The temple of great Indian food.

The rich setting, interesting art, romantic candle lighting and the conservatory are secondary details in London's temple of great Indian food. Chutney Mary is among the very best restaurants in London regardless of cuisine.

Part of the Masala World Group incorporating Amaya, Veeraswamy and Masala Zone

535 Kings Road, Chelsea, London SW10 0SZ
T: 020 7351 3113   F: 020 7351 7694
chutneymary.com

THE 2010 COBRA GOOD CURRY GUIDE

Joint Editor and Database Management:
Dominique Chapman (DBAC)

Design: PCP Graphics developed from Peter Ward's design
Pat's logo and graphics by Nick Warren at www.n9design.com

Text Editor: Ronald Laxton

Statistics: Taylor Nelson, Sub Continent Publishing

Researchers: Sarika Azad, Jonelle Bester, Zubin Bhedwar, Aftab Bhatti, Shahnoor Chowdhury, Roopa Gulati, Khurram Nelson, Horshang Noria, Ajay Patel, Biren Parikh, Buela Samuel, Samson Sohail and Puja Vedi.

Good Curry Guide Frequent and Prolific Reporters:
Dave Bridges, The Wirral; N.K.Campbell, Edinburgh; Hilary Chapchal, Surrey; Bill Parkes-Davis, Kent; Rod Eglin, Cumbria; Ray & Ruby Elliot, Worcs; Tony Emmerson, Lancs; Bob Giddings, Poole; Justin Harper, Hemel; Tony and Monika Hetherington, Yorks; Andy Glazier, London; Tim & Katherine Morgan, Scotland; Paul Motley, e-mail; Steve Osborne, Bucks; Grahame and Melinda Payne, Coventry; Dr Dirk Pilat, e-mail; Nigel Thomas, Lincoln; Ralph Warrington, Hyde; Cheshire (GM); Jeanette Wickes, Kent,; Malcolm Wilkins, Gravesend, Kent; Mick Wright, Beds.
plus many hundreds of others, without whom this Guide would not exist, and whose names appear at the end of this book.

This tenth edition first published in Great Britain in October 2008
Reprinted as Version 3 of 2009 edition
by The Curry Club, PO Box 7, Haslemere, Surrey, UK. GU27 1EP,
in association with John Blake Publishing, W14 9BP

Previous Editions of this Guide:
First edition 1984, Second: 1987, Third 1991, Fourth: 1995, Fifth: 1998, Sixth: 1999,
Seventh 2001, Eighth 2004, Ninth 2007, reprint of Ninth 2008, Tenth 2009

Printed and bound in Great Britain by Blackmore Printers, Shaftesbury, Dorset.
A CIP catalogue recommendation for this book is available from the British Library

EXTRA SMOOTH

2010
COBRA
GOOD CURRY
GUIDE

Chilli, cumin, coriander...
and the Good Curry Guide

Some things are essential to the enjoyment of great Asian food, and the Cobra Good Curry Guide is one of them.

Congratulations to Pat Chapman and his team, and to all the restaurants listed, on another fantastic edition.

2010 COBRA GOOD CURRY GUIDE

CONTENTS

Author's Notes

Sponsorship The continuing sponsorship by Cobra Beer as the Guide's sole sponsor, enables the author to finance the considerable costs of operating and producing this Guide, which include: maintaining the restaurant database on computer; subscribing to a press-cutting service and other information suppliers; printing a detailed questionnaire and mailing it to all 9,000 restaurants twice a year; mail-shotting the 1,500-plus restaurants that are selected to appear in the Guide; telephoning many for verification of information; producing, supplying and mailing the selected restaurants (free of charge) their wall certificates and window stickers; printing and mailing restaurant report forms for interested parties; collating and recording the info received (some 5,000 reports per annum) and operating the Awards Ceremony. *(see page 32).*

Accuracy The contents of this Guide are as up-to-date and accurate as possible, but we cannot be held responsible for any changes regarding quality, price, menu details, decor, ownership, health offenses or even closure, following our processing of the reports.

Connections Pat Chapman, the publishers of this Guide and the proprietors of The Curry Club wish to make it quite clear that they have absolutely no financial or ownership connections with any restaurants, including those mentioned in this Guide.

False Representation Restaurant reports are welcomed from any bona-fide source. We do not pay for reports – they are sent in spontaneously and voluntarily. Our own research and restaurant testing is normally done anonymously, the bill is paid, and often no disclosure is made as to our presence. On some occasions, such as openings, we accept invitations to visit restaurants as 'guests of the house'. Under no circumstances do we tout for free hospitality, and anyone doing so in the name of The Curry Club is an impostor. We have heard of cases where people claiming to be members of The Curry Club, or Good Curry Guide 'inspectors', request payment and/or free meals in return for entry into this Guide. In such cases, we would recommend that restaurants threaten to call the police. We would also like to be informed of any such incidents and we will not hesitate to take action against people acting illegally in our name.

Discounts We used to invite all restaurants selected to appear in this Guide to participate in a discount scheme for members of The Curry Club. We have now discontinued this scheme, but we urge all readers of this Guide to request a discount from any restaurant in this Guide, and if necessary to show the restaurant their entry in the Guide.

Certificates & Window Stickers We send all restaurants appearing in this Guide a 2007 certificate, hand-signed by Pat Chapman, and a 2007 window sticker. These items are supplied free of charge. Some choose not to display them, others display them proudly and prominently. You may observe that our certificate is not displayed alone. There may well be a host of others, some bigger and flashier than ours, including the Dome Grading certificates issued by Peter and Colleen Groves, which are genuine, as are certificates issued by London's Time Out, Ronay, local council health departments and certain others. Unfortunately, some certificates are a pure sham. They are issued to any restaurant who cares to pay for them, in some cases with a promise of entry into a Guide which does not even exist. We reported last time on a scam by Good Food Guide, yet again, but this is not <u>The</u> Good Food Guide. There is no Guide and this is the same outfit that were sued by the Consumers' Association some time ago and have now re-emerged at a different address. Masterchef returned after being exposed by BBC 'Food and Drink' in June. Certificates are on offer for £67.50 (£10 for extra copies) and £5 for window stickers. The Asian Food Guide was caught out on Radio 4. There are others on the bandwagon. Like Peter Groves, we would like to see this scam stopped. But how do you know that the Good Curry Guide certificate you see is genuine?

For those of you who like to follow events, we reported last time about a scam-operator called Ian Cowan of Inc Software, Paisley, Scotland. He was attempting to charge for Good Curry Guide certificates for a cost of £30. Remember, we give our certificates free of charge. -It seems that, as we predicted, he has sunk without trace. And so too has the mania to operate copy-cat websites. Infact we have become relaxed about it. If you want to read this Guide's words on some 'unauthorised' website, so be it. And if you are contemplating rewriting all the words on this Guide, I point out that there are 250,000 words to copy. Enjoy!

2010 COBRA GOOD CURRY GUIDE

County Index

See pages 341 to 343 for Town Index

The Good Curry Guide broke new ground when it was first published in 1984, by being the first restaurant guide to specialise only in the British curry. This is its tenth edition, marking its 25th year. We mark it with a special feature overleaf As usual, there have been demotions and promotions since last time. We want continuity in each edition of the Guide, and because we do expect changes, we feel it is important that each restaurant completes our questionnaire. For one thing, it means the restaurant actually wants to be in the Guide. It also verifies its current name, address, telephone number, and above all, prices. Despite our earnest endeavours, not all restaurants reply, even if they did so last time. So if we have not received a reply from a restaurant that was in the previous edition, after it has been sent a form three times, should it be delisted? I believe it should if it cannot be bothered, for whatever reason, to talk to us. But curry restaurants are a peculiar trade; communications aren't always easy and normal rules don't apply.

A completed form from a restaurant does not guarantee entry to the Guide. We rely on various other sources of information. We can only visit a handful of restaurants each year, and do not have a team of paid inspectors. Most important to us are the opinions of the customers – you, the diners. We do not pay for such reports, though from time to time The Curry Club gives prizes for your efforts. The report itself can be a simple short note, though we have a special form (see final page) for all who want one. A report may deal with a single restaurant or several. Some reporters write to us only once, others write repeatedly. For this Guide, we received about 5,000 reports, yielding information on up to 50,000 restaurant visits. We read and record every report, although it is becoming increasingly difficult to reply to all of them. I would like, therefore, to thank all those who have taken the time to tell us where they have found the best, good, mediocre and even bad curries.

Naturally, reporting standards vary, and the The Wind of India, Puddlecome-on-the-Marsh may well be reported as the best in the world by an ardent, novice, local fan (and I want such opinions), but may not rate highly if compared with London's best. Nevertheless, it will be a competent curry house in that area, serving standard formula curry. Numerous entries in this Guide come into this category, and they are here because someone, maybe more than one person, has taken the trouble to write in and praise the place, and to exclude it would be wrong. We want to know what you know.

Answering the question *'Name your favourite curry restaurant(s)'* may not always be as easy as it sounds. It is worth again quoting Sutton Coldfield's John Brockingham, a retired college lecturer: *'My favourite restaurants,'* he wrote, *'range from opulent establishments like Rajdoot, Birmingham, where I might take the family on special occasions, to cheap and cheerful places like Erdington's Balti Express, where a meal costs £11 a head. I have a favourite posh curry restaurant, when I can afford it, and a favourite posh Balti. But I have a favourite plonk version of both, and a favourite takeaway, and then there's a favourite lucky dip. Some of my favourites are good enough to tempt me in whenever I'm in the district, but could not be nominated for the highest accolade.'*

Of course we do not receive reports on every single establishment. On occasion a restaurant we normally receive good reports about gets damned. If this is the exception, we will probably still carry that restaurant. Some will have closed, and others should perhaps have been omitted. But none get into this Guide unless we have had at least one recent good report on it, preferably several. To get into the TOP 100 we need several detailed excellent reports, including at least one by one of our elite 60 or so regular reporters. As editors we visit a top 100 restaurant anonymously whenever we can, but it's impossible to go to them all within one year. We do our best to filter out 'good' reports on bad restaurants, particularly those written by their hopeful owners. As usual, we requested that restaurants selected for entry get their customers to write to us, and many did. This way, we have almost weeded out the few restaurants who previously sent us phoney reports, purportedly from adoring customers. However, even after twenty five years in the editor's chair, it is possible that I've been conned and a 'bad' restaurant has slipped in. Equally, I'll guarantee that we've missed someone's favourite, and that there are a few faux pas too. Please let us know about these. No doubt, we'll continue to get irate letters from people who won't have bothered to read this section, telling us that, because this or that restaurant was awful when they visited, 'it casts doubt on the credibility of the entire Guide'. We certainly do not enter restaurants just because they ask us to. After twenty five years of bona-fide operations, you would imagine that curryhouse owners would clamour to be in the Guide. Indeed some do. As I have said in previous Guides, more than one restaurant has made veiled references to the benefits that would be made available to the editors if that restaurant were declared the UK's number one. The very idea is abhorrent. Besides, if one did accede to such bribery, word would soon get round risking the credibility of both author and publication. The book is paid for through book sales, ads and sponsorship, not through bribes.

So what's new in this edition? Regular readers will know that we go alphabetically by county, then within that, by town and then restaurant. We are continuing with this system, since it is easier to see at a glance what alternative choices are nearby. We also continue with the town index at the end of the book. A new idea is to put in a restaurant name index to speed up finding your favourite. At the start of each county's entry, are our thumbnail county maps, which help pinpoint the location of that particular county, along with a list of adjacent counties. It should make this Guide more informative and finding your way around it easier. And that, after all, is what this Guide is all about finding good curries easily, and nothing else.

Finally, the winner of the 2007 Guide's **Win-Enough-Cobra-beer-for-a-Year** quiz was Colin Snowball of Glocestershire. Believe it or not he was the only entrant and he got the answers to all questions correct.

THE PREFERRED CHOICE OF TOP CHEFS

Map Trading Ltd
Specialist Suppliers of Indian Foods
Rice, Lentils, Spices, Pappadoms, Flours, Pickles, Pastes, Oils, Chutney etc.

Map Trading Limited
2 Abbey Road, Park Royal, London NW10 7BW, England.
Tel: +44 208 965 0193   **Fax:** +44 208 963 1184   **Email:** post@whitepearl.co.uk

w w w . w h i t e p e a r l . c o . u k

OR IN PEOPLE

There are many excellent reasons to dine at

MADHU'S

What's yours?

39 South Road, Southall, Middx. T: 020 8574 1897

There are many excellent reasons to dine at

MADHU'S

What's yours?

BIG CURRY

In aid of the Army Benevolent Fund

The Army Benevolent Fund's 3rd annual BIG CURRY takes place in April 2010. Their full time Fund organisers are such fans that they work hard on this one day event all year round. Result: it annually raises a six figure sum to swell the fund.

And the Cobra Good Curry Guide is helping.

Also helping the ABF cause are celebrities such as Kate Silverton, Jools Holland, and actor Charley Boorman, to name just a few. **We want you to get involved.**
Simply gather a group together, hold a curry party and ask them to donate.

Your imagination is the only limit when deciding where to hold your BIG CURRY.
At home
In your office
At a curryhouse (add £1 per person to the bill)
Up a mountain
In a canoe
…Anywhere! The crazier the better.
See **www.bigcurry.org** for help and advice.

For recipes, see **www.patchapman.co.uk**
On menu bar click <BIG CURRY>

If you'd like to get involved but don't have time to organise your own event, you can always visit one of the select group of curry restaurants across the UK and northern Ireland who raise funds for the cause in a variety of ways (watch out for their publicity material nearer the time).

Let this Guide know what you did and we'll publish the zaniest, prettiest, biggest event and note the ones who raised the most money.

Servicemen enjoyed their 2009 BIG CURRY at Iraq's Camp Bastion's and donated to the fund, pictured alongside by Corporal Rupert Frere. Other barracks did too, in the UK, Bulgaria, the USA, Germany, the Falklands, Helsinki and biggest of all, the Army Super Kitchen in Afghanistan's Camp Bastion Basra, where 4,000 troops enjoyed their spicy dinner. Nearer to home London WASPS Rugby Club held their own BIG CURRY, as did the House of Lords, Oxford University Student Union, and a multitude of civilians in schools, homes, and offices up and down the country.

The Ashoka Restaurant, Ashton Lane Restaurant, Hillhead Glasgow ran a BIG CURRY. Strathclyde University students Officer Cadet Faye Heslop, 18 and Katie Potts, 19 enjoy theirs with the help of Ashoka Chef Dali.

Take part in 2010's biggest Curry day.
Come to the Big City flagship event, the prestigious
2010 BIG CURRY LUNCHEON,
hosted by the Lord Mayor of the City of London at the Guildhall.

Join Royalty and the cream of the City of London, including members of the Livery Companies, the Lord Mayor, Sheriffs and Aldermen as well as a host of celebrities, senior army personnel, Army Benevolent Fund workers and some of the soldiers the fund has helped. Needless to say you'll in good company: they are all curryholics enjoying Noon curries, Cobra Beer and wines, all included in the ticket price .

> **The provisional date for the 2010 BIG CURRY is Thursday 29 April.**
>
> **Tickets are £95 each, and most of that goes to the ABF fund.**
>
> **To be one of this élite thousand, or for further ticket information email: tickets@bigcurry.org**

The event at London's prestigious Guildhall is unique. Royal attendance is guaranteed. Above we see Prince Charles arriving at the Guildhall for the 2008 BIG CURRY. A glittering scene awaits him in the Guildhall. A Gurkha piper plays a tuneful greeting, while inside the hall itself, a regimental band is in full play. The huge hall room is full of military personnel, of all ranks, from cadet to Warrant Officer and General, in full. There is plenty of Top Brass as well as Captains of Industry. But by far the majority is from the surrounding City of London and further afield, who have the ABF at heart. The atmosphere is convivial and elegant with excited anticipation caused by aromas of the curries to come, and the chance to win a magnificent prize or two in the fabulous draw or bid for the silent auction.

It's an all-win situation for the ABF; the more you spend, the more the Fund can help desperately needy servicemen.

No matter how small your donation, your BIG CURRY can make a big difference to soldiers, veterans and their families in times of need. For example to a person like Steve Gill. He was seriously injured by an explosive device whilst on patrol in Belfast. He lost his right leg above the knee, his left leg below the knee, his right eye and also suffered various internal injuries. With his ABF grant he bought a sports wheelchair, he is now a passionate basketball player.

"The ABF guarantee that the money actually goes to the soldiers and ex-soldiers that need it the most" says Steve, *"and I'm living proof of how it can change your life."*

April 2009. The Guildhall buzzes as diners tuck into their **BIG CURRY**. HRH the Duke of Kent chats with a liveryman, before taking his place at table, where the waitress explains the curries. Next to him, sporting the tattoos, is Steve Gill (see his story on the bottom of the adjacent page). HRH said of his **BIG CURRY** *"absolutely delicious'*.

THE CHEF'S STORY

Sainath Rao, Senior Executive Chef at Noon Products tells how the BIG CURRY for 1,500 diners was cooked

Noon Products are used to producing tens of thousands of curries daily for the likes of Sainsburys and Waitrose in the form of ready meals. We heard that our Curry King boss, Sir Gulam Noon had agreed to sponsor the ABF's BIG CURRY in 2008, by donating and serving 1,000 curry lunches at London's Guildhall. So when I heard that as Noon's Senior Exec chef I was going to be in charge of it, I was delighted, but a wee bit apprehensive. The the challenge was to prepare the food at our Southall factory, then on the day transport it through London's awful traffic) and serve a piping hot lunch for all the attendees who had paid no less that £95 each. True it was all for charity, but the diners rightly expected high quality food. It was hard work but the 2008 event went really well.

This year the number went up to 1500.

So how did we do it?

First I organised a meeting with Noon chefs (pictured below). Then Major Harry Lomas, representing the army, came to discuss logistics, resources and staffing. He was very pleased to find that we use only fresh ingredients, and to witness the level of food science that goes into our day to day production for all the supermarkets. He was impressed by our policy of not using any

Head of Development Chef Ravinayak, Rao (me), Chefs Mukesh, Ramesh and right Venogaran. In the turban is Noon driver, Brar Singh.

Noon Products donated the 1,500 curries. Backstage in a service marquee, Curry King Sir G.K.Noon inspects our work, while Ramesh watches anxiously.

preservatives, colours or artificial enhancers in any aspect of Noon's production. Our Southall site was next visited by environment and health executives from Westminster and Ealing Boroughs who certified all the staff involved as properly qualified. Next we agreed the menu.

On the day prior, Major Harry and his brigade of 12 army chefs arrived very early, to work together with our 12 Noon chefs to do the advance preparation. Then all the food was transported in a refrigerated truck van to the Guildhall. On the day our two teams had 4 hours to cook with active assistance of a third team of Guildhall chefs. Even twelve Noon chefs, twelve Army chefs and ten Guildhall chefs needed help servicing 1000 diners in two hours. We got it from an array of young uniformed cadets, scurrying with loaded steaming food in warming trays. The only way to describe the entire action is that it was done with "military precision".Timing was spot on and we started the first sitting service at the announced moment of 1230. Second sitting was 1.10 and third at 1.50. 500 cadets were rewarded with their BIG CURRY later. Total 1,500. The day whizzed past and we all went back to our daily routines, but this experience is still exhilarating. We all are proud to be of service to the army. I'm looking forward to doing it all again in 2010.

Why not be there yourself?

Chef Ravinayak, me in the blue hair net with Major Harry Lomas who has just given the thumbs up, then its all go for service..

Britain's Elite A-List & Top 100 Restaurants
As Chosen By You

Only one in every twelve of the nation's curry restaurants has achieved entry into this Guide, so they are all top restaurants and a cut above the norm. Put another way, all the entrants are in our **TOP 1000**. But, naturally, we are always asked to identify the best of the best, so to speak. And it is true that there is an élite number of really excellent restaurants including, by definition, those establishments about which we receive many consistently good reports. In our 1985 we pioneered a **TOP 30** list, and reflecting the improvement in standards this grew in our 1992 edition to our **TOP 100** list. As usual, this year there has been quite a lot of change. There is the usual demotion from that list because of a decline in performance or closure. Two, Le Raj Epsom and Khan's W2 have come out for neither of these reasons: they have asked to be delisted despite being in our TOP 100 list; they didn't like the minor criticisms from you. Fortunately, from the many you have brought to our attention, we have promoted a number of 'new' **TOP 100** entrants (indicated •). Once again we have more than an exact 100. As ever, if there are yet others you feel we have missed, please report to us. For a restaurant to remain in our top 100 list, we also need your views. There is a further, even more élite list, the cream of the cream, winners of our **AWARDS** all of whom attend the Guide's prestigious ceremony in London to receive their awards. For the record, all our previous award winners are listed below, since they all remain at the top the tree. We describe all these as our **A-LIST** (A for Awards + Nominees). At the request of the worldwide media, we commenced our **Best In The UK Awards** in 1992, in our third edition of this Guide. To date there have only been seven such winners, listed below. Although our judgements at the time were nearly always received with some surprise, we are proud they have all stood the test of time. Each of these restaurants continue to thrive and deliver outstanding food and service. Although so many of our best restaurants are in London, and probably most deserve the Best in UK accolade, we actively want to displace any perceived London bias, hard though this is. So in 2004 we moved a little outside London for the first time. In 2007 we went to the Midlands for our best. For 2009/10 we move to Milton Keynes to award a restaurant and its owner for his life-long persistence and eventual achievement in seeking the best.

The Hall of Fame
Our Ultimate Achievers
Best In The UK Awards

BOMBAY BRASSERIE, SW7
Lifetime Best Restaurant Award – 1982 to 2009/10

CHUTNEY MARY, SW10
Best in UK 1991-1994 – Third Edition of this Guide
Best in UK 1999-2000 – Sixth Edition

BOMBAY BRASSERIE, SW7
Best in UK 1995-7 – Fourth Edition

LA PORTE DES INDES, LONDON, W1
Best Indian and Best in UK 1998-1999 – Fifth Edition

THE QUILON, SW1
Best in UK 2001-2003 – Seventh Edition

MADHU'S, SOUTHALL, MIDDLESEX
Best in UK 2004-2006 – Eighth Edition

ITIHAAS, BIRMINGHAM
Best in UK 2007-2008 – Ninth Edition

JAIPUR MILTON KEYNES, BUCKINGHAMSHIRE
Best in UK 2009-2010 – This Edition

2009 COBRA GOOD CURRY GUIDE

Britain's Elite A-List & Top 100 Restaurants As Chosen By You

KEY:
A-LIST ~ see definition above
• = NEW TO OUR TOP 100
† = One of a group of restaurants

London

E1	† Cafe Naz A-LIST ~ Best Bangladeshi and Best Chef 2007-8
	Café Spice Namaste A-LIST ~ Best chef 1992-5 / 1996-8 / Culinary Excellence 2001-3
	• Kolapata
	Lahore Kebab House A-LIST ~ Nominated best Pakistani Restaurant 2007-8
	Shampan ~ Best Bangladeshi 2001-3
	Tiffin Indian
EC2	• Tiffin Bites **2009 GROUP AWARD WINNER**
EC3	Kasturi A-LIST ~ Nominated best in London 2007-8
N1	Afghan Kitchen
	Masala Zone A-LIST ~ Best New Concept Award 2004-5
N3	Rani Vegetarian ~ Best Vegetarian 2001-3
N16	† Rasa A-LIST
	Rasa Travancore A-LIST
NW1	• Ambala Sweet Centre
	Diwana Bhel Poori House
	Great Nepalese ~ Best Nepalese 2001-3
	• Royal Sweets
	• Zeen A-LIST **2009 MOST EXCITING NEWCOMER**
NW3	Eriki
	• Woodlands
NW4	Prince of Ceylon ~ Best Sri Lankan 2001-3
NW5	Chetna
NW6	Elephant Walk A-LIST Best Sri Lankan 2007-8
	Geeta South Indian
	Vijay
NW8	• Eriki **SE1** Bengal Clipper
SE1	Bengal Clipper
	Georgetown ~ Best Restaurant group 2004-5 See Kenilworth Warks.
SE13	Spice of Life
SE23	† Babur Brasserie A-LIST ~ Nominated Best in London 2007-8
	† • Mela at Herne Hill
SW1	† Amaya A-LIST ~ Nominated Best Newcomer 2007-8
	Cinnamon Club A-LIST
	Mint Leaf A-LIST ~ Best in london 2007-8
	The Quilon A-LIST ~ Best in UK 2001-3 and Outstanding Restaurant Award 2004-5 & 2007-8
	Saloos
	† Woodlands
SW3	† Haandi A-LIST ~ Previous Award Winner
	Rasoi Vineet Bhatia A-LIST
SW4	• Maharani TOP 100
SW5	† Masala Zone A-LIST
	Nizam
	Star of India
SW6	† Blue Elephant Thai A-LIST ~ Previous Award Winner
	Darbar
	• Memories of India on the River
	Nayaab A-LIST ~ Nominated best in london 2007-8

Savour the change at London's iconic Bombay Brasserie. A larger more spectacular setting serves up an eclectic ambience. Where authentic Indian flavours are transformed into a contemporary gourmet experience.

THE ONLY THING OLD ON THE MENU IS THE AUTHENTICITY

BOMBAY BRASSERIE

SW7   Bombay Brasserie A-LIST ~ Best in UK 1995-7
                     BEST INDIAN RESTAURANT IN EUROPE
             † Café Lazeez A-LIST
             Shezan Indian
SW10   † Chutney Mary A-LIST ~ Best in UK 1991-4 and 1999-2000. Permanent Outstanding
                                             restaurant award from 2004
             Painted Heron A-LIST ~ Best Chef Award
             Vama The Indian Room A-LIST
SW12   Tabaq A-LIST ~ Best Pakistani 1998-99 1999-2000 2001-3 & 2004-5
SW15   Ma Goa
SW17   Jaffna House A-LIST ~ Best Sri Lankan 2004-5 & Nominated 2007-8
             Radha Krishna Bhavan
             Sree Krishna
             • Vijaya Krishna
W1   Anwars
             Benares
             † Café Lazeez
             Chor Bizarre ~ Best North Indian 2001
             Chowki
             Gaylord
             Imli A-LIST AWard winner Best Indian 2007-8
             • Indian YMCA Canteen
             † Masala Zone A-LIST ~ Best New Concept Award 2004-5
             La Porte des Indes A-LIST ~ Best Indian and Best in UK 1998-9 / Permanent Outstanding
                                             restaurant award from 2004
             Ragam South Indian
             † Rasa A-LIST
             † Rasa Samudra A-LIST
             Red Fort A-LIST
             † Soho Spice
             Tamarind A-LIST ~ Best Newcomer 1995-97 / Best Indian 1998-9 / Best Chef 1999-2000
             Veeraswamy A-LIST ~ Best newcomer 1998-9 & Outstanding Restaurant Award 2007-8
             † Woodlands
W2   Bombay Palace
             Durbar
             Ginger ~ Best Bangladeshi 2004-5
             Khans
             Mandalay Burmese A-LIST
W4   † Woodlands South Indian Vegetarian
W5   Monty's Nepalese Cuisine A-LIST ~ Best UK Nepalese 2007-8
W6   Agni
             Green Chilli
             † • Indian Zing **BEST UK BOUTIQUE RESTAURANT AWARD 2009**
             Sagar A-LIST ~ Nominated best vegetarian 2007-8
             Tandoori Nights
W8   Malabar
             Zaika A-LIST
W11   Bombay Bicycle Club**W13**   Laguna
WC1   Hason Raja A-LIST ~ Nominated best Bangladeshi 2007/8
             Malabar Junction ~ Best South Indian 1999-2000
WC2   India Club A-LIST ~ Special Award Winner 1995-97
             Mela
             Moti Mahal A-LIST ~ most promising newcomer award 2007/8
             Punjab A-LIST ~ Best North Indian 1999-2000

England

BERKSHIRE
             Cookham   Malik's
             Slough   Baylis House A-LIST Nominated Best Indian 2007-8
             Sunningdale   Tiger's Pad
             Theale   Café Blue Cobra ~ Best in the West 1995-7
             Twyford   Hawelli
             Windsor   • Mango Lounge
             Wokingham   Sultan Balti Palace

BRISTOL
    • Myristica
BUCKINGHAMSHIRE
    Milton Keynes   Jaipur A-LIST ~ Best Restaurant Outside London 1995 to 2008
                        BEST RESTAURANT IN UK AWARD 2009/10
                        Jalori
                        Orchid Lounge at Jaipur A-LIST
                        BEST UK ORIENTAL ASIAN RESTAURANT 2007-2010
    Newport Pagnell Mysore
    Stony Stratford   Moghul Palace
CAMBRIDGESHIRE
    Cambridge   Cafe Naz A-LIST ~ Award winner Best Bangladeshi & Best Chef 2007-8
CHESHIRE
    Ellesmere Port   The Taj of Agra Fort ~ Best in the North 1998-9
    Northwich   † Bengal Dynasty A-LIST
DERBYSHIRE
    • Derby Anoki
DEVON
    Ilfracombe   Rajah
ESSEX
    Gants Hill   Kanchans
    Ilford   Curry Special
                        Jalalabad and •Jalalbad 2

HAMPSHIRE
    Fleet   Gurkha Square A-LIST ~ Best Nepalese 1998-9 & nominated Best
                                Nepalese 2007-8
    Liss   Madhuban
    Southampton   Café Mumbai
                        Kuti's Brasserie A-LIST ~ Best Bangladeshi 2007-8
                        Popadom Express
    Southsea   Bombay Bay
                        Golden Curry

HERTFORDSHIRE
    Abbots Langley   Viceroy of India
    St Albans   • Chez Mumtaj
                        Mumtaj A-LIST ~ Nominated Best In the South 2007-8

KENT
    Ashford   Zarin
    Bromley   Tamasha A-LIST ~ Best in the South 1998-9 and 2007-8
    Folkestone   Gurkha Palace ~ Nominated Best Nepalese 2007-8
                        India
    Halstead   • Calcutta Club
    Westerham   KINARA at Pitt's Cottage ~ Nominated Best Paksitani 2007-8
                        Tulsi

LANCASHIRE
    Adlington   Sharju
    Longridge   Victoria's India ~ Most Welcome Newcomer 2007-8

LEICESTERSHIRE
    Leicester   Curry Fever A-LIST ~ Best in the Midlands 2001-3

                        Ek Maya ~ Nominated Best in the Midlands 2007-8

                        Friends Tandoori

LINCOLNSHIRE
    Boston   Star of India
    Lincoln   Malabar Junction at Barbican Hotel
MANCHESTER, GREATER
    Altrincham   Barindar
                        Dilli
    Ashton-u-Lyne   Indian Ocean A-LIST ~ Best in the North 2007-8
    Rochdale   La Tandoor
MERSEYSIDE
    Liverpool   Gulshan ~ Best in the North 1999-2000 and 2001-3
MIDDLESEX
    Brentford   Pappadums

Britannia Spice

An award-winning voyage of discovery

Britannia Spice burst onto the Edinburgh dining scene in 1999, and went on to wow the capital city. Founded as the new millennium dawned, Britannia Spice has won widespread praise for its exotic multi-ethnic cuisine, bagging accolades such as Les Routiers Best Newcomer (2001), and the coveted Best in Scotland from the Best in Britain Awards. The restaurant has also enjoyed recognition as the 2008 Restaurant of the Year in the Irn Bru Curry Awards, an honour that followed three consecutive years as holder of the Best in Scotland title from the esteemed British Curry Awards. Britannia Spice specialises in exotic food from four countries: Bangladesh, Thailand, Nepal and India. Using only the finest ingredients, the chefs at Britannia Spice are proud to serve mouthwatering dishes as varied as Gaeng Kiew Wann and Bangladeshi Special Chicken. Gaining rave reviews from all corners of the media, Britannia Spice has proved itself one of the most loved restaurants in Scotland, being visited by both Alex Salmond and the Lord Provost.

"We are proud of our heritage and what we have achieved so far," says Wali Uddin. "But we are also looking forward to the coming year. 2009 marks our 10th anniversary, so we have plenty to celebrate. We've got some great events planned – we definitely want to make 2009 the year of Britannia Spice!"

"The unique appeal of Britannia Spice is that customers can broaden their palates by trying a taste of lots of different cuisines. Where else can a party of four people can each try a taste of Thai, Bangladeshi, Sri Lankan or Nepalese dishes without suffering jet lag?"

The Edinburgh Evening News

BRITANNIA Spice

Exclusive Exotic Cuisine

North Indian, South Indian, Thai, Nepalese and Bangladeshi cuisine served

For further information on any of the events happening at **Britannia Spice**, visit **www.britanniaspice.co.uk** or call **0131 555 2255**
Britannia Spice,
150 Commercial Street, Ocean Drive, Edinburgh

A-List and Top 100

(MIDDX) Edgware	† Haandi
Harrow	• Connoisseur Cuisine of India
Southall	Brilliant A-LIST ~ Best Punjabi Restaurant 1998-9, 2004 to 2008

Madhu's Brilliant A-LIST ~ Special Awards 1991-2000 ~
Best Restaurant in UK Award 2004-5; Outstanding 2007-8
Moj Masti
New Asian Tandoori Centre
Omi's
Palm Palace ~ Nominated Best Sri Lankan 2007-8

Sunbury-on-Thames	• Indian Zest
Twickenham	• Pallavi South Indian
• Tangawizi	
Wembley	Chetna's Bhel Puri
	Clay Oven
	Curry Craze
	† Woodlands

NORTHUMBERLAND

| Berwick | Magna A-LIST ~ Best in the North East 2007-8 |
| Corbridge | The Valley A-LIST ~ Best in the North 1995-7 |

NOTTINGHAMSHIRE

| Nottingham | Saagar |
| | • Spice Takeaway |

OXFORDSHIRE

| Oxford | † Aziz A-LIST Nominated Best Bangladeshi 2007-8 |

Also branches: Pandesia, Oxford, Aziz Burford and Aziz Witney

SOMERSET

| Bath | Eastern Eye A-LIST ~ Best in the West 2007-8 |

STAFFORDSHIRE

Kingsley Holt	Thornbury Hall Rasoi
Leek	Bolaka Spice
Lichfield	Eastern Eye

SURREY

Croydon	Planet Spice A-LIST
Esher	• Sherpa Kitchen
Oxted	Gurkha Kitchen A-LIST Nominated 2007-8 ~ Best Nepalese 1999-2000
Richmond	Origin Asia
Woking	Jaipur

SUSSEX

Crawley	Blue India
Nutbourne	Tamarind and Moonlight Express
Worthing	Indian Ocean Takeaway

TYNE & WEAR

| Gateshead | The Last Days of the Raj A-LIST nominated best in the north 2007-8 |
| Newcastle | • Rasa |

Sachins A-LIST nominated best in the north 2007-8
Valley Junction 397 A-LIST ~ Most Original 1999-2000
Nominated Best in the North 2007-8
Vujon ~ Best in the North East 2004-5

WARWICKSHIRE

| Kenilworth † | The Coconut Lagoon A-LIST ~ Best in the Midlands 2002-3 |

and Best Restaurant group Award 2004-5
† Raffles Malaysian A-LIST ~ Best Restaurant Group Award 2004-5

| Stratford on Avon | †The Coconut Lagoon A-LIST ~ Best Restaurant Group 2004-5 |
| | † Georgetown Malaysian A-LIST ~ Best Restaurant Group Award 2004-5 |

WEST MIDLANDS

| Birmingham | Adil ~ Best Balti House 1999-2000 |

†The Coconut Lagoon A-LIST ~ Best Restaurant group 2004-5
Itihaas A-LIST ~ Best in the Midlands 2007-8
Best in UK Award 2007-8
Maharajah ~ Best in the Midlands 1998-99 &1999-2000
Royal Naim ~ Best Balti House1995-98
Sweet Chillies Cuisine ~ Nominated Best In Midlands 2007-8

Coventry	Monsoon
	• Ocean
	• Rojoni
Solihull	Mango Tree
	Rajnagar International A-LIST ~ Nominated Best in the Midlands 2007-8

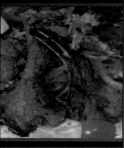

Welcome to Brilliant Restaurant

At the heart of ou
business is devotion
authentic, fresh an
superbly prepared foo
We do everything w
can to ensure that thos
who choose to dine wit
us have a 'Brillian
time.

We look forward to
welcoming you.

Gulu

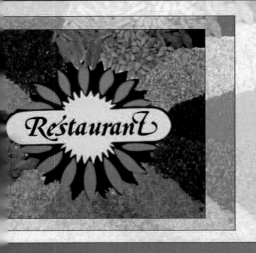

What they say about us:

'The best Indian food in the country'
(Michael Winner, Daily Mirror)

'... produces a lunch that betters the best in Europe'
(Victor-Lewis Smith, Daily Mirror)

'I can tell you it was a real treat'
(Fay Maschler, Evening Standard)

'Brilliant is a stayer'
(Sophie Grigson, Telegraph Magazine)

'Blissful experience, memorably excellent cooking'
(David Robson, Daily Express)

Brilliant offers:

- A new 'Healthy Options' menu
- Banqueting Suite for up to 120 people
- Full karaoke facilities for private functions
- Approved licensed premises for the Solemnization of Marriages
- Contract Catering at selected London hotels
- Private car park for up to 100 cars opposite the restaurant

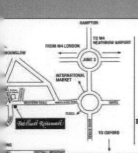

HOW TO FIND US:
72 – 76 WESTERN ROAD
SOUTHALL
MIDDLESEX UB2 5DZ

TEL: 020 8574 1928
FAX: 020 8574 0276
EMAIL: BRILLIANTRESTAURANT@HOTMAIL.COM
WEB: WWW.BRILLIANTRESTAURANT.COM

masala zone

real indian food
around £15 per head

each restaurant showcases a different
indian folk art or craft form.

enjoy
- mouth watering
  street foods
- fresh & healthy thalis
- regional curries
- spicy noodles
- fresh wines, beers & juices

- 9 marshall street, soho, w1
- 48 floral street, covent garden, wc2
- 147 earls court road, earls court, sw5
- 80 upper street, islington, n1
- 25 parkway, camden, nw1
- 73 bishops bridge road, bayswater, w2

no reservations.
part of the masala world group
incorporating amaya, chutney mary
& veeraswamy

WILTSHIRE
　　Marlborough　　　The Palm
　　Salisbury　　　Anokaa
　　Swindon　　　Rafu's Tandoori
WORCESTERSHIRE
　　Worcester　　　Monsoon
　　　　　　Spice Cuisine

NORTH YORKSHIRE
　　Skipton　　　† Aagrah A-LIST ~ Best Restaurant Group 1998-2000 & nominated Best Pakistani 2007-8 (also Aagrah Tadcaster and York)
　　York　　　† Jinnah
SOUTH YORKSHIRE
　　Doncaster　　　† Aagrah A-LIST ~ Best Restaurant Group 1998-99 &1999-2000
　　Sheffield　　　Ashoka A-LIST
　　　　　　Saffron Club

WEST YORKSHIRE
　　Bradford　　　Sweet Centre
　　Garforth　　　† Aagrah A-LIST ~ Best Restaurant Group 1998-2000. Nominated Best Pakistani 2007-8 (also Aagrah Huddersfield Pudsey. Shipley and Wakefield).
　　　　　　† Akbars and Akbar's The Grand
　　Leeds　　　Darbar
　　　　　　† Georgetown A-LIST
　　　　　　Hansa's Gujarati Vegetarian A-LIST　Best Vegetarian 1998 & 2007
　　　　　　Polash

Eire
　　Dublin　　　Jaipur
　　　　　　Shalimar

Scotland
FIFE
　　St Andrews　　　Balaka A-LIST ~ Nominated Best in Scotland 2007-8
　　　　　　　　　Best in Scotland 1995-7 & Best Bangladeshi 1999-2000
LOTHIAN
　　Edinburgh　　　Far Pavillion
　　　　　　Lancers Brasserie
　　　　　　Shamiana ~ Best Chef 1998-99
　　　　　　Verandah Best in Scotland 2007-8

　　Leith　　　Britannia Spice A-LIST ~ **Best in Scotland, 2009-10**, 2007-8
　　　　　　　　　Best in Scotland 2001-3
　　　　　　Gulnar's Passage to India ~ Best in Scotland 1999-2000
STRATHCLYDE
　　Glasgow　　　† Ashoka at the Mill A-LIST ~ Nominated Best in Scotland 2007-8
　　　　　　Café India
　　　　　　Koh-i-noor
　　　　　　Mister Singh's India
　　　　　　Mother India
　　　　　　† Murphy's Pakora Bar
TAYSIDE
　　Dundee　　　Dil See A-LIST ~ Best in Scotland 2004-5

Wales
CLWYD
　　Colwyn Bay　　　† Bengal Dynasty A-LIST ~ Best in Wales 2004-5 – fourth time
GLAMORGAN
　　Cardiff　　　† Cafe Naz A-LIST　Best Bangladeshi and Best Chef 2007-8
　　　　　　† Jubraj A-LIST ~ Best in Wales 1999/2000
　　Swansea　　　Bonophul
　　　　　　Phool Koli Bangladeshi Takeaway
GWENT
　　Monmouth　　　Misbah Tandoori A-LIST　Best in Wales 2007-8
GWYNEDD
　　Llandudno　　　† Bengal Dynasty A-LIST ~ Best in Wales 2004-5 – fourth time

INDIAN ZING
236 King Street,
Hammersmith, W6 0RF
020 8748 5959

Telephone: 0208 748 5959
Fax: 0208 748 2332
Email: info@indianzing.co.uk
website: www.indianzing.co.uk

Closest tube station:
Ravenscourt Park, District Line
Buses: H91, 190, 267, 391, N9, N11

**2009 Cobra Good
Curry Guide Award**

**Best UK Boutique
Restaurant**

Recently Opened Dil Se

Dine in elegant surroundings with an award winning chef and an executive management team. Dil Se is a family owned business that has placed itself as Scotland's premier Bangladeshi restaurant.

Dil Se has also received the Civic Award for the outstanding architecture of the building.

Amirjan House 99 - 101 Perth Road Dundee
T 01382 221501 | F 01382 221958

The Balaka
Restaurant

FULLY LICENCED BANGLADESHI RESTAURANT

3 Alexandra Place St Andrews Fife
T 01334 747825 | F 01334 476548

The Currination

Gastromone takes a light-hearted look at the world's curranigans

Big McCurry

A Malaysian appeal court ruled that McDonald's does not control the rights to every word with the "Mc" prefix. Mr Suppiah, 55, a former accountant, says his troubles began when in 1999, he shortened its name (Malaysian Chicken Curry Restaurant) to the snappier McCurry. Big Mac objected. Suppiah and his wife Kanageswary spent eight years battling in the courts for the right to retain the name of their business. In 2006 McDonald's lawyers forced them to operate as 'M Curry' and pay damages to McDonald's for using the name to associate its business with the fast-food chain. The appeal court overturned that 2006 decision. In granting the appeal, judge Gopal Sri Ram ruled that *"McCurry's Restaurant signboard would not result in persons associating McCurry with McDonald's."* McD have 185 outlets in Malaysia; McCurry have one. McD sell burgers; McC do not. McC sell curry; McD do not, yet bullying McD are threatening further court action.

Big sMac

When a London omnibus crashed into the branch of McDonalds, on Hoe Street, Walthamstow it did quite some damage. Luckily the Big Mac was unoccupied and it missed its neighbour, Guide entrant Priya (see page 84) so diners were not deprived one of E17's better curries. The Big sMac was quite a sight, which you wouldn't have got to see were it not for Martin Belam. [www.currybet.net/about.php] We publish it for two reasons; one that Priya narrowly escaped being demolished and secondly to put on record the disgraceful behaviour of a badly trained, power-hungry petty official with no real powers. This idiot was Police Community Support Officer (PCSO) JC 206. Says Martin *"he shouted 'why are you taking photographs of a crime scene?' Now in the first place it was a very silly question, as Hoe Street was full of people taking snaps for*

a bleedin' obvious reason. It's not everyday you see a double decker bus wedged into the front entrance of McDonalds. In the second place the crash site is not a crime scene until it is deemed that an offense has taken place. In the third place, it is not an offense to take photographs in a public place." Next the officious JC 206 demanded that Martin delete all the photographs taken. There are no lawful grounds for demanding that someone delete photographs. What's more not even a police officer can confiscate a camera without a court order. *"He asked for ID. I asked why I should supply it to him. At that moment a man from the press with a very large camera materialised and said very vigorously that anyone can take photographs in a public place. He produced a legal advice card and urged me to get in touch in case of difficulty. JC 206 didn't give up; I was required to wait with his colleague while he phoned for advice (presumably from the real police). Eventually I was informed I was free to continue taking photographs. The basic problem with PCSOs is that (i) they have an inflated sense of their own importance (ii) they lack the common sense, experience and professional knowledge of the law that a police officer possesses."* If imbecile JC 260 cares to identify himself, we will publish his name AND PICTURE next time. Don't hold your breath.

Cate has nothing to smile about

Mouse-ala Sauce

St Austell nursery worker Cate Barrett bought a £1.49 pot of ASDA Extra Special CTM sauce from her local store. When she emptied it into a pan of vegetables, she wondered what the lumpy object was which plopped out of the jar. On inspection she realised, to her horror, it was a dead mouse, complete with whiskers, legs, and a tail. I screamed to my boyfriend Nigel to come to see it. The couple took the jar and its contents back to the shop where a manager apologised and said it would be sent for examination. When asked for an explanation by Gastronome an ASDA

spokesman said it was 'to early to comment'. However, some curryholics are not too shy to comment. Chris G from Eastbourne asks *"was one of the 3051 products that ASDA priced lower than Tesco that week?"* Cat from Catford (!) suggests it should become a new line in cat food. Fergus asks *"was Brussels consulted?"?* Cate and many others all say *"we'll make their own CTM sauce from now on"*. And you won't get a better recipe than in Pat Chapman's books.

Baltistar Galactica

The higher you take cooked food above the earth, the blander it tastes. Airlines face a challenge making food taste good when reheated at altitude. So NASA 's problem in space was multifold. Millions were spent on developing it, none more than for 'space

kimchi' for the first South Korean astronaut. NASA admits early space food was *"a testament to the fortitude"* of the first spacemen. The maxim was that when an astronaut is happy on all fronts, performance is enhanced. India is now facing an even bigger problem. Her first astronauts are planned to launch by 2015, and with them will go curry. Indian nutritionalists are struggling to adapt their national cuisine to work in space. *"Curry is spicy and high in fat content,"* the lab's director said. *"It must not upset an astronaut's digestion. But neither can we afford to leave our astronauts without a taste of home."* Once Sir Richard Branson's cracks his public space trips, can we look forward to the first orbital curry house? Virgin Vindaloo at Branson's Baltistarhouse, perhaps!

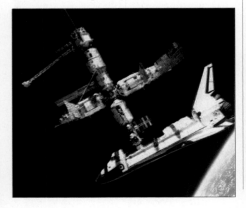

Don't Fool with the Curry Bomb

India's war with Pakistan on the Kashmiri border has been ongoing for five decades, and shows no sign of ending. Each side lobs off mortars and missiles over the disputed mountains tops as regularly as they play cricket together. Both sides have nuclear weapons, but will never use them, never that is unless, insurgent Taliban and al-Qa'eda get control of Pakistan. They go about their cowardly business, planting bombs dressed as civilians, and causing mayhem. Indian army weapons designers have come up with an ultimate weapon which they say can bring an insurgent to his knees in seconds, *"something frequently experienced by Britain's legion of Friday-night Vindaloo casualties"* says journalist Pamela Timms in Delhi. Indian Army scientists have created an 81mm grenade packed with red hot chilli, pepper and phosphorus. The searing mix chokes the enemy's respiratory tract, leaving targets barely able to breathe; their eyes, throat and skin burn and sting. Described as the 'curry bomb', it will be used both as a hand grenade by police and armed forces, and as a tank-mounted device. After being fired by a grenade launcher, it creates an effective smoke screen 90 metres away within seconds. Trials have been completed. Published: 12:01AM BST 01 Apr 2008.

There's nothing small about being pint-sized

Extra smooth Cobra is now available on draught.

Credit crunchy munchy

New research by **foodtv.co.uk** examines changes in the UK public's culinary behaviour in the 'credit crunch'. Four in five of us often (36%) or always (45%) keep leftovers after a meal but some are making their food stretch even further: 35% admit to eating food past its use-by date regularly and 28% confess to eating food that has gone mouldy (after removing the mouldy bits). 8% say they eat takeaways for breakfast. 35% of UK adults lick their knives while they eat and 23% confess to using their finger to clean their plate. 44% say chewing with your mouth open is the most disgusting food habit; a third say eating off the floor/ground is worse and 13% say licking your plate. Half of all UK households sit down for a roast together at least once a fortnight; with nearly a third eating a roast together every week. Meanwhile, 33% of households eat meals together once a day and 28% also watch TV while they eat. 39% of households say they are buying fewer ready-made sauces and salads and are cooking more meals from scratch compared to a year ago. And it seems that people actually care about what they're cooking, with 51% rating taste as the most important criterion for their family when it comes to deciding what to cook. We like to think we eat healthily but for 41% the main snack is biscuits/cake, 33% chomp on chocolate between meals. Nine in ten of us believe we're healthy but only one fifth always eat their fruit and vegetable allocation. Men are more likely to snack on unhealthy things than women. Meanwhile, 25% say their guilty food secret is eating a packet of biscuits in one sitting and 22% confess to eating ice-cream direct from the tub. 15% admit eating huge quantities of food in one sitting and 10% put their hand up to drinking out of the milk bottle. For full survey findings go to www.foodtv.co.uk.

Another survey, **Mintel's Ethnic Cuisine** report also detected a rise in home cooking, influenced by the need to save money and eat healthily – 62% said cooking ethnic food at home was cheaper than getting a takeaway while 61%, up 6%, said they enjoyed cooking and trying new recipes. More than a third reckoned their curries tasted just as good as a takeaway. Enjoyment of ethnic food is greatest with 70% those aged 25-44 enjoying it. There are those, however, whose taste buds are a little less experimental: 6% of the population claimed never to eat foreign food. **[This stat hasn't changed in 25 years – Ed]**. Mintel's report found consumers spent £1.32bn on 'foreign' cooking last year. forecast to hit £1.52bn by 2013 because of rising affluence, more women in work and a greater number of twenty-something shoppers and single households. The survey found that 83% of adults liked Chinese, ahead of the 71% who favoured Indian food. 32% have visited a Chinese restaurant in the past year compared with 30% who have been to a curry house. However in the UK supermarket, the curry still reigned supreme, with shoppers spending £556m on Indian £367m on Chinese food. Sales for Indian and Chinese went up 1% and their traditional stranglehold hold on taste buds is easing, falling from 77% of sales in 2003 to 70% last year as consumers experiment with newer styles of cooking. Shops sold 20% more Mexican food, the third most popular cuisine, but Asian foods recorded the most spectacular growth. Meals and ingredients for South-east Asian cooking, including Vietnamese, Indonesian, Malaysian and Singaporean, grew by 46% to £17m. Japanese food grew 44% to £13m. Cajun and Caribbean food rose 7%. During 2007 and 2008, sales of Chinese stir fry sales rose 37% and Chinese cooking sauces 13% while ready meals fell 7%. For Indian food, spices and other accompaniments were up 11% and ready meals down 2%

POSH prize

In a remarkable experiment, a school whose attendance records are below Ofsted standards, is offering parents the chance to win three curry meals a year if their children turn up to class. Despite teaching union NASUWT decrying the offer as bribery, absentee rates have halved since the scheme was launched. Joanne Dorricott, Southampton's, Glenfield Infant School's

head came up with the idea of holding one prize draw a term for the families of children who miss fewer than 5 per cent of their classes, with the winners getting £40 to spend at Southampton's POSH *Indian restaurant. She said: "we are delighted with the way it's going because the number of persistent absentees has decreased by over half. It is important it is to get children to school at this age, otherwise we have lost them."* So what does it cost the school? Nothing ... The £40 is covered by the restaurant, POSH (see page 194), with no money being taken from the school budget to fund the scheme.

Bibles Galore

Pat Chapman was the first to have a book published under the title Curry Bible. Hodder did it in 1997. So successful was it that they followed up with two more Pat Bibles: Balti and Vegetables. When they took them out of print, Pat's original Curry Bible was reissued as The New Curry Bible, and is still in print. Copies of all Pat's Bibles are available at his online shop on patchapman.co.uk

Book titles can't be copyrighted. As far as we know they are simply not copied; it's a matter of publishing honour. It was, that is until, in an unprecedented move which shocked the publishing industry, Random House plagiarised Pat's title with their Madhur Jaffrey Curry Bible, in 1999 (right). In 2008 M&S did it with Mridula's version (left), and this year she had the same title

pub by Parragon with two different covers. Also this year comes a Curry Bible pub by

Michael Joseph or is that Penguin, author in one version Jackie Passmore, or in another identical version, Gordon Kerr and in another, anonymous. Confused?

Stick with Pat's Bibles, pictured below. They actually deliver the curries you want, not airy-fairy recipes from Vietnam.

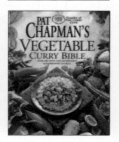

Fast Track Curry

Another Curry Bible with rather less publicity has just been published by Indian Railways Catering and Tourism Corporation. It has been sent to the hundreds of kitchens all over India run by the Corporation plus some 1,200 caterers licensed to provide meals for the 9,000 trains on which 16 million Indians who travel every day. It is an attempt to standardise the curries cooked at these units. Most meals are preordered by passengers at one station en route, then delivered to their seats at the next. New Delhi journalist Amrit Dhillon says in the Daily Telegraph *"rail travellers can buy a plate of sambhar (spicy lentil and vegetable dish with tamarind) and rice served with poppadoms and pickle for as little as 20 rupees (25p), or pay twice that for chicken biryani. The average middle class Indian earns around 500 rupees (£6.50) a day."* However, most seasoned travellers find these meals unappetising, and they bring their own picnics. Says Rakesh Tandon, MD catering, *"We've had decades of complaints over unreliable standards, and recipes that varied widely based on the cook's birthplace or whim. Some meat curries were far oilier and spicier than those on some trains. Vegetable dishes varied from pungent to very light."* He continues, *"we hope the Bible will fix this problem with our suppliers."* One such caterer is in New Delhi. Run by Rajeev Mittal; a private company turns

A 24 coach, diesel-hauled Shatabdi crossing the picturesque Pamban Bridge near Rameswaram.

which out 10,000 meals every day for India's so called superfast trains (max speed 80mph, average 50 mph), the élite Shatabdi and Rajdhani trains. There are 24 Shatabdi trains criss-crossing India and 36 Rajdhani trains with Delhi their hub. These trains have galleys where meals are reheated on the trains by travelling 'cooks' and waiter-served on trays to seated passengers. A typical breakfast on any one of these

A typical Rajdhani train breakfast, complete with chewed sandwich. Appetising, huh!

requires more than 1,000 slices of bread, 2,000 butter portions, 200 vegetarian curries, 300 meat curries, 300 omelettes and 500 tea bags. We can say from experience that these meals used to be as boring as airline meals, and Bible of no Bible, only silver service of steaming tureens of freshly cooked curries at tables with crisp white linen and silver-plated cutlery will compete with India's domestic airlines, who are quicker and cheaper than even the superfasts.

> Railways were first introduced to India in 1853 by the British. By their departure in 1947 the network was among the largest in the world which it still is today. It comprises 6,909 stations, 39,350 route miles, 200,000 (freight) wagons, 50,000 coaches and 8,000 locomotives. Steam is only worked on special tourist trains, as in the UK.

The world's costliest Curry

Credit crunch or no, the Bombay Brasserie has produced a curry dish that they claim is the world's most expensive, at £2,000 a portion. Called Samundari Khazana, or seafood treasure, is the brainchild of the BB's exec chef Prahlad Hegde. The dish requires a huge live Scottish lobster, £80, Turbot, which is highly prized for its delicate flavour, Devon Crab, four Abalone (sea snails) c£300 a kilo, White Truffle, Beluga caviar, morel mushrooms and edible gourmet gold leaf. The fish and seafood is first marinated in chilli and tamarind paste, before being gently pan-fried in a lightly spiced and chillied sauce. Then five tiny shavings of truffle costing £90, are placed on top "to give it a nutty flavour." Garnishes include hollowed out cherry tomato halves into which 30g of Beluga caviar, (£120) is pressed and then covered with a wafer-thin sheet of edible gourmet gold leaf (24 carat of course), Indian name 'vark', priced at, wait for it £1,000 per 150g. Four shelled quails' eggs are similarly treated with caviar and vark, and so too are four Morell Mushrooms. The dish is accompanied by ten year old vintage Derha Dun Basmati rice flavoured with saffron, the world's most expensive spice, (currently £per gram)and it comes with a glass of Krug vintage champagne. It looks incredible. Gold sparkled everywhere, including from the four pricey morel mushrooms. Not mentioned by the BB, but brought to your attention by Gastronome, this amazing dish has many aphrodisiac attributes. Sensual and mysterious, truffles were thought to be an aphrodisiac by the ancient Greeks and Romans. Saffron was given that attribute by the ancient Arab traders, Vark by the

Moghul emperors and caviar by the imperial Russians. Clearly aimed at getting plentiful press, (mission achieved), it also got detractors. Andy Morris (he who knows everything) wrote in GQ (formerly Gentleman's Quarterly and re-launched with the slogan 'everything a man needs and more'), *"No dish, no matter whether it's coated in precious metal or* *has so many lobsters it looks like Aquaman's breakfast, can justify such vast expense."* He goes on *"It cheapens the restaurant experience: in a hotly contested field, the Brasserie is one of the best Indian restaurants in London but by including such a preposterous item on the menu, they risk overshadowing the good work they do in the kitchen."* Miss the point about getting press did you Andy? Donna from Luton noted *"that's as expensive as my wedding ring!"* A Daily Mail reporter observed *"bagging the jackpot on Who Wants To Be A Millionaire is my only chance of trying this wallet-busting delight again.*

Chef Hegde, who joined the BB in 1991 as a sous Chef, and became Exec last year, quipped *"this curry is a real experience and there are still people out there with money to spend"* What he left unsaid was that he and the BB are happy to help them spend it. (Andy please note). And Gastronome notes overleaf who does spend loads of money.

Slumdogging it

Intentionally or not, the world's costliest curry was created, according to the BB's spin, to coincide with the DVD launch of Oscar-winning film Slumdog Millionaire, whose subject matter concerns the world's poorest inhabitants. Nobody knows how many there are. India just estimates it. The movie was a great yarn and earned itself mega millions, In reality slums are not

glamorous. 18,000 people to the acre; 15 per tiny dwelling plus the vermin. They are filthy, hideous, leak in the rain, and they stink and flow with you know what. The film got that right, but real slums aren't viewed in warm, air-conditioned Vue cinemas, on a velour seat, with popcorn and cola to hand.

Who's who on the C-List
the curry list of course

So who can afford the £2,000 curry? Actor Keanu Reeves treated five friends to a slap-up curry at an upmarket London Indian after a recent premier. Surprisingly he didn't go for the BB's that curry, he went instead Mayfair's Tamarind and spent a circumspect £1,200 on 17 starters between them, including scallops, lamb, chicken and aloo tikka salads. Mains included Saag Paneer Lobster Karikudi, Lamb Chetinaad, all helped with 'several' bottles of Chassagne Montrachet £95 and Tour Du Pin Figeac, £90. Pud was coconut ice cream. Gastronome can reveal that the bill came to £833.29. But add his bodyguard's bill of £200 and the tip, the total came to £1,200. I guess when you earn £10million a film plus 15 per cent of gross profits, the bill is really just a drop in the ocean, especially to those hangers-on. Other celebs at Tamarind have included the Sultan of Brunei, Tom Cruise, Sharon Stone, Mel Gibson, Nicole Kidman, Chelsea Clinton, Steven Speilberg, Eddie Murphy,

Right: A typical scene during a rush hour in 2009. Suburban trains like this serve every Indian city. They have a capacity of 1,200 passengers but often carry as many as 5,000. No attempt is made to control this astonishing spectacle, and some 1,500 deaths a year are caused by unfortunates falling off or being pushed off such trains. It represents the extent of the problems of over-population and poverty which hamper India's bid to become a superpower.

and Antonio Banderas and his wife Melanie Griffith. Tamarind Chef Alfred Prasad said *"they love their spicy kebabs and Chettinand dishes."* Mr Banderas was more specific. The couple flew from Madrid to Luton Airport for the British premier of Shrek 3. He revealed that he was so desperate for curry, that he'd phoned ahead to arrange for a takeaway tandoori to be delivered to his private jet on touch down. He'd also phoned Tamarind to tell them that the two of them, plus 40 of the Shrek production team, all of whom were curry addicts, according to Prasad *"wanted the best possible curry meal, so, we carefully prepared a big lunch of hara kebab , aloo tikki, lentils and spinach with tomato chutney, bhalla papri chaat, tandoori -grilled portabella, button and oyster mushrooms, mahi machchi tikka and grilled monkfish marinated with gram flour and ajwain."* Prasad won't be drawn on the bill, but he did say Tamarind prepared an an exotic lunch for 100 people (identity not revealed), billed at £40,000. Antonio strolled up the special green carpet for the charity film premiere in Leicester Square, and quipped: *"I just love the curry in Britain. It is delicious."*

Uma Thurman, Minnie Driver, Boris Becker, Mahesh Bhupati, and the King and Queen of Jordan like low-cal, non-spicy Indian dishes. Says Namita Punjabi (owner of Amaya, Chutney Mary, Masala Zone and Veeraswamy) *"we're not serving hurry-curry mixes. It's about sophistication of the curry for the elite. Everyone is willing to pay a huge amount for his pot of curry. It takes my chef 3 hours to prepare an exotic spread. The cost for the dish £40 pounds."* She should know; she's had the who's who of Britain eating at her classy restaurants: Prince Philip, Victoria and David Beckham, Hugh Grant, Liz Hurley, Monica Lewinsky, Rupert Murdoch and Cliff Richard.

Brad Pitt and Angelina Jolie recently opted not to eat at £120 per head ; instead they went to the Noor Jahan, South Ken at £20 a head. Shauyab Ahmed, part-owner of the restaurant, said: *"They booked a table for 12 at 7.30pm. They were joined by former supermodel Claudia Schiffer and her film director husband Matthew Vaughn, as well as actor Robert Downey Junior. The other customers loved it and were very happy to see them."* The party dined on a feast of

vegetable samosas, tandoori lamb chops and the house special, lamb pas anda at the 40-seat restaurant. *"They ate it all."* Mr Ahmed said: *"Matthew and Claudia are regulars. He always has pasanda".* Robbie Williams loves Pasanda too, he walks in every other day to Vama, just for that dish. Naomi Campbell and Jodie Kidd love Kerala curry. Johnny Depp is a Chicken Biryani freak, Bryan Adams, has a personal

Indian chef, and Kate Moss after watching Blur at their Hyde Park gig, and wearing a pair of hotpants, stopped off for a curryhouse Dhansak before turning in.

Phowll Air

An hour after a Frankfurt-bound Air India Boeing 747 Jumbo with 229 passengers on board, took off from Mumbai, a fire alarm caused a full emergency. The pilots activated the fire-suppression system in the cargo hold area and turned back and safely landed back in Mumbai. The passengers were evacuated to a hotel. Meanwhile, a check in the hold revealed nothing until a sniffer dog pointed to a soft leather bag. When the ground crew got a whiff, and looked inside they found two 3Kg innocent bags of curry powder. Once removed, the alarms stopped. Spokesman Jitendra

Bhargava explained that 747s have sensitive sensors that give alerts on detecting heat or smoke. In this case, the particles of the powder had escaped into the air in the cargo hold and triggered off the smoke detectors. *"In the past,"* he continued, *"mangoes and meat products, which generate heat, have been suspected of setting off fire alerts that led to delays, diversions and emergency landings on AI planes."* The curry powder belonged to a passenger from Gujerat, who said *"I was taking it to my mum. You can't get good curry powder in Germany. I declared the bag contents at check-in, and it had been accepted"*. It was duly confiscated and removed from the flight. This was of little comfort to the 229 passengers, who had suffered a 14 hour delay.

Drive in Curry

Diners at North Yorks Yarm's Raj Bari were shocked when a 45-year-old regular, who shall remain nameless to protect what little reputation he still has, was so desperate to get his takeaway, he drove right into the restaurant. Manager Mahfuz Ahmed said: *"It sounded like a bomb going off. It was very lucky only a few people suffered cuts and bruises."*

The Subcontinent

The subcontinent includes Pakistan, India, Nepal, Bhutan, Bangladesh, Myanmar (Burma) and Sri Lanka. Until 1947 this was one country ruled by the British. Now as independent states, each has its own unique culinary style. India has ten major regional cuisines and several minor ones, colour-grouped in the map. The main cuisines of the subcontinent are outlined in the following pages.

*Map from **India Food & Cooking**, courtesy New Holland Publishers, London. See page 62.*

It is a pleasant duty to enlarge this section for the fourth time in four editions. As we said before, the average overseas tourist expects to find a gastronomic desert when they visit the UK, although many it seems, are intensely relieved to find to that they can populate the proliferation of Macdonalds and its clones just as they do back home. Gourmets know better and head for culinary delights the like of which many can only dream of in their home countries. Despite our enduring reputation for boring, tasteless food, it is now several years since London has held the crown as the world's food capital. London boasts the unique and remarkable fact that every nation on the planet is represented with at least one restaurant serving its national food, and most of our bigger cities offer thirty or forty national cuisines. Their streets abound with serious cooks and restaurateurs whose mission is to produce good food and serve it well. Certainly that is the case in the 'Indian 'sector, whether it is haute-cuisine in highly-rated restaurants or simple home cooking in cosy, tiny venues. And the good news is that all over Great Britain standards are rising and authentic food is becoming more readily.

For years the majority of curry restaurants have been Bangladeshi-owned, profiting on a food style which is so alien to them they they won't eat it. In the last two decades, some have begun to 'come out' and declare their nationality, in some cases with a full menu of Bangladeshi dishes. Two do a fine job, the new Kolpata in E1 and the venerable Aziz in Oxford. There are rather less Pakistani, Sri Lankan, Nepalese and Indian restaurants. However most of these have always been true to their culinary roots, which is why we highlight as many of them as we can in this Guide.

In London you can dine in restaurants who specialise in the Indian region of their owners cooked to the highest, most authentic quality. Bengal, Goa, Gujarat, Hyderabad, Indian Kosher, Kashmir, Lucknow and Nawabi Dum Pukht, Maharashtra and Mumbai, Punjab and South India which itself has restaurants specialising in the cuisines of Kerela, Chetinad, Coorg, the Nairs, the Syrian Christians, Tamil Nadu and Udipi. They are all in London; their restaurants are all in this Guide and their cuisines and those of the subcontinent are outlined below and the next few pages. Not even India you can get such an array of good regional Indian cuisine in any one city. The A to Z of the Curry Menu (which follows) details every one of the items at these and all our British Asian restaurants. Outside London, regional restaurants are beginning to open up and down the country, but it remains a slow process. Sadly our sole Parsee and Rajasthani restaurants closed, proving that they were a bridge too far even for London. It is up to you the diners to keep the others thriving and become their regular diners.

Afghani Afghanistan's location had always held the strategic key to India until this century, for it was through the solitary mountain passes that the invaders came and possessed India from as early as 3000 bc. Located between Iran (formerly Persia) and Pakistan (formerly NW India), it brought the cuisine of the Middle East to India – and that of India to the Middle East. Afghan food features Kebabs and Birianis, and skewered spiced lamb over charcoal. See Afghan Kitchen restaurant, London N1. (See Pashtoon).

Balti Balti is a Pakistani phenomenon which does not exist in India and with Pakistan and India in a permanent state of war, communications between them are limited and bitter. The reality is that in north Pakistan's high mountains is the ancient state of Baltistan, sharing its border with China and India's Kashmir, and once on the Spice Route to China. Little may have been known about Balti food outside its indigenous area, had it not been for a small group of Pakistani Kashmiris, many from Mirpur, who settled in east Birmingham in the 1960s. There, they opened small cafés in the back streets, serving curries made aromatic with Kashmiri Garam Masala, and herbs, with plentiful coriander, in two-handled pots called the 'karahi' in India, but known here as the 'Balti pan'. Eating with no cutlery, using fingers and bread to scoop up the food, is the norm to the community, but a revelation to Birmingham's white population, who made Balti their own. Bear in mind that Balti served in the average curry house bears no resemblance to the real thing. See West Midlands, Birmingham Balti Zone for information.

Bangladeshi Most of the standard curry houses in the UK are owned by Bangladeshis and nearly all of those serve standard formula curries (from mild to very hot). Bangladesh, formerly East Pakistan, is located at the mouth of the River Ganges. Before Partition, the area either side of the Ganges was Bengal. Today Bengal is the

Indian state that shares its border with Bangladesh. Bangladesh is Muslim, so pork is forbidden. Unlike Hindu India, beef is eaten. The area enjoys prolific fresh and seawater fish – pomfret, boal, ruhi, hilsa and ayre, and tiger prawns – and specialises in vegetable dishes such as Shatkora (a kind of grapefruit used as an ingredient in meat/poultry dishes(and Niramish, (mixed vegetables) and some quite bitter dishes such as Shuktoni or shukti, meaning sour or bitter curry, eg using karela, bitter gourd. Until recently, true Bangladeshi cuisine was nigh on impossible to find in the UK. Now more of our Bangladeshi restaurants are serving the delights of their own country. Of these good examples are found at Aziz, Oxford, Café Naz E1, Hason Raja, London WC1, Kuti's Southampton, Shampan E1, and Spicery, Newcastle with maybe the most authentic of all at Kolpata E1.

Bengali Bengal is one of India's major culinary areas with Bengali cuisine India's second oldest-established. Mustard oil and seeds and the aromatic nigella seeds have been around in Bengali cuisine for thousands of years, as has the spice mixture unique to Bengal, Panch Phoran. Over time two states, East and West Bengal developed, their main difference being religion. In 1947 East Bengal was partitioned to Muslim Pakistan. In 1972 it became Bangladesh (see above). West Bengalis are mainly Hindu, and this proscribes no beef. Many dishes are common to both Bengals, for example, their adoration of sour tastes as seen in Dal Doyi Jhol – a runny lentil and yoghurt Soup, other dishes they have in common include Chachchori Morog – stir-fried mild chicken curry, Rezala Morgh – rich-tasting hot chicken, creamier curry than Korma in which green chillies are mandatory., Kalia – a thin red sauce. Aubergine (eggplant) were indigenous with Begun Shorshe, fried aubergines in yogurt and mustard sauce. while Baigan Burtha is the smoky puréed version. Niramish is another remarkable Vegan Curry. Potoler Dolma is a small wax gourd stuffed with a spicy filling. The 16th century Portuguese taught the Bengalis to make cheese (Paneer). Bengalis have a sweet tooth and they adore their sweet chutneys. J A Sharwood, a Victorian Raj merchant exported sweet Bengali mango chutney into Britain in the 1800s, and it is now a major feature at the curryhouse. It is not eaten in this form in India, but its basis was the Bengali Choti Mature sweet Mango Pickle. Calcutta is India's city of culture and in the 19th century it became famous for

those wonderful, sticky sweets, such Gulab Jamun, Jalebi, Ras Malai and Ros Gulla (see glossary). When he feels like doing it, you'll find authentic Bengali dishes at Udit Sarkhel's, Mango Sweet, London, SW14.

Chetinad A style of cooking from the southern Indian state of Tamil Nadu. A meat-eating community called Chetiyars, have been resident in the Madras area since the earliest times. Under the British, they became merchants and money lenders, owning large amounts of Burmese farmland. Fish Kozambhu – sour sauce tamarind & chillies. Chetinad dishes appear on menus all over the place but Coconut Lagoon restaurants (see Kenilworth, Warks) are owned by Chetiyars so are one of the few places to do them correctly.

Dum Pukht A cooking term meaning 'containing the steam'. The technique originated in ancient Persia deriving from the Persian word 'dampukht' or baked. A pot was filled with meat and spices. A tightly-fitting lid was sealed with chupatti dough. A hole was dug in the desert sands. and hot coals were placed in its bottom. Next the sealed pot was surrounded with hot coals, buried in the sand and left undisturbed to cook for a few hours. The magical moment comes when the lid is opened in front of the diners, releasing all those captured fragrances. This was the perfect vehicle for cooking Biriani. The contemporary exponent is Delhi master chef Imtiaz Qureshi. His modern versions use pastry as the lid, and of course the modern oven. Qureshi has not ventured to London, but we have the next best chef, Mohammed Rais. He also hails from Lucknow and he too claims ancestry back to the Nawab court and Qureshi is his uncle. Rais worked at the Red Fort (W1) from 1997, but moved to Darbar, SW6. See also Kasturi, EC3 and Naresh Matta (Rias' former assistant at the Red Fort) now at Eriki NW3.

Goan The tiny state of Goa had always depended on spices, fish and coconut. In 1492 it was taken by the Portuguese who occupied it until 1962. Christianity prevails and there are no objections to eating pork or beef. Modern Goan curries are based on all these ingredients, often combined with palm todi (feni) vinegar to create a gently unique sour taste. Goans are mostly non-vegetarian. Meat is usually confined to Sundays. Fish is mandatory at least once a day in the Goan diet. Bread-making was introduced by the Portuguese and though rice is important to Goa, bread takes precedence and is eaten with most

meals. Portuguese dishes, some unspiced, are to be found on the Goan menu. Many have evolved to be unique to Goa, with the addition of spices and coconut, yet have Portuguese names such as Cafreal, Xacutti and their most famous dish, Vindaloo. But it is not the dish from the standard curry house; the real thing is derived from the Portuguese dish Vino d'Alhos, traditionally pork marinated (the longer the better) in wine vinegar and garlic, then simmered until tender. To this the Goans added hot red chillies, creating a rich red curry gravy. But nothing is simple in Goa. Many dishes can appear with two different names in Portuguese or Goan (Konkani). And even same-named dishes can be cooked in different ways by the three different Goan communities. The majority of the population is Christian (Catholic) who eat everything including pork and beef and use plentiful chillies, todi-vinegar and sugar for piquancy, sweet and sour tastes. There is also a significant Goan Hindu population. Hindu Goans use less heat, tamarind or kokum for souring and jaggery for sweetening. The use asafoetida, chick peas, curry leaves, fenugreek, mustard and urid dhal. They don't eat beef, of course, and generally abstain from pork. Goa was occupied by Moslems for centuries before the Portuguese and there is still a significant Goan Moslem population. They do not eat pork or beef, mutton (goat) being their preferred meat, and the rather more complex dishes from Kashmir and the Moghals (Roghan Josh Gosht, kormas and birianis) are to be found in the Goan Muslim home. There is only one true Goan restaurant in the UK, Ma Goa in London SW15, although Goan dishes do appear at the better Indian restaurants such as Bombay Brasserie, SW7.

Gujarati Gujarat is a major culinary region, with a unique and abundant indigenous cuisine. It is home to more Hindi vegetarians (about 70%) than anywhere else in India, and their food is also India's least spicy. Despite her long Arabian Sea coastline, fish does not prevail. The Parsees (see entry) have lived in Gujarat for 1200 years (see below) and influenced the food with subtleties of sour and sweet. Prime Gujarati ingredients in savoury dishes are yoghurt, turmeric, gram flour, with a little sugar being added, displaying the penchant for sweet tastes. One dish exemplifying the Gujarati adoration of these ingredients is the primrose-yellow, soup-like dish called Khadi or Kari. Often served with with gram flour dumplings, this may have been

the very dish which gave 'curry' its name when in 1608, the first British diplomat docked at the port of Surat in southern Gujarat, to establish the East India Company's only trading post, until Bombay was built in 1674. With plentiful rainfall, Surat is the lushest of Gujarat's several main regions, guaranteeing ample supplies of grain, fruit and vegetables. Its signature dish is Undhyoo or Oondhiya in which chopped vegetables such as sweet potato, ratallu (purple yam), plantain, brinjal, green beans (papadi) etc are marinated in a spicy coconut paste and dry-fried in oil, often til (sesame) oil. Other Surati or Surti favourites are Ravaiya (baby aubergine stuffed with paneer paste) and Paunk, the winter-time delicacy of immature, fresh green millet grains is washed down with chass (buttermilk) drink. Breads made from wheat, millet and gram flour have names like Nankhatais, Ghari and Saglu Baglu Mithai. In the south west the lands of Kathiawadi (aka Saurashtra or Sorath) benefits from annual monsoon rains. Pulses dominate, used whole, ground or sprouted. Peanuts, and sesame prevail. Kathiawadi favourites include Debra (wheat flour mixed with spinach, green chillies, yogurt, salt and sugar). Breads include Phafda, (ajowan-flavoured assorted-flour puri). Methia Masala, a dry powder made from fenugreek seeds, chilly powder and salt, is sprinkled over raw vegetables and salads giving Kathiawari food a distinctive flavour. Sugarcane from which gur (jaggery) is processed is in famous sweetmeats such as Ladoo, the delectable Chhundo (hot and sweet shredded mango chutney) and Murabbo (sweet mango pickle). Central Gujarat loves its Farsan, crunchy fried snacks like Chakli, Doodh-Pak, Ghari, Nankhatai, Dhokla, and Khandvi. The famous Pakora/Bhaji also originated there, as did Dahi Vada (gram flour dumpling in a tangy yoghurt sauce), Murukus (crunchy, spicy snack nibbles made from a deep-fried spicy gram flour dough) known in Britain as Bombay Mix. Sev is the very fine vermicelli-sized version and Sevian Tamatar (wheat vermicelli noodles with tomato) is found there. North Gujarat food is non-spicy, virtually oil-free and best known for its thalis (once made of silver) consisting of rice, dhal, curry, vegetables, sprouted beans, farsan, pickles, chutney and raita. The north west province of Kutch borders Pakistan and Rajasthan in the arid Thar Desert. Specialities include Osaman (a consommée-like dhal soup flavoured with tomatoes, fresh coconut and coriander), Khichdi

(rice and lentils), Dhokla, a salty steamed cake, Doodhpak, a sweet, thickened milk confectionery and Shrikhand dessert.Gujarati vegetarian restaurants are prevalent in Leicester and Wembley, Middlesex, and they pop up elsewhere, too. Not all Gujaratis are Hindus or vegetarians. As a result of ancient Moslem occupations, there remains a small group of Gujarati beef-eating Moslems, called the Bohris Community. Unique to India they like soups such as Sarka, made with toovar oily dal, peanut and coconut. Their most outstanding dishes are Gosht Tikkea Malai ke Bohris (beef cubes marinated in cream, garlic and ginger, then coated with breadcrumbs and baked) and Lagania Seekh (egg-brushed beef kebab).

Hyderabadi (Andhra Pradesh) Andhra Pradesh (AP) formerly called Hyderabad, after its major city is the fifth largest state in India, both in area and population. In the 1930s, Hyderabad's royal ruler, the Nizzam was alleged to be the richest man in the world. The state is strategically situated in the south central India and forms a major link between north and south of India. It has a widely diversified agricultural base with a variety of cash crops. It is the granary of the south and produces a surplus of food grain. Hyderabad has been south India's strongest Moslem enclave since the 14th century. Today it is 40% Moslem. Hyderabad also has a Parsee population. Consequently, it is a meat-eating cuisine, but its cuisine is also one of India's hottest, as indicated by Mirchi Ka Salan, Chilli Curry. Mirchi means chilli, 'ka' means 'of' and Salan is a type of Urdu spicing speciality of Hyderabad and we encounter it twice more in Macchi ka Salan (Fish) and Baigan ka Salan (aubergine / eggplant. Biriani is a Hyderabadi speciality and we represent it with Tahiri a Vegetable Biriani speciality. Koftas and Kebabs are popular and the Parsee Khara Soti Boti Kebab, Omelette-enrobed Meat chunks Two dishes represent yoghurt's popularity, Chowgra a Yoghurt-based Vegetable curry and Churri a Herbal Yoghurt dip. Thoran lightly spiced Coconut and shredded Cabbage, is called Thoora in Andhra Pradesh.

Kashmiri Kashmir is India's most northerly state, located in the Himalayas thousands of feet above sea level. At partition in 1947 Kashmir was split between India and Pakistan, leading to conflict. On both sides of the border most Kashmiris are meat-eaters (even Hindu Kashmiris) whose rich sauces and ghee help to combat the cold. Lotus, apples, saffron and rice

but not wheat are specifically Kashmiri. The Moghuls built a summer retreat in the 16th century and brought with them aromatic spices, such as cardamom, cinnamon, clove, and aniseed. Nothing shows this off better than Kashmir's most celebrated dish, Korma. The Kashmiri Moslem wedding feast, the Wazwan at which the number of guests expected to attend always exceeds 500, is unique. Traditionally, the feast must contain exactly 36 different dishes, including chutneys and accompaniments. At least seven mutton dishes must be served. A 15kg male sheep is considered ideal. All parts are used; leg for dhaphol, ribs for tabak maz, neck for roghan josh, entrails for methi maz, quorma soured with apricots, jakhni soured with curds. Gushtaba giant meatball, with curd gravy, is traditionally the final dish, though a semolina might follow. See Chor Bizare, London, W1.

Maharashtran and Mumbai food Maharashtra is located in central India's Deccan plains. Maharashtran, or Marathi food has developed over the centuries as a minor cuisine. It is mild and delicately spiced and uses tamarind and fresh coconut. The climate is perfect for viticulture and supports two grape crops a year. One brand of method-champagne is widely exported under the name Omar Khyam. Mumbai (Bombay) is the vibrant, buoyant, commercial centre of India, with some of the highest property prices in the world, Bollywood, expensive restaurants, and home-delivery Pizza, contrasting with the shocking poverty of shanti-towns, and street-begging. Bombay was the creation of the British and as such it has never developed a large cuisine. A favourite UK curryhouse dish, Bombay Potato (see A-Z glossary) is not found in Bombay, but it is typical of Bombay tastes. Gujarat's Murukus was re-invented as 'Bombay Mix' in Southall in the 1970s. Sev *(qv)* is one ingredient of Bhel Puri, Bombay's favourite street food. It is served cold and is delicious. Restaurants such as London's Masala Zones, Bhel Puri Houses in Drummond Street, Wembley, SW16 and other places around London specialise in it. The original fishing tribes, the Kholis, however, had a couple of delicacies up their sleeve; Bombay Duck *(qv)* and Bangda (fish head) curry. Parsees migrated into Bombay after the British created their fortress trading posts there in the C18th to form India's largest Parsee community (see below).

Moghul Almost surrounded by Haryana is Delhi, the small state containing India's capital

city. Delhi has no cuisine in its own right; it was during the 16th century that Indian food was taken to its supreme culinary heights in the Moghul capital city of Delhi, as well as Agra, Lahore and Kashmir (see below). East of Delhi is the largely Muslim state of Uttar Pradesh, with Moghul Agra and its Taj Mahal in the west and the river Ganges flowing through its length. No one was richer than the Moghuls, and it was during their time, four centuries ago, that Indian food was perfected. Authentically, this style of food should be subtly spiced. The French may believe they invented 'haute cuisine', but they were pipped to the post by Moghul chefs, who did to Indian food what the French chef Varenne did to French cooking a century later; they perfected sauces using garlic, butter and cream with the addition of something uniquely Indian; a marriages of spices. They created supremely aromatics curries with sensual sauces like Classic Korma, Pasanda, Rhogan Josh Gosht and Raan, roast lamb. The standard curry-house has based some of its formula on mild, rich, creamy dishes such as these, albeit lacking the subtlety of the real thing. Rather more authentic interpretations can be found in an increasing number of 'haute cuisine' restaurants around the country, spelt variously Moghul, mogul, moglai, muglai mugal, mugul, etc.

Nawabi Of culinary importance, is Lucknow, now an Indian army city, and one which is of immense historical importance especially during the time of the wealthy Nawabs, who came to royal prominence as the Moghuls declined. One inheritance is Nawabi cuisine. Lucknow, being Moslem, enjoys meat, but its cooking is unique. Flavours are spicy aromatic and subtle and the food is luxurious. One process is called Dum or Dum Pukht. It means slow-cooking by steaming the curry or rice dish, in a handi or round pot, whose lid is sealed into place with a ring of chapatti dough. The resulting dish is opened in front of the diners, releasing all those captured fragrances.

Nepalese Beautiful Himalayan mountains, the world's only Hindu kingdom, home of Gurkas, sherpas, yak and yeti, Kumari the living virgin goddess-princess, Everest, and unique food. Some similarities to north Indian, with curry (tarkari), rice (bhat), and wheat breads (roti haru). Kukhura (chicken), Khasi (lamb), Dumba (mutton), Bhutwa (pork), Hach Ko (duck), Jhinge (prawn) and Maccha (fish) are cooked in the clay oven (chula) or curried. Specialities include Aloo Achar, potatoes in pickle sauce, Momo/Momocha, keema-filled dumplings, and Tama Bodi, bamboo shoots and black-eye beans, a dish showing Tibetan/Chinese roots. More examples will be found in the entries for Great Nepalese, NW1, Gurkha Kitchen, Oxted, Surrey and Gurkha Square, Fleet, Hants.

Pakistani Until independence in 1947, Pakistan formed the north-western group of Indian states. Located between Afghanistan and India, it contains the famous Khyber Pass. The people are predominantly meat-eaters, favouring lamb and chicken (being Muslim, they avoid pork). Charcoal cooking is the norm, and this area is the original home of the tandoor. Breads such as Chupatti, Naan and Paratha are the staple. Balti cooking originated in the northernmost part of Pakistan (see earlier). In general, Pakistani food is robustly spiced and savoury. The area called the Punjab was split by the formation of Pakistan, and it is the Punjabi tastes that formed the basis of the British curry house menu (see Punjab, London WC2). Bradford, Glasgow and Southall have sizeable Pakistani populations.

Parsee/Persian This is not a regional cuisine; it is the cuisine of a religious sect, and their unique cuisine has evolved over the last 1200 years from when the Parsees fled Persia to escape persecution from the newly Muslims. There are now only around 100,000 Parsees. Most live in Bombay, but there are other groups in Hyderabad and Gujarat. It is quite common to see Persian dishes listed on the standard curry house menu. Dishes such as Biriani and Pullao did indeed originate in Persia (Iran) while Dhansak and Patia. are Parsee dishes. However they are a pastiche of the real thing. Parsees have no religious proscriptions on eating, so they eat pork, beef as well as lamb and shellfish and they love egg dishes. Meat mixed with vegetables and fruit is typical of Persian and Parsee food, though the latter has now incorporated the Indian spice palette and sweet and sour combinations, typified in their Patia. The most celebrated and popular of all Parsee dishes is Dhansak, where in the real thing meat on-the-bone is incorporated with four types of lentil (polished moong, masoor, chana and toovar). Slow cooking in a heavy lidded pot amalgamates the flavours. During the cooking, a kind of ratatouille of aubergine, tomato, spinach and fresh chillies is added. Sweet and sour comes from jaggery (palm sugar) and a slight overtone of sour from fresh tamarind juice. Jardaloo Boti is

lamb cooked with dried apricots and the coriander coated fish dish, Patrani Maachli is a Parsee speciality. Their roasted vegetable dish, Oonbhariu is one of the best vegetable dishes in India. With the demise of the N19 Parsee restaurant it remains to south-west London's Bombay Brasserie and Chutney Mary, who both have Parsee chefs who cook authentic Parsee dishes, and of course, Cyrus, himself a Parsee, at Café Spice Namaste, E1.

Pashtoon It refers to tribal people and their language from the rugged mountain passes of Afghanistan *(qv)* and Pakistan *(qv)* in the former North-West Frontier Province, whose name for themselves is Pathan, Pashtun, Phuktana or Pukhtun. Afghan food is pretty basic, especially at tribal level, involving hunting wild life then grilling it or slow-cooking it in pots. Grills, Kebabs, Koftas and Birianis are popular, spiced with the unique Afghan spice mix, Char Masala (four aromatic spices) and cooked mostly in their own juices. Visit Tagore, Welling Kent and Kasturi EC1.

Punjabi For the purposes of this Guide we link together India's north-central states Haryana, Himachal Pradesh, Uttaranchal and Punjab. The former have little culinary interest, though the very best Basmati rice comes from Himachal Pradesh, which as its name suggests is in the foothills of the Himalayas: Dehradun Basmati is to rice what Krug or Dom Perignon is to champagne. The Punjab, like Kashmir was another state split into two after partition, with western Punjab and the Moghul city of Lahore in Pakistan. Food knows no boundaries, and Punjabi food is a major culinary style which is identical in both the Punjabs and in Haryana (meaning 'green land') Punjabi cuisine began to evolve from early in the first millennium AD. It is perhaps the best known Indian food because the original curry restaurants in the developed world based their menus on Punjabi cuisine. Dairy farming is a major Punjabi industry and its prolific wheat and grain crops, earn it the title 'the granary of India', and Parathas and Puris are staples. Oilseeds, spices, peas and beans and much else. grows prolifically in the area. The food is very savoury and fenugreek leaf (methi) and mustard leaf (rai) are virtually staples. Robust curries like Punjabi Keema, Methi Gosht, Aloo Ghobi Methi and Sag Paneer, Mattar Valor – pea and bean curry are typical. Best Punjabi exponents are found in Southall, but look out for other Punjabi references throughout the Guide.

South Indian South India consists of three sub-tropical and very fertile states, Karnataka, Kerela and Tamil Nadu and also includes the Konkan Coast or Karavali (800 miles of rugged and beautiful Indian coastline stretching from Mumbai to Mangalore). The area was first occupied in about 1000BC by the Dravidians, who are still the largest racial group. South India's cuisine has remained virtually unmodified since that time, making it India's longest-established cuisine. When the Dravidians first arrived and cultivated the area, they encountered South India's main indigenous ingredients: ginger, coconut, curry leaves, peppercorns, turmeric and curry leaf. The food is rice-based, with no wheat. Yoghurt and tamarind provide two quite differing sour tastes. Many dishes use all these ingredients, and many dishes are common to all three south Indian states, albeit under different names, and with subtle differences in flavourings. Common to all states is Dosa, huge, thin, crisp rice-lentil-flour pancakes, with a curry filling (Masala) and Idlis – steamed rice or lentil-flour dumplings accompanied by Sambar, a lentil-based curry, Rasam, a hot and spicy consommé and coconut chutney. Other rice-based items include Upuma and Uthappam (see A-Z glossary). Because of the intense heat and frequent high humidity, thin curries are preferred because they are more easily digested than the thick-sauced versions of the north. Day to day, much of the area's population is fish-eating or vegetarian, but most will eat meat or poultry on special occasions. Many exotic vegetables include, drumstick, mooli, snake gourd, doodi, bottle gourd, bittergourd (karela). tindoora, and long beans. Vegetable curries using them include Avial, Thoran and many others. Some specialist groups, such as Coorgs, Malabaris, Nairs, Mophlas, Syrian Christians and Jews (see below) eat meat and chicken dishes on a regular basis. Specialist restaurants have long been found been in and around London (especially Tooting SW17). The specialist food of Udipi (a small town north of Mangalore) is to be found at Sagar, W6. The first restaurant to bring south Indian meat, chicken and sea food dishes to the UK was Chutney Mary,SW10 the Quilon, SW1. But other restaurants have developed the theme as specialisations. The best are Kerela, N1, Rasa Travanvore, N19 and Coconut Lagoon restaurants (see Kenilworth, Warks). One conservation-minded, zero-cost serving method dating from 1000BC and still in daily use is the

Pullisseri · Avial · Thoran · Seeni · Olan · Curd Chutneys · Erisseri · Pickles · Sambar · Payasam Puddings · Papad · Banana Chips

The Sumptuous Sadya

banana leaf. This fleshy, pliable, ribbed, inedible leaf serves as your plate and on which is placed the traditional meal (the Sadya, all courses together, but with each item in an invariable position on the leaf, see picture above. No cutlery is needed and once you have eaten, the plate leaf is wrapped up and disposed of to bio-degrade. When will the Sadya appear in a UK restaurant as a trendy (and no doubt costly) dining experience, one wonders?

Sri Lankan Sri Lanka is the small, pearl-shaped island, formerly Ceylon, at the southern tip of India. Its cuisine is distinctive and generally chilli hot. They eat similar fare to that eaten in south India, i.e. vegetarian dishes, but they also enjoy very pungent meat, squid, chicken and duck curries. Look out for black curries and white ones, and devilled dishes. Hoppers are pancakes made of fermented rice, mixed with highly alcoholic palm toddy) and a little sugar, and are available in both sweet and savoury versions, String hoppers are rice-flour noodle nests. A festive dish introduced by a Dutch burger centuries ago is called Lampries (Longkirist). here a full meal of meat curry, kofta, rice and sambols is wrapped inside a banana leaf parcel and cooked. Samols made of coconut and onion accompany all meals. Good Sri Lankan restaurants include Palm Paradise, Southall, Middlesex, Prince of Ceylon, London N4, Elephant Walk NW6 and Jaffna House SW17.

Tandoori The ancient Egyptians created the side-entry clay-oven in which to bake their bread. Later they were used in ancient Persia where they are still called the' tonir', and their bread 'nane lavash'. A small variant seems to have been invented in India at the same time. Instead of having a side-entry, this egg-shaped vessel's entry hole was at the top, which was narrower than its centre point. It was the ancestor of today's tandoori oven. Its base had a small air-hole, below which was placed an even earlier invention, charcoal. Easily transported, this oven was probably invented to enable travelling traders to cook at their camp-sites. Corroborative evidence exists in the form of oven remains found all along ancient trade routes. By 300bc Sanskrit writings on cooking techniques describes meat spread with a honey-coloured spicy paste and cooked in the clay-oven, the 'kavan kunndu' (fire-container). Could kunndu be the derivation of the Hindi word 'tandoor'? The paste 'kunndu pachitam' (fire-paste) 'spread on meat' sounds remarkably like a marinade, the contents of which are unclear, but to achieve the colour as described, it could well contain yoghurt to assist in tenderising the flesh, plus spices, garlic, salt and indeed honey itself. For the first time we know that spiced meat, and probably poultry too was cooked in the tandoor.. The ancient Iranians also have a claim to the derivation of the word tandoor. It could have derived from their words 'tata', meaning 'hot', and 'andar', meaning 'inside'. Either way the tandoor remained on the Afghan/Pakistan border until modern times. The world's first tandoori restaurant, the Moti Mahal was established there in 1922. Partition forced its Hindu owner to move to Delhi in 1947. It remained as India's only tandoori restaurant until recent times. Even now, outside the five-star hotels, tandoori food is rarely found in India. Conversely tandoori food is ubiquitous in the UK and is some of the most popular dishes. Recently a Moti Mahal branch opened in London WC2.

The Cuisine of South East Asia

INDO CHINA South East Asia, called 'further India' is the peninsula between India and China containing Burma, Thailand, Malaysia, Singapore, and Indonesia. Britain is blessed with an ever-increasing number of restaurants serving these spicy cuisines, and this Guide lists just some of the best. Here we thumbnail their cuisines:

Burmese Burma (Myanmar), shares its boundaries with Bangladesh, India, China, Laos and Thailand. Since independence from Britain in 1948, Burma has been isolated by dictatorial communism. Our loss, because Burma is an exquisite country, with a gentle, bullied Buddhist population, whose food is a combination of these styles. There is the spiciness of India with ghee-fried curries using turmeric, pepper, tamarind and chilli (though less than in many Indian regions). There is the fragrance of Thailand, in the form of lemon grass, (though less of this than in Thailand) shrimp paste (Ngapi), fish sauce and coconut. From China comes steaming and stir-fry wok techniques, tofu, bamboo and soy sauce. Rice (Hta-Min) and noodles (kaukswe) are the staples. There is no wheat bread-making. There are no religious objections to eating pork (whethar) or beef (ahmai) and they enjoy lamb/mutton (seikthar) chicken (kyethar) duck (bairthar) fish (ngar) and shrimp (pazun). The only UK Burmese restaurant is the Mandalay, London W2.

Malaysian Malaysia's only border is a narrow strip at her north where the peninsula joins that of Thailand, and it shares many tastes in food. Such similarities include the love of lemon grass, shrimp paste (petis or belacan pronounced blachan) sweet lime (kaffir) and, above all chillies (the taste for really hot food diminishes in popularity as one goes southwards, away from Thailand). Differences include the use of tamarind (asam) to achieve a tart taste, turmeric for yellow colour and peanut to thicken. Instead of galangal, Malaysians use aromatic pink ginger buds with their flowers and or zedoary (cekur), both hard to obtain (ginger or galangal can substitute). Noodles are more ubiquitous in Malayasia than in Thailand, and curry with noodles is as common there as curry with rice. Try Laksa if offered it. Curries prevail, showing their Indian, Chinese and Thai influences. Thinner fragrant gravies, often based on coconut milk, also contain chillies, ginger, and lemon grass. A curry version of Satay is Inche Kabin, where curry paste is added to the sauce, which is coated onto a whole chicken, then grilled. Wet curries are flavoured with lemon grass and shrimp paste, along with the robust spices of India. Soto Ayam and Rempah are two of Malaysia's better known curries. Malaysia's population is composed of Chinese, Indians, and Malayans, and this results in a distinctive cuisine also known as Nonya. Best UK restaurants: Georgetown Malaysian, Nottingham, Stratford, Leeds and Kenilworth

Thai Thailand shares her borders with Burma, Laos, Kampuchea and Malaysia, yet her cuisine is hardly influenced by them. It is the combination of tastes which makes Thai cuisine unique. Key items are fragrance from lime leaves (markrut), lemon grass stalks (takrai) and holy basil leaves; heat from explosive tiny chillies and to a lesser extent from galangal, a peppery type of ginger. Savoury tastes come from from shrimp paste (kapi), sweet from palm sugar and seasoning from thin clear fish sauce (nam-pla) which never dominates, but enhances the other ingredients. Thailand grows dozens of vegetables which have no translation in the west. Appearance matters greatly in Thai cooking, and no where else on earth makes prettier carved garnishes than the Thai. Roses from radishes, carnations from carrots and coronets from cucumbers are examples. Chicken, pork, duck, beef, fish, shellfish are regularly in the diet. Wheat, dairy products, potato, tomato and potato are largely absent from the diet. Glutinous rice, tamarind, soy sauce, noodles and chops sticks are common to the far north. The south prefers fragrant non-sticky rice and coconut milk which gives Thai curries a creamy sauce. Indian spiced mutton is eaten in the Moslem far south, as one approaches Malaysia. The best UK Thai restaurants UK is Orchid Lounge at Jaipur, Milton Keynes, Bucks with Blue Elephant, London, SW6 and Rumwong Guildford close behind.

Singaporean Singapore is a small island country in Southeast Asia. It lies near the southern tip of the Malay Peninsula about where the South China Sea and the Indian Ocean meet. The sea is an arm of the Pacific Ocean. Singapore consists of a large island and more than 50 smaller islands. founded in 1819 by Sir Stamford Raffles, and was used by the British as their major trading post in the area, the legacy of which is today's major business centre. Singapore's population is the most cosmopolitan of the area, with Indian, Chinese, Malay, Indonesian and European influences. The Chinese or Hokkien predominate, and little wonder, so do noodles. Because Singapore, like Hong Kong were created from nothing, and then populated by such a mixture of races, there has been insufficient time for few, if any true Singaporean dishes to evolve. Fish Head Curry and Hokkien stir-fry Noodles are two.

Indonesia Adjacent to Malaysia is Indonesia, the former Dutch East Indies. It consists of in excess of 13,600 islands, some of which are uninhabited. The world's fourth largest population lives on the remaining islands, which include Sumatra, Borneo, Java, New Guinea, Bali and the celebrated Molucans, the spice islands, the original home of clove, mace and nutmeg, where the cuisine never uses these spices. Indonesia likes its spicy dishes although spices, ironically earn relatively little income for Indonesia. The Chinese introduced Nasi Goreng (fried rice with vegetables), and Bhami Goreng (noodles). The Indians brought their curries and spices, the Portuguese brought chilli, peanuts and tomatoes while the Dutch brought sweets and cakes, and of course Rijstaffel (a selection of up to 40 dishes of meat, vegetables and rice served in individual bowls). Satay, meat coated in a lightly spiced peanut sauce, originated here. Rendang is a popular beef (water buffalo) curry flavoured with galangal, lemon grass. shrimp paste (terasi or trasi) turmeric leaf, and chillies

INDIA: Food & Cooking
by Pat Chapman

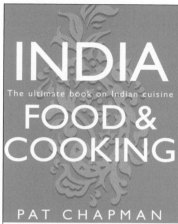

256 pages, 268 x 198 x 28 mm
Hardback ~ 40 colour pictures
ISBN-10: 1845376196
ISBN-13: 978-1845376192
£19.99
Special Offer £12 inc p&p
order online at **patchapman.co.uk**

Readers in the 'developed' world all know and love our local curry houses, but this is not a curry book, if by curry we mean the pastiche which is served at many curryhouses outside India herself.

This is a collection of recipes from real India and Pat Chapman has spent over three years travelling the length and breadth of India's 26 federal states collecting thousands of culinary secrets from home cooks, chefs, and foodies. The 200 recipes represent the tip of the iceberg from a country whose a landmass exceeds that of Europe, has several main culinary styles; with numerous minor variations.

The recipes give the reader the widest range of ingredients, tastes and methods, with all the principal signature dishes of each region included. They are in short, the dishes the reader is most likely to encounter whilst travelling in that enigmatic and contradictory land called India. They are cooked in the manner which Indian householders would be proud to offer to their friends and family. Each recipe includes a short introduction with regional or other relevant information.

Indian food began its development thousands of years ago. At a time when Britain was covered in ice and populated with individuals in bearskins and wode, whose main activities included picking berries and clubbing to death anything alive, including each other, India was already cooking refined spicy food.

To understand how India and her food evolved, the book goes on an exciting journey over the last nine millennia. The book comes right up to date by examining modern Indian food trends. Then it explains in detail the utensils and cooking methods, spices, herbs, and ingredients we need to cook Indian food.

The book is a good read, with every recipe enjoyable and easy to cook.

The Flame Grill

Shahi Noor Tandoor

Shahi Turbo Cooker

Shahi Tandoor

Mega Stock Pot

Romali Roti Griddle

Tel: 020 8896 2696   info@clayovens.com
Fax: 020 8896 2686   www.clayovens.com

The original bigger bottle

The 660ml beer bottle has become an icon,
but it almost didn't happen.

When we started Cobra in 1989, we had the only
double-sized bottle on the market. No one had seen it
before, and it was a bit of a struggle to get beer-
lovers interested. Luckily for us, a larger bottle is the
perfect size for sharing, and now you'll see 660ml
bottles all over the UK.

Just like Cobra, come to think of it.

cobrabeer.com

To the first-timer, the Indian restaurant menu is a long and complex document. This glossary explains many of the standard, and some of the specialised, dishes and items that you are likely to encounter. See also **The Cuisine of the Subcontinent** *(psee earlier)*. Spellings of vowel sounds will vary from restaurant to restaurant, reflecting the 15 languages and hundreds of dialects of the subcontinent. *(See Masala, Moglai, Papadam and Rhogan Josh Gosht for some examples.)* Our spelling here is as near as possible to the standard accepted way of spelling, when translating phonetically from the main languages to English.

A

AAM or **AM** Mango.

ACHAR or **ACHAAR** Pickle, such as lime, mango, aubergine, etc. Achar Gohst is meat curry, curried in a pickle base, Achar Murgh is the chicken version.

AFGHANI CURRY Nuts and fruit are added for the standard curry house interpretation.

ALOO Potato.

AYURVEDIC FOOD. Ayurveda is the ancient Indian holistic philosophy from 1100BC concerning body, mind and soul, which states that each of us has one of three different body types, or 'dosha' fixed at the moment of conception, which determine everything about us – our appearance, what illnesses we are likely to suffer from and what foods we should eat. The word is derived from the Sanskrit 'ayur', meaning 'life' or more literally 'lifespan' and 'veda', 'knowledge' and is intertwined with the Hindu sacred religious works, the Vedas. Ayurvedic medicine is still widely and successfully practiced in India using, amongst other methods, herbal infusions as cures. Ayurvedic dietary rules are complex, but in outline sweet foods cool the body (ie lower its metabolism) and increase its weight; salty foods warm it and increase weight; bitter/sour foods cool it and decrease it; pungent /savoury foods warm it and decrease it. However not only is this subject to seasonal variation, the detail is confusing. For example, vegetable oil cools the body while ghee *(qv)* heats it; fennel seed cools while aniseed warms and both garlic and ginger heat it. This is further confused by the contradiction of China's ancient Yin-Yang (cool-warm) food philosophy, where garlic, for example is Yin (which decreases body heat) while ginger is Yang (which increases it). This may explain why in India today at least 25% of today's Hindus dismiss Ayurveda saying science and common sense define how your meal must be perfectly balanced. Be that as it may, some restaurants offer Ayurvedic menus, such as London's Mantra EC3 and Quilon SW1, and Altrincham's Dilli. *(see Garam Masala).*

B

BAIGAN or **BEGUN** *see Brinjal.*

BALTI Balti originated centuries ago in north Pakistan's Mirpur, Kashmir and Skardu (Baltistan). It found its way to east Birmingham in the 1970s, where any combination of ingredients was curried in a two-handled pot known as the **KARAHI** *(qv)* elsewhere, but the Balti there. Served to the table still cooking, the art is to eat the food – which should be spicy, herby and aromatic – Indian-style, with the bread as the scoop in the right hand. In the 1990s, Balti spread rapidly all over the UK and beyond. The Balti found at the standard Bangladeshi curry house, however, owes its flavours more to Patak's acidic Balti paste than to Mirpur, and unless it is cooked in its pan and served cutlery-free, it will (correctly) never convince the Brummy purist that it is anything other than hype.

BARFI or **BURFI** Indian fudge-like sweet made from reduced condensed milk (koya or khoa), in various flavours.

BASMATI from the Hindi word for 'fragrant' is the name for certain varieties of rice grown exclusively in the plains of northern India and Pakistan. It has a characteristic aroma in both the raw and cooked state, and a distinctive shape, which on cooking elongates to almost double its length whilst its width remains the same and it slowly releases carbohydrates (i.e. it has a low glycaemic index compared with other rice).

BATERA Football-sized fried bread puri *(qv)* becoming increasingly popular.

BATTAR Quail.

BENGAL CURRY A curyhouse chicken or meat curry with chilli, sugar, potato cubes and halves of tomato.

BHAJI or **BHAJEE** Dryish, pan-fried mild vegetable curry.

BHAJIA Deep-fried fritter, usually with sliced onion, mixed with spiced gram flour batter, then deep-fried. Bhajia is the correct term, meaning fried. Bhaji or Bhajee is the anglicisation. For the real thing, visit Maru's Bhajia House, Wembley, Middlesex. *See also Pakora.*

BHEL PURI This is the delicious street food snack from Bombay. It is a cold combination of those crunchy squiggles you find in Bombay Mix *(qv)*, the smallest of which is called Sev. To this is added small-diced cooked potato, puffed rice (mamra), coriander leaf, onion and chilli. It is laced with brown sweet and

sour tamarind (imli) sauce, green coriander chutney (dhania) and red chilli/garlic sauce, and topped with crispy puri biscuit chippings. The result is an exquisite combination of crisp, chewy and soft textures with sweet, hot, savoury and sour tastes. Variations include differing amounts of ingredients, under various similar names, such as Sev Batata Puri, Dahi (yoghurt) Batata Puri, Chat Aloo Papri and Batata Pava. Bhel can be accompanied by **GOL GOPPAS** (q.v.). This delicious food is generally beyond the abilities of the average curry house, so is rarely found. Try it when you can *(see London's Drummond St NW1, Shahee Bhel SW16 and Masala Zone W1)*.

BHOONA or **BHUNA** Cooking process involving slowly frying out all the water content to produce a dry, usually mild curry.

BINDI A pulpy, rather sappy vegetable also known as okra or ladies fingers. Correct cooking of this dish is a good test of a chef's ability.

BIRIANI Traditionally, rice baked between layers of meat or vegetable filling, enhanced with saffron and aromatic spices, served topped with edible silver leaf – vark *(qv)*. The restaurant interpretation is a cooked rice, artificially coloured, with filling stir-fried in. It is usually heavily garnished and served with a vegetable curry sauce *(see Pullao)*.

BOMBAY DUCK A smallish fish native to the Bombay docks, known locally as bommaloe macchi. This was too hard for the British Raj to pronounce, so it

became Bombay Duck. It is dried and appears on the table as a crispy deep-fried starter or accompaniment to a curry. Following a senseless EU ban a decade ago, it is now allowed. An acquired taste!

BOMBAY MIX An age-old traditional Indian snack nibble, called muruku, made from a savoury, gram-flour, spiced batter called ompadi, which is forced through a press straight into the deep-frier, to give different shapes and thicknesses of squiggly nibbles. Nuts, pulses, seeds and other ingredients are added. It should always be really crunchy and fresh. Re-invented by GK Noon, owner of Royal Sweets in Southall, under the catchy name Bombay Mix, it will keep you going at the bar.

BOMBAY POTATO A popular invention of the curry house. Potatoes in curry sauce with onions and tomato.

BOTI KEBAB Marinated cubes of lamb cooked in a tandoor oven (see Tandoori).

BRINJAL Aubergine, also called baigan or began. In Baigan Burtha, aubergine is smoked, spiced and mashed, in Baigan Bhaji it is chopped and curried by pan-frying.

C

CTM ~ CHICKEN TIKKA MASALA The unshakable ledgend is that it waas invented by a British curry house chef (identity unknown) c1980, as a way to exploit his already popular Chicken Tikka by adding a creamy, pink, mild sauce made tasty by 'skilful' blending of curry sauce, tomato purée, tandoori paste, cream, coconut, mango chutney, ground almonds and a surfeit of red food colouring. It is a dish not found in India (because they do not have red food colouring nor Tandoori dishes). In any case India already had a dish from the 16th century Moghuls (See Murgh Makhani). CTM is now ordered by 65% of all diners. Not only that, it appears in supermarket sandwiches, flavours crisps, is a pizza topping and even spices

mayonnaise. If only that chef had copyrighted it, he'd be earning millions in royalties a year. See Tandoori and Tikka.

CEYLON CURRY Curryhouse concoction cooked with lemon, chilli, and coconut.

CHANA A yellow lentil resembling, but not identical to, the split pea, used in dhal (qv) and to make gram flour. Kabli Chana is the chickpea. Both can be curried or dried and deep-fried as in Bombay Mix (qv). See also Paneer.

CHASNI CHICKEN A central Scotland Pakistani restaurant name for CTM (qv).

CHAT or CHAAT Literally means 'snack', though often it can be a salad.

CHILLI Fleshy members of the capsicum family, ranging in heat from zero (the bell pepper) to incendiary. All chillies start green and, if left long enough, eventually turn red, the one being no hotter than the other. The chilli normally used in Indian cooking is the narrow 7.5cm (3in) cayenne. The hottest in the world are Mexican Habañeros, Caribbean Scotch Bonnets and Bangladeshi Naga (qv). People build up a tolerance to chillies, but they should never be inflicted upon the novice, not even in fun.

CHUPATTI A 15cm (6in) flat disc of unleavened bread, cooked dry on the Tava (qv). It should always be served hot and pan-fresh. The spelling can vary – Chupati, Chapatti, etc.

CHUTNEY The common ones are onion chutney, mango chutney and tandoori chutney. There are dozens of others that rarely appear on the standard menu. See Sambals.

CURRY The only word in this glossary to have no direct translation into any of the subcontinent's 15 or so languages. The word was coined centuries ago by the British in India. Possible contenders for the origin of the word are: Karahi or Karai (Hindi) – the wok-like frying pan used all over India to prepare masala (spice mixtures); Karhi or Khadi – a soup-like dish made with spices, gram-flour dumplings and buttermilk; Kari – a spicy Tamil sauce; Turkuri – a seasoned sauce or stew; and Kari Phulia – Neem leaves, which are small and rather like bay leaves, used for flavouring. The Dutch, who were in India in the 17th century have their own derivation. They say it was used in Malaya for their Malay curries, and that it derived from the word Lekker meaning delicious, or in colloquial Dutch, Lekkerie.

CURRY HOUSE See Formula Curries.

D

DABBA or DHAABA The subcontinent's version of the transport café, it's a ubiquitous roadside eatery usually made of tin sheets and thatch or tarpaulin.

Millions exist. If packed with truckers (their lorries parked all around) it's good. A limited menu offers dhals, spicy omelettes, mutton and vegetable curries, tea (chai) and soft drinks at truly low prices. Seating usually a charpoy or rope-strung cot in the open air in front of the eatery. Primitive kitchen fully visible. Vertical neon tubes are its night time symbol. Dabba dishes are appearing on some London chi-chi menus, at rather more expensive prices.

DAHI or DOHI Yoghurt, used as a chutney (see Raita) and in the cooking of some curries. Most curry houses make their own, and it is delicious as an accompaniment to curry, being less sharp than the shop-bought equivalent. Incidentally, Dahi, not water, is the best antidote if you eat something that's too hot for you.

DAHI VADA South Indian savoury gram-flour doughnut, deep-fried, cooled and dunked into cold, spicy yoghurt (see Vada).

DAL or DHAL Lentils There are numerous types of lentil in the subcontinent. They contain carbohydrates and protein and being inexpensive, they are the staple much of village India. The common restaurant types are massor (red, which cooks yellow), moong (green), chana (also used to make gram flour) and urid (black).

DEGCHI or DEKHCHII Brass or metal saucepan without handles.

DHANIA Coriander leaf, India's main herb or seed, her main spice.

DHANSAK Traditional Parsee meat dish cooked in a purée of lentils, aubergine, tomato and spinach. Curryhouses use dhal and methi, and sometimes chilli and pineapple.

DOPIAZA Traditional meat dish. Do means 'two', piaza means 'onion'. Onions appear twice in the cooking, deeply caramelised and second fried. This gives the dish a sweetish taste.

DOSA South Indian pancake made from rice and urid (lentil) flour, which, when made into a batter, soon ferments to give a superb sour taste. The batter is ladeled onto a hot plate and spread thinly to achieve a pancake shape.

MASALA DOSA is a Dosa filled with mashed potato curry spiced with onion, chilli, turmeric, curry leaf and mustard seed.

DUM Cooking by steaming in a sealed pot, invented by the Royal Nawabs (*see The Cuisine of the Subcontinent*), e.g. Aloo Dum, steamed potatoes. Also called Dum Pukt or Pukht (pron 'pucked')

E

ELAICHI Cardamom. Can major in curries – for example, Elaichi Murgh is chicken curried with a predominance of green cardamom

F

FOOD COLOURING Unlikely to appear on the menu except to state that the food excludes it. But if your food turns up in lurid, bright flourescent reds, yellows or greens, it does include it and it ain't natural! The ingredient is Tartrazine, which is coal extract and which can cause asthma attacks and hyperactivity. Despite endless attempts to get it banned in the UK, it is sadly still permitted in small doses. *See Pullao Rice, Tikka, Tandoori and Sheek Kebabs etc.*

FOOGATH Lightly cooked vegetable dish found in the Malabar area of South India. Any vegetable such as gourds or plantain can be used.

FORMULA CURRIES Many of our 'Indian' (*qv*) restaurants operate to a formula which was pioneered in the late 1940s. In those days, a way had to be found to deliver a variety of curries, without an unreasonable delay, from order to table. Since all authentic Indian recipes require hours of cooking in individual pots, there was no guarantee that they would even be ordered. So cubed meat, chicken or potatoes, dal and some vegetables were lightly curried and chilled, and a large pot of thick curry gravy, a kind of master stock, was brewed to medium-heat strength. To this day, portion by portion, on demand, these ingredients are reheated by pan-frying them with further spices and flavourings. At its simplest, a Medium Chicken Curry, that benchmark of middle ground, is still on many menus, though sometimes disguised as 'Masala', and requires no more than a reheat of some gravy with some chicken. For instance, take a typical mixed order for two. Chicken Korma (fry a little turmeric, coriander and cumin, add six pieces of chicken, add a ladleful of curry gravy, plenty of creamed coconut, sugar, almonds maybe and a little cream – result, a mild dish, creamy-golden in colour), with Vegetable Dhansak (fry some cumin seeds, dry methi leaves (*qv*), chopped onions, a little sugar, tomato, red and green capsicum with the gravy, add cooked dhal and some cooked veg – result, colourful, and still medium-strength). Meat Korma (as for the chicken, using meat), and Prawn Vindaloo (fry spices and chilli powder, add the gravy which at once goes red and piquant, then cooked peeled prawns, fresh tomato and potato, simmer and serve). Maybe also a Sag Paneer (fry cumin, some thawed creamed spinach and pre-made crumbled paneer together, add fresh coriander – done). The curry chef can knock all these up, simultaneously, in five pans, within minutes. Rice is pre-cooked, breads and tandoori items made to order by a different specialist. And, hey presto, your order for two! The curryhouse menu can be very long, with a huge variety of dishes, sometimes numbered, sometimes heat-graded, mild, medium and hot, hotter, hottest, and any dish is available in meat, poultry, prawn, king prawn, and most vegetables, too. That's the formula of the standard curry house. Just because this is not authentic does not make it bad. It can be done well. This Guide is full of many such restaurants, which are listed as YOU SAY OK..

G

GARAM MASALA 'Garam' means 'hot' or 'warming' but not in the coincidence of Ehglish 'hot' meaning piquancy. Rather, it refers to temperature, and specifically to Ayurvedic (*qv*) philosophy, where certain foods 'warm' the body, while others 'cool' it. 'Masala' means 'mixture of spices', in this case a combination of whole, aromatic spices including pepper which the mixture must coincidentally contain to achieve a little piquancy, (but never chilli or turmeric). It is much-loved in northern Indian cookery, which originated in Moghul (*qv*) Kashmir (*qv*) and is added towards the end of cooking in certain curries. It can also be used in curry masala mixes, and as a sprinkler on, say Onion Bhajis. Balti (*qv*) also originating in Kashmir, uses a type of Garam Masala to achieve its fundamental aromatic taste. There are as many recipes for Garam Masala as there are cooks who use it. Some Kashmiri recipes use up to 20 spices. However to get the best from Garam Masala, heat must be applied and the spices should be roasted, cooled and ground to release the essential oils (the analogy being roasting coffee). All factory Garam Masalas, ergo those used at most curryhouses are not roasted, thus depriving the diner of a fine home-made taste. *See also Ayurvedic Food and Masala*.

GHEE Clarified butter used in high-quality north Indian cooking.

GOBI Cauliflower.

GOL GOPPA (*see Pani Puri*)

GOSHT Meat, usually refering to lamb or mutton.

Barfi & Halva

Srikand

Gulab Jamun

Rasgulla

Indian Sweets

GULAB JAMAN An Indian dessert of cake-like texture. Balls of curd cheese paneer, or flour and milk-powder, are deep-fried to golden-brown and served in light syrup.

GURDA Kidney. Gurda Kebab is marinated kidney, skewered and cooked in the tandoor.

H

HALEEM A Muslim speciality found in Pakistan and Hyderabad (central India) where it is regarded as a delicacy to them but an acquired taste to everyone else. Pounded mutton is cooked with wheat, chillies, ginger, garam masala and onion tarkaI to become a sort of gruel. A bread called 'Girda' is traditionally eaten with Haleem. Found at London's Salloos SW1 and Lahori Kebab E1.

HALVA Sweets made from ghee (*qv*) syrup, milk and vegetables or fruit. Served hot or cold in small squares, it is translucent and comes in bright colours depending on the ingredients used. Orange – carrot; green – pistachio; red – mango, etc. Has a texture thicker than Turkish Delight. Sometimes it is garnished with edible silver leaf. *See Vark.*

HANDI or **HAANDI** A traditional round-bellied earthenware or metal, narrow-necked cooking pot used in many parts of India, and especially Gujarat. Pottery shards have dated the design to 2500BC.

HASINA KEBAB Pieces of chicken breast, lamb or beef marinated in a yoghurt and spice (often tandoori) mixture, then skewered and barbecued/baked, interspersed with onions, capsicum and tomato. Turkish in origin. *See Shaslik.*

I

IDLI Rice-and-lentil-flour steamed cake, about the size and shape of a hockey puck, served with Sambar (*qv*) a light lentil curry. South Indian in origin. *(Pictured top of next page)*

IMLI Tamarind. A very sour, date-like fruit used in cooking or chutney which is of purée consistency, sweetened with sugar.

INDIAN In 1947, the subcontinent of India was partitioned. To cut a long story short, in Britain and the West we still generally erroneously refer to our curry restaurants as 'Indian'. In fact, over 85% are Bangladeshi, with only around 8% run by Indians and 8% run by Pakistanis. There is a smattering of Nepalese and Sri Lankan restaurants, and only a couple of Afghan and a single Burmese restaurant in Britain. *See Formula Curries.*

J

JALEBI An Indian dessert. Flour, milk-powder and yoghurt batter are squeezed through a narrow funnel into a deep-

frier to produce golden, curly, crisp rings. Served in syrup..

JAL FREZI Sautéed or stir-fried meat or chicken dish, often with lightly cooked onion, garlic, ginger, green pepper and chilli.

JEERA Cumin or cummin seed or powder, hence Jeera Chicken, the signature dish at Madhu's Southall.

JINGRI or **CHINGRI** Prawns of any size.

K

KALIA Traditional Bengali/Bangladeshi meat, poultry or fish dish in which red-coloured ingredients are mandatory, especially red chillies and tomatoes. *See Rezala.*

KARAHI A two-handled hemispherical Indian kitchen dish. Some restaurants reheat curries in small karahis and serve them straight to the table with the food sizzling inside. *See also Curry and Balti.*

KASHMIR CHICKEN Whole chicken stuffed with minced meat. *See Kurzi.*

KASHMIR CURRY Curryhouse pastiche where cream, coconut and/or lychees, and/or pineapple and/or banana are added to a medium curry bse.

KEBAB Kebab means 'cooked meat' in ancient Turkish, traditionally cooked over charcoal, in a process over 4,000 years old. It was imported to India by the Muslims centuries ago. Shish, incidentally, means 'skewer'. *See Boti, Hasina, Nargis, Shami and Sheek Kebab.*

KEEMA Minced meat, e.g. as used in curry. *See also Mattar.*

KOFTA Balls made from ground meat, poultry or fish/shellfish or vegetables, then deep-fried and/or simmered in a curry sauce.

KORMA Probably derived from the Persian 'Koresh', a mild stew. The Moghuls made it very rich, using cream, yoghurt and ground almonds, fragranced with saffron and aromatic spices. But, traditionally, Kormas need not be mild. In Kashmir a popular dish is the 'Mirchwangan Korma', red in colour because it is full of Kashmiri chillies. To the curry house, Korma is terminology for the mildest curry, sometimes made sickly by the overuse of creamed coconut block, cream and nuts.

KULCHA Small leavened bread. Can be plain or stuffed, e.g. Onion Kulcha.

KULFI Indian ice cream. Traditionally made in cone-shaped moulds in vanilla, pistachio or mango flavours.

KURZI Leg of lamb or whole chicken given a long marination, then a spicy stuffing, e.g. rice and/or Keema (q.v.), then slowly baked until tender. This is served with 'all the trimmings'. It is many a curry house's Special, requiring 24 hours' notice (because of the long preparation) and a deposit to make sure you turn up to eat it). Often for two or four, it is good value. Also called Khurzi, Kasi, Kozi, Kushi, etc. *See also Murgh Masala.*

L

LASSI A refreshing drink made from yoghurt and crushed ice. The savoury

version is Lassi Namkeen and the sweet version is Lassi Meethi.

M

MACCI or **MACHLI** Fish. Today, fresh exotic fish from India and Bangladesh are readily available and, when a restaurant offers them, you have the chance of getting a truly authentic dish.

MADRAS You will not find a Madras Curry in Madras. It does not exist. But the people of the south eat hot curries, firing them up with as many as three different types of chilli – dry, powdered and fresh – added to the cooking at different stages. As the Brits got used to their early formula curries (q.v.), they began to demand them hotter. With no time to add chillies in the traditional way, one of the pioneer curry house chefs simply added one teaspoon of extra-hot chilli powder to his standard sauce, along with tomato and ground almonds, and ingeniously called it 'Madras'. The name stuck. *See also Chilli, Phal and Vindaloo.*

MAHARANI DHAL Classic north Indian dish, held in such respect that its name means 'lentil queen'. It obtains its gorgeous dark golden brown colour by the use of urid (dhal (black lentils), its flavour from butter-ghee and cream, and its texture by slow-cooking in a heavy pot for at least three hours.

MAKHANI/MAKHANI Butter. *See Murgh Makhani and next entry.*

MAHKNI/ MAKAHANI DHAL The invention of this dish is claimed by Moti Mahal *(see WC2)*. It is a development of Maharani Dhal *(qv)* with the same black lentils, cream and cooking time. In place of ghee, butter itself (makhni) is used and tomato purée provides its distinctive taste and chestnut-brown colour. The dish is a real test of a chef's skill. It is never seen at curryhouses, but when it is on a menu, try it.

MALAI Cream. So Malai Sabzi Kofta, for example, means vegetable balls in a creamy curry gravy. *See Rasmalai.*

MALAYA The curries of Malaysia are traditionally cooked with coconut, chilli and ginger. In the Indian restaurant, however, they are usually based on the Korma (q.v.), to which is added pineapple and/or other fruit.

MASALA A mixture of spices which are cooked with a particular dish, e.g. Garam Masala (q.v.). It can be spelt a remarkable number of ways – Massala, Massalla, Masalam, Mosola, Moshola, Musala, etc.

MASALA DOSA *See Dosa.*

MATTAR Green peas. So Mattar Paneer is peas with Indian cheese, Keema Mattar is mince meat curry with peas, etc.

MEDIUM CURRY *See Formula Curries.*

METHI Fenugreek, pronounced 'maytee'. Savoury spice. The seed is

important in masalas. The leaves, fresh or dried, are used particularly in Punjabi dishes eg Methi Gosht. At the curry house, the flavour of these leaves predominates in their Dhansak.

MOGLAI Cooking in the style of the Moghul emperors, whose chefs took Indian cookery to the heights of gourmet cuisine centuries ago. Few restaurateurs who offer Moglai dishes come anywhere near this excellence. Authentic Moglai dishes are expensive and time-consuming to prepare. Can also be variously spelt Muglai, Mhogulai, Moghulai, Moghlai, etc.

MULLIGATAWNY A Tamil vegetable consommée (molegno pepper, tunny water), adapted by the Raj to create the thick, meat-based British soup.

MURGH Chicken.

MURGH MASALA/MURGH MASSALAM Whole chicken, marinated in yoghurt and spices for hours, then stuffed and roasted. *See Kurzi.*

MURGH MAKHANI A 16th century Moghal dish. Chicken is cooked in butter ghee, in a creamy, lightly spiced red sauce, nowadays using tomato. This was the derivation of CTM *(qv)*.

NAGA Until 2000, the hottest known chilli was a Mexican Habenero variant, Red Savina. Well known for centuries to Bengalis and Bangladeshis was the Naga aka Bhut Jolokia or Tezpur chilli growing in the Indian Assam and Bengali hills, which had never measured for heat-level. It took British growers to confirm the chilli's status as the world's hottesti. Scientists found Red Savina measured half the heat level of Naga. Put into perspective, Tabasco measures 25 times less and those fat chillies at the supermarket, 200 times less. Nagas and other chillies can be bought from <www.peppersbypost.biz>. Naga curries are increasingly available at the UK curryhouse, and have a totally different characteristic to Phal, and should be avoided by those not used to 'heat'.

Ask at the Asian stores for the new Bangladeshi pickle called Mr Naga, though this is 'diluted' with onion, etc and is less hot then the actual chilli.

NAN/NAAN Pronounced 'narn', it is flat, leavened bread, usually made from plain white flour (maida) dough, but sometimes from wholemeal flour (atta). After the dough rises, it is rolled out and baked in the tandoor *(q.v.)*. It is teardrop-shaped and about 20-25cm (8-10 inches) long. It must be served fresh and hot. As well as Plain Nan, there are many variations involving the addition of other ingredient(s). Keema Nan is stuffed with a thin layer of minced, spiced kebab meat. Peshwari Nan is stuffed with almonds and/or cashew nuts and/or raisins. Garlic, onion, pineapple, tomato, indeed anything, can be added. Double- or treble-sized Karak, Elephant or Family Nans are offered at Balti houses to share to scoop your food up with.

NARGIS KEBAB Indian scotch egg – spiced, minced meat around a hard-boiled egg.

NIRAMISH A Bangladeshi mixed vegetable, often cooked without garlic, and spiced only with Panch Phoran – Indian Five Spice mixture.

OOONBARIOU/UMBERIO/OBERU Parsee vegetable dish which evolved from Undhui *(qv)* Gujarat baked vegetables using root vegetables slow-baked for several hours in a charcoal-lined pit..

OOTHAPPAM *See Uthappam.*

PAAN Betel leaf folded, samosa-fashion, around a stuffing of aniseed, betel nut, sunflower seeds, lime paste, etc. and eaten in one mouthful, as a digestive after a meal. The leaf is bitter, the mouth-feel coarse and the taste acquired; but more acceptable (to Westerners) small spices and seeds (supari), sometimes sugar-coated in lurid colours, are often offered by the curry house after the meal.

PAKORA The true pakora is a whole piece of vegetable, lightly coated in gram-flour batter and deep-fried, although at the curry house it is to all intents and purposes the same as the Bhajia *(q.v.)*.

PALAK *See Sag*

PANI PURI or **GOL GOPPA** are one and the same things, the latter name used in Bengal and the East and the former in Gujarat and Mumbai. They are mouth-sized puffed-up crispy biscuits, served with Jeera Pani (water spiced predominantly with chilli, black salt and cumin water) and Aloo Chaat (potato

curry) at Bhel Puri *(qv)* houses. To eat the correct way, gently puncture the top of the biscuit, pour in some Jeera Pani, and pop into the mouth in one. Chew and then add some Aloo Chaat.

PANEER Cheese made from milk by separating the whey (liquid) from the curds (solids) which, when compressed, can be crumbled, chopped, fried, tandoori-baked and/or curried (see Mattar). In Bengali, Paneer is called 'Chhana', not to be confused with the lentil 'Chana' *(q.v.)*.

PAPADAM/PAPAD Thin lentil-flour wafers. When cooked (deep-fried or baked) they expand to about 20cm (8 ins) and must be crackling crisp and warm when served. If not, send them back and deduct points from that restaurant. They come either plain or spiced, with lentils, pepper, garlic or chilli. There are many ways to spell papadam, using any combination of the vowels 'a', 'o' and 'u', and double 'p' and double 'd'. But, despite many people calling it so, it should never be referred to as a pampadom.

PARATHA Brown-flour dough combined with ghee *(q.v)* thinly rolled out and folded over itself to create a layered disc, like puff pastry. Pan-fried to create a soft unleavened bread.

PASANDA Meat, usually lamb, which traditionally is thinly beaten, then cooked in a creamy curry gravy to which some chefs add red wine. The dish and wine were both true treats of Moghul emperor Jehangir who, though Muslim, blessed the wine to make it 'holy water' thus circumventing the rules of Islam. Then he and his court proceeded to drink themselves legless while enjoying this dish.

PATIA Restaurant curry with a thick, dark, red sweet and sour sauce. Based on a Parsee prawn or fish dish.

PATRA A Gujarati speciality, in which colcasia (patra) leaves are rolled in gram-flour paste, like a Swiss roll, then steamed, sliced and deep-fried.

PESHAWARI NAN See Nan.

PHAL The hottest curry, also known as a Bangalore Phal, invented by the British curry house restaurateurs.See Naga.

PICKLE Pungent, hot, pickled vegetables essential to an Indian meal. The most common are lime, mango, brinjal and chilli. Though rarely seen at the restaurant, meat and game are made

into traditional and very delicious Rajasthani pickles.

PODINA/PUDINA Mint. A fresh chutney, puréed from fresh mint, chilli and onion.

PRAWN BUTTERFLY Usually a large or giant king prawn, cut so that it opens out and flattens, butterfly-shaped, marinated in spices and immersed in gram-flour batter, then deep-fried. A curry house invention, whose name could also have derived from 'batter-fry'.

PRAWN PURI Prawns in a hot sauce served on a Puri (*qv*) bread. Although sometimes described as Prawn Purée it is not puréed prawn or anything esle.

PULLAO Ancient Persia invented Pollou, with rice and meat and/or vegetables, cooked together in a pan until tender.

Following Muslim invasions it evolved into Turkey's Pilav, Greece's Pilafi, Spain's Paella and, of course, India's Pullao. In many curry houses, the ingredients are mixed after cooking, to save time. (*See Biriani.*) There are many other ways to spell it: Pillau, Puloa, Pillar, Pilaw, Polaw, etc.

PULLAO RICE The restaurant name for rice fried with aromatic spices, usually with rice grains coloured with yellow and/or red and/or green food colouring.

PURI Unleavened wholemeal bread: rolled out flat to about 10cm (4 ins) in diameter, it puffs up when deep-fried, and should be served at once.

QUAS CHAWAL/KESAR CHAVAL Rice fried in ghee (*q.v.*), flavoured and coloured with saffron (kesar).

QORMA Non 'u' Kashmiri translation.

R

RAAN is an absolute Moghul delight. Leg of lamb or beef is pared of fat, then marinaded in a paste made from yoghurt, oil, lemon juice, garlic, ginger, red chillies, fresh coriander leaves, ground almond and aromatic spices for at least 12 hours. It is then slow-roasted until so tender that the flesh literally falls off the bone. *See Raan restaurant, SE10*

RAITA A cooling chutney of yoghurt on its own or with a vegetable, e.g. cucumber or mint (sometimes called Tandoori Sauce) to accompany papadoms, the starter or the main course. *See also Dahi.*

RASGULLA Walnut-sized balls or ovals of paneer (q.v.), or semolina and cream cheese, cooked in syrup (literally meaning 'juicy balls'). They are white or pale gold in colour and served cold or warm. *See Rasmalai.*

RASHMI KEBAB Kebab of minced meat inside an egg net or omelette.

RASMALAI Rasgullas cooked in cream, served cold. Very rich, very sweet. They are the white spheres in the picture. To their right is Gulab Jaman, below is Rasgulla. Above are Indian sweetmeats, Burfi and Halva, In the bowl is Shrikand, the Bombay yoghurt sweet syllabub (*all qv*).

REZALA Bengali/Bangladeshi speciality. Lamb cooked in evaporated milk, rich and subtly spiced, it would be milder than Korma except that green chillies are mandatory. Traditionally no red- or orange-coloured ingredients should be used. *See Kalia.*

RHOGAN JOSH GOSHT Literally meaning 'lamb in red gravy'. Traditionally, in Kashmir, lamb is marinated in yoghurt, then cooked with ghee, aromatic spices and natural red colorants. It should be creamy but not hot. The curry house version omits the marinade and the aromatics, and uses tomato and red pepper to create a red appearance. There are many ways of spelling it – Rogon, Roghan, Rugon, Rugin, Rowgan, Ragan, etc, Just, Joosh, Juice, Jash, etc, Goosht, Goose, Gost, etc.

ROTI Generic word for Indian bread of any type, rolled out into thin flat discs. Often if you ask for it you will get a chupatti (*qv*).

S

SABZI Vegetable.

SAG/SAAG Spinach, also called 'Shak' in Bengali, Palak in Punjabi and Rai, although the latter are mustard leaves. Lalshak is delicious red spinach.

SAMBAL/SAMBOL A Malaysian and Sri Lankan term describing the chutneys accompanying a meal. Sometimes referred to on the Indian menu. Malaysians also refer to Sambal as a dish of various ingredients cooked in a hot sauce, e.g. prawn sambal.

SAMBAR A hot and spicy, runny, almost consommé-like south Indian vegetable curry made from lentils and exotic vegetables, such as the drumstick. In the Manchester/Merseyside area, the curry houses have a dish called 'Samber'. It bears no resemblance to Sambar, except that lentils and a lot of chilli powder are added to meat, chicken or prawn curry.

SAMOSA Celebrated triangular, deep-fried meat or vegetable patties, supreme as starters or snacks.

SHAMI KEBAB Round minced meat rissoles.

SHASHLIK KEBAB Shashlik in Armenia means 'to grill'. Cubes of skewered lamb or chicken are marinated (in an oil, garlic and chilli mixture) then grilled. *See Hasina.*

SHATKORA A Bangladeshi citrus fruit, the size of a grapefruit but sharper in flavour. Can be eaten fresh or used in cooking.

SHEEK/SEEKH KEBAB Literally means (from Turkish 'shish') a skewer. Spiced minced meat, usually coloured lurid red at the curry house, from proprietary tandoori/kebab paste irradiated with chemical food colouring (*qv*), is moulded onto the skewer, then baked in the tandoori and grilled.

SHRIKAND A yoghurt/cream syllabub from Mumbai, infused with saffron, nuts and cardamom.

SINGARA Bengali Samosa (*qv*).

STANDARD CURRY *See Formula Curries.*

T

TANDOORI An ancient style of cooking, which originated in the rugged north-west frontier of India (now Pakistan). It gets its name from the cylindrical clay oven, the tandoor, with its opening at the top, fired with charcoal in its base. Originally the ingredients were chicken and lamb, marinated for many hours in a spiced yoghurt-based sauce, traditionally slightly reddened with red chilli, then skewered and baked in the tandoor. Now the curry house product also includes fish, prawns, paneer (*qv*) and vegetables. But its lurid red or orange colour is created by the unnecessary use of tartrazine food colouring (*qv*) in proprietary ready-to-use pastes. *See Boti Kebab, Nan Bread and Raita and Tikka.* **TARKA** South Indian 'tempering' technique, whereby items are fried and placed on hot, wet dishes at table to create a sizzle. The ingerdeints vary from recipe to recipe and can include onion, garlic, curry leaves, dry lentils, spice seeds such as cumin and mustard seeds, dry red chillies and coconut shards.

TARKA DHAL A tasty, spicy lentil dish, the Dhal being massoor (red) lentils, cooked to a purée, to which the Tarka (in this case crispy, fried caramelized onion and/or garlic) is added. It should taste very slightly burnt (from the

Tarka), and be subtly, yet decisively, spiced, neither too thick nor too thin.

TAVA A heavy steel, rimless, flattish frying pan, used to cook items such as Parathas.

TARTRAZINE *See Food Colouring.*

THALI/TALI A round tray with a low rim, averaging about 34cm (12in) in diameter. It is a plate on which an entire meal is served. Dry items (rice, bread

and even dry curries) are placed directly on the thali. Wet portions (curries, dhals, soups and sweets, etc) are placed in matching serving bowls (tapelis), and they too reside on the thali. They were made of gold for the Moghul emperors, silver for the Maharajas, and stainless steel for the rest of us. To be found at certain restaurants serving 'special' meals.

TIKKA Literally, a small piece. For example, Chicken Tikka is a filetted chunk of chicken, marinated (see Tandoori), skewered and baked in the tandoor. Traditionally, the marinade is identical to Tandoori marinade, and cooks a naturally russet brown colour. Proprietary Tikka paste, as used in the curry house, is lurid orange or yellow because of the tartrazine *(qv)* it contains.

TINDALOO *See Vindaloo.*

U

UNDHUI/OONDHIYA Gujarati signature dish in which chopped vegetables such as sweet potato, ratallu (purple yam), plantain, brinjal, green beans (papadi) etc are marinated in a spicy coconut paste and dry-fried in oil, often til (sesame) oil.

UPPUMA South Indian dish. Lightly fried semolina with onion & spices.

UTHAPPAM/UTHAPPAM/OOTHAPPAM South India pancakes made of rice and urid *(qv)* dhal which is soaked and ground, then allowed to ferment. The rice should be sambar (south Indian) rice, a small oval-grained variety, available at the Asian store. Traditionally the batter contains dried red chilli,

ginger and onion. Recent developments include Pizza-style toppings of garlic, tomato, onion and green chilli

URID A type of lentil, with a black husk, when whole, and cream when split or polished. Available as a dhal dish in some restaurants, e.g. Maharani Dhal *(qv)*.

V

VADA/VADAI Lentil-flour spicy, savoury doughnut, enjoyed in Gujarat and south India. *See Dahi Vada.*

VARK Edible silver or gold leaf, made today in Hyderabad, but a Moghul speciality, said to be an aphrodisiac.

VINDALOO A fiery dish from Goa. It now means the second hottest dish (two spoonfuls of chilli powder), usually with a chunk of potato (Aloo). Also sometimes called Bindaloo or Tindaloo (even hotter). *See also Chilli, Madras and Phal.*

W

WAZWAN Kashmiri wedding feast, described in the Cuisines pages.

X

XACUTTI A popular Goan curry, Mutton, chicken, fish or crab is cooked with grated, roasted cashew, coconut paste, red chilli, tamarind and spice masala, including one of Goa's unusual spices, dargaful (poppy petals).

Y

YAKNI A spicy mutton, or meat-based stock, also called Akhni.

Z

ZAFFRON Saffron, also known as Kesar or zafron. The stigma (stamen) of the crocus flower. Though never as expensive as gold (2008 prices are $1000 per oz gold and $180 per oz saffron) it is world's most expensive spice, because picking is is laborious and expensive.

ZEERA Alternatively called Jeera, which is cumin. FP

The Entries – An explanation of our method

There is no perfect system for laying out a nationwide restaurant Guide. Many Guides simply list their entries in town alphabetical order. The problem here is that there is no geographical relationship between each town. Cheltenham, Glocs to Chelmsford, Essex via Chelsea, SW3 is 180 miles. The method we have adopted in our Guide is to record the entries by county since most people prefer their British counties. We list them alphabetically. Unlike some Guides, we do not group the counties in National Regions (such as 'The Midlands' or the 'West Country', etc), since this too lacks logic. Counties are not without confusion. In some cases, their once

sacrosanct borders have been altered by frequent local government tinkering. Greater Manchester is one example. When it was established as a 'Unitary Region' in 1965, it nibbled away parts of Cheshire and Lancashire. Many residents prefer to stick to these counties in their addresses, though we have adopted 'Greater Manchester' as a 'county' in this Guide. Other bodies, such as the Post Office, add to the confusion of recent years. Their postcodes are far from logical and do not follow county borders. BT also have their own system of geographical reference. It is because few people understand postcode logic, and even fewer understand phone

codes, that we use the counties. Following London, we cover the English counties. With the demise of Avon (which was in any case, not a county, but a Unitary Region), we now start with Bedfordshire. Within each county, we record the relevant towns alphabetically, and within each town, we record each restaurant alphabetically. In Bedfordshire, for example, the first town we record is Arlesey, and its first restaurant is Raj Villa, and so on. Following England, we then look at the Isles and Islands, Northern Ireland, and after some years of absence, Eire returns to this Guide. Then it's Scotland and finally Wales. We start with London, as is explained overleaf.

2010 COBRA GOOD CURRY GUIDE

THE ENTRIES

CENTRAL LONDON

Area: British capital
Postcodes: E, EC, N, NW, SE, SW, W & WC
Population: 6.125,000

For the purpose of this Guide we define Central London as its 1870 postal
districts, now known as postcodes. We run them alphabetically as follows:
E, EC, N, NW, SEW, SW, W and WC. Within each individual postcode, we run
numerically, starting with E1 and ending with WC2. As with all postcode logic, this
is not in any geographical order. For example, W5 Ealing, shares its borders with W13, West Ealing and
W3, Acton. For 95 years these postcodes comprised all of London. In 1965 Greater London, (GL) was
established. It includes these postcodes and expanded its borders, absorbing Middlesex and parts of
Essex, Hertfordshire, Kent and Surrey (shown in lilac in the drawing below). For GL (Greater London)
towns/boroughs in these areas, please see the relevant county (Essex, Herts, Kent, Middlesex and
Surrey) – see list on page 9.

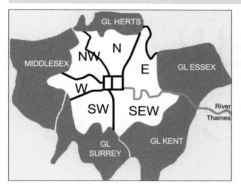

Greater London covers 1579 km² (609 sq. mi) and had in 2006, an estimated population of 7,500,000. The highest point is Westerham Heights, in the North Downs on the Kent / SE London border, at 245 metres. The River Thames flows west to east through central London, and forms the natural boundary between E and SE London and Essex and Kent

London E

Area: East London
Postcodes: E1 to E18
Population: 1.150,000

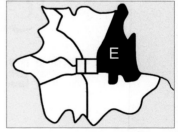

London E1

Brick Lane – Banglatown

Once predominantly Jewish, and bustling with tailors, salt-of-the-earth street markets and cab drivers, (to
emphasise its roots you'll still find a 24 hr fresh-baked bagel shop at 159 where cabbies queue for sus-
tenance) the long and narrow Brick Lane, has, since 1971, become home to the country's largest
Bangladeshi community. Running north between Shoreditch and Aldgate East tube stations, it is now called
Banglatown, indicating its proliferation of cheap and cheerful curry cafés, snack bars, restaurants and
provisions shops, run by the thriving community. Some of these establishments have remained fairly spartan,
and unlicensed (you can BYO). Others have redecorated and become licensed. We're not convinced that a
Balti house is PC on the street, but there is one. But the curry-hungry can get breakfast from 8am here
(Sweet & Spice, no 40). The late arrivals can get into Shampan until 2.30am. Many other on the Lane are
open all day. Here are your favourites:

Something for the weekend (and the other five days)

From the original Cobra Premium Beer to the Cobra Bite range of flavoured lagers, with Cobra Light, Cobra Zero% and King Cobra in between, the Cobra range has a beer for every occasion.

CAFE BANGLA

NEW ENTRANT

128 Brick Lane E1 6RL   0845 345 1723

Enjoy the wall paintings of 'Ancient Greek myths' vegetarian and speciality dishes. Venus in the oyster shell (variant!) And Princes Diana! But, says HEG *'It was full the first time I tried, but I booked to come back and it was fine, busy but fine.'* Daily: 11am- 2am.

CAFE NAZ

A-LIST

46 Brick Lane, E1 6RF   020 7247 0234

'Resolutely modern from its shiny black facade and chilli-patterned glass'n'chrome bar, Cafe Naz is sufficiently confident to allow itself the odd splash of kitsch such as the splendid, smoking fountain by the door. After all, this is Banglatown's buzzing Bangladeshi brasserie', says Cafe Naz about Caf'Naz. Presentation is very European, and just as well, as the large deep plates are necessary for coping with monster main courses such as Hyderabadi achar Gosht - chunks of lamb slow cooked on the bone in a dark rich sauce flavoured with pickling spices and limes.It enjoys a very busy and lively buffet lunchtime trade. Above the main restaurant there is a large room, which can be used for private meetings and functions. The food very good indeed, including some authentic dishes. All round very happy reports with some saying best in Brick Lane, though as these pages show, opinions about everything vary. *'Why have I never discovered Brick Lane before? What a colourful, vibrant and lively cobbled*

One Adam Gilchrist criticised this Guide on Amazon, saying we had included a restaurant that had closed five years ago. He did not tell us which one, but went on to say: *"It isn't a guide in the normal sense - it just contains comments that people have sent in."*

Adam, we invite you to TELL us which restaurant and we'll publish your reply.

Meanwhile anyone who wants to send us reports, to make this Guide better, please see page 339.

street this is, with every second building being a thriving Indian restaurant (including two in the Top 100). Café Naz is an excellent restaurant, very deserving of its Top 100 listing. Ambience is lively and the decor is bright and airy. The staff were welcoming, professional and efficient, coping with a large group of us from a local graduate art show, all of whom had to leave at different times. Dishes that really stood out were their Tandoori/Tikka Fish which was succulent, perfectly cooked and nicely balanced. The Lamb Korai was also very nicely balanced and the meat was truly melt in the mouth texture. Chicken Madras and Chicken Korma were also much enjoyed by my teenage daughters. Overall Opinion – excellent and would definitely return.' SO. *'Add perfect pilou rice and a nice fluffy garlic naan - if you're planning to sleep alone.'* Free Del over £12, 2m. Hours: 12-12 Mon-Wed-; 1am Thur & Fri; 6-1 Sat, and 1-3/6-12 Sun. Branches Cambridge, Cardiff, Café Naz at Corvino, 7 Middlesex St, Aldgate, Cafe Naz Express, 16 Brick La.   www.cafenaz.co.uk

LE TAJ

134 Brick Lane, E1 6RL   020 7247 4210

Opened in 1995, seats 40 diners, and linked to nearby Taj Stores grocers. Ignore the curryhouse stuff and order the authentic Bengali food, such as starters: Biran Mass – a slice of boal fish marinated in a mixture of freshly ground herbs, then fried with onions, £5.95; Jhal Puri Small diced chicken tikka cooked in a fiery chilli sauce resting on a bed of light puri bread. £5.20; Masser Kebab Bengali fish marinated in a special blend of spices.cooked over charcoal flames and served with a salad. £5.40; Shorisha Raja Chingri – grilled gholda king prawns in a chilli and fresh mustard marinade served sizzling, £6.50. Mains: Lau Gootha – pumpkin and King Prawn dish, extremely popular in the fishing districts of Bangladesh, £11.50. Beguner Borta – smoked aubergine pulp, muddled with green chillies, ginger and fresh lime. Pepe Bhajia – green papaya diced and tossed with light chillies and aromatic spices and Tomato Bhorta charcoal grilled tomatoes, puréed with a hint of spices, mustard oil and chillies, both £4.25. Set lunch: £7.50. Set dinner: from £15 to £22.   www.letaj.co.uk

PREEM
NEW ENTRANT

118 Brick Lane E1 6RL   020 7377 5252

Full name Preem Restaurant and Balti House, it stands on a corner site, its white frontage taking three units gives the clue that is's large (200 covers). Coffee-blonde walls, tables and chairs and ditto floor give Preem a Scandinavian look which is not surprising because it is owned by Hussein Aslan who worked in those parts before coming to London. The menu is typical curryhouse fare, although you tell us it is good and busy when others on the street are less so. Also it is the only Brick Lane venue to serve Masala Dosa. Aslan holds weekly curry cooking courses and he will tell you that he cares about healthy eating, banning ghee, using minimal oil and cooking meat (including beef) in its own juices. Daily 12-3/6-12

SHAMPAN
A-LIST

79 Brick Lane, E1 6QL   020 7375 0475

It's one of the few venues which give you real Bangladeshi food as opposed to Baltis and curryhouse stuff. If you are new to this, try Chef Anha's real Bangladeshi Special Thali, which at £12.95 provides a selection of dishes including Ureebisi Biran, Biran Mas, Chicken Rezala, Shatkora Dall, Pilau Rice, Paratha and yoghurt sauce. a la carte specialities also include Thetul Tanga Bujon, £6.95, Chicken/lamb/vegetable Kofta in a spicy and sour sauce; Shahi Murag Bujon, £11.95, Whole spring chicken, marinated in yoghurt, baked in the tandoor and then cooked with minced lamb and paneer. Tandoori Rupchanda, £7.95, whole flat fish marinated, baked and served sizzling. Sag Ureebisi Gatta, £6.95 ~ spinach and Bangladeshi runner bean seeds. Owner Mr Haque, the runs the annual September Bangaltown Festival. *'THIS is the place to go.'* says NP. *'delicious. Impressed with food, although wasn't cheap.'* Here's the fully licensed place for the night owls. Hours: 12am to 2.30am non stop, daily. Branch Clifton, E1 and Docklands. www.shampan.co.uk

SWEET AND SPICY

40 Brick Lane, E1 6RF   020 7247 1081

One of the Lane's oldest (1968). It's the cuisine you go for and it's Pakistani. Seats 40 diners in simple clean cafeteria style. Prices here are very good indeed, choose from the counter established favourites such as Seikh Kebab or Aloo Bora for 80p each. Chicken Karahi or Vindaloo or Korma for £3.95. Karahi Gosht or Madras Chuppatis, Puris and Popadoms are all 30p each. A favourite is the Kebab Roll from 90p to £2. Specials: Halwa Puri and Chana. Set lunch, set dinner, delivered to your table. Sunday Buffet: £4.50. One of the few places where you can get curry breakfast in London. Hours: 8am to 10pm non stop, daily.

Elsewhere in E1

CAFE SPICE NAMASTE
A-LIST

16 Prescot Street, E1   020 7488 9242

When he opened in 1995 Cyrus and his front of house wife Pervin Todiwala did busier lunch trades than evening and did not even bother to open on Saturdays! Lunch – weekdays remains frantic and the crew have

learned to turn around a full house within the hour!. The former magistrates' office had been wrecked by the DHSS, who seem to achieve immunity from Grade 1 listings, and it cost a packet to get it suitable for restaurant business. The secret weapons were Cyrus and Parveen friends of mine since 1982, he as Exec Chef and she as Maitre D at Taj Fort Aguada properties in Goa. I knew then that Cyrus can really cook, specialising in Parsee and Goan cuisine. The former because he is Parsee, Goan because he was in Goa where he learned to cook wonderful Portuguese-influenced curries. Cyrus is a great talker and dooer too, and we gave him his first Award in 1992, barely a month after he opened his first UK restaurant. '*Well presented and tasty food from a varied menu, in an attractive décor, with prompt lunchtime service*'. SH. '*Usual good food at this place. £3 for a small cobra is a bit steep. Pickle selection well above average. Nice touch on current menu is naming dishes after regulars. Interesting to conjecture how often folk have to go to get so honoured. "Jacobs" aloo chat at £4.50 was a cold dish, but very spicy."Jenny's" chicken was a hearty full breast portion at £12.75 with piquant sauce. "Danglers?" scallops made for a different ingredient at £14.95. The pork in "Carvalho's vindaloo could have been fat trimmed. Most disappointing dish was "Dhanki's" palakh, a very bland veg. curry for £4.75. Service very good, full by 8.30 on a Tuesday evening. 10% CC discount without quibble. Cost net £135 with 12.5 % service. Can see why it gets awards.*' C & MC. The small alfresco patio out back, with Indian snacks and cold beer, opens in summer. Cyrus is a bundle of energy, and he achieved one of his dreams to open an Asian cookery school. which it got him the MBE. See Zen Satori London N15. Main courses £10 - £17. Set meals £25 - £40 (min 2), Service charge: 12.5% Takeaway service; delivery service (within 2-mile radius). Hours: 12-3 / 6.15-10.30 Mon-Fri; Closed on Sundays. Branch Café T, W1. www.cafespice.co.uk

CLIFTON

1 Whitechapel Road, E1	020 7377 5533

The iconic Clifton closed in 1997 when its owner passed away. Though unable to build on the original site, current owner Shiraj Haque of Shampan fame, wanted to resurrect the name and recreate the fine cuisine and great reputation that Clifton once had, and he found a site virtually at the entrance to Brick Lane. It opened in 2005. With its beautiful Indian and Bangladeshi art in a variety of mediums adorning the walls on both the ground and lower ground floors, the eatery has a simple but modern feel and seats 200 covers. Chef Musavir Ahmed and his kitchen team have designed an extensive menu. The open-plan kitchen on the ground floor entices passers by and customers can see and understand how the dishes are prepared.

CLUB SPICE — NEW ENTRANT

30 Alie Street E1 8DA	020 7481 8288

Two coincidences here, one is that this was the site of Cyrus' first restaurant, 1991 - 95, and second , the name's not unlike Café Spice. Since Cyrus left in 1995 it survived as Café Indiya. Now, at lunch time it's an Indian restaurant, serving the city's financial men and women Indian food. In the evening it becomes Club Oops, a night club or to be more precise a table-dancing club (complete with a team of nudie dancers), which, I believe we now call a 'Gentlemen's Club' – all very strange! Our only review was anon and said '*very tasty!*' We don't know which dish this referred to! Lunch: 12-3. Night Club 4pm-3am. <www.cluboops.co.uk> tells you nothing about the restaurant, only of the club.

HALAL

2-6 St Mark Street, E1 8DJ	020 7481 1700

Established way back in 1939, making it the second oldest survivor in London. With a frequent throughput of Bengali sailors coming from India to the nearby docks, Halal was not alone in the east-end area. Earlier in the 1930s According to the Groves '*Abdul Gofur opened a cafe shop at 120 Brick Lane as well as others in New Road and Commercial Road and Ayub Ali Master came back from America in 1938 and opened Shah Jalal at 76 Commercial Street London. Shirref's in Great Castle Street opened in 1935 and Halal, which still thrives today, opened in St Marks Street E1 in 1939.*' P&CG. It certainly does and it has been at the same address all that time. '*It's better than the trendy places in Brick Lane with their freebie inducements. Cost £51 with a tip for 3 people. Still about the only place where I have meat vindaloo(£4.30).Have been going there for twenty years but still regarded as a newcomer-plenty of city retirees of older vintage still go for old times' sake. Good value for money, quiet in the evening, but 8 "city gents", obviously regulars came in.*' CC. Fully licensed. Hours: 12-12, Sat /Sun 12 - 10.30.

LAHORE KEBAB HOUSE — A-LIST

2 Umberton Street, E1	020 7488 2551

For anyone who has not been to either Pakistan or to Sparkbrook, the LKH is what it's all about. Despite Brum's claim to be the inventor of the currinary world, this gaff has been doing Balti, under what some say is its true name, Karahi or Karrai (sic.) since it opened in the 1963 – serving darned good food, geared to Asian tastes, without compromising it for Westerners. At least that's what it used to be. But its relatively new-found glory as a lunchtime dive for the money boys and girls from the City has permeated into the evenings, and it's had an effect on management. The redec has now become old hat, and tatty even, much to the delight of

LKH's aficionados and its Asian patrons, who were wary of such inventory as arty line drawings. Cutlery is still for wimps (though you no longer have to ask for it). But when in Rome, eat the correct way, please, using a piece of Roti to scoop up your curry, in your right hand only – too bad if you're left-handed. And expect limitations if you're a veggie. Halal mutton, chicken and quail are it, in the karahi, from the tandoor as tikkas or kebabs, or as steam roast (Choosa), with robust lentils and fragrant rice. Real veterans show their spurs by enjoying the celebrated, and very filling and satisfying, Paya (lamb's trotters), laced with the Hot Chilli Raita, followed by their gorgeous Kheer rice pudding. Service is swift and accurate, but don't expect pampering, and don't expect to pay more than a tenner, including tip, in cash, please – nothing fancy like credit cards. It has a different atmosphere at different times of the day, different again at the weekend, depending on who's eating when. The eight downstairs tables are communal, each seating 6 – 12. There are eight more tables upstairs. One wall is covered with mirrors. The restaurant is worn but clean. The main dishes are on display in a glass-fronted heater. *'I sat next to two businessmen and ordered Saffron Rice and Chicken Karahi. Almost but not quite – too hot. My Spinach and Potato offers a pleasant counter note, flavoured with nutmeg'* LB, Dallas. *'Service very good: they're used to large crowds with diners in and out very quickly. This place is my Mecca, my Garden of Eden, my Golden Temple. It's the best food anywhere.'* RCE. *'Please. please delist this restaurant from your Guide. It's already too busy, and we don't need you piling in more people.'* anon. Hours: 12-12 non stop, daily.

KOLAPATA
NEW ENTRANT & NEW TO TOP 100

222 Whitechapel Road E11BJ   020 7377 1200

Opened in 2004 its headboard bills it as a Bangladeshi restaurant and fast food takeaway. Nothing unusual there then – half the restaurants on Brick Lane make the Bangladeshi claim whilst really serving curryhouse to tourists. But this could be the very restaurant your editors have been waiting for. Kolapata, meaning banana leaf, avoids anything curryhouse (except its fish tank).

Decor, zilch, lighting, white and green neon lights' nothing fancy! It's USP is that it is the only restaurant in the UK to serve Bangladeshi food as they would know it in Dhaka. Its chefs previously worked at one of Dhaka's top hotels, the Purbani in Motijeel. The a la carte menu and Daily Specials are pure Bangladeshi, and the management tell us they rarely serve non Bangladeshis 'they find the food strange-tasting', they say, 'the complain that the fish has too many bones and they hate bitter (shukti) tastes.' That's as maybe, and it is something I have heard from many Bangladeshi restaurateurs around the country when they defend their serving of CTM. But not all dishes are bitter or have fish bones. Kolapata welcome all-comers, and the waiters are helpful and friendly and will advise you on what to choose. We cannot recommend it highly enough, which is why we have placed it into our TOP 100. Here are some Daily Specials Monday: Gura Mach (small fish); Fish Kopta (chitol fish) £3.95. Tuesday: Murgh Pilau, served with Borhani (spicy icy yoghurt drink like Lhassa but enhanced with chilli, £4.50; Prawn Bhorta (chatni) £1.95. (Bhortas are served cold like a chutney, and are a mash or purée of a soft vegetable, to which is added chopped raw onion, chilli and stir-fried spices. Other Bhortas on offer are Begun Bhorta (aubergine) £1.95. Wednesday: Lamb Rezala, (cooked in evaporated milk, rich and subtly spiced, it would be milder than Korma except that green chillies are mandatory) £3.95; Aloo Bhorta £1.95; Taki (tomato) Bhorta £1.50. Thursday: Moorighonto (fish head curry) £3.95; Ayer Fish £3.95. Friday: Bhuna Khichori (rice and lentils with dry-cooked mutton), served with Borhani £3.95; Lamb Chop £3.95; Whole Boal Fish £3.95. (Boal is a rather ugly ,long thin, round white fish with 'whiskers'). Saturday: Rupchanda (Pomfret) Fish £3.95; Bangladeshi Pithas (sweet desserts) Narial (coconut) Pitha £2.50; Patishapta Pitha (cream-cheeses- filled pancakes!) £2.50. Sunday: Neharee (lamb shank) £3.95; Luchi (white flour Puri) £1. www.kolapata.co.uk

MALA

St Katherine's Dock, E1   020 7480 6356

Located in the unique and beautiful St Katherine's Dock Marina, the 200 seat Mala was est in 1987 by clothing and property tycoon brothers Charanjit and Malkit Roy Sandhu initially as a place to entertain their clients. It is now run by Charanjit's son, Vinnie Sandhu. Chef Madhur Sheel has worked all over India and this reflects in his regional menu with dishes such as Malabari sea food and fish dishes from the south, to Chingiri Jhol from the east, to Dal Makhani from Punjab. There is also a range of curries and tandoori dishes. 'We visited after a reception in the Mayor of London's building for Charles Campion's new London Restaurant Guide. After nibbling on Tio Pepe, Spanish Hams and cheeses (which were all delicious by the way!), we decided that

something more substantial was need and headed off to Mala. It's a short walk over Tower Bridge. As we did a tourist boat passed under us, and we exchanged waves with the happy on-board wedding party, (complete with a newly married Oriental couple – she in a white wedding dress) all busy taking photos of the Thames , the bridge and us. We went down the steps and through the regenerated docks surrounded by views the Thames, moored yachts, expensive fashionable flats, trendy restaurants, boutiques and bars. The waiters are dressed in black tie, which I don't like, very old fashioned trolleys to deliver the food. It is busy, perhaps too busy and they are literally rushed of their feet and don't have any time for polite conversation. I am not saying they are rude, as they're not, they are perfectly civil but abrupt, looking tired, as if just going through the motions. Because of its location, the restaurant is not cheap. Clients clearly see Mala as upmarket and they all dress smartly. There are several groups of noisy men, who could have been taxi drivers or builders, but not city types, and were not going without, ordering many dishes and champagne like it was tap water. It was money-no-object but good humoured. Food delivered too quickly, didn't feel like I had been out, all to rushed. Some dishes very good – Lamb Biriani others ordinary – Murgh Makhani.' DBAC. Set Lunch: 3 courses £12.95 - (example) Chicken Tikka and Seekh Kebab; Chicken Jalfrezi, Bombay Potato, served with Popadom, Tarka Dal, Pullao Rice, Naan bread and Raitha; Antillais Caramel Banane (caramel and banana mousse on thick macaroon biscuit base) - Great Value! Sunday Buffet lunch. Daily: 12-3 / 6-11. www.mala-restaurant.co.uk

YOU SAY OK, LONDON, E1
Standard Curries at fair prices

BENGAL CUISINE 12 Brick Lane, E1 ~ 0120 7377 8405. 12-12, daily. Branch: Taja, E1.
EASTERN SPICE 2a Artillery Passage, Bishopsgate, E1 020 7247 0772. Hours: 12-3/6-12.
RUCHI 393 Whitechapel Rd E1 1BY 020 7247 6222
SABUL BANGLA 192 Brick Lane E1 020 7247 6666
SHAFIQUES BENGAL BLUES CAFE BRASSERIE 94 Brick Lane, E1 ~ 020 7377 9123. 12-12, daily.
SHEBA 36 Brick Lane, E1 ~ 020 7247 7824. 12-12, daily. Est 1970 by Abdul Milad.
TAJA 199a Whitechapel Road, E1~ 020 7247 3866. 11am-12, daily. Branch: 1 Brick Lane. E1

RIVER SPICE   NEW ENTRANT

83 Wapping Lane, E1W 2RW 020

Close to Wapping Tube, this 50 seat venue is very popular indeed. Some call it their absolute favourite. A generous frontage of plate windows pour light into the bar area and up into the main seating area. You go past the cerise voiles and admire the stone-coloured flagged floor, turmeric and indigo walls and discrete a/c as you

are shown to you spaciously placed modern blonde tables and chairs. Chef Abdul Alim says he has abandoned ghee and uses vegetable oil instead. But so does every curryhouse in the land and he claims to use beetroot powder for colouring, something Pat Chapman has advocated in his books for years, in place of tartrazine colourings. The spin also tells us the food and spice mixes are made fresh every day. And so we should hope. So why the rave reviews? Everyone likes the service. The lasses like the waiters, whom we hear are very friendly and very competent. But they like the food too. It's Bangladeshi curryhouse, through and through, with slightly disguised names. Shobzi soup, £2.95 which the spin says is *'our daily preparation of this authentic Bengali vegetable soup'* is just that. Piazi is onion bhaji - £2.55; Kurma is Korma. And yes, these are done rather well. But look for the unusual. Try starters of Murgh Paapiya, finely chopped chicken breast, seasoned, bread-crumbed and deep fried, £3.40; or Chingri Shemaik, Bengal prawns marinated in lime leaves and freshly ground condiments, coated in vermicelli and deep fried, £4.50; And Mains of Raj Hash, diced duck with baby potatoes cooked in a medium hot spicy sauce, £8.95; Kodu lamb, butternut pumpkin cooked in medium spicy sauce, £7.25 or Cod Roshany cooked with garlic flakes.pepper, medium spiced with fresh tomatoes and coriander - £8.50. And if you have room, finish with Gulab Jamun served with ice cream. Occasional live performances bring the dance floor into play. One correspondent bemoaned the demise of the venue's hookah following the arrival of the 2007 non-smoking regulations. Hours: 12-2:30 Sat-Thurs / 5:30-11:30.

SCARLET DOT

4 Crispin Sq, Crispin Pl, E1 6DW   0207 375 0880

The traditional Indian symbol for a married woman, the bindi, worn on the forehead, Scarlet Dot is the first Indian haute-cuisine restaurant in Spitalfields as a modern restaurant behind the famous indoor market. Neon floor-lights lead up the Scarlet Spice Bar, 30 feet of tropical wood, dark blinds and marble floors and walls, is open all hours. The adjoining 120-cover restaurant opens for a traditional Indian breakfast that is not to be missed. In the summer months, there is a further 125 seat eating area under an impressive glass and steel canopy. You can hire 'zones' in the chic bar for groups of up to 25 – complete with a DJ if you want one. *'We like their Express Lunch the Maharaja Thali, £9.95 served in Scarlet's designer Bento Box including a selection from: Vegetable or Meat Samosas, Aloo Tikka (minced potato patties with garam massala and peas), Murug Makhanwalla, chicken tikka cooked with fenugreek and massala sauce or Rogan e Nishat (lamb cooked with tomatoes, ginger, herbs and aromatic spices), Chana Limbu (chick peas*

in spicy sauce), both options served with Naan and Pilau Rice.' PV. Full range of menus on offer, from a la carte to drinks-only daily, 9.00am - to 11pm. www.scarletdot.co.uk

Above:
Scarlet Dot's relaxed al fresco environment.

Below Left:
One of Scarlet Dot's smart presentations uses a Japanese Bento Box, here containing, Chick-pea Curry, Tikka Masala, Pullao Rice, Salad, Raita, Nibbles and Samosa.

YOU SAY OK

You may get a discount of you show them this Guide.

E2: ALAMIN 483 Cambridge Heath Road, E2 – 020 7739 9619. Owner Abdul Noor. 39-seats. Hours: 12-2.30/6-12.
E4: PURBANI 34 The Avenue, Chingford, E4 – 020 8531 8804. Est 1983 by Tony Turu Miah. 54 seats. *'Bamboo Shoot Bhajia is different.'* HEG. Hours: 12-2.30/6-11.30.

TIFFIN INDIAN   TOP 100

165 Cannon St Road, E1 2LX   020 7702 3832

Abul Kalam's Tiffin opened in 1991 and has a '*Very dramatic and stylish glossy purple menu for the food, wine and*

---

other drinks are listed in an equally good looking orange and green menu.' RL. Start with Tiffin Special, £4.50, an absolute feast, including Murghi Tikka – chicken marinated in yogurt and spices cooked in a clay oven. Keema Chops – seasoned mince coated in finely mashed potato and breadcrumbs lightly fried. Sheek Kebab – finely minced meat mixed with onion, coriander and an assortment of rich exotic spices, skewered and cooked in a clay oven, all served with salad. The vegetarian alternative is also equally tempting, lightly spiced aubergine slices in batter; vegetables in a spicy sauce wrapped in filo pastry and fried. But do leave room for your main course, for example Friday's Catch £9.95, Specially selected Bangladeshi seasonal fresh water fish

fillets. Bohal, Ruhi or Ayre, consisting of onions, haldi coriander, green chilli, garlic and a few light spices to sustain the natural taste and cooked with 100% pure mustard oil, '*served saucy*'(sic) with plain rice and slice of lime or Murgh Ur Saag – chicken cooked in a dry sauce with spinach, onion and spices, £6.35 or Bathara, £9.95, tender quails cooked in a spicy garam masala sauce. Min charge: £8, set lunch: £5.95.
Daily: 12-3/6 - 12
Above:
Tiffin's chef, Dinar Ahmed enjoys the heat of the kitchen.

London E6   Upton Park

LAZZAT KAHAR

18 Plashet Grove, E6   020 8552 3413

Busy, cheerful, basic, friendly, buzzing and above all cheap! We add to that Punjabi so expect meats, savoury flavours , no holds barred on the chilli front, al denté-perfect rice and super breads. And let's add another

word: superb. You watch them cook, and you know it's fresh. The lettuce, onion, tomato, and chilli salad is free.. With main courses £4-£5 and starters much less, it's hard to spend a tenner here, so cash is best here. Alcohol not permitted.. Takeaway service. Hours: 11am-midnight daily.

London E7 Forest Gate

MOBEEN

224 Green Street, E7   020 8470 2419

An all-day caff which takes credit cards. Hm ... Bliss! Furthermore it has escaped gentrification. Because of it or despite it, it is busy-busy with Asian families high on the attendance list. The mainly Punjabi food is churned out by a battery of cooks, in view and female servers. Meat and veg dishes alike are competent, maybe not brilliant but ample and tasty. One veggie tried the Vegetable mince curry and rejected it because it tasted like meat – entertainment too! (it is made with granulated soya). And the balance of opinion favours the veggie dishes over the meat (just), so take your choice. Besides, it's hard to spend a tenner here, so what the heck! A 20-seat party room is billed, but it always seems to be a party here. Main courses £2-£5.50. Takeaway service. 11-10 daily. Branch Ilford, Essex.

VIJAY'S CHAWALLA

268 Green Street, E7   020 8470 3535

And just down the road is another all-day caff which takes credit cards. More bliss! Again, it's a non-nonsense value-for-money caff, but with a different food-style from Mobeen. It is Gujarati, which means considering its apt address, that vegetarian is king, and there is an abundance of gram flour, albeit used in rissole form, sauces, curries et al.Yoghurt also prevails in the cooking, as does the typically Gujarati sweetness in savoury dishes. Sev Khaman, is gram-flour dumplings with topped gram flour squiggles (sev) with yoghurt and sweet and sour imli (tamarind chutney). Ragada patties, balls of mashed potato stuffed with curried chickpea are deep-fried and served in a tangy sauce. *'I started with that delightful Bombay street snack Bhel Poori'* (see glossary) *'and it was sublime. Then I went on to a fab thali'*. HEG.

They dosh up good Indian desserts here, and someone, not sure if is VJ himself, makes Indian tea as it should be made (bring milk to the simmer with green cardamoms. Add too much sugar and serve in a large cup. Well that's what Chawalla means – tea maker! If you've not had it before, this is the place to indulge. Main courses £4 -£7. Thalis £7. Unlicensed. BYO allowed. Corkage no charge. Daily: 11-9.

London E11 Leytonstone

CHANDNI

715 High Rd, E11   020 8539 1700

Vegetarian food here including South Indian in this licensed café. *'I thought hang it, money is no object today ignoring the £5 thali, I splashed out on the top-priced version (£7). I enjoyed a platter of mixed vegetable pakoras (very fresh, very tasty) while I pondered whether I would regret this impulsive act. The rather bumbling but amiable waiter eventually ambled up with my thali, and placed it in front of me with a flourish I never suspected he had in him. Now I've had salvadors all over India, and I have to say this one was worth every penny the extra investment. I'll be back!'* HEG. House wine: £8. Credit cards OK. Hours: 11-11.

London E14
Docklands, Dogs, Limehouse, Poplar

ANUPANA NEW ENTRANT

Lumina Bldgs, 2 Yabsley St, E14   020 7515 7501

Modern art hangs from the white walls and down lighters highlight the pale wooden flooring. This restaurant is light and airy, with white and pale blue table linen, large wine goblets and classical cutlery. A long bar enables the diner to sit and enjoy a drink or two before sitting at one of the many tables. Anupana, meaning water dwellers, can accommodate 200 diners. If after dinner you wish to sit and have coffee, there is a area set aside with comfortable chairs. The venue benefits from the skills of Executive Chef Khilesh Kumar Anand, fresh from Mint Leaf and a short spell at Café Spice. Menu Snapshot: Yellow lentils soup with herbs and spices served with garlic nan £5.50; Piccata of lamb rump infused with crushed coriander and dry red chilli £6.95; Fresh white crab meat cooked with spiced in white wine, mango juice and cheese £5.50; Pickled chunks of moist Indian cheese grilled in Tandoor £5.25. Boneless chicken in aromatic karahi masala with green pimento's £10.95; Chunks of red snapper simmered in mustard flavoured gravy £11.95; Vegetable dumplings simmered in melon and cashew gravy £7.50; Tandoori roasted beef in star anise, clove and fenugreek £11.95; Pullao Rice £3.00; Peshwari Naan £3.25. Set Menus for lunch are exceptionally good value, so don't forget to check out the options, as their are several choices. Here is menu 1: Black tiger prawns perfumed with dry mango powder, traditional Calcutta-style monk fish cooked in tomato, chilli and coconut, served with pullao rice or naan and if you can fit in a dessert, please do – all for £15.95. The wine list is very reasonable starting at £13.95 a bottle.

www.anupana.co.uk

LIME RESTAURANT NEW ENTRANT

Regatta Point, 1 Manilla Street, E14 8JZ
020 7515 4500

If you like lime as a colour, you'll get plenty of it at this new venue, contrasted with orange furnishings and attractive naked bricks. *'Au corant, neoteric, modish and original'* is what Lime restaurant says of itself. The menu delivers all your favourites with a few Bangla specials thrown in. *We were early and it was empty. We asked for the amazing circular banquette seat (lime-green, of course) which houses a table for four though we were two and we loved it. We kept to the theme and ordered amongst other things Jhinga Lime Special, king prawns grilled with garlic, butter and mustard seeds, £5.50; Lemoni Lime Chicken, Marinated chicken stir fried with grated lime rind, spring onions and exotic herbs. £7.95 and Kashta Bhindi Aloo lightly spiced crispy okra and potato cooked with fresh herbs, £ 3.95, which hit the mark.* RL. Business lunch £8.95. Average spend £20. Hours: 12-2.30 / 5.30 -11; 11:30 weekends. www.limerestaurant.co.uk

DOCKMASTERS STOP PRESS RE-ENTRY

Dockmaster's House, West India Dock Gate, Hertsmere Road, E14 020 7345 0345

The huge house was built in 1807 by Thomas Morris, to house the all-powerful Dockmaster. A century later it became the Jamaica Tavern, then reverted the post-war dock manager's office. It was restored by the Docklands Development Corporation and was used by its marketing department. So successful were they that today the charms of this once prominent Georgian building, are utterly dwarfed by Canary Wharf's sky-tech towers, the snaking overhead tracks of the Docklands railway and the surrounding drab, gloomy overparked streets. The movie Batteries Not Included spring to mind, but such is progress. It is worth a visit, however. There are three elements. A 100-seat a/c restaurant with a satisfying range of Indian regional dishes. Down in the extensive cellars, is now a 200-seat bar offering a range of spicy pub grub. Outside there is a garden large enough to accommodate 100 seats which serves summer barbecues of Indian kebabs, grills and tandooris on platters alongside pitchers of beer. At least, that's how it was. Then in 2008, Dockmasters closed. Fortunately, it has just reopened, (in early 2009) and although we have not reviewed it, we hear of a big rebuild (costing £3m). Most prominent is the square, modern conservatory, turning what was a dark dining room into a bright and airy experience. The reason why we are entering the new dockmasters is chef Navin Bhatia. He cut his teeth with Tamarind's (W1) Atol Kotchar at , and Vineet Bhatia at Zaika, as well as Anurag Gaultam at the now closed Yatra. He had been exec at the now defunct Café Lazeez operation. *"Bhatia's starter highlights include smoked aubergine soup, green tandoori drumsticks, duck samosas. His mains include a mussalam of poussin, coriander-crusted stone bass and coconut chilli beef. Everything about this place oozes class and that includes the service"* Humayan Hussain, Editor Tandoori Mag. Your reports will be most welcome. Hours: Mon - Fri: 12-3 / Mon - Sat 6-11.30. <dockmastershouse.com>

MEMSAHEB ON THAMES

65 Amsterdam Road, E14 020 7538 3008

A bright a modern Bangladeshi restaurant with wooden floors in the bar area, where you can pop your self up onto a stool, and carpets in the dining area, where red upholstered chairs and white linen covered tables await you. Traditional art hangs on the walls and huge bouquets of beautiful exotic flowers decorated the restaurant. Mridul Kanti Das, managing partner puts on regular food festivals, specialising in regional food with delights such as Machli Amritsar – boneless pieces of white Indian fish in a spicy batter which is deep-fried. Murghi Lababdar – minced chicken cooked in a thick spicy tomato sauce, garnished with fresh coriander. Executive chef Enwar Hussain also cooks all the usual curries, from Bhuna to Vindaloo with a few specials, which include: Chicken Anarash £6.95 - cooked with pineapple, coconut and almonds in very mild sauce; Lamb Xacuti £6.95 - a popular Goan dish, with fennel, cloves, garlic, ginger (though I am not sure how authentic this dish is) and Panjabi Style Lamb Shank £10.95 - marinated overnight with spices, yoghurt, garlic,ginger, coriander, green chilli and lime juice, then slow cooked. Menu Snapshot: Assorted Starter £4.50 - chicken tikka, shish kebab, onion bhajia and meat samosa; Crab Puri £3.95 - crab meat cooked with spice and lime juice, served on a deep-fried puri bread; Kabuli Salad £2.95 - boiled chickpeas and egg mixed with onion, green chilli, fresh coriander, mustard oil and tamarind sauce. Takeaway is a very important part of their business, apparently 25% of their trade. Hours: 12.30-2.30 (closed Sat & Sun) / 6-11.30. And they do an Express Lunch Delivery - so give them a call! e-mail: table@memsahebuk.com

TIFFIN BITES   NEW ENTRANT

22 Jubilee Place, Canary Wharf, E14 5NY
020 7719 0333

This branch is in the Jubilee Place shopping precinct above the Canary Wharf tube Station. Up the escalator, M & S Simply Foods on the left. Tiffin Bites straight ahead. Full details, see EC2. Hours: 11–10; 9pm Sun. See EC2 and page 19.

London E15   Stratford

HEMALAYA TANDOORI   RE-ENTRY

178 The Grove. Leyton E15   020 8519 6887

Stratford is east London's new railway hub with Eurostar, DLR, mainline and tube train connections,and the 2012 Olympic spending spree is in full swing. Hemalaya was first mentioned in out 1991 Guide, and it has been there ever since. *'It's not one of the nicest areas – architecturally a disaster and sometimes a bit scary. On one of the trunkroads leading towards Leyton is a small, well kept restaurant, run for decades by the same family, serving the basic indian/bengali cuisine one would expect in this area of London. Nevertheless, there are some things that elevate this curry house from the rest of similar establishments: The proprietors really believe in Service with a smile: a broad grin awaits you as soon as you enter the premises, for regular patrons hands are shaken, one is led to the favourite table and out of nowhere beer, popadums and chutney arrives, and after a couple of minutes a sizzling sound marks the arrival of the most tender and tasty Lamb Tikka you can imagine. This is not the microwaved fare one gets so often: the lamb is well marinated and accompanied by sizzling onions. The starters and main course list does not differ much from the usual fare: Madras, Vindaloo, Tikka Masala, Korma, Pasanda in the usual variations are all present and well presented. The highlights of my visits have been the more unusual fare like Methi Gosht and Shally Lamb. I personally find their Dansak Balti especially well crafted, as the tanginess of the medium hot sauce goes well with the lentils and chicken. Cobra served and the prices are for London in the lower range. Certainly worth a visit.'* Dr DP.

London E17   Walthamstow

PRIYA   NEW ENTRANT

256 Hoe St, Walthamstow, E17 3AX
020 8520 5552

Opened 2006 and is the first south Indian/Sri Lankan restaurant in the area and finding itself, quite rightly, popular. The few such restaurants in London are mostly in SW. And though the food is so different to the curryhouse norm, it's captured imagination; it's full, and booking's necessary. You'll find some familiar dishes such as korma, etc but go for the specialities such as Masala Dosa, and accompanying Sambar and chutneys. But the dishes which intrigue Priya's diners are the devilled (ie chilli hot) stir-fried chicken and meat dishes. Whether or not it is all new to you, try the special set meal which provides many different items at a reasonable price. Being 100m from Walthamstow Tube and rail station, it is easy to find and should not be missed.

YOU SAY OK

You may get a discount of you show them this Guide.

E14: SPICE MERCHANTS, 38 Salter Street, E14 ~ 020 7987 8779. Managed by Mr Uddin. *'Goan lamb shank all excellent and around £8.00 p e r dish. . A very pleasant experience'* IC. www.thespicemerchants.com
E14: TALE OF INDIA, 53 West India Dock Rd, E14 ~ 020 7987 3418. Starters include: Iribeesi Baja – runner beans fried with onions. Lunch to 2.30 weekdays and dinner to 11.30.
E 15: SPICE INN, 22 Romford Road, Stratford, E15   020 8519 1399. *'Methi Gosht – best I've had since the untimely demise of the Shish Mahal in Dumbarton'* . DP.
E 17: SHISH MAHAL, Hoe St, Walthamstow, E17
E 18: MECHNA GRILL, 219 Woodford High Rd, E18 ~ 020 8504 0923. Owner Siddiqur Rahman Est1971 Half price Mondays if you book.
E 18: THE ROSE, 65 Woodford High Rd, E18 ~ 020 8989 8726. Owners Messrs Miah & Hoque. Est 1982. *'Food delicious, service exemplary, as ever' served in little china dishes (Villeroy and Bosch) with matching lids'. Try Garlic Mussels on Puri – in a garlic, red onion & white wine sauce.'* says SSTC. 12-2.30/6-11.30.
● E14: Atul Kotchhar, Mayfair's Benares' 'proprietor chef', is, we hear considering opening a fast-food outlet in Canary Wharf. If he does, reports please.

London E18   Woodford

THE ROSE

65 Woodford High Rd, E18   020 8989 8726

The Rose has been operated for 25 years by Messrs Miah and Hoque, who offer all the favourite tandooris and curries at sensible prices. *'Food delicious, service exemplary, as ever'* says SSTC. *'Chef's Rallwa – chicken or lamb tikka with prawns, keema and spring onions in ginger sauce, very tasty. Generous portions and rice served in little china dishes (Villeroy and Bosch) with matching lids.'* SSTC. Be more adventurous and try the Garlic Mussels on Puri – mussels cooked in a garlic, red onion and white wine sauce, served on a puri. 20% discount on collected takeaways. Lunch to 2.30. Dinner to 11.30.

London EC

Area: The City of London
Postcodes: EC1 to EC4
Population: 145,000

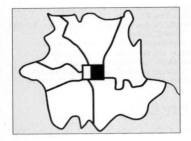

See page 72 for key to this map.

London EC1

Angel, Barbican, Clerkenwell,
Farringdon, Old Street, Smithfield

ANAKANA

Olivers Yard, City Rd, EC1   0845 262 5262

'Street-food' is the new thing on new trendy venue's menus, whatever street-food means. I take it to mean Indian items you purchase from kerbside vendors, and since you can purchase just about anything in this manner in India, I am still not able to define it in terms of the UK . Chef Simon Koo's definition is 'small-eats' such as mini tandoori quail and mini utthapam (south Indian pancakes). Menu Snapshot: A version of Patrani Maachli (seabass wrapped in banana leaves) a green vegetable Biriani, and char-grilled cuttlefish / black ink pilau are original. Char-grilled red pepper stuffed with vegetables. Pre Coca-Cola India's major fizzy drink brand was the cutely misspelled Thums Up, and it's here. Not cheap if you go for the works (over £90 for two for a starter cocktail and small-eat followed by a meal with beer and tip. Hours: 11.30-11 Mon-Sat; 10.30 Sun. Bar Sun-Wed -12 / Thur-Sat -2.

CAFÉ CULSHAN

33 Charterhouse Square, Barbican, EC1
   020 7600 7277

'A large restaurant, a very pleasant building in an excellent location. We had been there twice before, not long after it opened. We were always happy enough with the food but something was missing. This time it was different from the moment we stepped through the door. We were welcomed immediately, shown to an upstairs table, (before we had always been ushered downstairs even though upstairs was not full),

promptly handed menus and wine list and generally given the impression that the whole place was much more professional. Apparently the owner is the same but the whole staff has changed, with a 'proper chef', keen waiters and an ambitious manager who has already made changes and has plans for more. The food was very good, portions generous and prices very fair for central London. Very good to find an Indian restaurant with a better wine list and offering espresso coffee. Coffee is usually a dreadful let down in Indian restaurants. Unfortunately there wasn't a single Indian dessert.' HC.

CARDAMOM ROOMS

33 Charterhouse Sq, EC1   020 7600 7277

Launched in 2005 by brothers, Jay and Sal Abedin, India meets Thailand in this 140-cover restaurant. It is airy and spacious, combining dark wood floors and black marble with shades of cream, crimson and chocolate. Large round tables encourage a social dining experience. Chef Himmat Singh (ex Cinnamon Club) offers the Indian menu with signature dishes including Muglai Rost Gosht, slow-cooked lamb shank with whole spices and onion in a tomato and cashew based sauce. Chef Saowanee Franklin delivers the Thai menu, with dishes such as Plah Neung Si-ew, steamed whole sea bass with soya sauce, chilli, ginger and spring onions.

CHAWOL   NEW ENTRANT

5 Clerkenwell Road, EC1   020 7490 4468

'A great success. The decor is very bright and modern, menu fairly short and prices very average. The service was very good and extremely friendly. Three small spheres of Onion Bhajia, Butter Chicken - rich and creamy but definitely spicier than most and really fantastic Baigan Bhajee. All the food was delicious and well spiced and I thoroughly enjoyed the meal. Definitely a 'will return' restaurant. £28 for one, including one Cobra, one mineral water and one espresso which deserves full marks for being available!' DRC.

CURRY LEAF

20 City Road, EC1   020 7374 4842

Curry Leaf opened in 2004 by S. Rehman, T. Ali, P. Chowdhery, and S. Sohail who between them for over 30 years have built up a portfolio of twelve other top-end restaurants across London. This 120-cover restaurant is pretty and modern, with an intimate 15-seat bar / lounge area, a 25-seat balcony and the main dining area (70 seats) on the ground level. There is also a basement, with a private 35-seat room. The walls are noticeably bare and the only obvious embellishment is the arched Burma teak beams, which co-ordinate with the curved-back chairs and give the restaurant a bit of flair. The illuminated glass panel at the back of the restaurant enhances the chic simplicity and the generous space between tables again emphasises the minimalism

of the eatery, while allowing the diners a bit of privacy during their meal to a backdrop of Indian classical music. The bar area also projects a contemporary vibe, with comfortable bar stools for a small group of people and dim lighting to create a cool atmosphere for diners. The man behind the food, Executive Chef, Ramu Sharma trained in Dehradun's School of Food and Arts and worked for Moti Mahal group of restaurants in Delhi (see London WC2) before moving to London. He has emphasised the cuisine on north India, with regional dishes from across India peppered into the menu. Ones to try include Sikandari Raan, which is a leg of spring lamb soaked overnight in run marinade and oven-cooked, Allepey Seafood Curry, which is a mixture of seafood stewed in coconut milk with shredded ginger soured with raw mangoes and Lamb Hyderabadi Biriani. www.curryleaf.co.uk

INDIA

182 St John Street, EC1	020 7490 8295

After a wealth of family restaurant experience stretching back to the Shangri La in London's East End in 1967, Harun Khan, who owns four restaurants in the Chingford area and one in Upminster opened this 80 seater restaurant, India in Clerkenwell. The downstairs Saffron Bar is run by Mark Powers, former Saudi Royal family butler then beverage manager at the St James Club. The chef came from Chutney Mary and this reflects the menu. Reports please.

SMITHFIELD TANDOORI

4 Lindsey Street, EC1	020 7606 1652

This restaurant has always been one of our favourites. Mr Afsar Khan is an excellent manager and even mentioned that he had not seen us for some time. The decor is very plain but looks stylish with good glassware and white tablecloths. Prices a little more than average, but good value for quality. All the food is served on or in plain white china. Chicken Tikka Makhani, King Prawn Persian Curry with four vegetable side dishes, no rice or bread. All really goo, we ate every morsel of every dish, all different in flavour and colour, not always the case. £90 for two, including £39 bottle of wine.' HJC. *'All details as before. The food was even more exceptional. On our previous visit the Gulab Jamun was not fresh enough and this time the manager made a point of having a fresh delivery to ensure it was available for me. This is service. I love Gulab Jamun, but they have to be warm and served with no cream or ice cream, just the way there are - delicious! £87 for two which included a Sambuca, which the waiter brought properly alight with the correct number of coffee beans. Did you see in the papers that a waitress refused to light Sambucas in an Italian restaurant in Hampshire as directed by their local, obviously over-officious Health and Safety Dept!.'* HJC. Hampshire employ the bolshiest, most unpleasant 'officers' in the UK. It was Cicero who observed that such petty officials are our servants not our masters. Not

so in Hampshire. Perhaps we should count ourselves lucky that we can get hot food at all these days. If the nanny state got its way, cooking itself would be banned because it requires us to have a 'fire' in the kitchen!

London EC2

Barbican, City, Liverpool St, Moorgate

MEHEK

45 London Wall, EC2 5TE	020 7588 5043

Mehek means "fragrance"and whafts of delicioso came to us as we approached the venue. A pretty Indian girl, who takes coats etc, shares space with a comfortable leather sofa (for the takeaway customer). An extremely long bar leads to tables at the back. Throughout our visit, suited men, men and more men arrived. Some perched themselves on high stools, drank pints of beer and talked loudly while crunching on popadums piled high in woven metal baskets. From the short menu, we chose a starter of Bhalla Papria Chaat – light, fluffy buns of fermented and steamed rice flour, smothered in natural yoghurt and imli which were quite plain. I decided on Aloo Tikki, three nicely shaped patties of spiced potato and green peas were delivered with salad and yoghurt dip. The main course Achari Gosht, tender lamb, mildly spiced, was too sweet for us both. Madri Murgh, a new twist on CTM, dish contained Vodka (and that's why I ordered it!). Side dishes of Jaipuri Bhindi, diagonal slices of okra, deep-fried in a very light batter of besan and sprinkled, too sparingly, in my opinion, with mango powder and kala namak. Though

still a good dish. Our benchmark Dal Makhni was well cooked, creamy, not over salted, wonderful. It is a testing dish for the chefs, and Ashok Kumar, formerly at Tamarind, handles his dishes admirably. We decided to indulge in the real Indian sweets on offer. We shared Dudhi (marrow) Halwa. Service charge 12.5% and the credit card slip was returned, closed – congrats!

TIFFIN BITES   GROUP AWARD WINNER

Tiffin Bites is a group of outlets run by Andy and Arjun Vama (see page 121) in locations strategically placed to catch London's busy City workers at all times of day from early breakfast to dinner. The menu is identical at each, and some of the food is cooked at a central kitchen with finishing off taking place at branch. The Vamas are particular about health and ethics. The group do not use ghee, and the little oil they use makes their food lighter. The story of their costly but well-publicised decision only to use free-range chicken is told on page 36, and their CTM is of course no 1 at Tiffin Bites. The philosophy is that the only true way to eat Indian cuisine is to eat it the correct way – the way it has been prepared and served for centuries as if you were eating in India – in traditional Tiffin boxes. *(see piece overleaf)*. All the premises are licensed and their long hours mean that diners can grab a drink at the bar or at table, get a speedy meal (Halal) and watch the latest Bollywood film on a large screen TV. Asian clientele love it. After 5pm Tiffin Bites serve a different menu more suitable for the evening. Menu Snapshot: For breakfast you can have Naan bread at £2.75 with light curries, washed down with coffee, chai, smoothies or lassi. Later in the day you can buy Chaat and Bhel £3.95, Kebabs, Samosa and Bhajis, £1.50 or Wraps containing organic fillings c£3. and a wide range of Indian sweets and hand-fried crisps. Choice of three tiffin boxes (bespoke plastic trays) eg CTM, Veg Jalfrezi and Pilau Rice at £5. See page 19.

TIFFIN BITES   GROUP AWARD

3 Russia Row, Off Gresham Street, St Paul's EC2V 7PG   020 7600 4899

The flagship 260-seater St Pauls' branch is appropriately enough only yards from that wonderfully named City Street, Poultry. See above! Hours: 11.30–10; Closed at weekends. See page 19.

TIFFIN BITES   GROUP AWARD

24 Moorfield, Moorgate, EC2T 9AA   020 7638 3951

Take-aways can be phoned through first so that it´s ready when you arrive or you can pop in and grab your choice from their selection of pre-wrapped chilled dishes: wraps, light bites, freshly baked naan breads, or a main dish that are neatly packed in little Tiffin boxes which can be heated up in store or taken back to your office microwave and are ready to eat in three minutes. Hours: 6.30am – 9.30pm; Closed at weekends. See page 19.

Tiffinbites, Russian Row, EC2

TIFFIN
WHAT IS IT?

Tiffin derived from an English slag term, *'tiffing'*: eating or drinking outside of meal times, and a *'tiff'*, a draught of liquor or beer. By the time of the Raj in India it had come to mean a light lunch, though in today's India the term Tiffin is generally used to mean an in-between-meals snack. In Mumbai it has a more significant meaning. Most office-workers commute from the suburbs to the city centre. When it comes to lunch, restaurants and fast-food outlets are too pricey to visit, besides there aren't that many. Also there's nothing like home-food. So a unique service has evolved over the last 100 years or so, to provide a unique door-to-door delivery service. After the worker has left home, his wife or mum cooks his or her lunch and packs it in a three or four tier stainless-steel,

circular containers, which clip together and become one unit with a carry handle. This is called a **tiffin** or **tiffin**-box. A curry will be in one tier, rice and/or bread in another, dhal in another and possibly a sweet in the fourth. At around 11am, a man on a bike arrives at the suburban home. He is a **Dabbawala** and he collects the tiffin. At 12pm he boards the nearest train with a loaded crate of tiffins weighing 60kg, and heads

for central Mumbai, barefoot, crate on head. There he meets dozens of other Dabbawalas and there is a midday sort out of tiffins. Each Dabbawala next has a delivery destination (office blocks), with dozens of tiffins on his trolley or tray. The right tiffin arrives at the right desk at 1pm ... one happy diner! At 2pm the process reverses. The Dabbawala collects his empty tiffins and the right tiffin arrives at the right home at around 4pm. Around 200,000 tiffins are delivered each day by 5,000 Dabbawalas, who being illiterate, use a system of coloured squiggles to identify in and out locations. The cost is £3 per month per diner! The system is said to be so efficient that there is only one mistake for every million deliveries. More info on <www.mydabbawala.com> and **Wikipedia**, to whom thankyou for use of the photos.

TIFFIN BITES   GROUP AWARD

22 Liverpool Street, EC2M 7PD

020 7626 5641

Opposite Liverpool Street Station main entrance, it is designed for a quick meal in reasonable comfort, on benches. Food & drink is swiftly served, and with a smile too, and it can cost less than a tenner. Hours: 6.30am–9.30pm; Mon–Fri; 11–5 Sat & Sun See also branch at Canary Wharf, E14, previous page and p19.

London EC3
Aldgate, Fenchurch Street, Tower

KASTURI   A-LIST

57 Aldgate High St, EC3   020 7480 7402

Right out-side Aldgate Tube, we hear that Nur Monie has cut back his menu a bit. You can get all the usual

curries which may say it all. Because if that's what you want got to nearby Brick Lane and stuff yourself for half the price. In late 2002 he teamed up with Bashir Ahmed (owner of five popular Kohinoor restaurants in Holland) to open their 80-seater Kasturi. It has the current look of blonde wood floor, bright lights, colourful walls and pot plants. Management tell us, Kasturi means 'the strong scented secretion found in rare musk deer, used in expensive perfumes'. Phew! I don't know about that, but the scent of the tandoor is more likely to be encountered. Kasturi has an ace up its sleeve – Head Chef Rajandra Balmiki. He trained at the Delhi's Mauyra Sheraton Hotel, under chef Imtiaz Qureshi of Dum Pukht fame and former training chef, the highly respected C.P Rahman. Maurya has the best Tandoori restaurant in the world, the Bukhara. What a background. Kasturi claims to specialise in Pakhtoon cuisine. It's a far cry from Delhi and Welling. It refers to the tribal people of Afghanistan from the rugged mountain passes in the former North-West Frontier Province, whose name for themselves is Pathan,

Pashtun, Phuktana or Pukhtun. Afghan food is pretty basic, especially at tribal level, involving kebab-skewer cooking and slow-cooking in pots. Koftas and Birianis are popular, cooked in their own juices. Try Kadak kebab Samarkand – minced lamb roll stuffed with cheese and grilled, or Mahi-e-Ghazni, whole pomfret fish marinated in fresh coriander and mint and roasted in the Tandoor £9.95, or Grilled Seabass – marinated in a sauce of yoghurt and olive oil with black and white pepper £10.95. Any of the Birianis will *'blow you away'*. HEG. Our benchmark Dal-Dera Ismail Khan – *'A harmonious combination of black dal and herbs, simmering on slow charcoal fire'* (aka Dal Makhani) is just £3.50. Kasturi has attracted rave reviews from our reporters But such a menu and such a skilled Indian chef will of course bring adverse comments from what Monie calls *'those with their brains closed'*. He's prepared for it, and he offers them formula curries. [How sad.]

MANTRA VEGETARIAN   NEW ENTRANT

37 Crutched Friars, EC3N 2AE 0871 4263587

Colleagues out for three-course meals, friends out for a few drinks, families, celebrating a special event, couples looking for a quiet meal are who you'll typically find at Mantra. The dimly-lit main restaurant has 30 covers, and can fit an extra 20 for a reception. A smart private basement room can accommodate a maximum of 25 seated, 50 standing. Choose from an a la carte, canapé or buffet menu. Its blend of Asian and Western influences works really well. Don't expect your average curry menu either. Mantra is 100% vegetarian, yet tellingly, the majority of diners aren't. They just enjoy tasty, expertly cooked food. A versatile menu lists creative dishes such as curried Bombay potato in pitta bread lined with chutney, as well as traditional meals such as saag aloo and palak paneer. The veggie chicken curry is fantastic. Good pre-theatre meal deals. Smiley service. Top marks all round. Ayurvedic see A-Z glossary.

YOU SAY OK, LONDON, EC3
You may get a discount of you show them this Guide.
MATAB'S 76 Aldgate High St, EC3 ~ 020 7481 4010. Owned by Matab Choudhury, of the Bangladeshi Caterers Association. **PLANTERS INN** 25 Great Tower Street, EC3 ~ 020 7621 1214. 64-seater, opposite the Tower. Partners Vernon Menezes, formerly of Zaika and Chor Bizarre Chef Joydeep Chatterjee, from Calcutta. **RAJASTHAN**, 49 Monument Street, EC3 ~ 020 7626 1920. *'Not Rajasthani food, but curryhouse which varies from OK to good. Fast service, nice decor.'* NP. Hours: 6-11.

STOP PRESS ~   NEW ENTRANT
OPEN FROM JUNE 2009
BANGALORE EXPRESS
1 Corbet Court, 6 Gracechurch Street, London EC3

We safely predict that this 'quirky' venue will be as successful as the original branch. See pages 101 and 121.

London N

Area: North London
Postcodes: N1 to N22
Population: 1,250,000

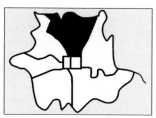

See page 72 for key to this map.

London N1

Islington, King's Cross, Shoreditch

AFGHAN KITCHEN   TOP 100

35 Islington Green, N1   020 7359 8019

Afghani food is served here, as the name suggest, in this intimate restaurant. It is not dissimilar to northern Indo-Pak, though it is less spicy. The names are similar. Bread isn't Naan, it is Nane Lawash – thinner, glazed and basket-shaped. Qurma is Korma, etc, etc. It's Muslim, big on Halal goat (here they use lamb) and goat's milk. Banjon Borani - fried aubergines, flavoured with garlic and cumin. Yoghurt always accompanies a meal. Try Dogh – Savoury Yoghurt with mint, and the Tourshis or chutneys. *'Not knowing anything about Afghan food, four of us were delighted to find that it bore a close resemblance to Indian with the Murgh Kofta – chicken meat balls in sauce, Gosht Qurma, a type of meat Korma, Suzhi Gosht – meat with spinach spiced with Char Masala (a four-spice version of India's Garam Masala), each £4.50 with the bread as the staple, chilli pickle to liven up the delicate spicing, house wine to wash to it all down.'* GR. Small menu. No credit cards. Av spend £10. Hours: 12-3.30 / 5.30-11. Closed Sun & Mon.

EMNI   NEW ENTRANT

353 Upper Street, N1 0PD   020 7704 8323

Emni opened in 2006, bringing what it called an

'upmarket Indian restaurant' to the area. Bags of money have been spent on decor:smoked glass windows, wooden floor boards, white walls, black furniture and artifacts a l'Indiennne. *'Pretty place'* says RCF. Some enjoy the upstairs bar for people watching in the street below. The food gets mixed reviews. Presentation is a prerequisite for the ex-Indian-hotel chefs who do not subscribe to the belief that the squeegee tubes are out; here they reign supreme with on-plate graffiti in greens reds browns and yellows. They play safe with curryhouse items such as Korma, CTM and Roghan. But there are other interesting items to try: Malai Scallops in a herb and yoghurt sauce; *'Bhindi Gosht (lamb with okra), Pasilyan chops, Doora Kebab and Tandoori Duck were are good'* RCF. Hours: 12.30-2.30 Fri-Sun / 6-11; 12 Fri.   www.emnirestaurant.com

INDIAN VEG BHEL POORI HOUSE

92 Chapel Market, N1   020 7837 4607

'Although I have sung the praises of the excellent value eighteen e-a-m-a-y-l buffet dishes, I feel I must praise it again. I now lunch there once a week and the quality is always consistent. Occasionally there is a superb mashed potato and onion curry. Always a friendly welcome and my half lager is now brought automatically.' TN. *'All the dishes are superb, and I'm no veggie. The Bhel Puri is still my favourite though.'* ME. Hours: 12-11.30.

MASALA ZONE   A-LIST

80 Upper Street, N1   020 7359 3399

This is the second of five Masala Zones. They are a clever idea from a clever family. Briefly it is basic food, but cooked as is Mumbai Indian street food. You can't reserve, and it is inexpensive. Hard in fact to exceed £15 per head (more with wine). You won't find better real Indian food at such prices. Mon-Fri 12-3 / 5.30-11.30 (12-11 Sat & Sun). Full menu description and list of branches, see Masala Zone, W1.

ROOBUROO NEW ENTRANT

21 Chapel Market, N1 9EZ 020 7278 8100

What's a Rooburoo; a burrowing marsupial? No its gem of an all day Indian restaurant which opened in 2006 in what they call a culinary desert (but is in fact a restaurant-packed area). Paintings adorn the walls. One is of Britain's first Asian MP – Dadabhai Naoroji, elected 1893 in Islington and loads of others featuring Indian subject, old and new. And Rooburoo is Indian with Indian chefs which ensure you get Indian diners. The owners won't mind my gag because the menu's full of them. Rooburoasts are tandoor items, Rooburosalads include Tun Tuna Tun £8.50, lightly spiced tuna, seared and served on green leaves with tomatoes, topped with chick peas and omega seeds; Kakra Aloo Anarkali £8.75, crab and potato. On the beverage list (named Rooburrefresh) you'll find Lassi and Nimbu Pani both sweet or salty, £2.75 or Rooburtini is a cocktail of gin, vodka, fresh lime juice and passion fruit.' while Rooburlini is mango liqueur, mandarin juice and sparkling cava. It's got the familiar favourites on the menu (Rooby Murray Curries and Rooburbiriyanis). But Rooburoo goes further than that. Hard to find Romali Roti is (aka handkerchief bread) giving the clue that is is very thin and rather large, a hanky in fact) is here and is one of the wraps along with paratha and chupatti and banana leaf which encase a choice of interesting subjects such as fish chicken and meat curry stir-fries and bakes. Patrani Machli is a great starter (fish wrapped in banana leaf). And unusual items include Kerka bitter gourd, doodi marrow and mooli white radish vegetable dishes. Puds are authentic too. chocolate dalchini fudge sponge cake with cinnamon and crushed pistachios; mishti doi, sweet, baked Indian yoghurt topped with molasses syrup A good meal can set you back just over a tenner. Their final gag: '*The only 'e' number is in our postcode*'. [wrong actually, Turmeric is E100!]. Service 12.5%. www.rooburoo.com

YOU SAY OK

You may get a discount of you show them this Guide.

N1: PARVEEN 6 Theberton Street, N1 ~ 020 7226 0504 60 seats on two floors est 1977: '*Faruk and staff are so amazing, makes everyone feel special. Food lovely and decor fantastic.*' JO'B. '*By far the best Indian in Islington, highly recommended.*' CR. Hours: 12-3 / 6-12.

N1: RAJ MONI 279 Upper Street, N1 ~ 020 7354 1270. 50-seater. Lunch and dinner daily. Del evenings only.

N2: COCHIN 111 High Rd, East Finchley, N2 ~ 020 8444 5666. South Indian vegetarian. Thali set meal from £8.95. A-la-carte meal for two with wine and service: c£60. Hours: 12-2.30/6-11.30.

N2: MAJJOS 1 Fortis Green, N2 ~ 020 8883 4357. Est 1993 by Mrs Ashraf, mngr S Mogul. A shop with seating for just 10. Enjoy meat curries £4.50; veg £2.50 then shop for your Indian groceries. Hours: 10.30-10.30; 10 Sun.

London N3 Finchley, Fortis Green

RANI VEGETARIAN
PREVIOUS AWARD WINNER TOP 100

7 Long Lane, N3 020 8349 4386

Jyoti Patni is front of house in this venue tastefully decorated in shades of turmeric and red, with Georgian chairs and glass-topped tables. Rani means Queen, and the term could as well refer to the cooks, Jyoti's wife and his mother, because their Gujarati vegetarian food cannot be bettered anywhere. The menu features mainly Gujarati items which are tasty enough to please all but the most obdurate non-veggie. India's most western state, Gujarat, is the home of mild, slightly sweet dishes, with a love of yoghurt and gram flour. The soup-like curry Khadi is one dish showing Gujarati adoration of both. The famous bhajia also originated in Gujarat, as did the lesser known Dahi Vada, a gram flour dumpling in a tangy yoghurt sauce. Kachoris – Spicy mashed potato and peas spicy ball, coated in batter and deep-fried. Bhel Puri are all there along with Gujarati curries e.g. Undui – five vegetable stew, and a Gujarati national dish. Traditionally the five vegetables are beans, aubergine, red pumpkin, sweet potato and a further vegetable. These are cooked in a sauce made from gram flour, asafoetida and yoghurt. It is often served with besan kofta balls in it. Another superb dish is Lasan Bateta, literally garlic potato, but it's not that simple, it is baby new potatoes, stuffed with spices and red chilli. It is dipped in gram-flour batter, deep-fried and served in imli (sweet tamarind chutney). Wow!!! Innovations to prevent diner boredom make this restaurant different. How about pizzas (which are after all just Naan bread cooked in the oven) with Indo-Italian toppings, such as banana (plantain) methi with green chilli and mozzarella. Great stuff. And they are innovations retaining the ethos of Indian, rather than fusion food which does not. '*The menu has some cold starters which are "to die for". Rashia Vall, great. Rice and breads as good as usual.*' CT. Says the highly critical RL: '*Menu includes unusual and tasty dishes. Recommended to me by so many people. Aloo Shai Poori (crispy pooris, potatoes, onions with yoghurt) and Vall Papri (spicy beans and onions on pooris with tamarind and yoghurt), both a taste of heaven. This restaurant is pure quality. It's world class.*' RL. 6-10.30 daily. Sun lunch 12.15-2.30.

London N8
Crouch End, Hornsey, Turnpike Lane

MASALA DELI BAR

59 Park Road, N8 020 8442 9222

Gujarati food, predominately vegetarian, e.g.: Kachori 60p – minced peas / split mung beans in pastry balls.

Patra 50p, spiced gram flour wrapped in arvi leaves. Pani Puri £2.50, six small puffed puris filled with sprouted mung beans and potato, served with tamarind and date dressing (yum yum!). Roti Wraps £1.50, bread filled with a choice of sweet corn; potato and nut; shredded cabbage with carrot and lime. Light lunches include: Tuna Thali £6, plain rice served with spicy tuna, a vegetable dish or your choice, a roti and a juice drink. Falafel Meal £3, spicy lentil fritters with salad in pitta bread. Hours: 11-9.30.   www.masala-uk.com

London N12 · North Finchley

FINCHLEY PAN CENTRE

15 Woodhouse Road, N12   020 8446 5497

A tiny, unlicensed Indian snack bar, frequented by Indians. Kebabs, samosas, veg rissoles, etc., very inexpensive. Friendly service. Cash please. Oh, and as for Pan or Paan, it's not a cooking vessel, it is a collection of edible ingredients, ranging from very bitter to very sweet wrapped in the paan or bright dark green paan or betel leaf. Paan is an acquired taste, used as an aid to digestion. The observant visitor to India will have noticed very busy street kiosks dispensing paan all hours. We only know of a few other Paan houses (in Asian communities such as Southall). See A-Z of the Menu. Hours: 12-10; (Fri, 3.30-10); closed Tues.

YOU SAY OK

You may get a discount of you show them this Guide.

N4: JAI KRISHNA 161 Stroud Green Rd, Stroud Green, N4 020 7272 1680 Vegetarian, BYO, cash only and the WC is accessed from outside. '*Home-style, plentiful and wonderful.*' RL. Hours: 12-2/5.30-11 Mon-Sat

N7: BENGAL BALTI HOUSE 6 Brecknock Road, Tufnell Park N7 ~ 020 7609 7075. 86-seater est 1984 by Ashik Ali since 1994. Hours: 12-2.30/6-12;12.30 Sat. Branch: Hillmarton Tandoori, Hillmarton ce, N7.

N10: TASTE OF NAWAB 93 Colney Hatch Lane, Muswell Hill, N10 ~ 020 8883 6429. Est1996 by Abdul. '*All dishes are large, reasonably priced and tasty. Service great!*' SM. Del: 3m/ £10. Hours: 12-2.30 / 6-12. Sun buffet 12-5.30, e-a-m-a-y-l.

N11: BEJOY 72 Bounds Green Road, New Southgate, N11 ~ 020 8888 1268. 54-seater est 1995 by Abdul Sukur and chef M Rahman. Del: 2m/ £8. Hours: 12-2.30 Sat-Thurs / 6-12 Mon - Sat. Sun buffet. 12-11. Branch: Sunderban, N4.

N13: DIPALI 82 Aldermans Hill, Palmers Green, N13 ~ 020 8886 2221. This popular restaurant has appeared in all our Guides. Hours: 12-2.30/6-12. Sun buffet 12-3.30.

N14: BEKASH 8 Hampden Square, N14 ~ 020 8368 3206. 55-seater est 1995 by Nazrul Miah (manager) and Harun Ali (chef). Hours: 5.30-11.30 (12 Sat).

N22: AKBAR TAKEAWAY 13 Salisbury Rd, Wood Green, N22 020 8881 7902. Chef Proprietor - Mostakin Miah (Mintu) est it in 1988. Is it London's cheapest Popadum? Hours: 5.30-11.30.

London N14 · Southgate

ROMNA GATE · RE ENTRY

14 The Broadway, Southgate, N14 6PH
020 8882 6700

'*Of the many restaurants in Enfield (which includes Oakwood and Southgate), only three are listed in the current guide. My local in Southgate deserves a mention – but then again as it's so popular it probably doesn't need it but it surprises me that no one has bothered to write to you, so here goes. 'Romna Gate' in Southgate (just opposite Southgate tube station) is a great, traditional restaurant. It's always busy, the food is great and the staff are helpful and friendly. My husband swears their Chicken Jalfrezi is the best (and he's tried a few around the UK). It's the only restaurant I have visited which gives complimentary Popadom starters.*' JN.

London N15 · Stoke Newington

ABI RUCHI

42 Church Street, N15   020 7923 4564

South Indian serving Keralan meat, fish and shellfish, as well as vegetable dishes. '*Had Veg Pakodas (bhajias) crunch and fresh and for mains Bekal Meen Kootan, fish curry with smoked tamarind and Koonthal Masala, spiced baby squid, stuffed with tomato, pepper, coconut, and chilli. Friendly helpful service.*' BD. 2 course set lunch £5.95 veg, £7.50, non-veg. Hours; 12-3 / 6-11 Mon-Thu; 11.45 Fri & Sat; 1-10.15 Sun.

London N16 · Stoke Newington

RASA · A-LIST

55 Church Street, N16   020 7249 0344

South Indian vegetarian. Cochin-born Shiva Das Sreedharan's and his wife Alison's first restaurant. He worked at a Delhi hotel before coming to England to manage a small restaurant. Believing he could do things better, he set up this restaurant in 1994 in this then unfashionable street serving then unfashionable south Indian vegetarian food. To make his statement he had his frontage a blackcurrant yoghurt shade shocking pink. Das just loves it, and it has indeed brought him good luck. It's now the signature colour of the many branches which continue to follow plus menus and his web site. Thanks to passion that Das has imparted into his ventures, we know that there is so much more to Keralan food than Masala Dosas. Rasa chefs are expert vegetarian cooks. Cooking uses coconut, mustard, curry leaves, curds, chillies, lentils and rice. Exotic vegetables include plantains, drumsticks, gourds, sour mango, and beans. The differences between the cooking of the five

Keralan groups is intensely subtle, including the names of the similar dishes. But differences there are, so try it out. Ask managers Usha or Bhaskar or the staff for advice. Menu Snapshot: Banana Boli £2.75 - plantain slices in batter of rice and chickpea flour with black sesame seeds, fried, served with peanut and ginger sauce; Kathrikka £2.75 - slices of aubergine dipped in coriander and chilli batter, fried, served with tomato chutney; Chilli Onion Rava Dosa £5.95 - crispy pancake of semolina and rice flour, with ginger, green chillies and cumin seed, served with Sambar - lentils and vegetable sauce, coconut chutney and spicy potato masala; Cheera Parippu Curry £3.75 - fresh spinach, toor dal, garlic, tomatoes, green peppers and curry leaves; Kerala Salad £4 - guava, avocado, shallots, fresh coconut, lemon juice and chilli. This is the only UK venue where you can get Nair Dosa – a Keralan speciality, usually eaten during festivals and celebrations: a rice and black gram flour pancake filled with a mixture of potatoes, beetroot, carrot, onions and ginger, served with sambar and fresh coconut chutney, c£6. Chef Narayanan's signature dish is the Rasa Kayi, a mixed vegetable speciality from the Southern State of Karnataka. A spicy curry made of beans, carrots, cauliflower, potatoes and simmered in a sauce of garlic, ginger and fennel, c£4. Cheera Curry is Paneer and spinach cooked with garlic, peppers and tomato in a creamy sauce, c£3. For pudding, if you have room, try Banana Dosa, the Palakkad Iyer (Brahmin) speciality with a difference. These tiny pancakes are made from bananas, plain flour and cardamom. Mango Halwa £3 - puréed Alphonso mangos, with cashew nuts and raisins, an interesting twist on the traditional Carrot Halwa. Service: 12.5%. Hours: 12-3 Sat & Sun only/ 6-10.45; 11.30 Fri & Sat. Branches: next entry, London NW1, W1, WC1 & Newcastle. www.rasarestaurants.com

RASA TRAVANCORE   A-LIST

56 Church Street, N16   020 7249 1340

Nearly opposite the original at Rasa 55 (see above). Go in past the pink frontage into more pink (table cloths and menus and decor) amidst the wooden temple carvings. We normally think of Kerala as a vegetarian state. In fact there have been passionate non-vegetarians – Muslims, Jews and Christians – living there side by side for centuries, each with a distinctive cooking style. As for the latter, St Thomas the Apostle landed in Kerala in AD50 and made many converts to Christianity. His language was Syriac Armenaic, his converts known as Syrian Christians. To this day they eat offal, chicken, duck, fish, shellfish, beef, and wild boar. Das brought such dishes with very unfamiliar names to London and they vie for attention on his menu. A great introduction is the Travancore Feast, where you get a good selection of dishes for c£22. Chicken Puffs, spicy chicken masala stuffed in puff pastry are frankly Anglo Indian Raj stuff, but they're great stuff, c£4, and eat them with Meen Achar – Chicken pickle. In fact all the Rasa venues serve

unusual pickles and chutneys seemingly quite expensive at £2.75 a shot. However, these are not just any condiments, they have been carefully made by the kitchen staff, so worth every penny with the Rasa a twist on popadums as your pre-starter nibble. Try Murukku £3 - crunchy sticks made from roasted rice flour, black sesame and cumin seeds. More traditional Syrian Christian specialities include Kerala Fish fry, £4, king fish marinated in a spicy paste made of ginger, green chillies and coriander, then shallow fried in the traditional fashion. Chicken Stew, £5.50, chicken cooked in fresh coconut milk, with finely chopped ginger, green chillies and flavoured with cinnamon, cardamom, cashew nut and raisins. Erachi Olathiyathu £6.95 - boneless cubes of lamb, dry cooked in turmeric water, then stir-fried with black pepper, curry leaves, and slivers of fresh coconut – a spicy dish (I can still recall the first time I ate this dish, it was in Trivandrum and the Sea Shells restaurant - wonderful! dbac). Nadan Kozhy Curry £5.25 - boneless chicken, pepper masala from garlic, mustard seeds, curry leaves, green chillies and ginger (eat with Lemon Rice). Tharavu roast, c£7, duck cooked in a thick sauce with ginger, garlic, onion and coriander. Rasa in Sanskrit means amongst other things, taste, flavour, liking, pleasure, delight and essence. There is so much more: You can even get the house pink in dish form – try Beet Bhindi Pachadi, beetroot with yoghurt. The venue is managed by Jinu and Mustafa. Let them and the staff guide you. Service: 12.5%. Hours: 12-3, Sun only and 6-10.45; 11.30 Fri & Sat. Branches: see previous entry. www.rasarestaurants.com

London NW

Area: North West London
Postcodes: NW1 to NW11
Population: 680,000

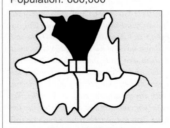

See page 72 for key to this map.

London NW1
Drummond Street, Euston

Drummond Street , west of Euston Station, has always been a second heaven for curry aficionados. In 1951 M. Mahammed opened the Shah restaurant at 124 Drummond Street (in the same block as today's Royal and Zeen). It was London's fourth Indian restaurant and survived until 1989. (Its descendant is the Star of India run by Mahammed's exhibitionist son, Reza (see

page 115). In 1958 Laxmishanker Pathak opened a shop (called Virani) on Drummond Street, selling spices, groceries, fresh Indian vegetables and snacks such as samosas made by Mrs Pathak in her upstairs kitchen. Before long this humble enterprise became brand-leader, Patak's (see page 42). Virani's descendant is The Indian Spice Shop (at 115). Diwana opened in 1981 (at 121), pioneering Bhel in Britain (see previous page and p94). Drummond Street will not win any beauty awards, and it lacks the ethnic glamour of Southall and Wembley, or the intensity of purpose of Brick Lane. Today its assets include greengrocers, a Halal butcher, a liquor store and a concentration of extremely good, mainly inexpensive Indian food vendors. Here in alphabetical order are your Drummond Street favourites including the latest arrivals Zeen and Royal Sweets (see entries) which opened in early 2009. Here in alphabetical order are your Drummond Street favourites:

AMBALA SWEET CENTRE   TOP 100

112 Drummond Street, NW1   020 7387 3521

Ambala started trading in 1965. It specialises in takeaway-only savoury snacks (Pakoras and Samosa, etc.), Indian sweets (Halva, Jalebi, Gulab Jamun, Barfi, etc.) and a few vegetarian curries such as chickpea. Established initially for Asians, it now has branches in Birmingham, Bradford, Derby, East Ham, Finchley, Glasgow, Leicester, Leyton, Luton, Manchester, Slough, Southall, Tooting and Wembley. All branches serve identical items at identical prices. The quality is first-class and the prices are always reasonable. Be prepared to queue, and pay cash. Open daily 10am-11pm.

CHUTNEYS

134 Drummond St, NW1 2PA   020 7388 0604

100% vegetarian. *'My first visit but recommended by my father who had been there previously with colleagues. 100% vegetarian Indian restaurant so perfect for me. Cuisine mainly Gujarat (Thali etc) or southern Madras (Dosa etc) and my dishes had almost no oil so much healthier than most restaurants. Quiet, clean and quite small (about 50 covers). Wooden floor and tables and earthy wall colours. Traditional Indian music but very discrete. Service very quick, efficient and happy to help with any questions or requests. Very flexible; managed dairy free for one customer and also able to cater for diabetics. Quiet before 7pm but quickly filled up afterwards with a wide international clientele. Simple menu on 2 sides of A4 with no standard curries and, being vegetarian, no CTM!. Some daily specials and lots of special dishes I'd never had or seen before – very tempting! Examples from the menu: Starters: Onion bhaji £3.50, 3 x samosa £3.50 Mains: Thali £7.95 - £10.50, Utthapam £6.95, Muttar Panir £4.70, Pillau Rice £2.95 My meal. Appetiser: Spiced Popadum (x2) and chutneys £1.20. Starter: Aloo Tikka Chat £3.60. Fresh, fragrant and flavourful with yoghurt and chutney dressing. Main: Dosa Paneer £6.95 with sambar and coconut chutney.*

An enormous triangle (12" to a side!) of light rice flour pancake filled with a mix of delicately spiced potato and vegetables. Drinks: Cobra £4.50 for 660ml bottle. Kingfisher and other lagers also available plus choices of lassi, bottled water and other soft drinks etc. Wines and champagnes and a choice of organic and vegetarian wines! Didn't have desert but complimentary mixed red/green masala and selection of fruit served at the end! Portions more than adequate and very light and fresh tasting (lack of oil / ghee). Food beautifully prepared and wonderfully different from the norm. Really interesting tastes and variety not found in my experience. Would heartily recommend to anyone wanting Indian food without the 'heaviness' of most restaurants. As far as I'm concerned it's "the Indian I've been waiting for!" (Shame I

live 275 miles away!!!) Food £12.95, Drink £9, Service £ 5 tip (I was really happy!) = £25.75.' GC, Durham.

DIWANA BHEL POORI HOUSE   TOP 100

121 Drummond Street, NW1   020 7387 5556

It's a café-style, unlicensed, open-all-day, still very cheap, highly successful 100-seat restaurant, divided into two ground-floor sections plus a further floor. The food is all vegetarian, with much vegan, and above all, it's all fabulous, and it's most certainly all authentic. Diwana pioneered Bombay pavement kiosk snack food (see p 94) in the UK and is undoubtedly still the best of its kind. The ownership change could have dethroned Diwana, but it has remained one of London's iconic eating-holes. *'Not to be visited for the decor, nor for a long and relaxing meal – sitting on the floor would be more comfortable than sitting on the bolted-down benches, so opt for chairs if you can. I have the same thing every time I visit, Popadum with Coconut Chutney, Rasam, a soup, whose chillies without fail give me attention-drawing hiccups, then a Dosa £3 to £4.60 depending on type, with more Coconut Chutney, with its mustard seed and chilli and Sambar. If Pat and I share, I try to get all the drumsticks before him. And of course I never miss out on one of their adorable Bhel Puris, their masthead and their most ordered dish.'* DBAC. Bhel Puri, or Poori, is defined on the A_Z of the Menu. Diwana offers several types – Batata Puri, Dahi Batata Puri, Chat Aloo Papri and Batata Pava, all £2.10. Bhel can be accompanied by Gol Goppas . A super alternative starter is Dahi Vada. By now you've spent £5 or £6, and you're probably full.

But try to leave a little space for the Diwana's desserts. Their legendary Kulfi, perhaps, or *'the highlight of our meal, the Falooda – an Indian knickerbocker glory – probably the best in London. The quality of the food outweighs the numbness in your backside!'* DB. *'All first class. Reasonably priced.'* MW. *'Consistently good quality and low prices. Never changes.'* JR. *'On one of the hottest days in July, I needed lunch in Drummond Street. I chose Diwana because of the jug of water that is automatically provided. It was too hot for alcohol and lassi is too filling when there is serious eating to be done.'* bs. *'Will certainly go back, but not for buffet.'* np. *'The back of the bill has a questionnaire. I was pleased to tick excellent for everything.'* HC. Booking is hit and miss, and they won't even try on Fri to Sun so expect a queue (especially at peak hours). Great value and don't forget to BYO (no corkage charge). Off-license with chilled Cobra available at Viranis up the street. Thali from £4.00 to £6.00. E-a-m-a-y-l lunch to 2.30, £4.50. Hard to exceed £12 for a good veggie blow-out! *'Visited after many years absence. My top of the range Thali cost nearly £9 plus they added 10% service charge, I was not brought water as requested, I will not be returning !'* MD. Despite that it remains in our TOP 100. Hours: 12-11.

GUPTA CONFECTIONERS

100 Drummond St, NW1   020 7380 1590

Overshadowed, perhaps by the nearby Ambala, Gupta is nonetheless a very good, long-established, less flashy vegetarian snack and sweet takeaway. Samosas and Pakoras, plus their unique, delightful, and often still-hot Pea Kebab, a Gujarati speciality, are freshly cooked in the kitchens behind. Their sweets achieve a lightness of touch, and seem to avoid the taste of tinned evaporated milk that sometimes spoils those made by others. Cash or cheque. Branch: Watford Way, Hendon, NW4.

RAVI KEBAB HALAL

125 Drummond Street, NW1   020 7388 1780

Not the first on the street, but one of the longest stayers (opened 1978). It's a Pakistani venue. 'Kebab' tells you it's very much a meat place, halal that there's no pandering to Western tastes, as one can tell by its local mostly Muslim patronage (so no alcohol permitted). Grilled and curried meats are all there at bargain prices. There are some vegetable and dhal dishes but this is no place for the veggie. *'One of my favourites. Cheap & cheerful. Food superb. Sheek Kebabs amongst the best anywhere.'* RE.

RAVI SHANKAR

133 Drummond Street, NW1   020 7388 6458

Vegetarian restaurant similar to the Diwana which it followed into the Street. Prices are still very reasonable and it is usually busy at peak hours. Recommended are the two Thali set dishes, the Mysore and the Shankar,

and the Shrikand dessert. *'Every dish was excellent – flavoursome, spicy and delicious. Prices are extremely reasonable.'* MW. Daily specials under £4. Hours: 12-11. Branches: Chutneys, and Haandi, both on the Street.

ROYAL SWEETS   A-LIST

126 Drummond St, NW1 2PA   020 73884015

Sir Gulam Noon is accredited for creating the name 'Bombay Mix' (see page 65) when he estabished his Royal Sweets brand in England in 1966. He had renamed the family's Bombay Mithai business to 'Royal' in 1953. This fascinating story, (and all of Noon's other accomplishments) is published in Noon's book, 'Noon with a View' published by Whittles. It's not just sweets

A Noon facctory

(such as Barfi, Halva, Jalebi, Gulab and Kulfi, defined on pp 64-70), it is savoury mixes and snacks (Samosas and Pakoras), and chilled fresh curries (made downstairs in Zeen – see below). This flagship branch is made all the more remarkable because you'll not find higher standards of presentation and hygiene anywhere. Thoroughly recommended. Hours: All day till 7.30pm. Branches: Royal Sweets, 92 The Broadway, Southall, Middlesex UB1 1QF. Tel : 020 8574 0832. And: Unit 3, Ground Floor, Tesco Extra, Brunel Way, Wellington St, Slough, Berkshire SL1 1XW. Tel: 01753 570223. See page 28.   www.royalsweets.co.uk

ZEEN – flavour of India   A-LIST
MOST EXCITING NEWCOMER, 2009

130 Drummond St, NW1 2PA   020 7388 0606

Every now and then a star is born. It is rare in any industry, but Zeen is undoubtedly one such star. It is the brain-child of Sir Gulam Noon's daughter, Zeenat. She has a fascinating background in the food industry. She is married to Arun Harnal, Director of Britain's top restaurant, the Bombay Brasserie (see p117). They met while training in food and beverage management at the Taj Palace Hotel Mumbai. Her career began as she says, *"cutting vegetables in the kitchens, then working up the Taj management tree"*. When offered the opportunity to

130 Drummond St
NW1 2PA
020 7388 0606

ia

Zeen's Thali: 'An artist's palete containing' Murgh Makhani, Vegetable Curry, Dhal, Rice, Cutless, Popadums, Chutney and Naan Bread

ZEEN   *(continued from previous pages & page 95)*

130 Drummond St, NW1 2PA
020 7388 0606

become Operations Director at Noon Products (see p48) she jumped at it. Noon had begun producing ambient curries and had obtained orders from Sainsburys and Waitrose. Zeenat's remit was to run and expand the factory and grow the brand. As testimony to her success, Noon now annually produces millions of curries as own-label products in all the nation's supermarkets. Mission achieved, Zeenat harboured another long-term ambition ... to open an Indian restaurant in central London. With some 9,000 'Indian' restaurants in Britain, and with 1,500 of them in London, and in the midst of a recession this might, at first sight, not seem like good business sense. Furthermore, the choice of Drummond Street might be perceived by some to be a dubious location for such a venture. As stated on page 94; it will not win any beauty awards. It is certainly not Mayfair nor Knightsbridge. Furthermore it is located in basement premises, whose narrow frontage cannot indicate what lies within.

Zeen's soft-shelled crab

If such disadvantages put off prospective diners, they would be missing one of the best treats to have opened in decades ... for they have not reckoned on the Noon family's record of achievement and perfectionism. The arrival of a new upmarket restaurant, for upmarket it is, with prices which are affordable, as our menu 'snapshot' below shows, is a revelation.

The site was chosen because it belongs to the Noon empire, and the notion to place the new flagship Royal Sweets above is canny. Drummond Street attracts the discerning, where Indian food is concerned. Royal is the magnet for Zeen. Royal's huge plate-glass windows reveal a wealth of Indian commestibles within. Load up with a bag full to nibble at home, then tank up at Zeen, entrance on your left (located below Royal). Like Tamarind and Dr Who's Tardis, Zeen has a small frontage. Its orange signage tempts diners to enter and descend the elegant staircase to reveal a spotless, smart, contemporary dining room. All the furnishing is bespoke: smart chairs with stainless-steel frames and orange leather-work, face black ebony wooden tables, simply laid with glasses and place settings on orange napkins. On one wall, an angled, full-length mirror makes the room look larger, whilst carefully selected Indian artwork adorns other the walls. Lighting is a carefully designed mixture of hidden-source backlighting, illuminating the walls, and above each table, a sensibly bright spotlight, housed in a rectangular translucent orange housing, located , allows the diner to read the menu and see the food. The bar does not intrude, and diners can enjoy pre or post dinner drinks seated on the bar stools.

The room is bright and comfortable, yet relaxed, and the diners at other tables on the day we went, were enjoying the atmosphere of intimate friendship. We were fortunate enough to dine with just Sir GK and Zeenat for company. I make no secret that they are old friends,

but as I have said on these pages before, many of the greatest restaurateurs are our friends, and it in no way influences our judgement. I cannot fault the food or service. I can say with intense pleasure that I have not eaten Indian food, here or in India, tastier, more delicious, better presented, better served and in more pleasant surroundings than at Zeen. Every dish on the short menu is exquisite, and if you're not sure what to choose ... let them choose ... you can be certain that every dish will please. Editor DBAC says: *"The chefs prepared us a large mixture of starters: Chicken Tikka £3.75 - absolutely perfect, definitely the best chicken tikka we have ever eaten, and that includes India; Lamb Pattice £3.50 - potato cutlet stuffed with spiced ground lamb; Dahi Batata Puri £3.50, (pictured right, desribed as 'puffed puris with potato and sweet yoghurt', which does not do them justice; if you have never eaten them, order a plate to share – wonderful! Next came two seafood starters. Normally, the smell of seafood and fish, even the smell of the sea, turns my stomach. However, this was not the case in sampling Soft Shell Crab £5.95 - cooked with garlic butter sauce. I tore off a leg and nibbled it. A huge bowl Mussel Moilee £5.25 arrived, with a slice of garlic and chilli bread to soak up the lovely light yellow sauce flavoured with coconut, turmeric and curry leaves. All starters are generously served with a dainty, shredded salad and lime wedges. After all those starters we took a deep breath and braced ourselves for the intermediate course. Whole Fresh Konkan Crab £11.75 - cooked in ground coconut, red chilli, cardamom and coriander seed, served with a baby Naan. I can report that it was quite delicious, no horrid smell or taste of the sea. Pat tells me that this is because it was super fresh! Our waitress gave us all a 'shell cracker' and a 'pick' which proved very useful. The baby breads were very good too and turned out to be just perfect in mopping up any stray sauce. "I was quite surprised that after eating all of the above, I managed to fit in some main courses. Try the cashew-nutty, Chicken Cafreal £7.95 - roasted spiced chicken, served with butternut squash and parsnip mash. Or Lamb Chettinad £6.25 - another one of my favourites. , correctly flavoured with dargaful. Dal Makhani £4.25 - black lentils with red kidney*

*Zeen's
Dahi Batata Puri*

beans and cream. A very rich dishes, not for the faint hearted, using plenty of cream and butter - delicious! Tomato Pilau £3.00 - not a rice dish that you see on menus often, lovely. For pudding, Zeenat ordered us small Falooda £3.25, made with vermicelli and tapioca, rose syrup and milk. but the waitress, clearly thought we needed feeding up, as she brought us deliciously huge sunday glasses. A truly wonderful evening" DBAC. Service is every bit as good as the food. As an example, my napkin fell off my lap onto the floor. Before I could move to pick it up, a waitress served me a new one, and scooped up the old one for disposal. Zeen serves Indian contemporary food at its very best without 'modernisation', without 'fusion', without 'over-fussy' presentation and without over-pricing. When I am in India and I am offered food by the chef, I say *"would you serve that to your mother?"* Once I get the message home, I get great food. Zeen's chefs should be happy to serve their food to their mothers. We have given Zeen a big Award in advance of its opening for full service, so confident are we that Zeen will live up to our expectations, and we wish them well. House Wine: £2.95 a glass (red/white) £3.25 (rose); £9.95 a bottle (red/white), £14.95 rose. Service not included. Credit Hours: Daily: 12- 3 / Mon - Fri: 5:30- 11:30 /Sat 6 - 1130, Sun 6 - 10.30. www.zeenrestaurant.co.uk

Zeen's Masala Dosa with Sambar, Masala Aloo and Yoghurt

Elsewhere in NW1

Camden Town, Chalk Farm, Marylebone, Regent's Park

GREAT NEPALESE   A-LIST

48 Eversholt Street, NW1   020 7388 6737

Started by Gopal P Manandhar in 1982, this cosy Nepalese restaurant has stood the test of time. When you enter view the pic of the Queen and the Duke with five Ghurkas, all VC holders. Chef is son Jeetendra, whose charming wife Mandira also adds her culinary expertise, especially with Nawari (an Nepalese ethnic group) food, for example the starter, Momo, or Momocha – steam-cooked meat-filled pastries, £4. Other Nepalese specialities include Masco Bara, black lentil pancakes with curry sauce £4, Kalezo Ra Chyow (chicken liver). Main courses include Dumba (mutton), Pork Bhutwa (the Nepalese have no proscriptions of either pork or alcohol) and Hach Ko (duck) curries. There is also a range of eleven Nepalese vegetable dishes. Add those to sixteen 'standard' curry house vegetable dishes and the vegetarian will be spoilt for choice. In addition, the Great does all the standard curries and tandooris, from Phal, 'very very hot', to Shahi Korma, 'very very mild', though why you'd go there for these is beyond me. Go for Nepalese food, and if virgin to it, ask the staff to explain. Ask Ghopla for a shot of Coronation rum. Brewed in 1975 in Kathmandu, its bottle is kukri-shaped, its contents lethal. *'Following the recommendation of your guide I visited this restaurant reasonably early at 18:30 but still busy. As a single diner I was made to feel welcome. My table was a little small and squeezed in to fit the room available in the restaurant but not bad for that. I am already familiar with the restaurants in Drummond Street but fancied something different and the idea of a Nepalese restaurant was enticing. Should probably have had the Momo starter, in fact had the chicken liver starter which was perfectly fine but seemed like something I could have cooked for myself. Nothing wrong with that, of course. Main course a Nepalese variation on a prawn curry was nice, with some bread and coriander sauce to accompany. Nice and hot with large prawns. I didn't have a dessert. £26 including large Nepalese beer but excluding service. Was not hurried but left at about 19:30 and the restaurant was clearly busy. Observed another lone diner who also seemed very satisfied. Will happily go back again for an early meal and a later train home from Euston Station.'* JF. Set Nepalese meal c£14. Takeaway: 10% discount. Del: 5m £12 min. Hours: 12-2.45 / 6-11.30; -2.30 / 6-11.15 Sun.

RASA EXPRESS

327 Euston Rd, NW1 3AD   020 7387 8974

The great thing about this lovely inexpensive takeaway, is that the small menu is designed around light meals or snacks. Great if you are feeling like a quick, spicy bite! And here is the entire menu! Mysore Bonda £1.50 - potato balls, laced with ginger, fresh curry leaves, coriander, cashew nuts and mustard seeds, dipped in chickpea batter and crispy fried; Fish Cutlet £1.50 - tuna mixed with boiled cassava, aromatic spices and crumb fried; Medhu Vadai £1.75 - silk soft dumplings made of lentils, green chillies, onion, ginger and shaped like a doughnut and deep-fried; Plain Dosa £2.50 - paper-thin crispy pancakes made with rice and black gram, served with fresh coconut chutney; Masala Dosa £2.75 - dosa that comes with a refreshing filling of mashed potatoes with ground turmeric, onions and ginger, served with fresh coconut chutney; Rasa Meal Box £2.95 (veg)/£3.50 (meat) - basmati rice, bread, three curries and a dessert; Chicken Biriyani £3.50 - combining basmati rice, tender cubes of chicken and exotic spices, served with bread, three vegetable dishes and a dessert - what a feast! Credit cards: over £15. Hours: 10-5, Mon to Fri only. Branches: Rasa London N16, W1 and Rasa Express, 5 Rathbone Street, W1T

London NW3

Belsize Park, Hampstead, Finchley Road, Swiss Cottage

ATMA   NEW ENTRANT

106c Finchley Rd, NW3   020 7431 9487

Walls decorated in earthy colours – absolutely lovely, complemented with tables dressed with white linen, large drinking glasses and simple cutlery. Tea-lights in coloured glass, light up the tables. Arched mirrors hang from the walls. There is a feeling of elegant calm. Atma, meaning 'soul' in Sanskrit, tell us their team have worked at the likes of Zaika, Tamarind and Benares. Menu Snapshot: Starters: Two great tastes of scallops £7.25 - selection of rosemary flavoured chargrilled and stir-fried with raw mango and ginger, served with cassava mash; Soft Shell Crab £7.25 - batter fried baby soft shell crab with sesame and crushed pepper, served with black rice noodle cake. Main Courses: Tandoori Sarson Red Deer Venison £16.25 - grilled Scottish venison in a tandoori marinade of mustard and curry leaves served with potato and fresh fenugreek leaves; Smoked Chicken £12.95 - juicy corn-fed chicken supreme with paprika, cumin and yoghurt simmered in smoked tomato sauce served on a bed of aubergine mash with raitha ice cream. Side Dishes: Aloo Gobhi £6.85 - cauliflower florets with potato cubes; Punjabi Salad £1.95 - salad of red onions with toasted cumin, chaat masala and coriander. Good value set lunches include Lamb Sheek Kebab £10.50 or Paneer Tikka £8.50 - fresh cottage cheese and peppers wrapped in yoghurt, cardamom, saffron and glazed golden in tandoor. All served with a vegetable curry of the day, dhal, raitha, mixed pickle, rice and naan bread! Desserts include Gajar Halwa £5.25; Rasmali £4.95; Gulab Jamun £5.20 served warm with Mango Kulfi - I'll have one of each! Or there's Fig & Ginger Ice cream. Hours: 12-2.30 / 6-11 Tu - Sat; 1030 Sun.   www.atmarestaurants.com

CUMIN

02 Centre, 255 Finchley Rd, NW3
020 7794 5616

Opened in 2005 by Pam and Sirneet Kalwan who like to think of it in Wagamama terms. It certainly has uncomfortable Wagamama-style bench seating and a technicolour interior. King Prawn Peri Peri, chilli- fried in the Goan style sit comfortably with many old favourites. *'But some seem to work and others don't. We wondered whether the menu might work better if it were shorter.'* RL. For a bright quick turnaround, this is for you.

ERIKI   TOP 100

4 Northways Parade, Finchley Road, NW3
020 7722 0606

Entrepreneur Sat Lally opened here in 2002 in a former Italian restaurant. It's a 75-seater with a modern Indian look with orange and magenta walls, Indian cushions, carvings and chairs and a huge bar. Sat requests that you don't nick the trendy cutlery imported from Rajasthan; it's for sale if you fall for it! The place has a homely yet upmarket feeling. It is a place which could well become your local. The welcome is certainly one for regulars and newcomers alike: friendly, swift and sure-footed. Lally has recruited serious talent here: Naresh Matta was for many years one of Amin Ali's Indian chefs at Jamdani then the Red Fort, W1, working under Mohammed Rias, a Dum Pukht practitioner (see page 56) and more latterly at Soho Spice. Matta learned Goan cuisine from former head chef Jude Pinto (ex Goan specialist at Veeraswamy and Chutney Mary). He says *"The menu offers a tour of India, with dishes starting from the northern regions of Hyderabad, Punjab, midway through Delhi and Bombay (Mumbai), moving south to the coastline of Goa"* Mains £8-£12. 1 course Set lunch £7. Service : 12.5%. Hours: 12-3 Sun-Fri/6-11. See NW8 branch for menu details.   www.eriki.co.uk

WOODLANDS   TOP 100

102 Heath Street, NW3   020 7794 3080

Fourth branch (of four) of the much -loved vegetarian chain. See SW1 for details. Hours: 6-11, M - Th; 12-11 Fri - Sun.   www.woodlandsrestaurant.co.uk

YOU SAY OK
You may get a discount of you show them this Guide.

NW1: CAFÉ INDIYA 71 Regents Park Rd, NW1 ~ 020 7722 5225. Seats 28 in 2 rooms. Service: 10%. Hours: 12-2.30 Sat only / 5.30-11.30; 6 Sat; 12-11.30 Sun.

NW1: CINNAMON SPICE 14 Glentworth Street NW1 ~ 020 7935 0212 Partners: Rahman, Uddin and Khan are child friendly, so take the family! www.cinnamonspice.co.uk

NW3: FLEET TANDOORI 104 Fleet Road, NW3 ~ 020 7485 6402 *'Sun buffet is a must for those who wish a cheap alternative to meat and two veg.'* AD. Good prices enhanced by 10% discount if you show them this Guide

NW3: BOMBAY BICYCLE CLUB 3a Downshire Hill, Hampstead ~ 020 7435 3544. 70-seater. Signature dish Barra Chana Shahi, spicy and aromatic. Hours: every eve and all day Sun..

NW6: BENGAL SPICE 245 West End Lane, NW6 ~ 020 7794 5370. Established 1957. 'Highly satisfactory at £15 per person.' AIE. Hours: 6-12; 12.30 Fri & Sat.

London NW4   Hendon

KAVANNA

60 Vivian Av, Hendon, NW4   020 7722 0606

There are, it seems, 1,000 Indian-born Jews in the Hendon / Golders Green area. One of these is Nathan Moses who was born in India, lived in Israel and came to Hendon in 1978, where he runs a kosher and Indian bakery in Vivian Avenue, Hendon. Moses felt sure there was a demand for a kosher Indian restaurant, and Kavanna is it. We have not heard directly from this restaurant, but soon after it opened in 2005, it came to the notice of our scribes, thrilled to tell us of yet another first in London's Indian cuisine: Kosher Indian. There are kosher Chinese restaurants in Philadelphia and New York, and Moses claims there is a kosher Indian in Paris. Kosher is a protocol for orthodox Jews. Any food style can be kosher if it is prepared and supervised in accordance with certain laws. Kosher and Halal rules have in common meat slaughtering rules and a proscription on pork. Kosher goes further with stating no shellfish and that meat cannot be cooked or eaten with dairy and according to some views, fish with meat. Moses employs Indian chefs, who make traditional Indian recipes kosher. Meat and chicken cannot be marinated in yoghurt, cooked in ghee, nor mixed with cream; soy or coconut milk substitutes. At the Kavanna, non-Jews are welcome, and will hardly notice any difference. Apart from the absence of prawns, the menu reads much like the standard curry house, at normal prices. Hours: 5.30 - 11, Sun - Thur.

LAHORE ORIGINAL KEBAB HOUSE

150 Brent Street NW4   020 8203 6904

Lahore Kebab House E1 was, of course, the original the food being pure super Pakistani / Punjabi food, geared to Asian tastes, without compromising it for Westerners. Meat is the main player; Halal meat is a given, with dark, thick-gravied, pungent, savoury curries served in the karahi, or with items from the tandoor in the form of succulent tikkas or kebabs. But the observant tell of a seed change here. There's a Kenyan Asian twist with an emphasis on vegetable dishes such as Paneer or Chilli mogo, cassava stir-fried with garam masala and a heap of fresh coriander and chillies, then combined with tamarind sauce. The lentil dishes, a great test of the cook's skills, are to die for. Try the Mung Makhani (a green lentil version of black urid makhni dhal. Prices remain excellent, eg: Mains £5-£6.50. Takes some credit cards. Party room seats 35. Takeaway service. 11-11.30 daily.

PRINCE OF CEYLON   TOP 100

39 Watford Way, NW4   020 8202 5967

Abdul Satter has been here since 1979, during which time it has grown to 150 seats split over five rooms. Manager Nelson presides over a kind of bamboo / coir jungle with yellow-ochre and brown linen, olive green leather seats, and a lot of natural dark wood – tables given privacy by carved wood screens. The Prince's standard menu of tandooris, kebabs, curries and all the business, all perfectly competently cooked, are not what you go there for. It is the Sri Lankan specials. And if these items are unfamiliar, ask the waiter's advice, but be patient if explanations are unclear at first. It is a rice (Buth) cuisine. Jaffna Thossai, soft pancake made of soaked and ground urid dal, served with coconut chutney. Devilled curries are there, including Squid curry. Fried Cabbage with onion £3. Coconut Chutney £2. Hoppers or Appas are rice and coconut-flour pancakes; String Hoppers, like string made of wheat or rice flour dough, but resembling vermicelli nests (10 for £3.50); or Pittu – ditto dumpling. These or straight rice are accompanied by pungent watery curries, in which coconut, turmeric, tamarind, curry leaves and chillies feature. But they can be mild, too. Look out for aromatic black curries and fragrant white ones. Fish dishes, such as Ambul Thial (a Sri Lankan national dish – a sour, spicy tuna fish dish) and the Ceylon Squid (Dhallo) curry are popular. And there are substantial curries such as Lampries (chicken, meat and egg). Sambols, or relishes, include dried fish and chilli. Av spend £15. Sun buffet, 12-5 £8.50. Hours: 12-3 / 6-12; 12-12, Sat and Sun.

London NW5   Kentish Town

CHETNA

56 Chetwynd Road, NW5   020 7482 2803

Established as the Indian Lancer in 1990, then Indian Brasserie in 1999 this 42-seater's owner Edward Graham has decorated in a minimalist style with very pale pink walls, redwood furniture with pinky red cushions, modern spot lighting and red carpets. His chef, Ramdas, was Gujarati region chef of the year 1993 and has held post as executive chef at the Sayji group of hotels in northern India. Ramdas' signature dishes include: Dover Sole Kaliwala, fresh dover sole, cooked with red chillies, yoghurt and curry leaves, spicy!, Chicken 65, dry-fried Hyderabadi style in a light batter, topped with fried green chillies and curry leaves, Phaldari Kofte Paneh Phoran and Chicken Malwari. The most popular dish ordered is Dum Pukht Gosht – a royal favourite. Set lunch: c£3.50 to £5.50. Hours: 12-2.30; 4 Sun / 6-12; 11 Sun. Closed Monday.

London NW6   Kilburn, Hampstead

ELEPHANT WALK   A-LIST

98 West End Lane, NW6   020 7328 3308

Kannan Rajapakse and his Chef wife, Deepthe opened in 2005 a stone's throw from fashionable St. John's Wood and Lord's. They specialise in Sri Lankan & south Indian food. The couple make no secret of the fact that the decor was largely from IKEA installed by friends and family. If true this puts the TV makeover bore-shows to shame – it's gorgeous. The floors are hardwood, the furniture is ebony black solid wood. Batik paintings by Sri Lankan artist, Manawadu grace the walls. Located , Elephant Walk seats 42 in the main dining area, with a downstairs 30-seater function room. The front patio opens its folding doors for outdoor dining, while the rear outdoor patio, complete with canopy, is more zen-style. The charm is that Deepthe serves dishes her own mother prepared for her in their family home. Typical Sri Lankan treats include String Hoppers, steamed noodle made of rice flour and Kotthu Rotis, a flatbread that is shredded and chopped in a wok with vegetables and other ingredients and served with sauce on the side. Devil Dishes, mainly served the clubs in colonial times – dry dish served on a hot plate. Planters introduced some European vegetables to Ceylon, as it was then known. Try curries like Beetroot & Potato Kari, Green Cabbage stir fried with coconut, Green Beans kari, Swede kari, Leeks stir-fried with coconut, Turnip Kari. There are some unusual exotics like Breadfruit, Manioc, Drumsticks, Bitter Gourd, Pumpkin, Snake Gourd, Aubergine and Green Banana. Thalis and Masala Dosai also on. 12-3 (Sun: buffet min 12 items 12-5) 5-10:45; from 12 weekends.   www.elephantwalk.biz

GEETA SOUTH INDIAN   TOP 100

57 Willesden Lane, NW6   020 7624 1713

A homely feel here with mainly south Indian vegetarian food at which Geeta excels, and has done since the 70s, with never a decline in standard. Geeta and son work front of house and safe-hands, an elderly male chef commands the kitchens. Try his Dosa, Idli, Sambar, Upamas Karela (bitter gourds), drumsticks (long pithy marrow which you suck to extract the tender flesh), Ravaiya – baby aubergine and plantains stuffed with a coconut spicy filling Rasam – and more. And with most of these around the £2 mark, and providing you keep off the carnivorous items, you'll fill up for less than a tenner, with drink. You can get standard meat (inc beef) and chicken curries, et al, and from the reports I get, the thoroughly devoted following adore it. It's all fine stuff, served in less than glamourous, but typically Indian surroundings, to a thoroughly devoted following. '*This and Vijay (below) are different and should not be missed.*' DMW. Hours: 12-2.30 / 6-10.30; 11.30 Fri & Sat.

KOVALAM

12 Willesden Lane, NW6 7SR   020 7625 4761

Kovalam is a rather good government-run (Ashoka Group) beach hotel at the town of Trivandrum, just 30 miles north of India's southern most tip. Actually it's probably the best hotel in that chain. Coconut palms, temple elephants, white dotis, sea, sun and sand. Ah me! Their restaurant is called Sea Shells and it serves a range of south Indian dishes, protein as well as vegetable. I digress; Trivandrum is a far cry from Willesden, but you'll get the picture from the pictures on the wall. It opened in 2001 and as at Sea Shells, the food is spot on. It offers south Indian dishes such as dosai, Idli, Sambar, Upamas and Vaadia (see page 58). Pazham pori plantain pakora make an unusual starter. It also does Keralan seafood and meat dishes. Try the traditional Lamb Fry where the meat is dry-fried with pepper, coconut and curry leaves. Though we can't imagine why the do it, the south Indian chefs offer curryhouse dishes. Del 3m, over £15. Hours: 12-2.30 / 6-11 Sun-Thur, 6-12 Fri & Sat.   www.kovalamrestaurant.co.uk

SURYA

59 Fortune Green Rd, NW6   020 7435 7486

Mr (front of house) and Mrs Tiwari (chef) really pack 'em in at this tiny, 34-seat vegetarian, licensed restaurant – there's no room to move, almost literally – it's always full. The dish of the day (it changes daily) excites several of our regulars. We hear well of Gujarati dishes such as Patra and Kaddu Kari and inexpensive prices. Hours: 6-10.30, and Sun lunch. Branch: Shree Ganesha, 4 The Promenade, Edgwarebury Lane, Edgware, Middx.

VIJAY   TOP 100

49 Willesden Lane, NW6   020 7328 1087

Vijay was founded in 1966, and predated nearby Geeta (see above) by several years, so takes the crown for being the earliest to provide south Indian food for NW6, and its menu contains all the vegetarian items listed in Geeta's entry, at much the same prices. Indeed my remarks are the same, since Vijay like Geeta does carnivorous dishes too. Vijay has its own clan of loyal regulars who know they'll get *'very nice tasty food.'* B&WW. Prices are much the same, perhaps just a tad higher here, but again, even with the ridiculous 10% service charge (please get rid of it) you'll only spend a tenner if you stick to the scrumptious vegetarian delights. *'This and Geeta (above) are different and should not be missed.'* DMW. Hours: 12-2.45 / 6-10.45 (1145 Fri & Sat).

London NW7   Mill Hill

ATITHI   NEW ENTRANT

418 Watford Way, NW7   020 8203 6573

We generally dislike opening nights because we feel it fairer to let a restaurant bed in for several weeks before we review it. But being friends of curry author Mridula Balkjjekar, cuisine consultant and partner with Mesba Ahmed and Abdul Khalique we went. Atithi means 'guest' and inside was ready and we were made welcome guests with cold drinks. Mridula was in a striking fuschia pink sari with royal purple and gold border. And we sat with another old friend, Bill Buckley of LBC Radio fame nibbling on starters, made by Mridula herself, followed by a tasty main course. Decoration is clean and simple, white washed walls, tiled floor, black and glass bar. Menu Snapshot: Hariyali Murgh Tikka £4.95; Jhinge Machli ki Tikka (rice crusted prawn and smoked haddock cakes £6.95; Nadhru Kabab (lotus root kebab) £3.95; Boti Sali (Persian-style lamb curry with potato straws) £8.95; Macher Kalia (spiced trout in a Bengali-style vegetable sauce) £8.95; Phaldari Kofta (North Indian fruit dumplings in a creamy tomato sauce) £7.95; Chana Masala (chickpeas with pomegranate extract) £6.95; Hare Matar ke Seekh (sausage shaped green pea kebabs) £6.95; Gajar Mattar ke Tarkari (carrot and green peas in a roasted and ground chickpea sauce) £3.95; Dhal Makhani (Punjabi-style slow-cooked mixed lentils with spiced butter) £3.95; Missi Roti (wheat and gluten free bread) £1.75. We wish the venture well. Reports please.

London NW8   St Johns Wood

ERIKI   NEW ENTRANT & TOP 100

122 Boundary Road, NW8   020 7372 2255

We have eaten at their NW3 branch and can confirm that owner, Sat Lally, certainly knows how to run a top notch restaurant as this new branch shows. Bright and colourful decoration, lime and paprika walls. Everything we ate, and we tried a lot, was fabulous! Menu Snapshot: Lazeez Kastoori Tikka £4.95 , tender pieces of chicken marinated with garlic kastoori methi, mild cheese,

yoghurt and spices, delicately grilled in the tandoor; Calamari Mirch Fry £5.95, ocean calamari rings stir-fried with pure Keralan spices served on a leafy salad; Palak Pyaz Pakora £3.95, a medium spicy onion and spinach bhajia served with a mango sauce; Khas Tandoori Aloo £3.95, baby potatoes marinated with tandoori spices and flame grilled in the tandoor; Pistachio Murgh Korma £8.95, delicately flavoured slices of chicken breast with a pistachio sauce and flavoured with mild spices; Laknowi lamb Chop Masala £10.95, four tender lamb chops in a spicy masala and denghi mirch, ginger and fresh lime; Pudina Lacha Paratha £2.95, fresh mint paratha baked in tandoor; Malabar Tawa Paratha £2.25, crispy buttery layered bread, pan fried on a griddle; Phirni (Kheer) £3.95, home-made rice pudding flavoured with cardamom and garnished with crushed pistachio. Set menu's start at £18.95pp. Branch: NW3.   www.eriki.co.uk

London NW9 Kingsbury, Neasden

LAHORE KEBAB HOUSE

248 Kingsbury Road, NW9   020 8424 8422

Once but now no longer connected to the celebrated London E1 original, it is popular locally. It's licensed, and the kebabs are good and the curries. For the menu see the E1 Lahore Kebab House E1 review. No credit cards. 1pm to midnight, daily

TANDOOR, GREAT EASTERN

232 Kingsbury Rd, NW9 0BH   020 8205 1450

'An impressive place that opened in late 2003 in a barely converted pub, where instead of serving overpriced gastropub nonsense, here you get authentic Indian food, as evidenced by the high proportion of Indians actually eating here. Pops are free (remember those days?) and the menu is interesting. As well as the curry regulars there is a variety of different vegetarian dishes, and a wide range for carnivores also. I started with a form of Chicken Kebab, that had more than half a dozen large pieces of chicken marinated and then wrapped in a spiced batter, then cooked in the tandoor. The chicken was very tender, though the batter was rather floury, and I'm not sure the chicken would not have been better without it though it did keep it moist. Main courses were much better. I had a fine Chicken Biriani, in a little casserole dish, sealed with pastry. The chicken was moist &tender, the rice suffused with spices, with distinct grains – delicious. Aloo Jeera had good potatoes laced with cumin, cooked with spinach which kept its flavour well. Khumb Kaju Matter consisted of mushroom and green peas in gravy made with cashew nuts. Garlic Naan had plenty of garlic taste and had a pleasingly soft texture. Even better was Romali Roti, the thinnest Indian bread made on a very hot steel hemisphere. Hot towels are the proper variety (no lukewarm paper imitations here). Dessert featured Kulfi that they actually make on the premises, and

this was very good, the texture smooth. Service was mostly good, though attention was erratic. Overall this was a place to which I will definitely return, and has really authentic cooking from a chef who cooked for over 20 years in various Indian hotels. One point to note – portions are vast, so if you order normally you will have enough for a complete takeaway meal as well. Av £25' AH. AndyHayler.com   Hours: 12– 2 daily.

London NW10
Harlesden, Kensal Green, Willesden

GALLE CAFÉ

91 Dudden Hill Lane NW10   020 8459 7921

A Sri Lankan in the area is a precious gem. Named after the town (pron Gaul) in south Sri Lanka, it's an unpretentious café with unpretentious prices, very popular with local Asians. And look at the hours. Fancy breakfast? There is the typical British greasy spoon stuff: eggs, bacon, beans et al, but why not try String Hopper (steamed noodle) with a thin curry or Egg Hopper (ditto with an egg) The dishes of the day are on the board. Main stream curries may include, Cashew, or tuna fish, or beetroot. Meat might be beef or it might be lamb. Sambols (chutneys) add to the fun. Cash only (and not much of that either). You can exit with filled tummy for a fiver! Hours -8, Mon-Sat

SARAVANAS

77 Dudden Hill Lane, NW10   020 8459 4900

As if Sri Lankan on the street (see previous entry) the lucky locals have a South Indian too, and it too is popular with the Asian population. It is vegetarian, and inexpensive.(even so it does take credit cards): There are two dining areas, the formica tabled café and the cane-seating 'smarter' room with bar. South Indian food is described on page 85 and in the A-Z glossary. The Rasam soup and Sambar are competent, as are the curries, and the Thalis (£6 to 8) are a splendidly filling, economical meal. Hours: 12-10.30, Tue-Sun

YOU SAY OK
You may get a discount of you show them this Guide.

NW7: DAYS OF THE RAJ 123 The Broadway, NW7 ~ 020 8906 3477. Very smart 100-seater est 1989 by S Miah. Serv 10%. E-a-m-a-y-l lunch buffet daily £7. Del: 3m £12 min. Hours: 12-2/ 5-11.30.

NW10: KADIRI'S 26 High Road, Harlesden, NW10 2QD ~ 020 8459 0916. Jamal Kadiri's venue been around for over 30 years - well, that's an achievement in its self!

NW10: RAJ: 43 Chamberlayne Rd, NW10 ~ 0208 960 7090. Misbah's smart and popular venue. Del min £10.00. 10% disc on collected orders over £15. Hours 12-2/6– 11.30. www.rajlondon.com

London SE
Area: South East London
Postcodes SE1 to SE28
Population: 910,000

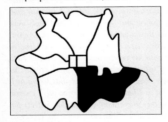

*See page
72
for key
to this
map.*

London SE1
Borough, Elephant & Castle, London Bridge,
Old Kent Road, Southwark and Waterloo

BANGALORE EXPRESS   NEW ENTRANT

103 Waterloo Road SE1   020 7021 0886

This Guide's Top Chef 2004 and 2007, Yogesh Datta
and partner Charles Hill have achieved acclaim with
their the Painted Heron, SW3. This is their latest
restaurant. As you would expect Yogesh serves the most
delicious food, in good hearty portions at a reasonably
price. Hooray for that! I think the architect's inspiration
must have come from Japan. It definitely has a feeling of
a Tokyo eatery. Little four seater booths line the ground

floor perimeter. Little four seater booths line the walls!
This extra dining space is accessed from bunk-bed style
ladders. The designer was obviously given the problem
of a dining room with high ceilings and came up (and
literally up!) with this elevated / alternative seating. I am
surprised that the dreaded Health and Safety
Department didn't squash this idea. Myself, I prefer the
ground floor and not in the heaven's . High heels, short
skirts and a bottle of wine, are not recommended for
climbing a ladder to reach tables on the upper deck.
However, it is an interesting idea, though I am sure that
the waiting staff find it a pain. The concept is popular
with the younger element who also like the free wi-fi.
Weather permitting, the venue has an outdoor seating
area. The menu is a brief one-page document with what
they call 'tapas-style' items – starters include tandoori
chicken, duck cashew nut and raisin roll, fenugreek-
marinated chicken drumsticks, dosa. Mains include
'build-your-own-rice-and-curry-plates' of items such as
chicken curries, lamb jalfrezi, sweet potato salad, sag rice &
tamarind rice. Fully licensed-11.30. Hours: 11am-12pm.
Branch EC3, see p89 & 121.
www.bangaloreexpress.co.uk

BENGAL CLIPPER   TOP 100

Cardamom Building, 31 Shad Thames, SE1
                                    020 7357 9001

Finding it is the problem. It's a fair walk from the tube!
Taxis will find it (it's behind Conran's). If you're
driving, and you've squeezed through the narrow one-
way streets, you'll then have to find a parking space (min £4).

Once inside, you'll find Kenneth Lynn's sophisticated and expensive interior. Chef Ram Das turns out excellent curry house food, and the Bangladeshi dishes are the best bet. *'Another good value lunch, with fairly quick service, whilst the food, as ever, is tasty and quite hot as they go.'* SH. Average c£30. Lunch and dinner daily. Branches: Bengal Trader E1; Bengal Mangrove, Halstead, Kent; Bengal Lancer, Chislehurst, Kent. www.bengalclipper.co.uk

CASTLE TANDOORI

200 Elephant & Castle Shopping Centre, SE1
020 7703 9130

Mr Uddin's Castle is a spirited place, and a regular entrant in our Guide. He once told us, and will tell you, if you care to be entertained by him, that he's outlived twenty-two Hoovers, two recessions, and several prime ministers, and served enough naan bread to stretch from Waterloo to Paris. Still no update on this yet; but I expect he's calculating anew. The menu is pretty much formula (135 items) but includes duck, lamb chops and trout in various guises. Reports tell of the value for money. We know of no longer hours in London (let us know if you know better). So, if you're an insomniac curryholic, or just a late-night reveller, note this place well. Hours: Lunch Mon-Fri / 6-1 daily; -2.30 Fri & Sat.

LOVAGE   NEW ENTRANT

15 Queen Elizabeth St, SE1 2JE
020 7403 8886

Opened in 2005 as Hara and changed name and ownership ion 207. It is set on two floors, with the 80 seat restaurant on the mezzanine level overlooking the stylish bar. Located in Butler's Wharf 200 guests can be accommodated for pre or post-dinner drinks before dining. Designed by Europe's famous Zoran Zafaria, he bar front is fitted with a translucent marble pieces sourced from Rajasthan and finished in Italy. Modern European furniture and a mixture of dark brown leather seating and elegant stools are scattered round the bar. Hours: 12-3/6-12. See page 41.

SILKA

6 Southwark Street SE1 1TL   0207 378 6161

With the pedigree of cheffing at Tamarind, Chutney Mary, Three Monkeys and the Red Fort, Abdul Mushahid turned proprietor and opened his 80-seat Silka, managed by A. Hannanin, 2003 in the basement of a Grade II listed building between London Bridge and Tate Modern. There's a backlit wall clad with Indian rosewood, ebony and makore. The eye leads to Mushahid's window kitchen with his Ayurvedic principles (see page 64). *'Our starters included Baked Lemon Sole wrapped in a banana leaf, Stir-fried Baby Squid, and Mixed Sprout Lentil Soup – a modern take on a traditional Indian staple. Interesting salads such as a lotus leaves coated with white sesame seeds and spiced gram flour batter is refreshingly innovative and served with a typically tangy tamarind chutney. Other gems include Wild Duck braised with delicate spices, Roasted Cauliflower marinated with cheese, yoghurt and cashew nuts and fiery Peri Peri Prawns. Try the tasting Ayurvedic platters. Potatoes cooked in a creamy sauce, and spiced vegetable and rice, served with tiger prawns is one example of the choice on offer. Side dishes include pan-fried fresh mustard leaves and the steadfast Indian favourite of simmered black lentils.'* RG. *'Despite being put off by the tacky street-level door, a good friend was keen to enter so we took the plunge, as it were. But on entering the main restaurant area the service was polite, attentive and helpful. One dish immediately struck me – Bombay Duck!! The portion was hardly substantial (two very thin slices) but my friend enjoyed it very much. I have to say I was not so sure. The rest of the food was very good. We shared a spinach and potato kebab and cashew nut roll to start and both were delicately spiced and flavoured and cooked very well. Again, not exactly substantive, especially for £4 each, but fine as starters. Ordering with my vegetarian hat on, I could have gone for a couple of interesting sounding Paneer dishes. I'm sure they would have been very good indeed. But seeing as I had a few beers, and as I have no willpower at all, I craved something spicier so they knocked-up a vegetable Jalfrezi for me. There was a distinct lack of fresh chillies in it but otherwise it was excellent and the vegetable content was really good. My friend ordered 'Lamb with Apricot', [Jardaloo Sali Boti, a Parsee dish], and proclaimed it to be excellent, reminding him of a Moroccan dish. Tarka Dhal good, excellent okra and a good stuffed paratha. The Pinot Grigio kept flowing and went very well indeed with the meal. One aspect worth a special mention is the toilets – you enter via a completely wall-to-wall mirrored room, which totally confused me (not difficult). Though the mirrors were not in the toilet itself, I still have an aversion to seeing myself in the mirror I'm afraid. So overall it was a very enjoyable experience the food and service were good. Not your usual restaurant, certainly not your usual menu, and Silka should be given credit for that if nothing else, just for having Bombay Duck'.* AG. Lunch platter at c£9. Dinner average £26. Free Delivery. Valet Parking. Hours 12-3 / 6-11.   www.silka.co.uk

THE THAMES

79 Waterloo Road, SE1	020 7928 3856

52-seater established by Kalkur Rahman in 1985. Managed by Amirul Islam. It's still there under the railway bridge, and, yes, its neighbour, the fab-named Fishcotheque [it's a fish & chip shop for those new to

this Guide] is still there. *'We have been to this restaurant numerous times, but I am sending a report as it has changed its name and image from Thames Tandoori. The waiters now all wear darkish plain grey shirts with similar ties. Claims it provides 'contemporary Indian cuisine' and the board on the pavement outside states 'exquisite Indian cuisine'. I do not think either is entirely accurate but the food is exceptionally good and some dishes are attractively presented – but still a long way from the 'picture-on-a-plate' style. I'm not that keen on Brinjal Bhajee cut into such tiny pieces it resembles the onion salad served with the Popadums.'* DRC. And on another occasion: *'Consistency good and reliable. Butter Chicken sensational, the value excellent. A meal here is always a pleasure. Not the sort of restaurant for a whole evening's dinner with guests. Only slight niggle, we've been going here for years and there is no recognition or any personal touch to service - very odd.'* DRC. And again: *'This time I had a starter of Tikka Paneer – so attractively served: cubes of cheese were spaced on the square plate and at the corners the sauces were contained in an onion ring. Simple but very effective. Danny was asked by a business friend where is the nearest recommended Indian restaurant to Westminster? The friend had two Dutch businessmen with him and wanted somewhere quick rather than smart, so The Cinnamon Club was not suggested. All three were very impressed by the food and thoroughly enjoyed it. Good to have our opinion confirmed.'* HLC. Del: 2m, £20 min. Hours: 12-2.15 / 5.30-11.45.

YOU SAY OK

You may get a discount of you show them this Guide.

SE1: TOWER TANDOORI 74 Tower Bridge Road ~ SE1 020 7237 2247. *'8 mins walk from the bridge. Prices very favourable.'* NB.

SE3: TASTE OF RAJ 9 Royal Pde, Blackheath Village, SE3 020 8344 2823. *'Continues to be VG indeed'.* AG.

SE8: TANDOORI XPRESS 111B Deptford High St, Deptford SE8 ~ 020 8320 2555. Punjabi-style takeaway with a couple of tables Cooking is done in view and it's no frills, no toilets and no credit cards. c£5 for a good fill. Hours: 11.30-11 Mon-Sat; 12-3 / 6-10.30 Sun

SE9: CROWN TANDOORI TAKEAWAY 7 Lingfield Cres, SE9 ~ 020 8294 1313. Owned and managed by Saiful Abedin, since 1997. Del 3m. Hours: 5-11.30.

SE9: CURRY GARDEN 144 Westmount Rd, SE9 ~ 020 8850 2250. Owners from 1999 A Miah (mngr), F Haque, S & K Miah. Koleze Puree £2, chicken liver with pancake. Del: 5m £15 min, not to high rise buildings. Hours: 5-10.30.

SE19: RUCHITA TAKEAWAY 31 Avery Hill Rd, SE9 ~ 020 8850 1202. Miss Salma, Mohammed Yousuf's & Chef A Mukid's Ruchita 1975 takeaway is licensed. Del: 3m £10min. Hours: 5.30-12.

SE10: RAAN For the record it was an Indian inside the O2 Arena, run by Iqbal Wahhab of Cinnamon Club fame but it went bust in late 2007 and is not Indian any more

SE11: CHANDI'S HOURS: 347A Kennington Rd, SE11 020 7735 9015. Est 1983. MPs like it, they say! Hours: 12- 2.30 /6- 11.30

SE11: KENNINGTON TANDOORI 313 Kennington Road, London, SE11 4QE ~ 020 7735 9247

E13: BENGAL BRASSERIE 79 Springbank Rd, SE13 ~ 020 8461 5240. Syed Ahmed's 60-seater *'The spinach in Lobster Saghee makes this a fine dish.'* ES. Min ch £15. Service 10%. Cover ch £1. Del: 3m. Hours: 5.30-11.30 (12 Sat).

ARRU SUVAI 19 Lee High Rd Lewisham, SE13 020 8297 6452. Sri Lankan caff complete with Bollywood telly, fruit machine, Devilled dishes, Kotthu Roti, Pittu, Tuna Curry, Vadai, and wonderfully light Masala Dosa . Cash only, but you can fill for a fiver. Hours: 10-11 daily.

SE13: BABU SAHEEB 406 High Street, SE13 ~ 020 8690 7667. Del: 3 m £2 charge. Hours: lunch by apt / 6-12.30. Branch: Ladywell Tandoori, 81, Ladywell Road, Lewisham, SE13.

London SE13
Hither Green, Lee, Lewisham, New Cross, Deptford, Lewisham & Catford

GREEN CABIN SRI LANKAN

244 High Street, SE13	020 8852 6666

40 seater opened in 1996 by SE Jebarajan and serving Sri Lankan and South Indian food as well as the safe-bet Korma-through-Vindaloo range. Forget all that and go for the real stuff – you won't be disappointed. Meat Roll (diced lamb, onions, chillies and potato wrapped in a pancake, bread crumbed and deep-fried, served with spicy sauce), Potato Kulambu (deep-fried cubes of potato cooked in coconut milk with dry roasted chilli), Cabbage Mallung (shredded cabbage stir-fried with mustard seed, turmeric and spices), Kotthu Roti, soft and thin as a silk cloth sliced into pieces and mixed with shredded chicken on a hot griddle and blended together). Delivery: £15 min, 2m. T/a 10% disc, £15 mini. Hours: 12-3 / 6-11; closed Mon.

EVEREST CURRY KING

24 Loampit Hill, Lewisham, SE13	020 8691 2233

Don't be fooled by the name. It's yet another Sri Lankan in SE13. Everest is 1500 miles to the north of Sri Lanka, but it's the food which counts. It's a typical caff with no menu, just items on display in the cabinet. Fill up, pay up (and not much of that and by card if you wish) and have a superbly tasty, authentic experience. Hours: 11- 11.30 daily

SPICE OF LIFE   TOP 100

260 Lee High Road, SE13   020 8244 4770

Owner, Mahmud (Moody) Miah's fully licensed, a/c venue seats 58. *'Small, cosy restaurant which is hard to fault. Well above average.'* C&GM. *'The Spice holds a very special place in my heart – there is no Indian restaurant that I would choose to dine in; it's simply that good. When I saw it had been promoted to the Top 100, it almost bought a tear to my eye! But it had been seven years since our previous visit and a lot can change in that time. Our worst fears were so nearly warranted; the only family member still involved is Moody, and he was on the brink of selling up, but he got his son involved and hunted long and hard for a new chef. Moody was his usual charming self and was delighted to see us. He didn't need to ask if we wanted popadums. He just bought them over with the exceptional, as ever, pickle tray. Why can't other restaurants do these simple but important things as well as this? The Spice's menu almost bought a tear to my eye for the second time – they have included the full entry from the Curry Guide in bold letters on the back, so there were my initials on The Spice's menu! How honoured could I be??!! What also caught my eye was just how much effort this restaurant makes. They still have a 'specials board', something one so rarely sees in an Indian restaurant, which listed some real gems. After the pops we shared bhajis, samosas etc. Moody asked if I was still vegetarian and I told him I eat fish nowadays. Although it was nowhere to be seen on the menu he said I must try the tilapia dish. It was firm but soft and retained all its flavour whilst still being well spiced and just beautiful. We also ordered my old favourite, the garlic chilli vegetables, although this too wasn't on the menu. We had no need to worry whatsoever about the new chef – the smoky garlic flavour was just as prominent, he had added just the right amount of extra chillies and it was bursting with flavour and fresh vegetables. None of the food remotely disappointed – the rice continues to be light and beautifully presented, the naan soft and the dhal just the right texture. All this plus a bottle of decent dry white wine came to £38 – amazing. The Spice remains an absolute diamond - it warrants a spot so high in the Top 100. We have promised that we will not leave it so shamefully long before we visit again and that we will try to keep in touch more regularly with Moody. Places like this, and people like this are very, very, hard to find.'* AG. T/a: 10% disc. Lunch and dinner daily.

London SE15   Peckham

GANAPATI

38 Holly Grove, Peckham   020 7277 2928

A simple café, on an easy-to-spot corner site, especially in the summer with its 4 outside tables (4 more in the 'garden'). Ganapati (aka Ganesh) by the way, is the the elephant-headed god and the bringer of good luck. So lucky Peckham, enjoy the South Indian delights on offer. The Thali is great stuff with Rasam soup, bean

curries, shredded veg curry (Thoran), lentils (Sambar) gourds and the like. Lunch £5 to £6 and Mains £8 to £11. Service: 10%. Credit cards accepted. Hours: 12-10.45 Tue-Sun; Closed Mon.

SE22: AL AMIN TANDOORI, 104b Forest Hill Road, East Dulwich SE22 020 8299 3962. Est 1994 by Kabir Khan. Try Chuza Mossala, baby chicken with thick gravy. Del: 3m min £15. Hours: 5.30-12.

THE CORIANDER

120 Lordship Lane, SE22   020 8613 1500

Sister to the Coriander in Buckhurst Hill, Essex under owner J Islam. *'A visit to either is a MUST. The food is of a consistently high quality and is always freshly cooked. Portions are generous in size. I visited with my husband and to start we had: Hara Kebab, spinach and potatoes stuffed with cottage cheese and roasted cashew nuts – superb £3.50 and Coriander Special, a mixture of starters - chicken tikka, lamb tikka, onion bhaji and hara kebab - great value, £3.75. We followed with Mahi Masala, salmon cooked with special masala sauce – the salmon is succulent and tasty, c£8 and Adha Diya, lamb or chicken cooked with garlic, ginger, coconut and cream – absolutely delicious, c£7.50. The main dishes were accompanied by brinjal bhaji and sag bhaji - first class - £2.50 each and mushroom rice - great - £2.25. The staff are helpful, efficient, polite and friendly and you receive a warm welcome on every visit and knowledgeable about the ingredients of each dish and the way it's cooked. The restaurant is spotlessly clean (as are the toilets). It is tastefully decorated and has comfortable seating. Both establishments are WELL WORTH A VISIT.'* MF.

PISTACHIO CLUB

44 Lordship Lane, SE22   020 8693 7584

Try Pista Murgh, chicken whose sensuous sauce is made from cream, yoghurt, garlic, ginger, chilli and turmeric, punctuated with succulent fresh pistachio nuts. Their Raan, roast lamb Lucknow-style is marinated with cardamom, kewra water (screwpine) and saffron and served with a thick aromatic sauce. Bangladeshi fish such as ayer, rui and boal are available. Reasonable prices. Hours: 12-2.30 / 6 - 11.

SURMA CURRY HOUSE

42 Lordship Lane, SE22 020 8693 1779

Give me a place like the Surma Curry House. Est 1976, it is exactly what is says it is. It's a gem. No pretensions, no frills, old hands running it, a heap of happy regulars and a regular entrant in our Guide. It serves the standard menu with all you favourite starters: Bhajis, Samosas, Kebabs and Chaat. Tandooris and Tikkas, and curries,

side dishes and accompaniments. All are cooked just as they should be – perfectly. *'We just love going here. We go with our parents and with our kids. What more could you ask for'* AAR. The picture shows owner Muzazid Ali receiving a local Award from customer Angela Burgess. Show Mr Ali this Guide and he might give you a discount. Lunch and dinner, daily. Sun 12-11.

London SE23   Forest Hill, Honor Oak

BABUR BRASSERIE
BEST IN LONDON

119 Brockley Rise, SE23 1JP   020 8291 2400

Babur established the Moghul Empire in 1483 through his courage and daring in capturing Delhi. This restaurant captured Forest Hill in 1985, though its ownership by the dynamic Rahman brothers did not occur until 1992. Quite simply, it's in our AWARD-WINNING category because everything the Rahmans do, they do well. The restaurant was completely rebuilt in 2006, introducing a new menu, new wine list and new (and very strong) kitchen team. Head Chef, Jiwan Lal is from the Punjab and has featured the richly-spiced cooking of his homeland during the Punjabi New Year - Basant Lal came from the Oberoi Cecile Hotel in Simla. Sous Chef Praveen Kumar Gupta came from the Oberoi Rajvillas in Jaipur.

The restaurant frequently hold regional food festivals. For their Rajasthani festival the family visited the region to research the food. and these items were on the special menu: Jodhpuri Lamb Chops - marinated in aniseed, cumin and vinegar from the tandoor; Paneer Ke Sule - rounds of paneer rubbed with clove, chilli and coriander with papaya chutney; Maachli Kali Mirch - Bekti (fish) in black pepper, gram flour and yoghurt marinade; Lal Maas - classic Rajasthani clove smoked lamb curry in a spicy masala, served with steamed rice; Maas Ki Kadi - venison escallop in yoghurt and yellow chilli, served with jeera rice; Makki Ka Soweta - braised kid goat and sweet corn with cinnamon and red onion, served with tawa paratha; Khumb Mongodi Ki Subji - ground lentil and mushroom dumplings in tomato and onion sauce; Pushkar Ke Phool - tandoori broccoli marinated with yoghurt, cheese and spices. Indian puddings: Gehwar - crisply aerated griddle cake with chikoo ice cream; Jaipuri Bread Pudding - millet and maize-bread steamed pudding; Moong Dal Halwa - served with caramelised apple, sprinkled with almond and pistachio!

Continued overleaf:

BABUR BRASSERIE
BEST IN LONDON

119 Brockley Rise, SE23 1JP
020 8291 2400

Art is integral to Babur. The Kalamkari by Ajit Kumar Das in the entrance lobby is contemporary in design and the use of calligraphy (Sanskrit words written in Bengali characters) is a hallmark of his work.

The a la carte menu offers exciting dishes year round. Starters: Sandalwood Ostrich £7.50, Ostrich infused with fenugreek and sandalwood;

Bengali beetroot cutlets £5.95, beetroot and potato cakes coated with crispy sago, pictured left.

Chicken Chettinad £10.95, redolent of pepper, in a rice dosa crown (pictured below)

Babur's own home-made vanilla Kulfi, with figs (pictured right)

Ajwaini Macchi £5.95, crisp white bait with garlic, pepper and carom seeds Vegetable Beggar's Purse £5.95, pastry filled with potato, peas, cashews seasoned with chat masala. Mains: Batakh ka Seena, £12.95, pan-fried Barbary duck breast glazed with honey and coriander; Old Delhi style Khargosh £11.95, curried rabbit in ground aromatic spices; Bhikaneri Macchi £14.95, lack cod in spices and mustard oil, with mustard mash. Sides:: Asparagus Kali Mirch 6.75, asparagus and baby corn in roasted peppercorn masala. Zucchini Masala 5.95, courgettes tempered with five spices

In summary, at Babur everything is as good as it gets. and here. All you have to do is get there. Honor Oak Park station is just 5 minutes walk away. Turn left when leaving the station and walk about 150m to the first traffic light. Turn right and walk about 100m along Brockley Rise to Babur. Bus routes 122, 171, 172, P4 and P12 all stop at the junction of Brockley Rise and Honor Oak Park. Delivery: 6-12, phone: 0208 291 1853. Restaurant hours: 12-2.30 (not Fri) and 6-11.30 daily. e-mail: mail@babur.info   www.babur.info
Branch: Planet Spice, 88 Selsdon Pk Rd, Croydon, Surrey.

An apology: The cover of our 2007/8 Guide included photos of Babur's food, and we neglected to credit it.

London SE24
Herne Hill

MELA AT HERNE HILL
TOP 100

136 Herne Hill, SE24   020 7738 5500

110 seater formerly Three Monkeys opened in a former bank building in 1998. In late 2004 the restaurant changed ownership. to chef-proprietor Kuldeep Singh. The cooking is highly accomplished and there are regular menu changes. See Mela W1 for details. Prices are very fair. Two course set lunch from £7.95 / dinner £12.95 Sun to Thur 2 course. Sun buffet £6.95. Service charge: 12.5.% Hours: 6-11 Mon-Sat; 12-10.30 Sun. Branches Mela, Chowki and Soho Spice W1 and Dilli Manchester.   www.melarestaurant.co.uk

Pictured above: Kuldeep Singh, far right, with his brigade of exec chefs and managers.

London SW
Area: South West London,
Postcodes: SW1 to SW20
Population: 715,000

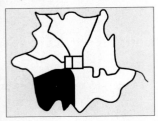

See page 72 for key to this map.

London SW1
Belgravia, Knightsbridge. Pimlico, St James's, Sloane Square, Victoria, Westminster

AMAYA
TOP OF A-LIST

Halkin Arcade, 19 Motcomb Street, SW1
020 7823 1166

Without doubt the cleverest restaurateurs not just in London, but anywhere, are the owners of this restaurant. Their continually growing portfolio now consist of seven Masala Zones, Chutney Mary and Veeraswamy. It makes a formidable portfolio. Masala Zone for the quick in-and-out dining experience. The other two for Indian regional fine-dining. Amaya at the higher price range. The average meal costs over £60 and you can add drink and service to that. And the clients flock in. And this is what they find. The decor is stunning. First there is a most attractive bar, encased in rosewood and vibrant red panels. The private dining room seats 14; the main room 150. Colourful, bright art sparingly decorates the walls in this sleekly dark restaurant. Day time provides a totally different atmosphere to night where the moody crystal chandeliers, spotlights and candles do the work. I don't know which I prefer. Statues, dark wood fittings, Indian sandstone and rosewood panelling; tasteful use of colour, subtle table settings, separate areas yet it is all one. And above all, a view of the kitchen running full-length at the end. The owners call it the India Grill. But this is no ordinary grill. There on view are a wide range of cooking implements used in India for thousands of years such as Sigrhi (open fire grill), Tawa (griddle), Mahi Tawa (walled griddle), Kadhai (wok), Lagan (steam pot) Shilajit Stone (special stones from Hyderabad, said to have aphrodisiac properties) and of course the Tandoor. Expertly positioned spotlights illuminate the equipment and the food, but not the chefs, discretely dressed in black. A big range of kebab

AMAYA *(continued)*   **TOP OF OUR A-LIST**

Halkin Arcade, 19 Motcomb Street, SW1
020 7823 1166

creating a culinary spectacle. Other dishes are seasoned with subtle marinades. These sit alongside fragrant light soups and exotic salads. The food is designed to be shared and is served as it is prepared. There are no conventional first courses or main courses. The staff warn you of this but can lead to complaints from those who like to get things in the order they believe they should be served. This is also how items are served at Masala Zones. Others complain that this is not 'curry' as they know it. The Panjabis explain this very tactfully. *'Our restaurants are very different from the inexpensive neighbourhood curry restaurants started in Britain by enterprising non-Indian entrepreneurs who developed their own brand of curry totally different from the tastes of real Indian food.'* Put it another way, curryhouse they are not. And of course we hear about it being pricey with small portions to boot. DBAC says: *'this restaurant is for some for that special occasion, but not necessarily for a table for two. Portions can be on the small side, but that's what makes it really lovely, you can share all those deliciously delightful little dishes, with your closest friends. The bar area is just perfect for a light lunch of perhaps, The Amaya Platter - eight little wonders, beautifully presented - all for £16.25. However, if you have a little more time on your hands and wish to linger over a longer lunch or perhaps dinner, retire to the main dining room with comfortable leather chairs and watch the chefs prepare kebabs and salads. Main course dishes are superbly presented on plates of different sizes and designs.'*

Presentation, like the venue's design, is seductively striking. But that alone is not what makes Amaya one of the most highly rated restaurants in this Guide. It is attention to detail in all departments, originality, careful service, cleanliness, immaculate food and sheer excellence. It is also only the fifth Indian restaurant anywhere to get a Michelin Star, though why Veeraswamy and Chutney Mary are still waiting for theirs, only Michelin can explain. As to those prices, you can pay two or three times more for higher-rated Franco-British restaurants in town (see page 17), but you won't get better quality. Main courses £10 to £28. Dinner with wine c£65 pp. Many desserts are light, and some are sugar-free. A favourite is plum compote with chilli custard and rose sorbet. Three-course lunch of less than 400 calories Hours:. 12.30-2.15 Mon-Fri; 2.30 Sat; 12.45-2.45 Sun / 6.30-11.15 Mon-Sat; 10.15 Sun. www.realindianfood.com

See pages 1, 36, 90, 114, 119. 139 and 153

CINNAMON CLUB   A-LIST

The Old Westminster Library, Great Smith
Street, SW1   020 7222 2555

The conversion of the former Westminster library is well documented. It was a labour of love by its founder who has now moved onto other ventures. The location is genius. To put it in catchment terms, it is one of the nearest restaurants to the House of Commons, the Lords, vast numbers of media types, numerous parliamentary offices, an expensive convention centre and a million tourists. Excluding the latter, the average wage of the indigenous workforce is in six figures. And there are thousands of them; ministers, shadow ministers, MPs, peers, civil servants and diplomats. And they love the Cinnamon Club. It's a great name too; because there is a membership-only bar and lounge at £1000 pa for the privilege. And so you are more than likely to see some of these high-flyers along with a sprinkling of celebs from all walks of life. Indeed when the House is 'sitting' the venue now echoes to the sound of the Division bell. This also happens at the previous curry king of the castle, the Kundan, Horseferry Road, and I ran a much copied gag about *'when the bell goes and the suits evacuate, its not the fire alarm it's the division bell!'* So location, location, location is perfect. The other maxim at the forefront of a venue owner's mind is utilisation. If your venue is only open for lunch and dinner, or worse just dinner, then its fixed costs are higher per hour than if it operates 24 hours. Unlike New York, London is not a 24 hour city, but this venue operates some of the longest hours of any restaurant in this Guide. It opens at 07.30 and diners often leave after midnight. Its current success is largely down to its chef. Chef Vivek Singh ex Jaipur Raj Vilas Hotel. He once cooked for President Bill Clinton. Here he has a brigade of 20 chefs. And he needs them. Breakfast Menu Snapshot: Spiced scrambled eggs on layered bread £14; Bombay spiced vegetables with cumin 'pao' £14; Utthapam - traditional rice pancake with coconut chutney and lentil broth £14. Or there's Anglo Indian Kedgeree If you must, there's a Full English or Continental breakfast. Average price £25. The lunch and dinner menu literally changes daily, so this review gives you just a flavour. Lunch: Stir-fry crab with roasted coconut & spices; tandoori breast of black-leg chicken with peanut and dried mango; Galouti kebab of green plantain and red kidney bean with raitha; Rajasthani sangri beans. Dinner: Carpaccio of cured organic salmon with onion seeds, horseradish raitha; French black chicken breast with pomegranates and spices, morel korma sauce; Smoked rack of lamb with Rajasthani corn sauce; Roast saddle of Oisin red deer with pickling spices; Tandoori grilled Portobello mushroom, morels and girolles with layered paratha. Dessert: Spiced pumpkin tart with clove and milk ice cream £7.50; Date pancake with vanilla and toasted coconut ice cream

£7.50; William pear poached with cinnamon and port; Batter fried rice pudding with grilled Victoria pineapple All food is beautifully presented on fine china. We agree with others that Vivek has moved the frontiers forward. It is an experience all true devotees of Indian food should try. *'on our first visit, we sat in the buzzing bar, I drank Gimlets – really good, 2nd best I've tasted – (best in Goa's Fort Aguada, by the pool). After a relaxing chat, we moved to the dining room, where a cleanly laid table, situated in the corner awaited us. We dined on fab food – all delicious.'* DBAC. The caveat remains. A lot of diners have found Cinnamon Club not to their liking, as is to be expected. It is far removed form the curryhouse formula as can be. No pickles and pops, and a futuristic / fusion slant on the food. And it still has a telephone attitude problem, noted by one of our most reliable reporters: *'We thought we'd give ourselves a treat and go to The Cinnamon Club. The woman on the phone was absolutely no credit to the restaurant and made us feel a real nuisance for telephoning. She finally agreed to let us have a table which we would have to relinquish by 8.30 and told us that "two hours is more than enough time to eat a meal and you can always take your coffee to the bar." After thinking about this later we decided it would all be too much of a rush and telephoned again to cancel. No "thank you for letting us know," as opposed to just not turning up, so we didn't feel so sorry about not going. Too many restaurant receptionists are far too officious and make you fit in with them rather than making them feel their custom is appreciated.'* HC. *'Having another free evening in London, we tried the again. We were told very firmly that they did not take reservations for 8 or 8.30, so they obviously operate a two sitting system and if you can not or do not want to go early or late, that's your hard luck. I doubt we shall ever go here'* We are finding increasing examples of staff rudeness. A sign of the times? Main courses £12-£26. 2 course set lunch £19; 3 course £22. 5 course set dinner £60. A-la-carte av £80 + drinks. Party rooms seating 30 and 50. Service: 12.5%. Bar Hours: Library Bar: 11am-11.45pm Mon-Sat. Dining Hours: 7.30-9.30, Mon-Fri, 12-2.45 / 6-10.45. Sunday closed. www.cinnamonclub.com

MINT LEAF   A-LIST

Suffolk Pl, Haymarket, SW1   020 7930 9020

This 4,000 sq ft basement 140-seater is simply gorgeous. The decor is breathtaking. It is intensely dark, but its spotlighting creates the most sexy environment. You enter the bar down the stairs. Watch the cocktails being 'thrown and juggled', and have some bar-snacks. Cocktails include Pomegranate Margarita - Patron silver, fresh lime, fresh pomegranate, and Grand Marnier Centenaire - sounds good to me, but I think Marieann would love the Lemon Mimosa - Pallini Limoncello, fresh lemon and Jacquart Brut NV. Bar snacks: a platter of crisp chicken rolls, scallops, prawns and soft shell crabs (non vegetarian); or a platter of stuffed mushrooms, stuffed potato barrels, char grilled stuffed peppers and vegetarian sheek kebab. When you do

move into the main dining area, it is in fact several areas, expertly divided, yet all in vision. There are private areas and public areas. New chef Ajay Chopra, from the Marriott, Bombay and has rewritten the menu to include seafood and game. Menu Snapshot: Duck kebab; or Guinea fowl, with yogurt and chilli, tomato and fenugreek sauce; Quails, roasted with ground mustard and honey; Baby lamb shanks. tandoor roasted with caraway and yogurt, Turbot.Seared with chilli, basil

and lime, all £8/£14 (small/large); Duck leg, slow roasted and spiced with star anise and coriander, £12/£20; Lobster £15/£26, braised, 'Upma' with curry leaf and coconut drizzle, Soft shell crab, £7/£12, crisp fried, curry leaf and dry mango Baby aubergine,.£6/£10, spicy eggplant and cumin mash with goat's cheese, Potato cakes, £6/£10, cased with green pea and raisins. Curries: Sea bass, £25, poached in a fenugreek and tomato sauce; Chicken Chettinad, £18.50, braised with tomato, curry leaf and Chettinad

spice; Morel and green peas, £20, with cashew, crushed tomatoes and ginger; Paneer, £17.50, tandoor-grilled, braised with onion, tomato and fenugreek. Vegetarian tasting platter, £17; Seafood tasting platter, £25; Salads: Sour mango and mustard salad; Tandoori pineapple and pepper salad..both £6/ £10.We were asked to recommend a venue for a pre-Christmas office party for 6 senior execs of a multinational US company. They wanted a venue where they could arrive at lunch time and relax until evening. We suggested Mint Leaf. '*We enjoyed the pre-lunch drinks and lunch, then we returned to the bar sofas and enjoyed our drinks. Next I knew it was midnight and they were closing. Our bill £1200 +Tip. Worth*

every dime!' GR. Service charge: 12.5%.Hours: 12-3, Mon-Fri / 5.30-11 daily. Bar: 12-12 Mon-Weds; to 1am Thur-Sat; from 5 Sat & Sun. mintleafrestaurant.com

THE QUILON TOP OF OUR A-LIST

St James Court Hotel, 45 Buckingham Gate, SW1
020 7821 1899

Taj Hotels Group have owned London's unique Bombay Brasserie (SW7) and the elegant St James's Court Hotel for many years. But it took until 1999 to open an Indian restaurant here. Though within the complex, the restaurant is only accessible from the street. It is modern, with clean lines and sparkly mosaics running discreetly around the room and a splendid monkey mural on one wall. It's a modern, light and airy restaurant, seating 92 diners in two areas. The restaurant's name comes from Quilon, an unremarkable town on the coast in the south of Kerala, not far from India's southernmost tip. This is the clue that the food is from the various states of south India. Indeed, the restaurant reflects what has been happening in Taj Hotels across India, where regional food of a high order is on their menus. In fact, Taj piloted this restaurant in Bangalore in 1988. Called Karavali, (meaning coastal food) it has become one of the city's favourites. Karavali owes its success to its original chef, Chef Aylur V Sriram. He originally trained with his father at the Hotel Sriram,

and went on to work in some of India's top hotel restaurants. While at Karavali, the New Statesman described him as '*One of the top five chefs in India.*' In 1999 he opened Quilon; his mission to recreate Karavali in London. Chef Sriram is a master; his spicing lyrical; his balance of flavour dreamlike; his menu a super choice of meat, fish and vegetable dishes. Unlike others in town, Sriram proves that there is no need for flamboyance, spin or new wave, '*Do not take a traditional dish and mess around with it*' he says. In typical understated Taj style, he simply and quietly goes about his business of producing perfect Indian cooking (others please note).His reward is that he is now Quilon's General Manager as well as Chef. His small but perfectly balanced menu awaits you. It's an education. '*We were lucky to get tickets to see 'Beating Retreat' at Horse Guards*

Parade followed by an invitation to Wellington Barracks Officers' Mess for a cocktail party. It was a great evening's entertainment. We decided that dinner at Quilon was in order, as it is just around the corner. It was quite late, getting on for 9.30, so while we decided what to eat, we nibbled on the popadums and lotus root basket and the two coconut chutneys (one spicy red, the other creamy green), which accompanied the basket and of course, it gave the waiter a chance to serve drinks. After a quick discussion, it was decided that we would share two starters, Mini Masala Dosa £7 - thin rice and lentils pancakes filled with tempered potatoes, served with sambhar and Crab Cakes £8.50 - crab meat sauteed with curry leaves, ginger, green chillies and cooked on a skillet. Chef Sriram, very sweetly, plated these two starters onto four plates, so it wasn't really two starters, more like three, so kind. The Dosa was curled into a cone and placed upside down, covering the potato filling like a little straw hat. The crab cake was served with a generous, artistic scribble of mustard sauce and the tiny accompanying salad was nicely dressed with a lime juice concoction. All was delicious and portions wise, perfect, as we all cleared our plates. For mains, Alison and I both chose the Manglorean Chicken (Kori Gassi) £18.50 - succulent pieces of chicken cooked in finely ground fresh coconut and roasted red chilli, peppercorns, cumin, coriander with a tempering. Paul, the Chicken Masala #18.50 - spiced chicken supreme cooked with aromatic spices and Pat, Malabar Lamb Biryani £20.50, Basmati rice and lamb cooked wit traditional Malabar spices in a sealed pot, served with pachadi and a lamb sauce. We all ate an Appam £2 each with Lemon and Coconut Rice £3 each and a bowl of Pachadi £3 - pineapple and pomegranate mixed with yoghurt, ground coconut, cumin and mustard (because Alison and Paul are both chilli lightweights!). The Biryani was huge and Pat struggled to finish it, so I helped him out a bit - it was delicious. The rice was so fragrant and the lamb so tender, it literally fell apart. Paul's chicken must have been good, 'cos he ate the lot! and Alison and I enjoyed our Kori Gassi, especially, as we dipped our Appam's in the rich, spicy gravy! We finished off (well, Alison and I did and Paul was given an extra spoon) with Bibinca and Dodal, served with a perfect sphere of home-made ice cream . What a wonderful evening! As you can see, the prices are typical for the area, so, please try the lunch time special offer, it really is excellent value for money - two courses for £17 or three (including coffee) for £20 (and don't forget the 12.5% service - though you do get the popadums basket with chutneys as a trade off). DBAC. 'I do love a good Appam, a soft centered, lace edged rice pancake and I think Quilon makes the very best! - especially, as the bread chef makes them for you in the restaurant, as you watch - delicious when dipped into the gravy of my favourite, Kori Gassi! 'Quilon is absolutely wonderful. Right from the way the telephone reservation was made, everything was right (very different from the Cinnamon Club's treatment of hopeful diners) and we were made to feel welcome. The decor is very attractive, light, spacious and modern. The serving staff are all young and in very casual, but tidy clothes and all extremely helpful and friendly. The menu is a mix of fairly traditional dishes and modern versions of Indian food. The number of dishes is similar to most English restaurants of good quality. All food was served on plain white plates of different shapes and all dishes that could be plated in an artistic way were. The Popadums were the lightest, crispest ever had and were served sprinkled with dry roast lotus root, delicious and very 'moorish' - like English crisps and peanuts. Served with marvellous relishes and chutneys. Two small niggles, the food was lukewarm, probably due to the plating and the lamb Biriyani was one-dimensional. All starters were excellent and main courses were served with assorted sides. Not cheap at £280 for four, including 2 bottles of wine, but superb, the place to go for a whole evening.' HC. You are quite right re: plating, the poor chefs are under such pressure to get the food out hot, but plated food, like it or not, and we do not, seems to be the trend today. In conclusion, a restaurant with management of this calibre means its quality remains rock-solid. It won our Best UK Restaurant award, which means what it says. Though this award goes elsewhere this time, it remains Best in the UK. Service: 12.5%. Mains £8.50-£23. 2 course set lunch £12.95, 3 course £15.95 Service: 12.5%. Hours: 12-2.30 Mon-Fri / 6-11 Mon-Sat. www.quilon.co.uk

SALOOS   A-LIST

62 Kinnerton Street, SW1 020 7235 4444

M Salahuddin's Saloos is a Pakistani institution. This 1st floor restaurant been around for decades and at the beginning it set a new standard of service, decor (chandeliers, white linen and screened windows – rather like being in a hareem) and yes, expense. Not the place to eat if you are a vegetarian, as the menu is meat biased, but never-the-less a great place to dine in you are not on a budget .Even 20 years ago, it was easy to spend £100 for two there. The elegant Farizeh Salahuddin (daughter of the house – she can be heard out of hours on the answer machine) handles bookings with considerable aplomb. It's still much hallowed by my Pakistani and Indian friends, well-educated wealthy citizens, who ignore politics when it comes to conviviality. But I am beginning to wonder if it has become overtaken by so many really excellent newer venues. Being Pakistani, meat, meat and more meat predominates ('A vegetarian-free heaven' says RA who, like Bernard Shaw, despises vegetables). The faithful still adore it. 'Succulent, natural-coloured, divinely-flavoured offerings like Chicken Shashlik, Lamb chop and Shami Kebab are insurmountable' HEG. Tandoor/Kebab items are the always recommended, served with breads, rice and raitha. Hard-to-find, acquired taste Haleem, (see glossary) is one speciality. But we get somewhat reserved reports about Saloos from occasional or first-time visitors these days. The place is an institution and is worth at least one visit. The last time we were there seemed to be family day. There were kids all over the place (well behaved ones, Asian and white), thoroughly enjoying themselves as were their parents, the staff and us. An unmissable treat for the aficionado. High in our A-LIST. Set lunches:£13 &

£17, (2 & 3 courses). Main courses c£11-£16. Cover ch £1.50. Service 12.5%. Hours; 12-2.15 / 7-11 Mon-Sat

SEKARA

3 Lower Grosvenor Pl, SW1   020 7834 0722

A combination of Indian and Sinhalese Sri Lankan cuisine. Go for the latter, and if you like it hot, ask the helpful personnel for it done as it would be back home. Menu snapshot: Sri Lankan Starters, mutton Rolls or Fish Rolls £3.50 two deep-fried crispy pancake rolls stuffed with a mixture of lightly spiced savoury lamb or fish and potato; Vadai £2.00, two deep-fried crunchy, spicy lentil cakes. Some mains: Mutton Lampreys £12.95, deep-fried pieces of mutton mixed with basmati rice flavoured with saffron and spices and served with mutton curry, aubergine and seeni sambola (fried onions). Lampreys or Lamprais (from the Dutch word, 'Longkirist') was a festive dish introduced to Sri Lanka by a Dutch burger centuries ago:a full meal of meat curry, kofta, rice, and sambols is wrapped inside a banana leaf parcel and served like a hot picnic. It is rare to find this dish even in Sri Lanka. Chicken Koththu Roti £8.95, soft home made roti bread chopped up and stir-fried with chicken, fresh leeks, tomatoes and carrots to a historic recipe. Tandoori Mixed Grill, £14.95, pricey but contains all you need: King prawns, lamb tikka, chicken tikka, tandoori chicken and sheek kebab served with salad and naan bread; String Hoppers £10.95, steamed Sri Lankan noodles served with seer fish curry and pol sambola (coconut); Devilled chicken, pork or squid £5.95, with sweet green and red capsicums, onions and fresh green chillies in a rich, sweet, spicy-hot sauce. Dessert: Wattalapam £4.95, coconut milk, sweet jaggery, cashew nuts and pure kithul treacle and spiced with cinnamon and nutmeg. A postscript. We were going to nominate this restaurant for best Sri Lankan (see page 23) but the manager / owner told our researchers that they weren't interested in the Guide, nor in receiving an Award. So we dropped it. Inexplicable behaviour but we do get 'em from time to time. Normally we drop those-that-think-they-don't-need-help from the Guide altogether, but we do believe this restaurant has plenty going for it, not least the Lampreys, though this is no further helped by open credit card slips with the 10% service charge already added. To stay in the Guide, it needs your opinions. Hours: 12-3 / 6-10. www.sekara.co.uk

WOODLANDS   TOP 100

37 Panton Street, SW1   020 7930 8200

Long-established (1985) licensed, vegetarian, south Indian 55-seat restaurant, just off Haymarket. It is the tiniest of UK Woodlands. There some 30 are branches in India, Singapore and LA, each serving an identical menu. Bhel, Dosa, Idli, Vada, Samosa, Pakoda,

Utthapam . *'I particularly like southern Indian food, and find the menu so appealing, it makes choice difficult. We chose one exceptionally good-value set meal, Thali, £6.50, which was quite generous, with good variety, and the Paper Dosa, £3.95. Upamas, £2.95, Lhassi, £1.25, and Chana, £3.75 are as good as ever. Also glad to have a choice of Indian desserts. Good value.'* HC. *'Gulab Jamun, slightly chewy cardamom-scented fried milk balls in a sticky syrup, Kulfi, Indian ice-cream in a variety of flavours and Carrot Halva, a dense pudding that has the consistency of fudge, are enough to satisfy any sweet tooth. And, if you missed out on a Dosa for your main course or want to continue the pancake theme, you could always end the meal with a butter dosa with sugar'.* TY. *'Enjoyed my lunchtime visit, indulging in the vegetarian buffet. Plenty of flavoursome dishes.'* RL. Lunch,c £8; Dinner c £20. Service 12.5%. Hours: 11-2.45 / 5.30-10.45. Branches: London NW3, W1, W4 & Wembley, Mddx.

YOU SAY OK
You may get a discount of you show them this Guide.

SW2: PUKKA BRASSERIE 89 Streatham Hill SW2 ~ 020 8671 1171. Kebabs good. Tues Banquet Night.Hours: 5.30 (Sunday from 12) to 12.

London SW3
Chelsea, King's Road, Sloane Square, Knightsbridge·

HAANDI   A-LIST

136 Brompton Rd, Knightsbridge, SW3
                              020 7823 7373

North Indian cuisine with Kenya influences. restaurant with bar and two entrances. One at the rear on Cheval Place is at street level, while the one on Brompton Road is down a generous staircase, leading to a bright, clean and tidy reception and the bar, which serves snacks, and on the left is the restaurant. The lemony-yellow decor, with inviting tables and chairs, give a cheerful sunshine welcome. *'We propped up the bar on high stools, and sipped glasses of red wine, which Ray (proprietor) had chosen for us – very good. We chatted about India, its food and his Kenyan connections (Ray has a highly regarded restaurant there). We enjoyed Kebabs and Tikkas – a chef speciality; you can see them cooking through a plate glass window, followed by Chicken Tikka Butter Masala , fantastic, not overly tomatoey, creamy, smoky, with a little chilli kick, Gosht-Ki-Haandi , one of Pat's favourites with Dal Dera Ismail Khan , creamy black lentils, rice and Pudina Nan £2.10, quite thin, not doughy, sprinkled with finely chopped mint – lovely (Pat liked it and he's not a bread fan!). All dishes cooked properly, presented carefully, served professionally and in generous portions.'* DBAC. Other diners think the same. *'Excellent menu, food and presentation with a warm welcome. A wonderful restaurant.'* RB. *'Chakula Mzuri Sana is Kenyan for Good Food!'* NH. *'Absolutely gorgeous, good food, wine and service.'* JH. *'A great experience, not only the place was relaxing, the*

atmosphere and the staff really helpful. We had one of the best Indian meals we have ever come cross. We'll definitely go back.' NM. *'I have become a regular. Absolutely amazing food, a great ambassador of Indian cuisine.'* AB. *'Absolutely love Haandi. Food so flavourful, spicy and delicious. Courteous staff are welcoming.'* CM. Menu Extracts: Khajy Til Rolls, vegetable roll with cashew nuts and mint. Bindya Prawns £12.20, crispy queen prawns. Diwani Haandi, mix of peas, corn, carrots and beans. Gosht Kabuli, lamb with chickpeas, lentils and fresh mint. Lunch Menus: from £9. Bar Hours: drinks served between 12-10.30, light meals and snacks available all day. Hours: 12-3 / 5.30-11; - 11.30 Fri & Sat. www.haandi-restaurant.com

RASOI VINEET BHATIA   A-LIST

10 Lincoln St, Sloane Sq, SW3   020 7225 1881

This restaurant is chef led, but Vineet Bhatia is no ordinary chef. He is one of the most determined hard-workers I know. He worked his way up via the Star of India to Zaika, Chelsea then South Ken, where he gained his Star, Michelin, that is. But he also wanted total freedom, and he settled for a tiny venue (38 seats) where he could cook as he calls it 'properly rather than for a 300 cover factory with a more hands-on approach'. Rasoi appropriately meaning 'kitchen' is housed in a 100 year old property which was previously home to Richard Corrigan's English Garden restaurant. Vineet, with his wife Rashima, has revamped the Chelsea property into a mini-Indian palace. It is divided into two floors; the lower is the main dining area and bar and the upper level is split into two private function rooms and named after Rajasthan's twin cities – Udaipur and Jaipur, seating 8 and 15. A myriad of rich eastern treasures creates a regal air. Rajasthani jharokas, – beautifully crafted wood frames, wedding saris draping the walls, a stunning Kashmiri rug, vibrant Benares saris framing the windows and antiquated Indian chests placed throughout the restaurant. All embody the rustic charms and colourful culture of India. Being perfectionists, Vineet and Rashima have not overlooked their staff. Together with Rashima, Bobby Gudka who has designed clothes for some of India's biggest fashion houses, including Satya Paul has exclusively designed the staff uniforms using a theme of chocolate brown and turquoise. Vineet and Rashima have globe-trotted to source many of their furnishings and crockery. Chic chocolate brown dining tables are imported from Turkey, plates (there are over fifty types) have been brought in from countries like Spain and America, the silverware is from France and the Rosenthal glassware is German. A glass covered wall adds depth to the modest space and overlooks the teak wood surface of the bar. Frequently reported is the *'delicately explosive individual spicing'* RCF countered with *'rather bland. but enhanced with some green chillies'* JGS. As you would expect Vineet varies his menu and he experiments with non-Indian ingredients. Samosa fillings the like of spinach and sultana, chopped asparagus tips mixed with south Indian coconut chilli and curry leaf chutney, and shiitake mushroom with chopped roasted peanut are not liked by all. But the Tandoori platter gets universal acclaim for the different marinades and subtlety. There is an array of chicken, lamb, king prawn, fish, lobster and Indian vegetable main dishes. And you will find ingredients we do not normally associate with Indian food; items like broccoli, chestnuts, beetroot, pine nuts, Stilton (in the Naan) and honey. Vineet's Dum Pukht Biriani has always been fabulous. GM Thomas Heimann, also the sommelier has carefully selected an extensive range of wines, in addition to spirits and cocktails. Jancis Robinson. Slightly understated Jancis; the list is as fabulous as the food. Not cheap though, the wines, nor the food. Mains £15 -£36. Set meal £60 - £70. Service: 12.5%. Hours: 12-2.30 Mon-Fri; 6-10.30 Mon-Sat. www.vineetbhatia.com
Branch: Urban Turban, W10

SHAHEEN OF KNIGHTSBRIDGE

225 Brompton Road, SW3   020 7581 5329

With Shaheen 150 yards from Harrods, if you are feeling a bit battered and worn, elbowing your way past the tourists, why not drop in at Shaheen to revive yourself and rest your feet! It's a long-standing restaurant, which understands its regulars and tourists equally well. *'Very happy with the meal. Decor plain and menu short. Prices very fair, considering location. All food very good and all chose something different, so had a good range. Full marks for having a dessert menu that wasn't the usual fancy ice-creams. Very pleasant Gajar Halva'* HJC. 12.30-3 / 6-11.30; 12-11.30 Sat & Sun.

London SW4

Clapham

MAHARANI

117 Clapham High St, SW4   020 7622 2530

The 104-seat Maharani was established in 1958, at which time there were under 200 curry houses in the whole of the UK. It was not only Clapham's first curry house, opened long before Cla'am became trendy ma'am, it was one of the first to open in a London suburb. It has always earned its keep by providing good, bog-standard, formula curries; indeed, owner SU Khan was one of the pioneers of the formula. Under the same ownership for all these years, Khan has kept up with the trends, though, and everything is as it should be. Hours: 12-2.30 / 6-12; 12-12 Sun.

London SW5

Earls Court

MASALA ZONE   A-LIST

147 Earl's Court Rd, SW5   020 7373 0220

London's most exciting chain. Its distinctive decor and food make it stand out. From a simple selection of street food dishes to a thali – a complete meal on a plate, noodle bowls, curry & rice plates, tandoors & grills and Masala burgers. Most meals served within five minutes of ordering. *'Quality Very good Quantity Adequate Decor Minimalist Service Prompt and pleasant Comfort Adequate and very clever Comments Starters: Chicken Vada £3.95 dry and subtly spiced. Slightly too salty; Aloo Tikka Chat £3.50 lovely flavours, well spiced. Main Courses: Clove Smoked Lamb Korma £7.45 intense flavours and subtly spiced. Chicken Mangalore £6.55 very rich sauce, extremely tasty. Accompaniment: Vegetable side £1 delicious. Drinks: Stella £2.75; Cobra £3.15. Bill: £31.19. Mark: 8 / 10'* G&MP. Delivery phone: 08700 841 330. Delivery lunch offer – 25% off. Del. Hours: 12.30–2.30 / 5.30–10. Sit-in hours: Mon-Fri 12 -3 / 5.30-11.30; 12-11 Sat & Sun . See pages 1 & 36. Branches: N1, SW & W1, W2, WC2.

YOU SAY OK

You may get a discount if you show them this Guide.

SW4: CLAPHAM TANDOORI 10 Clapham Common S ~ SW4 020 7622 4470. Clapham's 2nd oldest (1971); 72-seater owned by Abdur Rhaman Choudhury. Del: 3m £10 min. Hours: 12-2.30/6-12.

NO GO? Masala 4 Hogarth Road, London, SW5 0871 4263431. *'Went to this joint by mistake; we was looking for Masala Zone. Food was pretty poor.'*

NIZAM   TOP 100

152 Old Brompton Rd, SW5   020 7373 0024

The Nizam was the former ruler of Hyderabad. Until partition he was the richest man in the world, and his dining table seated 101 guests, yes, at one table! On it was a silver model railway which chugged around the table dispensing whisky et al to the guests. M Mian's 1989 vintage Nizam is rather smaller, seating 65 on several tables in two rooms. *'Attractive appearance and warm reception. The food was varied and excellent with a number of dishes new to me and my guests. Chicken and prawn main courses with excellent vegetables, especially the smoked aubergine. Service was superb throughout.'* RH. Service is exemplary, with smartly waistcoated waiters, exuding expertise. NW Frontier and Moghul cuisine is carefully executed by chef M Riaz. Specialities include smoky Baigan Burtha, (charcoal-grilled aubergine, its flesh then mashed to a purée), Prawn Piri Piri, (coconut milk and chilli). Cover charge £1. Takeaway 10% discount. Del: £12 min. Hours: 12-2.30 / 6-11.45.

STAR OF INDIA   TOP 100

154 Old Brompton Rd, SW5   020 7373 2901

Reza and Azam Mahammad run this startling restaurant. I say startling for two reasons. One is because Vineet was once chef here. (see Rasoi Vineet Bhatia, SW3, earlier). Vineet is a larger-than-life character, but he fades to insignificance alongside Reza. Get him talking to you and you'll see what I mean. It is startling too because the decor is a dead-ringer of Michael Angelo's Sistine Chapel. Starters include: Galouti Kebab, smooth mince lamb patties, served with onion and cumin relish. Samundri Ratan, Saffron infused chargrilled scallops served in a creamy sauce. Chenna Samosa crispy parcels filled with a trio of goat, buffalo and cow's cheese, mixed with leeks, ginger and green peppercorns, served with a spiced tomato and chive chutney. Main courses: Murghabi Tawe Wale, escallops of mallard marinated with garlic, nutmeg, lemon and chilli oil, pan fried on an iron griddle. Raan Mussallam (serves two), roasted leg of baby lamb marinated in a mixture of spices then cooked over a gentle flame in a rich onion and tomato gravy, flavoured with nutmeg and flambéed with rum. If you can spare room for a pudding, try either the Dum Malai Chikki, steamed milk pudding scented with nutmeg and cardamom, topped with caramelised jaggery and carom seeds, served chilled, or the Phalon Ka Muzaffar, home made seasonal fruit compote, served with cardamom ice cream, or have both! Lunch and dinner daily. Some say the Star has passed its zenith. Tell that to its regulars! Hours 12.30-2.30 / 6-10.30.

London SW6
Fulham, Parson's Green, West Brompton

BLUE ELEPHANT THAI
A-LIST

4 Fulham Broadway, SW6   020 7385 6595

The benchmark for best Thai restaurant anywhere, this group, headed by Belgian Karl Steppe, and his Thai wife has branches world-wide, including a cookery school in Bangkok. London's Blue Elephant has always been the group's flagship. The stunning Blue Bar, based on the Royal Thai Barge, enhances the whole experience. The bar menu includes a salad of young sour mango, palm sugar and roast coconut. On entering this enchanted kingdom, allow yourself to be taken on a wonderful journey, tasting some of the finest Thai cuisine in the country. Cross the delightful bridge stretching over a picturesque lily pond and enter the heart of lush jungle, exotic blooms and thatched Thai dining 'Houses'. Bundles of redolent orchids, freshly imported from Bangkok's famous floating market fill the light and airy interior. Specialist chefs prepare the finest in Royal Thai cuisine, ensuring each dish possesses the stamp of authenticity. Friendly and efficient staff are at hand to recommend and advise from the extensive menu that boasts a fabulous array of vegetarian dishes. The spectacular Sunday Brunch includes entertainment for children and unlimited servings for £25! All this is why we have frequently rated it the best Thai restaurant in the country. Hours: 12-2.30; 3 Sun / 7-11.30 Mon-Thu; from 6.30 Fri & Sun, from 6 Sat. See page 27. www.blueelephant.com

DARBAR
TOP 100

92 Waterford Road, SW6   020 7348 7373

Pravin Chauhan's family run the very successful London's Diwan-e-Am, But Pravin wanted his own venue and Darbar, (meaning royal court) is the outcome. His choice of chef shows the astrologers were smiling on Pravin. He got Mohammed Rais from the Red Fort London W1. His final ace is his advisor. Kris Patel owned the fabulous Diwana Bhel Poori House, Drummond Street, NW1, in fact he pioneered this type of food into Britain. He sold up a few years ago, but the restaurant bug didn't leave him and he is now a sleeping partner, advising Pravin on the running of the restaurant. This combination ensures the restaurant is promoted into our TOP 100. Although Rias has now returned to the Red Fort, his Dum Pukht (see page 56). legacy remains Starters include Galouti Kebab, the smoothest patties of minced lamb and spices. These are often cooked at your table to add to the drama. Teetar Gilafi kebab, spiced roasted minced partridge. Monkfish tikka, chunks of monkfish smoked with ginger. For main course, the wallets love Dum ka lobster – lobster steamed in a delicate sauce of mace, cumin and saffron, £28. But the Dum Pukht cognoscenti go for any of Rais' Birianis cooked in a sealed pot: Avadhi gosht Biriyani – Rais' 300 year old family recipe of lamb and rice. Samudari Biriyani, scallops, squid, prawns and rice. Subz Biriyani, moist basmati rice, vegetables and spices. Desserts include Strawberry Shrikand, yoghurt flavoured with fresh raspberry couli, £6. Not cheap, but this is Chelsea. Min spend £25 lunch and £45 dinner.

LILY TANDOORI

86c Lillie Rd, W. Brompton SW6   020 7385 1922

'Everything very good - the food, service, the price! The original Bengali cuisine, the one I was brought up with, the old fashioned taste. The Vindaloo was fantastic and the people so friendly. We were working at the Ideal Home Ex, erecting stands for a week prior to the opening and again, a month later to dismantle them. I'm in my 50's now and was pleased to get that authentic taste. We need more old fashioned restaurants as they used to be, not the fancy types which we are getting now.' PC. Peter, you are not alone with this comment.

MEMORIES OF INDIA ON THE RIVER
NEW TO OUR TOP 100

7 The Boulevard, Imperial Wharf, SW6 2UB
                                  020 7736 0077

They have changed name to 'Memories of India on the River' due to a legal entanglement relating to the name Memsaab, which has been copyrighted by a third party. The 96-cover venue is Bilal Ali and Abdul Jalil's third restaurant, the others being Memories of India, at Brighton Marina and Chichester. Situated in Chelsea's Imperial Wharf, the interior is stylish. Don't expect a river view though: it overlooks the railway. New station promised one day. For pre-dinner drinks there is a 16-seater lounge area where brown leather furnishings and American walnut hardwood flooring invite guests to enjoy custom cocktails like the Attitude Adjuster and Bombay Swinger, before heading off for some food. Cool toffee-coloured leather chairs and banquettes, cherry hardwood floors, traditional carved wooden screens and special Cold Cathode lighting are just some of the interesting features in the main dining area. Blown up pictures of various spices in Indian markets deck the walls and offer an ethnic flavour, but the focal point is a specially preserved palm tree that adds a touch of the tropics to west London contrasting with smart tableware and place-settings. South Indian Head Chef Muraalindharan, formerly at Chutney Mary, has created an a la carte menu that encompasses some of the best Indian cuisine. We had a huge plateful of mixed Tandoori items, which was super. Menu Snapshot: Punjabi starter of Chana chickpeas and Aloo Chop, fried potato cake with a whisp of chilli; Chettinad Quails;

Madras pot-roasted quails with shallots, star anise and toasted garlic; Palak Tikka Masala, roasted pepper with spinach patties served with tomato cumin sauce; and Quilon Sea bass, fillet marinated in red Keralan style masala pan fried in banana leaves. Special desserts include Kheer Brulée and fresh fruit skewers with honey yoghurt. Lunch £6.95, meat curry, boiled rice, paneer, and yogurt. Dinner for two with wine and service: around £80. Mon-Sat 12-11.30 / Sun 11 www.memsaabrestaurant.co.uk

NAYAAB   A-LIST

309 New Kings Rd (jnct'n Munster Rd), SW6
020 7731 6993

Praveen Rai has been around for a long time (est 1981) and this ensures that he runs a very good upmarket restaurant and superior Indian cooking will greet you. There are a lot of lovely dishes to choose from by chef Mohamed Raiyaz and his Pakistani brigade, so take your time and enjoy! Praveen's menu is full of *'some dishes you won't recognise and some that you will'*. The former are Indian and Pakistani specials cooked by head chef Akeel Ghani. Menu Snapshot: Lamb's Liver £5 - medium spiced, sautéed with onions and plum tomatoes; Baigan Pakoras £4 - gram flour coated aubergine roundels filled with cheese and herbs, crispy fried; Dhingree Chicken £6 - supreme breast of chicken stuffed with delicately spiced garlic mushrooms, rolled in gram-flour batter and deep-fried; Nihari £8 - lamb shank, slow cooked, pot roasted, sautéed, sealed, spicy sauce, slow cooked; Chuza Anardana £8 - whole poussin rubbed with home-made chutney (mint, pomegranate, spices) grilled in tandoor, hot and tangy; Monk Caldini £13 - spicy fish curry, cooked with 'kokum' (butternut berries), coconut, palm vinegar, garlic, curry leaves; Red Pumpkin £4 - lightly spiced, sautéed with onions, mustard and garlic; Mooli Ka Paratha £3.50 - multilayer bread stuffed with spiced grated white radish. This is all dedicated stuff, and well spoken of by the regulars. For the if-you-must-brigade, Mr Rai offers 'old curryhouse favourites' which include everything except Phal (he'll explain how it came to be 'invented by chefs as a revenge against the lager lout – and he'd never serve it or them!'). So if you are chilli-addicted, as Praveen himself is, then choose the hotter specials. Praveen is from the old-school of owner-management. He is gracious, articulate, witty and thoroughly good company. We cannot recommend it highly enough. And the added advantage is the discount: Show Praveen your copy of this Guide and receive a generous 10% discount on food bill. Set menus for two at £13 and £16 pp. Above prices approx. Reservation recommended. Del: 3m £10min. Hours: 6-11.45; 11.30 Sun. Closed 24-26 Dec & 1 Jan. www.nayaab.com

seasoning
RESTAURANT | BAR
84D - 86, Lillie Road ,Fulham,SW61TL
020 8836 0303

SEASONING   NEW ENTRANT

84D - 86, Lillie Road, Fulham, SW6 1TL
020 8836 0303

The 100 seater 'Seasoning' opened in April 2009 as the result of collaboration between two well-established restaurateurs, Nitin Munglanai and Gaylord's Salal Bhatia (see page 131) aiming to provide high quality authentic Indian and Fusion Indo-Chinese cuisine in a relaxed modern environment at affordable prices. The menu provides a mix of ethnic culinary styles prepared by chefs from India. Cuisines range from the exotic mughlai to the simple home- cooking styles of the north India with each dish ensuring authentic taste and flavour. The menu offers a wide selection of vegetarian and non-vegetarian dishes that can be custom prepared to your taste. Dishes include kebabs, curries, biriyani's, Indian breads and a choice of Indian desserts. The wine list includes 'Bollywood mocktails'l. The restaurant can also accommodate up to 100 people in its on-site function suit, complete with resident DJ Anil Arora who provides Modern Indian Electronica, Bollywood Beats etc. Seasons offers to project manage events from start to finish, including a party catering service, and packages for hotels Hours: All day: 11am to midnight. www.seasoning-restaurant.co.uk

London SW7   Kensington

BOMBAY BRASSERIE
BEST INDIAN RESTAURANT IN EUROPE

14 Courtfield Close, Courtfield Road, SW7
020 7370 4040

The Bombay Brasserie (BB to its friends) pioneered Indian regional cooking in this country, in fact the world when it opened in 1982. It hadn't even been done in India It is now the 50-strong Taj Hotel Group's flagship venue, earning millions of profit each year. It is an icon. Director Adi Modi has retired now after being there

since it opened. Arun Harnal remains in charge and the management is exemplary. Staff turn-round is minimal. Locals and regulars, of which there are very many greet the same staff faces year after year. Of our many thousands of reports received each year, we typically get around 100 about the BB. It way out does any other venue. Despite seating a considerable 265, you are advised to book. Some nights they serve 400 guests, split between a stylish restaurant and conservatory. It's nothing to see Madonna on one table, Hugh Grant on another, and the odd politician or peer on a third. None of this phases the waiters. The chefs are all Taj-trained regional specialists And this is some of their work: Samosa Chaat, vegetable samosas, served with chick peas, sweet yoghurt and a medley of chutneys. Aloo Tuk, crispy fried baby potatoes in jacket, topped with sweet yoghurt and imli (tamarind chutney). Sev Batata Puri , small biscuits like puris topped with cubed boiled potatoes, gramflour straws, sprouted lentil, coriander leaves and covered with a mix of mint, tamarind and chilli chutneys. And for mains: Chicken Tikka Makhani, chicken tikka immersed in a spiced butter sauce – fantastic CTM done the proper way. Lamb Chops with ginger and green herbs, French cut, English lamb cooked Indian style. Margi Ni Sali , chicken curry topped with straw potatoes. *'Pat and I enjoyed a candlelit dinner for two, sitting in the conservatory. After finishing a bottle of well chilled champagne in the bar, we sampled an abundance of delicious starters and main dishes and enjoyed everything immensely, but we always do at the BB! We finished off in the bar with their unique Cobra coffee - if you haven't had it, you don't know what you are missing!! It's absolutely fabulous as is the whole BB experience.'* DBAC. *'A friend booked six of us after our annual 'Messiah from Scratch' at the Royal Albert Hall. The BB is the sort of restaurant in which to spend a whole evening, and our concert made us late, but it was still such a treat. Surroundings are lovely, menu different, wonderfully tempting, food fantastic. Usual grumble – service. Professional when it came but had to attract attention to order drinks, ditto food. But atmosphere made up for everything. First class restaurant whatever its cuisine. Not cheap but top quality never is. Haven't been since 1984, so*

118

pleased it has kept up high standard. Had an out-of-this-world lobster dish. All superb, generous, and individual. Most impressed, we all were. £72 per couple.' HC. *'Attended the London International Trade Fair at Olympia and stayed in a hotel near the BB. Booked a table for 12 and entertained my colleagues with a top-class Indian meal. On arrival we were warmly greeted as we drank glasses of Omar Khayyam. Shown to an excellent round table in the conservatory and served us Chef's Choice. What followed can only be described as a procession of exceptional food with a variety of dishes too numerous to remember or name, washed down with 6 bottles of fabulous white wine. All who dined, thought it was the best meal they had ever eaten and would return again on special occasions – or when the company was paying!! £735 for twelve.'* DL. *'We go to enjoy the pianist as much as the food'* RCF. *'We moved to the curry desert of Devon from Berkshire and regularly ate at the Bombay Brasserie, a great exponent of the skills of cooking great Indian food.'* AF. Daily lunch buffet: £20. Min charge: £30.00. Service 12.5%. Hours: 12-3/7.30-12.. Branch: Quilon, SW1. See pages 20, 24 & 25.

YOU SAY OK

You may get a discount of you show them this Guide.

SW7: DELHI BRASSERIE 134 Cromwell Road, SW7 .020 7370 7617 Owner Mr A Jabber's and Chef Ram Singh's comfortable spacious 60-seater. Hours: 12-11.30.

SW7: KHAN'S OF KENSINGTON 3 Harrington Rd, SW7 020 7584 4114. 60-seater, est. 1991 by Mr Khan Hours: 12-2.30 / 6-11.30;12-12 Sat; 12.30-11 Sun.

SW9: OLD CALCUTTA 64a Brixton Road, Oval, SW9 020 7582 1415. Old-hand Abdul Mazid's curryhouse has been in this Guide since 1984. Del: 3m,£12 min. Hours: 12-2.30 / 6 -12. Go on the web site to hear some lyrical Ravi Shankar music. www.calcutta.co.uk

SHEZAN INDIAN　　　　TOP 100

16 Cheval Pl, Montpelier St, SW7　　020 7584 9316

This long-established (1966), very traditional 120-seat Pakistani restaurant, is in a residential street a block north of Old Brompton Road. The downstairs dining room, past the bar, is elegantly simple, with its downlighters, pewter plates, long-rolled napkins, traditional Pakistani chairs, all made theatrical by strategic lighting and candlelight. Chef Khan's food is as sophisticated as the service. It's traditional authentic Pakistani food done as it would have been for the royal courts. No innovation, no nonsense. Not even CTM (but its originator dish, Murgh Makhni) £12. The prices are Knightsbridge, but it's worth every penny just for regal service and care. Our favourite is still on: Choosa e Shezan – a chicken (whole poussin)-and-egg story described on the menu as *'a speciality of our dear old Khansama (cook)'*, and billed at a dear old £20! Set lunch £14. Mini charge dinner £25. Service 10%. Cover charge £1.50. Takeaway 20% off. Shezan branches in New York

London SW8
Battersea, South Lambeth, Vauxhall

CAFÉ ZIA

811 Wandsworth Rd, SW8　　020 3202 0077

In 2002 renowned chef and restaurateur, Manju Choudhury took leave of his successful group of over 20 restaurants (the Hawelli Group, well known to this Guide) to explore the flavours, food, and ingredients that make up India's famously diverse culinary world. After a four-year hiatus, he made the world's biggest onion bhaji (62kg), to raise money for charity and listed in the Guinness Book of Records. and he has produced a stunning menu at his new flagship restaurant, Café Zia. Manju's brother, Mosru Choudhury co-owns and manages the 100-seat restaurant. The contemporary design is fresh, with curtained windows and natural lighting offering a homely setting. Collaborating with his Head Chef, Govinder Prasad-Gurung, who joined the restaurant after ten years as Head Chef of Battersea's Bombay Bicycle Club (also well known to this Guide), Choudhury offers diners signature dishes like Bhuna Gosht Khybari, tender lamb flavoured with a hint of coriander and ginger cooked in a garlic and onion sauce; Chicken Aishwarya, slices of tender butter chicken breast marinated in lemon and methi leaf and cooked in a rich almond sauce; and Mala King Prawns, that are simmered in wine, garlic and almond sauce. Del: 4m. Hours: 12- 2:30 / 5:30- 11.

HOT STUFF　　　　NEW ENTRANT

19 Wilcox Road, SW8 2XA　　020 7720 1480

In London's SW1 you'll find the most expensive, haute decor restaurants in the UK. Not so far away, you'll also find a gem like this one which has been around since 1988. Decor is not a consideration here, and in that respect it's like India. And that is the beauty of this

Hot Stuff's Raj Dawood

Guide. We love them at any level so long as they deliver. *'Pat, everyone is raving about it. And when you find it don't give up because it looks so drab – go in, but not before you've stocked up at the office next door. It's BYO.'* JGS. Owner, waiter (and for all I know chief bottle washer too) is Raj Dawood. Let him guide you to your meal. Whatever he suggests is good. I had bhajis for starters, £1.50, followed by. hot chilli chicken and Raj told me to have the Magic Mushroom Rice with it. What a trip! Here it's hard to spend a tenner for good gutsy Pakistani food. In between his multitasking Raj is a raconteur too. He'll tell you that 'My Beautiful Launderette' was filmed nearby, implying that the crew all ate there. It is packed at times. Hours:12-10 Mon-Fri , 3-10 Sat

London SW10
Chelsea, West Brompton

CHUTNEY MARY
OUTSTANDING RESTAURANT

535 Kings Road, SW10   020 7351 3113

Chutney Mary opened in 1990. From the beginning they had a brigade of six chefs each from a different region of India, each dispensing their own speciality dishes. This was not the first to do this, but Chutney Mary did it rather well. We are proud of the fact that we gave Chutney Mary the first ever Best Restaurant Award back in 1992. And we did it again in 1999. Owners Camellia and Namita Panjabi and Ranjit Mathrani have since become well-established in the restaurant industry and have become renowned for their high quality Indian restaurants. They next bought Veeraswamy (W1) then opened one after another revolutionary Masala Zones (See W1). and more recently, the stunning Amaya, SW1 – all Award winners in this Guide. Amaya won the ITV Tio Pepe Best Restaurant of the Year Award and in 2007 it was awarded a Michelin star. Such awards are not given lightly, and it's time Chutney Mary was similarly recognised. Upstairs there is a bright and airy private dining room. The stair wall is made of sparkling Indian mosaics (a glass ball is made, and then smashed, the pieces are then gathered to make the mosaics) and it takes you down to the main restaurant. This is decorated with works of modern Indian art, concealed spot lights, and masses of candles held in clear crystal glass, specially designed Indian glass candelabra which effectively create a romantic ambience similar to the twinkling of a moti mahal. Hi-tech lighting gives a moonlit effect to the legendary conservatory, decorated with its forest of Indian greenery, its tree and sparkling fairy lights. A sumptuous, thickly woven carpet and dark wood furniture swathed in silk cushions helps to create a luxurious yet relaxed atmosphere. The wine list by wine writer Mathew Jukes is definitive, and would do justice in any restaurant. It features over 100 wines, kept in a glassed-in, temperature-controlled wine room in the restaurant where customers can see the ideal conditions in which their wine has been kept. Jukes promises relatively low mark-ups on the more expensive wines – 'to encourage experimentation'. Taj-trained Chef Nagarajan Rubinath has taken the mantle from Hardeep Singh, who is now at the Group's Masala Zone. The menu constantly changes. although some old favourites remain constant. Some years ago, Mathrani asked me how presentation could be improved at Indian restaurants. I recall blubbering some inconsequential answer. I know now that the Panjabis already had the issue in hand. Food presentation at Chutney Mary is revolutionary and it is still unique in the Indian market. Each dish has its own bespoke high-quality white platter or handmade glass plate chosen for shape and utility. on which it is plated with its own food-layout by the chefs. Nothing illustrates this better than the starters. For example, the magnificent Tokri Chaat (see overleaf); a potato-lattice basket exudes home-made imli and yoghurt-based 'street-food' studded with fresh green coriander and red pomegranate seeds.

It not only looks good, it tastes good too, and this alone could be my last dish on earth. The Kebab Platter is equally elegant. There are other favourites: Chandini Tikka (cornfed chicken breast tikka using white spices) or Konkan Prawns with asparagus. Starters (£6.25 to £10). Main courses (£16-£22) include four different Chicken Tikkas, Duck with Apricots (a Parsee favourite – Jardaloo), fanned slices of pink duck breast, drizzled with a spicy minced sauce with halved apricots, a fab Tandoori Crab, and other modern crab dishes that are all the rage in Bombay seafood restaurants. Wild Sea bass Alleppey (pan-grilled in a coconut and coriander sauce with green tomato salsa) or Mangalore prawn curry (with chilli hot sauce with tamarind and coconut). Vegetarians have a choice of two platters – one is a traditional North Indian platter of vegetables and dhal. The other comprises unusual vegetarian dishes such as stir-fried banana flower with coconut, baby courgette masala, okra and water chestnut in a selection of 7 items. Desserts from c£6 include the legendary Dark Chocolate Fondant with orange blossom lassi. Mains come plated, which some don't like because it makes sharing hard. There is a good selection of sides and breads, including Black Urid Dal (Maharani) – [DBAC's

Chutney Mary's Tikka Selection

Above: Exemplary presentation: Chutney Mary's starter, Tokri Chaat, a potato-lattice basket exudes home-made imli and yoghurt-based 'street-food' studded with fresh green coriander and red pomegranate seeds.

CHUTNEY MARY   *(continued)*

favourite] dark, rich, creamy, aromatic spices, swirl of cream. Suffice to say, the bold redec venture paid off. The place is more gorgeous than ever. Its regular clients are back, and loving it all the more. One way to try it all is to order the Tasting Menu of seven courses at £70 per head. Chutney Mary deserved its 1992 and 1999 Awards and it deserves it again. Nobody does it better. The Panjabis are the most innovative restaurateurs in the Indian sector. They stick to their beliefs, which is to offer Indian food done exquisitely well. Chutney Mary, their first venture got off to a slow and timid start. But that was years ago. It is now a huge success and a visionary pioneer. The team are now as confident as can be, and we can only await their future ventures impatiently. Meanwhile Chutney Mary remains my all-time favourite Indian Restaurant. 3 course set lunch £17. Service: 12.5%. Jazz lunchtime Sundays. 24-seat party room upstairs. Hours: 12.30-2.30, Sat & Sun only / 6-11, daily; 10.30 Sunday. Branches: see page 1. www.realindianfood.com

MOKSSH   NEW ENTRANT

222 Fulham Rd, SW10 9NB   020 7352 6548

Mokssh, meaning 'Nirvana' is a 75-seat restaurant and late-night cocktail bar family-run by Racchitt Khanna (former Hotel Manager of the Mandarin Oriental) and brother Rohett. The interior mixes brightly coloured artifacts and sumptuous fabrics sourced from India with modern sleek lines and smooth curves. Background music is Bhangra and the venue's low seating is said to 'hark back to traditional communal eating customs whilst providing an informal lounge atmosphere'. There are now-common tapas-style items and a light lunchtime menu of wraps and salads, with an evening selection of mains and a variety of lighter items such as tandoori items. Menu snapshot: Adraki Lamb Chops, £7.75, marinated in ginger then grilled; Dhal Makhni,£6.75, black Lentils and red kidney beans tempered with ginger, garlic, butter, cream and spices; Ajwaini Prawns, £7.50 marinated in with yoghurt, lovage and fennel then chargrilled. 12-3 / 6-1. Closed Mons. www.mokssh.com

PAINTED HERON

A-LIST

112 Cheyne Walk, SW10   020 7351 5232

It's between Albert and Battersea Bridges, on a corner site. Parking is difficult; there are few single yellow lines. The restaurant is tastefully decorated, under the minimalist banner – white walls with modern prints. Tables are simply laid, white linen cloths, napkins, contemporary cutlery and a single wine balloon. Rounds of moulded glass contain coloured oil with wick to light each table inadequately. Chairs are painted black wood, seated with leather and comfortable. Lumber floors are polished and the large plate glass windows are dressed with wooden slatted blinds. We perused the menu and sipped Shiraz (£17), over a large oval platter, generously piled high with fresh Popadum strips, accompanied by three chutneys – Beetroot, Coconut and Mango and Chickpea with Chilli. All handmade and all fabulous. Staff are smilers - smart, clean and very willing. The Painted Heron's young owner decided in 2003 to get into the Indian restaurant business. It wouldn't be my advice, but he's in property and owns the building, and he seems to have an instinct for it. His ace card is his choice of chef – Yogesh Datta. He's Taj-trained, and it is amazing just how good Taj chefs are. Yogesh has

absolutely no ego (others take note). He is totally dedicated to hands-one cooking. He enjoys a challenge and he's very much hands-on. His menu, which changes every few days, has no long, meaningless narrations, just short, concise definitions, or perhaps the best explanation, honesty! And Yogesh runs the kitchen with Kansili Brahmanand (ex Sheraton India) and just one other chef. (others take note). The food sometimes has an innovative signature, but it is glorious Indian food, all carefully crafted and accurately spiced. For starters, we settled on Pheasant Breast with Green Chilli and Garlic, a good piece of foul, carbon-tinged from the Tandoor – tender meat on a minuscule bone, accompanied by a

salad flavoured with ajwain and ginger – delicious. We also had Chutney-stuffed Paneer Cheese Tikka, an oblong of exquisite handmade cheese, split into two, rather like a sandwich, stuffed with Podina (mint). As if that wasn't enough we couldn't resist Gol Goppa, a wheat-flour mini 'flying-saucer', loaded with a spicy small potato cubes drizzled with imli and a trickle of natural yoghurt. Main courses were a quarrelsome choice, with so many delectable dishes. We agreed on Chicken stuffed with green chilli pickle in hot Rajasthani curry', a very clever dish of chicken breast which Yogesh had lightly beaten, making it flat. Chilli pickle had been positioned and the chicken rolled in a cylinder then baked. The enrobing spicy, creamy sauce contained curry leaves with long slivers of lightly sautéed onion. Ingeniously innovative but very Indian in taste.'Lamb Shank with aromatic spices, was served in a impressive, round, shiny, white metal bowl with a wide flat rim. The portion was so large it could have generously fed two and was so tender it literally fell of the bone. I choose side dishes of 'Wild Mushroom Pullao', Basmati rice, oval-plated, good flavour with tonnes of garlic and delicate slices of different fungi varieties. Since giving up wheat, I am now appreciating rice much more than before and can tell the good stuff from the dud! Simply described as 'Black Lentils' urid dal, well cooked, creamy, with a whirl of fresh cream decorating it surface. Quite chilli hot, but with a full, rounded flavour, not raw. Pat requested a Mint Paratha. He thought it would harmonise his meal well and he was right. It was delivered in a basket, rolled very thinly and sprinkled with finely chopped, dried, mint leaves. Pat's words 'VERY nice.' Full to the gills, we resisted Gulab jamun with chocolate ice cream £4, or Coconut tarte with coconut ice cream and chocolate syrup £4. We were delighted to give Yogesh our Best Chef Award. Nobody anywhere does it better. Main courses from c £10. Discretionary 12.5% service charge. Garden seats. Hours: 12-2.30 weekdays. Dinner 6-11 daily. Branch: Bangalore Express, SE1.   www.thepaintedheron.com

VAMA THE INDIAN ROOM   A-LIST

438 Kings Road, SW10   020 7351 4118

Vama, meaning 'womanhood', was established in 1997 by brothers Andy and Arjun Varma. Stylishly decorated with ochre walls and teak chairs, handmade crockery from Khurja, and a fossil-stone floor. It is quite obvious to see why the 110 seat Vama is so popular. The Varmas (different spelling) are charming men, who are very relaxed chatting to their many regular clients including Lloyd Webber and Rowan Atkinson. The cuisine is North West Frontier. This takes us from the Afghan border to the Punjab. Specials: Mahi (Salmon Tikka) Ajwaini £8.75. Tandoori Jhinga, Tiger prawns marinaded in yoghurt, chilli-oil and fennel, roasted on charcoal, £13.50, being the most popular dish ordered. Mains include duck, partridge or quails. And it is a

venue where you get the rare paper-thin Romali Roti ('handkerchief bread'). We certainly rate Vama's and are delighted to keep it in our TOP 100. Good weather seating outside on the patio: four tables to choose from. Entertainment: cabaret and belly dancer. 35 seat party room. 4 patio tables. Service 12.5%. Cover charge £1. Hours: 12.30-3 / 6.30-11.30. Vama-Ji, is the brothers' Indian cuisine delivery service. Cooked at their state-of-the-art, new Central Processing Unit in Battersea it delivers to homes and businesses within a 10 mile radius of Battersea, ring 020 7736 2300. Vama-Ji have opened four concession counters and two diners in Selfridges food halls in Manchester, Birmingham and London.

London SW11 Battersea

COROMANDEL NAME CHANGE

2 Battersea Rise SW11   020 7738 0038

Previously the Swayam Ruchi Coromandel is still a south Indian restaurant with a smattering of Sri Lankan and northern dishes on offer too. It really is such a treat to see such good south Indian food served here. The chef had been at Taj Malabar Cochin, where the food is sensational. Menu Snapshot: Achappam £2.95 - a flower shaped snack made of rice flour, coconut, black sesame, cumin; Pickles and Chutneys £2.50 - mango; lemon; garlic; fish; mixed vegetable pickle and coriander chutney; Medu Vada £3.95 - soft silky dumplings, lightly fried, crisp crunchy case, made from urid dhal, black pepper, fresh green chilli served with coconut chutney; Potato Bonda £3.95 - potato balls fresh ginger, curry leaves, coriander, black mustard, dipped in chickpea flour batter, crispy fried, served with creamy coconut chutney; Konju Varathathu £5.95 - crunchy battered fried prawn with corn flour, egg, chilli, ginger, garlic. Ruchi Kadal Soup £4.25 - £3.45 - peppery broth of lentils, garlic, tomatoes, spices, tamarind; Alleppey Konju Masala £9.95 - stir-fried prawns, ginger, curry leaves, chilli, mustard seed, crushed black pepper; Crab Thoran £12.95 (one of Pat's) - crab meat stir-fried, grated coconut, green peas, shallots, mustard seeds, served in shell. 'Rasam is of my favourites, another is Erachi Olathiyathu £7.95. The first time I ate this dish, we were staying in South India, where a green lizard lived behind the bathroom mirror. The hotels' restaurant, called the Sea Shells, because of the huge shell chandeliers that hung from the ceiling, served this rich aromatic dish, flavoured with roasted coconut, turmeric, red chilli and onion. While we ate, a cockroach crawled up the wall and disappeared behind a picture. No such visitor at Swayam Ruchi though.' dbac. Back to their menu: Masala Dosa £6.95 - a paper thin pancake made of rice and black gram, folded in half with a filling of spicy potatoes, cooked with onions and ginger. 'If you have never eaten a dosa, I insist that you try one, share one! Some years ago, when we stayed at the Fort

Aguada, Goa for a weeks holiday, I ate Masala Dosa with Sambar and Coconut Chutney every day for breakfast. We then flew to Bangalore to visit Raji and Balan of Mysore Breweries. Raji laughed long and loudly, when I told her my eating habits! Rasam is her favourite too, and she serves it from a Wedgwood Florentine teapot!' dbac. Back to their menu: Beetroot Pachadi £5.95 - fresh beetroot, yoghurt, coconut, mustard seed and curry leaves; Appam £2.65 - a crispy, spongy rice pancake - delicious! Hours: 12-3 / 6- 1.

London SW12 Balham

BOMBAY BICYCLE CLUB TOP 100

95 Nightingale Lane, SW12   020 8673 6217

The Bombay Bicycle Club (BBC) was a typical Raj venue where only white civil servants and military officers were allowed. Members would take tripsto the countryside to picnic with the food delivered by cyclist servants. Like Kava Khanna (teahouses), it was a place to catch up on local Raj gossip and events. Today's BBCs are open to all who love Indian food. It has grown to three restaurants and 15 on-line delivery outlets which all have in common a great logo of a turbaned Raj-style waiter holding a serving dish while riding a penny farthing. Decor, like at Rasa, has a penchant for pink and is *'luxurious and elegant; a massive vase of flowers dominates the room, charming staff, starched white tablecloths and napkins. In the winter, it's cosy and snug, in the summer the windows and doors are thrown open, the colonial ceiling fans whir, and it all looks extremely pretty.'* RL. Hours: 7-11.

Restaurant branches: Hampstead, Holland Park. Del: Battersea, Chiswick, City, East Dulwich , Friern Barnet, Fulham, Greenwich, Islington, Little Venice, Putney, Tooting, Surbiton, West Hampstead, Wimbledon , Weybridge. www.thebombaybicycleclub.co.uk

NANGLO

88 Balham Hill Road, SW12   020 8673 4160

One of the few Nepalese restaurants in the country actually serving authentic Nepalese food, which you

should try, rather than the unnecessary curryhouse items. Modern decor invites you to tread the blonde boards and observe the bright turquoise walls. The menu invites you to try all sorts of goodies. Starters include (all £2.70): Shekpa Soup, noodles, chicken, lamb and spices. Tareko Chyau, mushrooms covered with spice lamb mince. Soaltee Alu, potato patty with lentils, onions and herbs, cooked to crisp on the tava, served with sweet yoghurt and Sekuwa goat, sadly timidly done with lamb here. Main courses: Khorsani (meaning chilli) Chicken or Lamb £5.70, fiery dish with, , ginger and yes fresh green chillies; Pokhareli Lamb with potatoes, peppers and tomatoes named after the town of Pokhara; Nepalese Sam £7.70, noodles with chicken, lamb, vegetables, served with side sauce; Fewa Fish £8.50, spicy salmon, medium hot; Pahelo Pharsi £3.50 - pumpkin, tomato and onion; Paloong Sag with spinach said to 'popular with Kathmandu farmers'. *'I am a retired Major - 6th Gurkha Rifles, who lived in Nepal for 5 years. The food we had was authentic Nepalese, very tasty, large portions. Service excellent. A clean, fresh and modern decor (no garish painting of Mount Everest! All staff Nepalese. Head chef is Anand Kumar Gurung who is cultural secretary of the Yeti Nepal Association in the UK.'* JT. Hours: 12-2.30 / 6-11.30; 12 Fri & Sat; 11 Sun.

London SW14   Putney, Sheen

MANGO & SILK   NEW ENTRANT

199 Upr Richmond Rd, SW14 8QT

020 8876 6220

The once Bombay Brasserie super-chef Udit Sarkhel, former patron of Sarkhel's SW19 has been through a bad personal patch, leading to the closure of that superb venture. His other SW14 address is now owned by Radhika Jerath, and together, they bring Udit's homestyle regional Indian cuisine to this 38-seater. *The dining room is narrow and the decor simple, with fairly comfortable wicker-backed chairs and assorted prints of Indian scenes on the cream-coloured walls. Popadums (50p) come with decent but shop-bought chutneys (mango, lime) and a home-made yoghurt and mint sauce. I began with Goan Prawn Balchao (£5.50), a few prawns in a spicy masala sauce served with Naan bread. The prawns were nicely cooked and the sauce was spicy and lively, the bread good. This was better than Bombay Ragara (£3.95), essentially a deconstructed Aloo Tikki with a vegetable pattie, curried chickpeas and chutney (mint chutney and a rather watery tamarind chutney). The chickpeas were tender but the potato pattie rather dull. Main courses also showed inconsistency. Chicken Biriani (£8.95) was advertised as being cooked in a sealed pot, so I hoped to see a clay pot with a pastry seal, as an authentic biriani should be, but instead just a dish of rice and chicken appeared. The rice was cooked nicely and the chicken was pleasant if a little dry but they are missing an opportunity here. Malai fish curry was cooked with a mild coconut curry*

sauce, but the fish itself was rather tasteless, the sauce lacking vibrant spicing. On the other hand Okra (£5.50) was excellent, cooked carefully with onions and tomatoes , Channa (£5.50) had tender chickpeas and naan bread (£1.50) was very good indeed, light and fluffy. Yet a simple bowl of steamed rice (£2.50) had a clumpy consistency. Apparently Udit is single-handed in the kitchen with just a couple of helpers, and it would appear that he is over-stretched. This is a real shame as he is a fine cook, and I would love to see him return to his best form. Meal price £30 inc wine'. AndyHayler.com. Udit is very much a hands-on chef, and yes his work can be a bit variable. But no one I know has more passion for cooking nor works harder than Udit. He must succeed. Hours: 12-2.30 /6-10.30.

YOU SAY OK

You may get a discount of you show them this Guide.

SW14: TASTE OF THE RAJ 130 Upr Richmond Rd, SW14 ~ 020 8876 8271. Owned by the charming and personable Shawkat Ahmed. Lunch and dinner daily.

London SW15   Putney

MA GOA   TOP 100

244 Upr Richmond Rd, SW15   020 8780 1767

Opened in 1993 by the Kapoor family. Deepak looks after the diners, while Sushma is the chef. In fact she's his mum, so easy on the Ma Goa gags! The restaurant seats 50 and has had a modern-look makeover. We describe Goan food in some detail on page 00. Goa is one of India's 24 states, not a country in its own right, as some think. It is on the western coast of India and, because it was Portuguese for nearly 500 years, it inherited different characteristics from the rest of India, including a small pork-eating, Christian population. Goan cooks were prized in the Raj (because they would handle beef and pork and could cook well). Until a few decades ago, Goan cooks were frequently to be found in merchant ships. In the 1960s Goa was 'discovered' by hippies, and more recently, it has been 'discovered' by holiday companies offering the cheap package at formerly beautiful, exclusive, caring hotels. Goan food is rarely found in Britain. And what of Sushma's food? As

a regular visitor to Goa, I can vouch that it's as near to home-cooking as it gets. Goan food is unique, having that Portuguese influence – any meat goes and pork is the favourite, as is the chilli. Good examples at Ma Goa are Goa Sausage £475, (Chorizo) pork meat sausage with cinnamon, cloves, garlic, palm vinegar and red chilli, topped with spicy onion salsa, and Porco Balchao, Shrimps in tomato and Goan pickling masala served with Goan steamed bread £4.50. Vindaloo £9, this is the real thing, based on the Portuguese dish, Vinho d'alhos. In the Goan version, pork is marinated with palm (toddy) vinegar, garlic and roasted spices and plenty of red Goan chillies. It is then slow-cooked to achieve maximum penetration of flavours. Ma Goa serve it in traditional earthenware. Aunty Belle Goa Lamb Tomato, clove, garlic, ghazi chilli, palm vinegar & curry leaf sauce with diced lamb £8.95. Ma's Fish Calvin Escolar steaks (white boneless fish) in a fine coconut, mustard & fenugreek seed sauce £10.50 . The daily specials board makes this restaurant an adventure. Goan delights, with unique names such as Cafreal, Balachao, Assado, Temperado, Buffalo, and Recheiado all appear at one time or another. If these dishes are new to you, advice is forthcoming. Also they do cook regional dishes other than Goan, but our advice is to stick to Goan. 'If you ask for Goan heat, you'll get it hot! For loonies like Pat, look under side orders and accompaniments for Taliwi Mirch £1 (fried green chillies in mustard oil). There are even Goan puds, such as Bebinca, a heavily sugared egg layer-cake, with cashew nuts — fantastic but sickly!' dbac. But a word of caution. Please be patient. Sushma will not be hurried in the kitchen. Relax with their chilled Portuguese Vinho Verde wine, or Ambari beer, brewed in Goa, £2.25 and nibble something while you wait for your order to be cooked. 'Had one of the best evenings we have ever had. Definitely the sort of restaurant to enjoy the whole evening. Interesting food, good portions, well presented and fabulous. Faultless service and atmosphere. Mature clientele. Not cheap, but reasonable, superb for the value.' hc. Service 12.5%. Takeaway: 10% discount. Hours: 6.30-11 Mon to Sat; 12.30–3 / 6.30-10 Sunday. Branch: 194 Wandsworth Bridge Rd, Fulham, SW6 0207 384 2122. www.ma-goa.com

MUNAL

393 Upr Richmond Rd, SW15   020 8876 3083

Khem Ranamagar established his 65-seater in 1991. You'll find at least 100 of your favourites here. But this is Nepalese and the 'always-polite' crew would love you to try some of chef Bijaya Thapa's few Nepalese items on the menu, such as the starter Momo, meat dumpling with tomato chutney. Or Sadheko Meat or chicken, marinated, cooked, served hot, mixed into a salad and quite spicy. Nepalese mains include Meat or Chicken Bhutuwa, a dry-fried dish. 'This restaurant is where I took my wife on our first dinner date together,' says RAC. 'A frosty evening but welcome was as warm as ever. Chicken Pakora and Dal Soup, served hot and spicy. Butter King Prawn (huge) Masala, Boiled Rice, Tarka Dal and Keema Nan. Only grumble, Dal was cold.' 'I just thought to tell you about my daughter's wedding reception. We agreed on a three course meal with a set menu for 45 people and champagne. The starter was Chicken Tikka, Prawns and Vegetable Samosa .The main course was a buffet style serve yourself affair. The choice was Chicken Tikka Masala, Lamb Bhutuwa and a beautiful Masala Fish Curry. Also Tarka Dhal, Rice and a wide selection of Naan breads. Dessert was a wedding cake provided by us but fruit salad and coffee was available. The cost of this was £650 which included all drinks from the bar and seven bottles of champagne.' dab. Min charge £10. Del: £12, 3m. Hours: 12-2.30 / 6-11.30 (12 Sat & Sun).

London SW16
Norbury, Streatham, Streatham Hill

CHILLI CHUTNEY   NEW ENTRANT

20 The High Parade Streatham High Road, Streatham, SW16 1EX   020 8696 0123

Neelofar Khan is young and energetic and his mission is to make authentic and contemporary Lahori food accessible to the European and young Asian palate. Deciding that what was needed was as they put it ' a thoroughly modern and vibrant ambience'. Following, they say, frequent visits to India and Pakistan to develop the concept,and source qualified Lahori chefs, the 130-seat restaurant opened in late 2003. It very soon became the official caterer for the UK Pakistan High Commission. 12-11 daily. www.chillichutney.com Branch: Chilli Chutney at Alders Mall Croydon, Surrey

SHAHEE BHEL POORI VEGAN

1547 London Road, SW16   020 8679 6275

Vegan food is vegetarian without any animal products such as dairy products and honey . Lebas Miah's licensed

75-seater, opposite Norbury Station, serves Gujarati vegetarian and some south Indian vegetarian dishes, and some of which are vegan. As you can see on page 00, there are many goodies in this style of cooking. Thalis and Dosas are still, we hear, the most popular dishes served. Specials include Chapatti Chana (hot), chick peas marinated in a balanced blend of spices and sauce, served with green coriander. Bhel poori (cold), delicious mixture of Indian savouries blended with spices and exotic sauces which make this dish unique. Dahi Vada (Bhalle) (cold), spicy black-pea-flour fritters, with yoghurt and sweet and sour sauce, all c£2. Rava Onion Dosa, a crispy onion vegetable pancake stuffed with delicately spiced potatoes, served with coconut chutney and Sambar, £4.25. Hours: 12-2.30 / 6-11.

SHAMYANA

437 Streatham High Rd, SW16   020 8679 6162

Another good value Pakistani Punjabi caff, opened by Mohammed Tanveer in 1998. No frills. Seats a huge 130 in two black-and-white tiled floored rooms. Enormous menu, some 130 dishes, cooked in an open kitchen. Starters: Masala Fish (white fish in spicy sauce), Dhal Bhajia (spiced lentils deep-fried in chicken pea dough), Zeera Chicken Wings £2.50 (wings marinated in spicy sauce). Main courses: Masala Karela Gosht (lamb cubes cooked with bitter gourd), Ginger Chicken, Lamb Biriani (lamb with stock flavouring the rice). BYO. Daily specials. Del: 3m, £14 min. Service 10%. 50 space car park at rear. Set lunch: £5. Sunday buffet £5.50, 12-6, Hours: 12-12.

London SW17   Tooting

Upper Tooting Road (UTR) has reached a maturity, though with less street (pavement) trading than Southall. For years, the area has reflected the varied roots of its Asian population. In the half a mile, between Tooting Bec and Tooting Broadway tube stations, there are restaurants serving nearly every style of authentic food from the subcontinent. Nowhere else in the world has such variety cheek by jowl. South Indian restaurants include Sree Krishna, 192 UTR, Radha Krishna Bhavan, 86, and Kolam, 58. There are now more than one Sri Lankan outlets, the best of which is still Jaffna at the Broadway. Milan, 158 UTR and Gossip, 180 are two Gujarati vegetarian havens, and largely vegetarian Kenyan Asian food is to be found at Kadiri, 32 UTR, and Kastoori, 188, while at Masaladar, 121, you get this food plus Bhel Poori and meat curries alike. Handis, 164 and Lahore Karahi at the Broadway are Pakistan and fill the carnivore gap, Southall-style. As if that were not enough there are two formula Bangladeshi curry houses, the Peacock, 242, Calcutta Indian, 116, and Raja, 169. Veggy Indian sweet and snack takeaways include Ambala, 48, and Alaudin, 98, with Royal beyond UTR (north of Tooting Bec). The shops are getting better and more varied. Competition is rife with more and more excellent rivals opening, all displaying their wares on UTR itself, many until late, every day including Sundays. Sakoni, 204-208 UTR, is still the best Asian veg shop in London and there is no better Asian grocer than next-door Dadus, 210. There are several Sri Lankan grocers too. Utensils shops, sari boutiques and halal butchers have sprung up too. My prediction that parking would become impossible has come to pass. But with the tube so convenient, UTR is an all-day curryholic's theme park. Here's more detail:

APOLLO BANANA LEAF   NEW ENTRANT

190 Totting High Rd, SW17 0SF

Tamil decor (dysfunctional) and Sri Lankan Tamil food highly functional and you can't eat the art'. No regard is paid to the Scoville scale and if you like mild, it's hot, hotter hotter. Dosa, Rasams, Hoppers, Black Curries, Devilled dishes ~ it's all here for a minimal cost made even nicer with BYO (it's U) and no corkage. Hard to spend a tenner yet credit cards OK. Hours 11-11.

HANDIS

164 Upr Tooting Rd, SW17   020 8672 6037

A 60-seater Pakistani restaurant owned by Mrs S Sheikh and managed by Mr J Sheikh. Cooking is down one entire side. The Handi, a cooking pot, and dishes are served either in this or in the karahi. It's kebabs, tikkas, tandoori meat and chicken dishes in which this type of venue excels. There are a number of Punjabi-style vegetable dishes, such as Aloo Sag, and well cooked side dishes. One correspondent loves their chupattis. CT. Hours: 11-11.

JAFFNA HOUSE   A-LIST

90 High Street, SW17   020 8672 7786

We are often asked how do you choose a restaurant to go into the Guide. Our answer that four letter word beginning with 'C' : Care. This means the service is good and above all the food is good. Michelin have a different perspective, and good luck to them, because Jaffna house will never ever win a Michelin Star, yet they can cook better than-90% of the UK's Michelin-starred chefs. For those who must have meaty tandoori items and north-Indian curries, you've got your own side entrance and dining room, with food cooked by Aziz and Kannan. I've no idea how good it is; but do enjoy (and tell us about it, if you like). Where the serious palates boldly go (through the front door) is into K Sivalogarajah's and M Sivanandan's Tooting Broadway place, which built its name on its authentic, no compromise, chilli hot (as-it-should-be) Sri Lankan and south-Indian dishes with its particularly popular different Friday, Saturday and Sunday specials. Tastebud-tantalising stuff like Vadai – gram flour

doughnut, drenched in home made yoghurt and sprinkled with garam and (if you are lucky) chopped fresh green chilli, Masala Dosa £1.75 – must be one of the cheapest in the country. Sri Lankan specials are delightful, with Pat's benchmark crab curry scoring really high because it was searingly hot, and used fresh crab. *'Wow!! this was the second TOP 100 restaurant in 24 hours. lucky or what !'* [Yes] *'and we didn't break £50! I have LOVED this restaurant/cafe for years, eight or nine at least. It remains magnificent value for wonderful food. Potato Bondas and Onion Bhajia simply the best, and this before we got to Mushroom Curry, Chana Curry, Coconut Rice – fragrant and so light, almost floated off the plate! Vegetable Kottho – substantial, full of fresh vegetables. Curries clearly freshly prepared, very chilli-hot, just beautiful. We were stuffed full, long before we finished the food. all for £9!! Wonderful!!!'* AG. *'We holidayed in Sri Lanka and were longing to try the food again. Starters were the best – delicious Masala Dosa and lovely spicy Devilled Chicken which was very reminiscent of the food we had sampled in Sri Lanka. Chicken and String Hoppers, but they came all mixed together, which made it taste a bit like vermicelli or chow mein – anyway I shall definitely try again.'* NP. Set lunch: c£5 from 12-3. Hours: 12-12.

KADIRI

32 Upper Tooting Rd, SW17   020 8672 0710

A Kenyan Asian licensed restaurant, it does tandooris, kebabs, and regular curries and all the trimmings. Try Cassava chips (mogo) with imli as a good substitute for popadums, served with authentic imli, sweet and sour tamarind chutney. Fried fish Masala, Thali Hui Jhinga, breadcrumbed, deep-fried prawns, and Tandoori King fish, that tasty fish so loved in south India, are three unusual starters. Jeera Chicken or Butter Chicken are *'just like the Brilliant's'* AN. (see Southall Middlesex) while BD was *'smitten by the biriani.'*

KASTOORI PURE VEGETARIAN

188 Upper Tooting Rd, SW17   020 8767 7027

The Thanki family hail from Kathiyawad in Gujarat, via Kenya and specialise in both Gujarati and Kenyan-Asian vegetarian and vegan dishes. The former include Veg Samosas, Dahi Vadai, Kadhi (yoghurt and besan sauce, with dumplings), and Katia Wahd, a tomato-based curry and Karela Bharah, stuffed bitter gourd. Cassava Chips, Chilli Banana, £4.50 (green banana stuffed with chillies and served with pickle), Kasodi, c£4.50 (sweetcorn in a peanut and yoghurt-based sauce), and Matoki, plantain curry. Their Bhel Puri is a crunchy snip at c£2.50, but their Corn Bhel didn't work for RL: *'I hoped for a new type of Bhel Puri, but this was a salad of diced potato, tomatoes and canned sweetcorn mixed with imli (tamarind sauce).'* This is one of the few places where you can experience Bhatura, giant puri bread, £1, which puffs up to balloon-size when deep-fried. Thali curry selection is extraordinary. Hours: 12.30-2.30 (Mon. & Tues. closed) /6-10.30, daily.

KOLAM

58 Upper Tooting Rd SW17   020 8767 2514

Established in 1982 by S Rajakumar. Seats 52 in one long thin dining room. The food is authentic South Indian, as they have it in Tamil Nadu, plus standard north Indian items. Service is very friendly, albeit at freeze-frame slowness. Mañana is far too fast, which reminds one greatly of India. Patience will reward you with a good inexpensive meal, and, as ever, go for the South Indian delights, which is what they know best. BYO allowed: £1 corkage. Hours: 12-2.30 Tues-Sun / 6-11, daily (12 Sat).

LAHORE DREAMS

200 Upper Tooting Rd SW17   020 8682 9777

Average £14-£17. Unlicensed. No corkage charge. This is quite an upmarket restaurant (for Tooting) which adds to the super local mix. The food is Pakistani and the decor evokes the Moghul Lahori atmosphere (Lahore was one of the emperors' four major fortress-cities). So none of your minimalist décor, hard surfaces and and lurid dayglow colours. Here it is olde-worlde Indi-pics on the walls, carved chairs and lamps and good old sensible service. But it is Tooting, so expect ridiculous prices; cheap that is! Buffet lunch £5 / £8 dinner eat your fill. Even a la-carte won't set you back more than c£15, and it's unlicensed with BYO with no corkage. Hours: 12-11.30.

LAHORE KARAHI

1 High Street, SW17   020 8767 2477

This was the first Karahi-house on Tooting Broadway opening in 1995. It has been copied a fair bit so the formula is now quite well-known; stand at the counter and order your takeaway – or if you plan to eat in, sit down and wait to be served, with the cooking on view. Typical Pakistani Kebab House menu. Starters include: Masala Fish, chunks of marinated fish, fried. Sheek Kebabs. Main courses: Chicken Jalfrezi. Veggies might try the Karahi Karela, bitter gourd, Methi Aloo or saag Paneer. Cash preferred. No credit cards. Unlicensed, BYO, no corkage. Average meal £10. Hours: 12-12.

MASALEDAR

121 Upper Tooting Rd, SW17   020 8767 7676

Smart frontage with its smoky plate-glass window Terracotta tiles on split-level floors. Plants in pots and trailing leaves. Smart up-lighters behind large halved karahis. You can sit outside watching all this through that window, at the five pavement tables. Service is slow, but they really do cook it fresh to order in the open kitchen. Many old favourites on the menu, all good. Starters include Bhel Puri, and Mandazi, samosa-shaped

deep-fried bread with an African-Asian name. Mains: *'Rich, vivid Punjabi-type curries. Ginger Chicken and Methi Gosht very good. Cumin-flavoured Pilaw Rice (just like you get in Rusholme). Reasonable prices, thoroughly recommended.'* JR. Seek out the unusual: Dekchi Gosht, Halal mutton, on-the-bone, slow-cooked in a metal-waisted cooking utensil without handles. Strict Muslim rules apply: no alcohol permitted so BYO is not permitted. Credit cards accepted. Branch: Norbury, Middx. Hours: 12-12.

MILAN VEGETARIAN

158 Upper Tooting Rd, SW17 020 8767 4347

Taj Mehta's vegetarian café is just the sort of place we like to recommend. It's unpretentious, unexpectedly licensed and air-conditioned. But for the vegetarian, what more could you ask for. If I were you, I'd ask for popadums and their adorable fresh home-made relishes. Next I'd ask for their fabulous Bhel Poori. I'd avoid the Masala Dosa (they do it better at Sree Krishna), and I'd go for its subtly-spiced Gujarati curries, made largely from besan flour and yoghurt, spiced with turmeric and curry leaves. If it's new to you, ask for help. The dish of the day is always a good option. And do try the fresh Rotla (millet bread). Leave some room for the terrific Indian sweets on display. And buy some fresh 'Bombay mix' items. For a complete filling meal, try the Thali – a good selection of vegetarian curries including something sweet for pudding – at £6 a real feast. *'Another good one'* SM. Minimum charge still a ridiculous £2. Average meal under £10. Takes no credit cards so cash needed. Sunday lunch £5.75. Hours: 10-10.

PEACOCK TANDOORI

242 Upper Tooting Rd, SW17 020 8672 8770

When this 50-seater curry house opened in 1988, Tooting's current crop of fine authentic restaurants didn't exist. But the Peacock has stood the test of time. Owned and managed by Mr Yogi Anand, it does the formula to a high standard. Well, it has to being on that street! But look for the unusual, for example, Paneer Pakora (curd cheese, dipped in spiced gram batter and fried), Brinjal Pakora (sliced aubergine coated with batter and fried, served with salad) as starters. Mains: Sag Kamal Kakri (lotus roots cooked with spinach and onion), Batair e Khas £7.95 (quails in mild curry sauce with fresh coriander). Weekend buffet c£8 (u12, half price). Service 10%. Takeaway: 10% disc. Hours: 6-12.

RADHA KRISHNA BHAVAN   TOP 100

86 Tooting High Street, SW17   020 8682 0969

This restaurant was opened in 1999 by H.K.Haridas, an experienced Keralan restaurateur, following a partnership row at the Sree Krishna. Haridas got the head chef and set up this Krishna down the road. It

specialises in South Indian Keralan cuisine, with dishes from the cities of Cochin, Malabar and Travancore. Have the Rasam (hot and spicy soup, with floating slivers of garlic, curry leaves and a red chilli! – this is a DBAC benchmark, which if she doesn't get hiccups, it's not hot enough for her!). Masala Dosa, Sambar and Coconut Chutney are as good as it gets. Some have that choice for starters and go on to curries. I don't know how they do it – I'm too full for it. But the curries are worth trying. You can stay vegetarian if you like. All their vegetable curries are spot on. Contrary to popular belief, meat, chicken and fish dishes are commonplace. Even the Chicken Korma (if you must) is given the South Indian touch – creamy, coconut with ground almond. But don't forget the wonderful Lamb Cutlets (patties of spicy minced lamb, bread crumbed and fried, served with tomato sauce and salad), King Prawn Fry (with ginger, garlic, spices and sliced coconut), Malabar Chicken (with coconut, curry leaves, garlic and mustard), Spinach Vadai £3 (fried crunchy doughnut of Chana dal, green chillies, onion, ginger, curry leaves and fresh spinach served with chutneys). And if you have any room left Banana Leaf Cake, rice with sweet filling of coconut, banana and jaggery wrapped in banana leaf and steamed – divine. Mains from £2.50 to £7, Sunday Thalis, £7-£9. Min ch: £6. Service 10%. Licensed. Credit cards OK. Hours: 12-3 / 6-11;(12 Fri & Sat).

SREE KRISHNA   TOP 100

192 Tooting High St, SW17   020 8672 4250

Pravin Pillai's Sree (pron Shree) was the the original Tooting Krishna restaurant. And now there are three (see Radha above and Vijaya below). Regular readers know it's a regular haunt of ours, involving a round-trip of 90 miles. Look out for the corner site on the left (coming in to London). Parking is usually OK in the evening. Despite a redec it retains all the old charm which lets you pretend you are in India while you indulge in no-nonsense, efficient and friendly service., and they're used to full houses (120 seats). The menu offers all the same south Indian items as Radha, and this Krishna cooks them just as competently and accurately. To me there's too much curry house food being dispensed. Blame the customers for demanding it, I suppose, but they should go the the Peacock, and leave

the Krishna to do what they do best, which is anything South Indian, and preferably vegetarian. It's more satisfying than any carnivore realises. So read the caveat, and note we retain its TOP 100 cachet. Set thalis, Sun lunch, £6-£8. Service 10%. Credit cards OK. Hours: 12-3 Sun-Thur; 6-11 Mon-Thur; to 1145 Fri & Sat.

VIJAYA KRISHNA   TOP 100

114 Mitcham Road, SW17   020 8767 7688

The third Krishna in the trilogy opened in 1995 by Vijayan Mullath who also manages front of house at his 40-seater and keeps a watchful eye on the kitchen, where he poached the sous chef from Sree Krishna at the time of the partnership row. His restaurant is decorated with scenes of South India. The Keralan specialities don't disappoint. Popular authentic dishes such as Masala Dosai, a light rice flour pancake, rolled over a firm, gently spiced potato curry, Avial, a fluid curry made with yoghurt and mixed vegetables, and Sambar, a runny lentil curry (see definitions in A-Z glossary, from page 64) *'containing, if you are lucky, many drumsticks, with which you are to scrape the flesh off with your teeth – lovely'* says DBAC, who also enjoyed Kozhi Varutha Curry, chicken in garlic and coriander sauce. Green Banana Bhajia are served. PS, she adds: *'please ignore the curryhouse favourites and enjoy Kerala!'* Del: 2m, £12 min. Serv: 10%. Hours: 12-3/6-11; 12 Fri & Sat.

London SW18
Earlsfield, Southfields, Wandsworth

KATHJMANDU VALLEY

5 West Hill, Wandsworth, SW18
                                                 020 8871 0240

Owner Uttam Basnet, took over the reigns of this very cosy 38-seater in 2005 and serves Nepalese delights. Remember that Nepal boarders India and China, so don't be surprised to see Spring Rolls £2.25 on the menu. Menu Snapshot: Kalejo Bhutuwa £3.50 - chicken livers fried with Nepalese spices - a favourite of mine; Lamb Sekuwa £6.50 - Nepalese spiced tandoor lamb chops; Chicken Chitwan £6.95 - spicy hot; Gurkha's Lamb £7.50 - with tomatoes; Nepalese Murgh Masala c£7 - spicy sauce, mushrooms and peas. Licensed: stocks Cobra £3 a bottle, house wine c£9. Del: 3m, £7 min. Hours: 6-11.45; 12 Sat. <www.kathmanduvalley.com>

YOU SAY OK
You may get a discount of you show them this Guide.

SW20: HOUSE OF SPICE Kingston Road, SW20 ~ 020 8542 4838

London SW19   Colliers Wood

SUVAI ARUVI

96 High St, Colliers Wood, SW19
                                                 020 8543 6266

For such a small venue, the range of Sri Lankan food on offer is impressive. Devilled dishes (prawn, meat and chicken are suitably hot, and the Kotthu Roti (slices of Sri Lankan flatbread, chopped up with curry), is light and moreish. Sambols, such as Sambol (coconut or onion chutney) are a must, as are Hoppers (noodles). The takeaway trade is brisker than the sit-in. No credit cards. Cash needed. Hours: 11am-midnight daily.

London SW20   Raynes Park

COCUM

9 Approach Rd, SW20   020 8540 3250

Cocum or Kokum is a plum-like, dark, purple-black fruit, dried by wood-smoking. Also called Fish Tamarind, Kodam Puli, Kudam Pulli, etc. the words Kodam Puli are Malayalam (language of south India) for 'fish' and 'tamarind' (puli). However it is neither, but it gives us the clues that it is sour and used with fish. It is used by Kerala's small Syrian Christian community at Travancore Unlike most Keralans they eat offal, chicken, duck, fish, shellfish, beef, and wild boar. 'So what do we find at Cocum, SW19 *'No glamourous decor, but a friendly welcome and swift seating and advice to try the fish and prawn pickles with Achappam (flower-shaped wafers made of riceflour and coconut with black sesame, soonf and cumin seeds). Their fish dishes included Meen Vevichadu, red in colour and flavoured with cocum and chilli. Vevichathu Surmai (Kingfish) also uses cocum. Meen Patiichadu with mango and coconut chippings. There are plenty of vegetable dishes and we had Thoran and Lemon Rice. Again taking advice we had Payasam, rice-pudding boiled with coconut milk and jaggery and garnish with fried cashew nuts. Open slip noted.'* Main courses £4 - c£8. Service charge: 10%. . Takeaway and del:3m over £15. Hours: 12-2.30 Sat-Thur; 5.30-11 Mon-Thur; 11.30 Fri & Sat; 10.30 Sun.

London W
Area: West End
Postcode: W1
and West London
W2 to W14
Population: 630,000

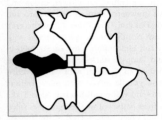

See page 72 for key to this map.

London W1
The West End

ANWARS   TOP 100

64 Grafton Way, Tottenham Court Rd, W1
020 7387 6664

Treat Anwars as the forerunner to the numerous successful Lahore Kebab Houses. It opened in 1962 as a 52-seater to serve local Asians, drawn to the area to buy spices next door at the then renowned Bombay Emporium, which later closed and went on to become BE International (Rajah brand), which is now owned by ABF. Anwar's itself was taken over in 1985 by Muhammad Afzal Zahid. who keeps to the old ways. It serves gutsy, spicy Pakistani food. You walk in, make your choice from the dishes of the day (no menu as such) on display in the serving counter, pay – they do accept credit cards – then carry your tray to a formica table, jugs of water in place, and enjoy it. *'Everything, including bhajis and naan bread, is microwaved. Seekh kebabs, Karahi Gosht was really tasty. ambience and, more importantly, the food all remain unchanged. Set lunch, £6 for Chicken Curry, ladle of mixed vegetables, ladle of Chana, ladle of Sag Aloo over a mound of rice, with a Puri and a cup of tea.'* MW. The vegetarian version is £5. Unlicensed, BYO no charge. Hours: 12-11, daily.

BENARES   TOP 100

12 Berkeley Sq, W1J 6BS   020 7629 8886

Benares is named after India's holiest city (formerly Varanassi). Upstairs is an expensive, architect-designed shiny black granite bar area, with smart Indian furniture hidden between ornate wooden partitions and the water pool with floating candles and petals. The Benares Bellini mixed with liqueur mango, passion fruit or strawberry-topped, with prosecco, is very popular. They serve bar snacks such as mini vegetable parcels with mint and tamarind chutney and crisp fried cod in a spicy batter. There are three private dining rooms off this area. The main dining room has polished grey limestone flooring, textured and sculpted white walls, and interspersed with artifacts, and is undoubtedly expensive but unexceptional. Chef Atul Kochhar is Oberoi-trained and worked at their Delhi Hotel. He was poached by an Indian magnate who opened Tamarind in 1994. At first Atul was understaffed and produced timidly spiced dishes for an underwhelmed clientele. But we saw the talent and awarded Tamarind our MOST PROMISING NEWCOMER AWARD in its first year (1995), Best Indian 1998 and best chef 2000 which finally caught the attention of Michelin. *'As part of his culinary exploration Atul's menu has a monthly regional menu. Starters such as Makali Sukhem (squid salad with coconut shavings, coriander leaves and tamarind) and Jal Tarang (a salad of scallops, prawns and oyster fritters with grapes-ginger dressing) are unmistakably Indian dishes presented in a modern European style. Main courses range from the traditional Murgh Makhani and Roghan Josh to Lagosta Xec Xec Goan lobster and prawn masala, served with tomato and red onion salad. The restaurant also holds regular master classes, where groups of between four and six are invited into the kitchen for two hours at a time, where they can be privy to Atul's kitchen secrets'.* PV. *'Having failed again to get into Cinnamon Club, we tried Benares, how different. We were spoken to as if we were actually human diners and not nuisances. the reservation was for 8.30pm and we did have a few minutes wait in the bar while a lovely corner table was relaid. The bar area is very attractive with a pool covered with rose petals. The main dining room is large, light and plainly modern, certainly not obviously Indian. The atmosphere was wonderful. From its reputation, it had a lot to live up to, and it excelled. The menu is fantastic with a modern twist to traditional dishes. The food was sensational and beautifully presented. The service was excellent and it was a fantastic experience. Mixed tandoori starter, chicken, huge prawn (fabulous) and lamb served with a delicious chutney, Soft shell crab, the restaurant's signature starter, superb, a whole crab spread out over the plate over a pile of purple potato, spicy squid and delicate salad, a wonderful dish. Brinjal in a coconut sauce, outstanding. The food is expensive but fairly typical for Mayfair. Starters £12 to £16, main courses £18 to £38. Wines are expensive, but quality. We did not have desserts but were very tempting and very ornately presented. We cannot praise this restaurant too highly. £149 for two, expensive but not outrageous.'* HC. Of course Atul has become a star TV chef now and he works less and less at Benares. He is planning new ventures at Wickham Vineyards, Southampton, Canary Wharf, and in Westfield, Shepherd's Bush, W6 which will prove interesting. Service charge 12.5%. Hours: 12-2.30 weekdays / 5.30-10.30 Mon to Sat; 6-10 Sun. www.benaresrestaurant.com

CAFE T

Asia House, 63 New Cavendish Street, W1
0207 7307 5454

Asia House promotes the arts and cultures of countries from Iran to Japan and from the Central Asian Republics to Indonesia. It stages talks, events and conferences, lectures and performances and regularly changing art exhibitions. Cyrus Todiwala's new venture opened in 2006. The name Café T comes from the wide range of teas offered as well coffees, a light lunches with wine or Asian beers or afternoon teas. It serves pan-Asian snacks curries sandwiches and soups. For example: Thai prawn & coriander baguette, £4.45, prawns, tossed with Thai green curry mayonnaise; Frango Espeto Peri-Peri, £4.45,Chicken marinated in Goan style peri-peri masala, chargrilled, sliced and filled with sliced cucumber, tomato & coriander. Country Chicken, £4.25 from the Taj Mahal Hotel, chargrilled chicken tikka finely diced blended with mayonnaise, finely minced chilli,mango chutney, mustard & fresh coriander. Mains include Parsee Lamb Dhansak, £9.25 served with brown onion & star anise flavoured rice and a meatball kebab and Vindalho de Porco £7.75 the classical Goan version. There is even Bento Box £13.95. Hours: 11-5, Mon-Sat, 1pm. Closed on Sundays & All Bank Holidays

CHOR BIZARRE   A-LIST

16 Albemarle St, W1S 4HW   020 7629 9802

Delhi's Chor Bazaar is a kind of permanent cart-boot-sale, where you can buy anything at knockdown prices. Meaning 'thieves' market' it was originally the place where the villains pushed stolen goods. Entrepreneur Rohit Khattar, owner of Delhi's 32-room Hotel Broadway, hit on the idea to exploit this image. The hotel restaurant needed a revamp, and he cannily renamed it Chor Bizarre exploiting the linguistic twist from 'Bazaar' to 'Bizarre'. The spin told Delhi it was furnished from the real Chor Bazaar. No two chairs or tables are the same. An aged car is the salad bar, and it took Delhi by storm. Mr Khattar set his eyes on Mayfair. When Mahendra Kaul's 85-seat Gaylord site became available, in 1997, it was perfect. Managed by Anshuman Saxena If you dine alone, you won't be bored; there is so much to look at in this fabulously interesting restaurant. 'Antiquities' abound. As in Delhi, everything is mismatched, all the chairs and tables are different; one, for example is encased in an '18th-

century four-poster bed' from Calcutta. Sadly Mayfair is spared the car. Chefs Deepinder Sondhi and Manpreet Ahujas cook dishes from all India but specialise in Kashmiri dishes. It is the only UK restaurant where you can get Goshtaba. '*It's one of a Wazwan wedding feast dishes where velvety spheres of finely minced lamb are flavoured with cardamom and cooked in a yoghurt sauce.*' DBAC. Menu Snapshot: Pakoras £5, assortment of batter fried spinach, aubergine, cauliflower, onion and potato served with strawberry chutney and tomato and white radish salad; Dakshni Crab cakes £7, white crab meat flavoured with South Indian spices served with salad and chutney and Shikampuri Kaba £6.50, melt in the mouth ground lamb kofta kabab flavoured with cinnamon & cardamom stuffed with spiced curd prepared on an iron griddle served with mint yoghurt chutney and tomato and white radish salad; Aloo Tikka Chaat £5.50, pan fried patties of mashed potatoes filled with spiced lentil and green peas, served warm, topped with yoghurt, and mint chutney. However, if you feel like a slightly more substantial starter then go for the Tak-a-Tan Kaleki £6.50 from Pakistan; after the chef starts frying the dish, in this case chicken liver tossed with coriander-flavoured masala, he takes the two steel, flat-edged spatulas and rapidly bangs them one after the other on to the pan to chop, mash and mix the ingredients. The dish gets its name from the noise made – taka-taka-taka-tan. It is served with a flaky Reshmi Parantha. The Tandoori items are also very good, especially the Adraki Chaampen £18, tender lamb chops marinated with fresh ginger and tandoori spices. Now for the main courses: do try the Baghare Baingan £8, a Hyderabad favourite, sautéed aubergine simmered in piquant peanut, and sesame-seed sauce. Main course Chicken Chettinnad £13 turns up on many a menu, usually cooked totally incorrectly. But here it's perfect, cooked in a hot sauce with a predominant flavour of pepper, aniseed and curry leaves. It comes from Tamil Nadu and is wonderful eaten with a Malabar Parootha £3, a south Indian layered paratha (good for mopping up the sauce!). Other Kashmiri dishes include Nadroo Yakhani, lotus stem in spiced yoghurt gravy. Marz Wangun Korma, lamb cooked with loads of Kashmiri chillies (yes chillies in a Korma) with cardamom and cloves; Haaq, spinach cooked with aniseed and Rajmah, red kidney beans and Chaaman, (lotus stem). A neat way to try these and other Kashmiri dishes is to order the Tarami c£30. Our benchmark Dal Makhni, thick black lentil flavoured with tomatoes and cream, immersed overnight on the tandoor; here it's masterly. '*We probably spent more time standing outside deciding whether or not we could afford to go in than actually eating! Once inside, it didn't disappoint. Food, it has to be said, was fantastic but expensive so baked beans for a week.*' AR. '*Friendly service, cheerful and efficient. Absolutely superb food, well spiced, good initial ingredients in good portions. A first class lunch – lucky that my new office is in the same street! £97 for two, very typical for lunch in Mayfair.*' DRC. Wines matched to each

dish by Charles Metcalfe, available by the glass. Culture evenings: e.g. book readings, comedy evenings, creative writing workshops to theatre/movie festivals. Food festivals. Private room downstairs, seats 30. Serv 12.5%. 12-3/6-11.30, 10.30, Sun. www.oldworldhospitality.com

CHOWKI   TOP 100

2 Denman Street, W1D 7HA   020 7439 1330

Chef Kuldeep Singh spearheads a valuable group of restaurants. Valuable because their food is expertly cooked, and is real Indian food. He opened Mela in 2000, and to prove its success Chowki opened in 2002, in a short street behind Eros, better known for its formula curry houses. But Chowki isn't one of those. Indeed Kuldeep's mission is ' *to return to the roots of India's culinary tradition.*' Operating with 120 seats in three areas, it changes parts of its menu monthly, with food from three different Indian regions at a time. And with the chef brigade all being Taj-trained it's well within their capabilities to cook highly accurate dishes. For example it's Punjab, Sikkim and Kerala one month, then Pakistan, Calcutta and Coorg another, and so on. The format is three starters and four mains from each region, all available a-la-carte, or priced at £11.95 for three mains and any four starters, and with lunch from £6.50, you can't complain (except you do, about the uncomfortable seats mostly). It's cheap and cheerful. Busy at peak times but usefully open all day: 12-11.30; 10.30 Sun. Branches: Dilli Manchester, Mela, Croydon Surrey & WC2, Soho Spice W1.   www.chowki.com

GAYLORD   TOP 100

79 Mortimer Street, W1W 7SJ   020 7580 3615

When it opened in 1963 Gaylord was not only Britain's first upmarket Indian restaurant, it also pioneered the Tandoori oven in Britain. The name is a play on the names of the original owners Gai and Lamba, who had opened one of Delhi's very first Indian restaurants called Kwality in 1948. By the 50's there were Kwalities all over India. But they were little more than caffs. Having made a fortune producing ice-cream, the pair decided to go upmarket, with their first Gaylord which opened in Delhi in 1958. Other branches followed soon after in Bombay, San Francisco, Kowloon, Kobe Japan, Bahamas and Manchester. '*We enjoy excellent quality curries and the dining experience is very important as we make a night of it. All four of us agreed it was a wonderful curry with such different tastes. We started with tandoori fish, onion pakora, vegetable samosa and chicken chat. The starters were good quality with the chicken chat being made up into a salad, very interesting and quite spicy, but not too spicy. Chutneys were good with an especially hot green 'harassi like' substance the favourite of us all, though to be used with caution. Diane had to wait for her starter of samosa a bit longer than the rest of us because according to the waiter the chef had discarded the first lot because they were not up to standard!!! (A good sign I*

think) Main courses were superb, sag chicken – the best we've ever tasted! Chilli chicken tikka had an excellent char grilled flavour, chilli lamb was some of the tenderest lamb ever in a curry and my Chana Kabuli was stunning, very hot with lots of taste and small pieces of raw chilli – all excellent. The side dishes were good too, with Aloo Zeera being our favourite'. KW. Serv 15%. Cover cha: £1.20 – includes a Popadum and pickle. Delivery. Takeaway: 10% disc. Hours: 12-3 / 6-11.30; 11 Sun.

GOPALS OF SOHO

12 Bateman Street, W1   020 7434 1621

Gopal, real name NT Pittal, was Amin Ali's exec chef first at the Lal Qila, then at the celebrated Red Fort whose names he helped to build by cooking superb food. Feeling his career was going nowhere, he opened his own restaurant in 1990, and the accolades poured in. Mr Pital jnr, Gopal's son, runs the place while Dad competently cooks classic Indian food to the standard menu, with the full range of starters from bhaji to kebabs, tandoori and curries, but a closer look reveals specials from Goa to Kashmir, Lucknow to Hyderabad: 'Father of a French student came over for a conference at OFSTED Headquarters. I met him at the appointed hour, to be faced with the prospect of an evening with not one, but six Inspectors – his colleagues coming along as well!!! I had done by homework the night before. I called up Gopal's on my mobile – I had stored the number – reserved a table and whistled up a couple of cabs. Gopal's was very good indeed, helpful with the menu, and very tasty indeed.' JRG. Hours: 12-3 /6-1.30.

IMLI   A-LIST

167 Wardour St W1F 8WR   020 7287 4243

'Imli' in Hindi means 'Tamarind' and this gives you the clue that Michelin-starred restaurant, Tamarind has branched out with a new baby – a casually sophisticated eatery in London's West End. Spread across 2,000 square feet over two floors, Imli is a 124-seater casual and informal all-day diner. To decor delicately blends the simplicity of the modern world and combines it with traditional Indian elements including an eclectic mix of Indian art and artifacts. Modern characteristics of bold form, colour and scale are mixed and layered with traditional Indian elements of craft, pattern, and texture to create a unique and inspiring culinary experience. Tamarind's Sous Chef, Samir Sadekar was promoted to the role of Executive Chef at Imli. Originally from Goa, Samir studied Hotel Management at India's prestigious Institute of Hotel Management in Bombay, and then spent two years training at the Maurya Sheraton, where he cheffed at the world-class Dum Pukht and Bukhara restaurants. Samir has created an exciting menu, taking influence from the dabbas (roadside stalls) mainly of the coastal areas of southern and western India. The 'light and refreshing' dishes are the ultimate in snack foods Papdi Chat £3.95, whole wheat crisps and bean sprouts with vermicelli, sweet yoghurt and mint chutney; Bhel Puri £3.85, a medley of puffed rice, cucumbers and roasted peanuts tossed with assorted chutney ; Dahi

Pakodi £3.75, lentil dumplings stuffed with crushed coriander and raisins topped with yoghurt and chutney; Ragda Potato £3.95, crispy potato cakes topped with yellow peas and chutney; Crab and Prawn Cakes £4.75, combined with creamed corn, served with roasted red peppers; Chicken Shammi £4.45, pan fried chicken cakes with brown onion and ginger served with mint chutney. If you feel you can manage a little more then choose three dishes from the main tapas menu, Chennai Fish £5.45, batter-fried tilapia fish with paprika and curry leaf, served with mint chutney; Prawn Masala £7.25, simmered in a cumin and ajwain masala sauce served with rice; Masala Grilled Chicken £7.50, with coriander and avocado dip, served with cumin and turmeric mash; Southern lamb £5.95, lamb sautéed with chillies, coconut and south Indian spices, served with rice. Desserts include Indian Caramel Custard £3.50, coconut milk and jaggery crème caramel. Formidable value are the 'tasting' menus starting at c£17. At affordable prices, even with the service charge of 12.5%. Imli proves that London's west end need not break the bank. Takeaway available. They claim max wait time, if any, is 10 minutes. Rajesh Suri Group CEO launched a new cocktail bar in 2008 'introducing exotic Eastern-inspired drinks'. Here are three of DBAC's favourites, Bollywood Bash, gin, whisky and triple sec, topped with orange juice; Bombay Crush, white rum, orange curaçao, topped with lemonade and Sunrise in Goa, vodka, white rum, topped with lychee juice and grenadine syrup, fabulous! All cocktails are priced at £5.50. Del: £15 min to W1. Hours: 12-12, Sun to 10. (On Fri & Sat nights bookings are only taken for 4 or more people.) Branch Tamarind, W1.   www.imli.co.uk

INDIAN YMCA CANTEEN   TOP 100

45 Fitzroy Street, W1 6AQ   020 7387 0411

Like this place, this entry hardly changes, though the acceptance of credit cards, a longer lunch time and non-resident access to dinner are new, as is the price rise – up by an inflationary 10 pence per curry! To find it, follow your nose north up Fitzroy Street – the large modern block on your right may already be permeating curry smells from its basement kitchen. Enter, and out of courtesy, please ask at reception, (manned by gentle young Indians) if it's OK to use the canteen. The canteen, on your right, is clean, with brown functional

formica-topped tables. It's deserted 5 minutes before opening time, then as if the school bell's rung, it's suddenly packed full with Asians, many of whom are students, and this is their residence. Like all YMCAs, residency is open to anyone. All students of good curry, should visit here before they can graduate as aficionados. These are the rules: Be punctual, (opening and closing times and rules are as sharp as the Post Office); no bookings, no smoking, no license, no alcohol, so no BYO, and no nonsense! And Bec warns us the if the food runs out, tough! So get there early. (and thanks Bec for your pic below). Unlike the Post Office, everything works, and the staff care. Take a plastic tray, join the always-busy queue at the stainless-steel servery. It's basic, and unsophisticated but authentic expertly spiced and cooked Indian school-dinner-style – food, like you get at streetside Dabbas the length and breadth of India. Chicken and fish curries, lamb curry from £2.50, vegetable curries all £1.50 and lentils £1. Your choice handed to you in bowls. Top up with chupatties, tea or coffee, and pay at the till. It's absurdly cheap – hard to exceed a fiver, and it's remarkable that they now take credit cards. Then jostle for space at a shared formica table. The food may not be five-star but the company can be, when you share your table with talkative, friendly students. Men in white coats tidy up after you. *'Marvellous.'* MW. Set lunch £5 two courses, Sat. & Sun. Two function rooms seat 30 & 200. Hours: 7.30am-9.15 / 12-2 /7-8.30pm Mon-Fri; 8am-9.30 / 12.30-1.30/ 7-8.30pm Sat-Sun and Bank Holidays

THE KERALA

15 Great Castle Street, W1   020 7580 2125

This 40-seater is decorated in a very Indian way, with artifacts hanging off the walls including golden umbrellas used by temple elephants. Owner's wife Mille is in charge of the cooking. The food is pure south Indian, with a full list of protein and vegetable dishes. And for the most part it's reasonable, but it's not memorable. *'It was, I feel, very authentic, but not particularly good. We shared a Dosa – spicy potato in a wrap – fabulous! But Vardi – lentil cake in yoghurt is probably an acquired taste. Prawn Biriani was ridiculously hot, nice rice, fabulous Paratha. £33 for three courses including lager – very reasonable.'* MG. Hours: Lunch 12-3 / 5.30-11.

LAZEEZ @ SOHO THEATRE

21 Dean Street, W1   020 7434 9393

Lazeez, meaning 'delicate and aromatic', was founded by Ms Sabiha Kasim and her brother Zahid. Now under new management, Lazeez rents its 100 seat, all-day bar/restaurant in the basement below the new 150 seat Soho Theatre. Chef Shenoy says *"I keep in mind the flavours and simplicity of my mother's food"*. *'Really excellent'* say KB&SS. Hours: 9am - 1am Mon to Sat. /Sun varies. www.sohotheatre.com

Masala Zone's entertaining murals

MASALA ZONE   A-LIST

9 Marshall Street, W1F 7ER   020 7287 9966

This, the first of seven Masala Zones [inc two more mid 2009] was established in 2001. The concept is to serve real Indian food cooked by a fresh new wave of young Indian chefs at a price point of around £15, which appeals to a new young wave of customers. It's a concept so simple that one is unaware, perhaps of just how brilliant it is. As you approach the interior is revealed behind full-length, full-width plate glass windows. There are 160 seats, some at street level, and the remainder a few steps down on a lower lever, overlooked by the higher level, giving the venue character. Chairs and tables are light and modern, on a wooden floor. Wall decor is inspirational, and deserves your attention. It was painted on a mud-like terracotta background by Indian tribal artists, who paint cartoon-like line-drawings in white with sticks. They'd never been outside their village, let alone to London. Doing what the tribe has done for centuries, they tell the history of mankind, in a series of episodes. The drawings carry humour, pathos and perception. And the artists were so awe-struck with the capital, that they added a new penultimate episode – scenes of London, including some things they'd not seen before – Buck House, some guardsmen, the Tower, and their favourite – a stretch limo. Their final episode is drawn around the restaurant's bar servery hatch and depicts mankind getting drunk and falling over. There's not much chance of that at Masala Zone, only soft drinks, wines and beers are sold, and customer turnround is fast. This is because service is fast, from smartly uniformed young men and women and the kitchens are fast too. But this is no criticism. It's fast if you need it, but if you want to dwell, we've never noticed pressure on you to leave, no matter how busy it gets. The actual cooking takes no shortcuts – curries are slow-cooked to maximise flavours in the large kitchens behind, which includes a completely separate vegan kitchen, with its utensils coded so that they never touch meat. There is a further kitchen in view, with a series of smallish warmers containing ready-cooked food, which are constantly refilled by the chefs behind. Cold food emanates from one side of the kitchen, hot on the right. Your order is immediately doled out to the waiter. This leads to what some reporters complain about as being chaos. This is because dishes arrive at your table as soon as the chefs issue them. Some things take longer than others, and your order may arrive mains first, starter last, in any order. If it bothers you, order your starters first and then further food later. A few other aspects of Masala Zone already noted: price, queues, youth and fun may be likened to Wagamama But the resemblance is skin-deep. Service, rather than self-service is an obvious difference, as are comfortable chairs. Most importantly, Masala Zone's food is much more complex. Wagamama's is noodle nosh doshed out by non-skilled cooks. All Masala Zone food requires very high skill levels to cook. Snacks (or starters) include several types Bhel – Bombay street food. Chicken Samosas, lightly spiced, finely minced chicken with green peas; Shikampuri Kebab, melt in the mouth, aromatically spiced, minced lamb croquettes. Malabar Seafood Bowl, prawns, calamari, fish kofta with flat noodles in a richly curried soup. Everything is available a la carte., but way-to-go is with the Thalis (see page 70). Items do change weekly, but this is an example -- snacks of Khandvi, Dhokla (a pancake of besan flour, spiced and rolled up like a swiss-roll and cut into slices, served chilled).

Yoghurt Curry, Potato Curry, Dal, Aubergine and Plantain Curry, Rice and Chuppatis served with chutneys of Mango and Coriander. Add to that your choice of Achari Chicken Curry or Prawn Curry or Lamb Curry. There is a vegetarian Thali, and a weekend children's Thali. Noodle Bowls with Bombay-style Indianised Chinese is a spicy take on regular Chinese cuisine. Desserts: Caramel or Mango Kulfi, Shrikand with Fresh Fruit, Gulab Jamun with ice-cream, Caramelised Carrot with ice cream all priced at £2.50 each. *Fantastic concept. A top quality Indian meal cooked in front of your eyes for less than a tenner in a prime West End location! It is a large split-level, modern café-style restaurant with the cheerful and confident chefs practising their art with a flourish in full view at the back of the establishment, as you dine. A nice piece of theatre for the West End! Food quality was first class. Minced Chicken Kebab, Chana Jabal Roti (chick peas) was particularly good, as were the Chicken Mangalore, Rogan Gosht and Chicken Vindaloo (one of our party was feeling brave!). The Thalis looked particularly good with a choice of meat or vegetarian, and appeared to be the most popular items on the menu, being ordered by every second diner in the venue. The great thing about their Thalis is you get to choose the main dish(es) and the smoked clove lamb dish was truly sensational. The accompanying vegetable dishes and the mixed meat starter were also excellent, as was Anita's vegetarian thali. The dishes were all characterised with excellent flavours although they did tend to err on the hot side of spicy (which was nice). Good-sized portions and outstanding value for money. Service was efficient. Overall opinion – very good even without the exceptional prices. Factor in the prices and location as well and it would be daft not to return (and I will!). Would highly recommend. This establishment truly is a gem.'* SO. Lunchtime treats also include spicy sandwiches. Spend between £8 and £15 plus drink. No reservations, so queuing is possible at peak times. Takeaway menu offers a good selection of street food and curry and rice dishes. Delivery free over £10 and covers the many central and west London postcodes. 25% discount is also available for delivery lunch orders over £40. Service: 10%. Hours: 12-3 / 5,30-11 Mon-Fri. Sunday 12.30-11. Branches: Masala Zones, 80, Upper Street, Islington, N1; 25, Parkway, Camden, NW1; 147, Earls Courts Rd, SW5; Fulham SW6; Bayswater W2; 48, Floral St, Covent Garden, WC2.

www.realindianfood.com

PALMS OF GOA

12 Charlotte Street, W1   020 7636 1668

'After lubrication in the Bricklayers Arms round the corner, Palms of Goa is the usual destination. Rapidly becoming one of my favourite haunts. Lamb Xacutti is very good, as is the Goan Chicken and fish dishes. Not as authentic as Ma Goa, SW14 but very tasty. Good rice and breads, excellent attentive service and the best Tarka Dal I've had in a long while. Good value in the heart of London.' AR.

LA PORTE DES INDES
OUTSTANDING RESTAURANT

32 Bryanston Street, W1   020 7224 0055

Owned by the Blue Elephant Group (see SW6) it opened in 1997, under the management of Sherin Modi Alexander with her husband, Mernosh Modi, in charge of cooking. Both Taj-trained they have really grown into the role. Their professionalism cannot be bettered. Once a ballroom which blossomed in the wartime 1940's, and lying derelict by the 1980's, owner Karl Steppe applied his Blue Elephant decor yardstick here, and went all-out with a £2.5m spend. Unlike others whose budget claims are greatly exaggerated, you can easily see how transforming this vast place cost all of that, particularly since its layout isn't an easy one to deal with. Features include a sandstone arch, a 40-foot waterfall, a sweeping staircase made of white marble with pink sandstone balustrades, imported especially from India's pink city, Jaipur. Airy, domed skylights enhance La Porte's daytime atmosphere, making it a different place in darkness. There is a forest of jungle plants, a wealth of Indian artifacts and antiques, and the range of eating rooms, including the tiny private dining rooms seating 12 and 24 respectively, and three more dining areas bringing the total seating up to 300. The lunch presentation of food on raised copper salvers is opulent and attractive, and you can e-a-m-a-y-l for £19.90. *'We've eaten lunch here many times and have not been disappointed'*RL. *'I love this restaurant. From the welcome at the door to the presentation of the bill. The food, is just superb. Murgh Makhani (CTM) is just how it is in India and just how it should be. Flavoursome chicken pieces from a whole chicken – not the usual chunks of tasteless chicken breast – are smothered in a delicious, creamy, delicately spiced crimson gravy. Potato-stuffed parathas are buttery and light. You will want to eat them even if you are full to bursting. Big, fat, juicy King prawns floating in a light, mustard seed, turmeric coloured, coconut milk sauce. The puddings will not disappoint. The frequently held themed food festivals are a remarkable education in Indian regional food.'* DBAC. *'Deservedly TOP 100, my all-time favourite restaurant.'* SO. The Curry Club held a unique 25th anniversary reunion here on 24 Feb 2008. On that day in 1983 the Club's first-ever gourmet tour departed to India. Jointly led by Pat and cookery author Meera Taneja, eleven others went on the tour, including one elderly couple who proposed in Agra and subsequently married. Sadly they and some others, including Meera have passed away. It's a tribute to the tour's success that eight people enjoyed a fabulous Sunday buffet lunch of reminiscences and laughter in the private dining room at La Porte thanks to the incredible hospitality of Sherin and Mernosh. We continue to remain impressed by La Porte. La Porte's ambience, decor, service, food is all as good as it gets. La Porte has become an Indian's Indian, with an ever-increasing clientèle from the subcontinent. We gave it

our **BEST IN UK AWARD** in 1998. This Award is a permanent accolade, and does justice to Mernosh's fabulous food and Sherin's tight management. Average spend £50. Service discretionary. Cover charge £1.50. Hours: 12-2.30 Mon, Fri; 3 Sun / 7-11.30 Mon, Sat; 6-10.30 Sun. Branches: Blue Elephant Thai, SW6, and others in Europe. See page 27. www.laportedesindes.com

RAGAM SOUTH INDIAN　　　TOP 100

57 Cleveland Street, W1　　020 7636 9098

Established in 1984 this cosy restaurant seats 34 upstairs, 20 downstairs, and has a strong following. Chef Nair cooks standard curries and, being from Kerala, authentic south-Indian food. All the south Indian favourites are there, and we recommend the Fish Mooli, white fish simmered in a sauce of garlic, mustard seed, curry leaf and coconut milk. It remains in our TOP 100 because you say it should. Don't forget the lunchtime 'quick meal' £5 for curry, rice and bread! Service, 10%, not included. Delivery: min £10, local area only. Hours: 12-3 Sat, Thurs; 6-11.15 Mon, Sat; 10.30 Sun.

RASA　　　　　　　A-LIST

6 Dering Street, W1S 1AD　　020 7629 1346

Opened in 1998, this is the second of three restaurants established by Shivadas (Das) Sreedharan and his wife Alison. It's a rather more formal dining room than the original Stoke Newington Rasa. The menu features many of the vegetarian delicacies of that eatery, but includes some lamb and chicken dishes from northern Kerala and superb cooking by Chef RS Binuraj and his team. Menu Snapshot: Nibbles include Pappadavadai – paps dipped in batter and sesame seeds and deep-fried and Acchappam – rice batter crisp made from a mould (acch). Starters include: Banana Boli – ripe plantain dipped in besan flour and black sesame, fried, served with peanut and ginger sauce; Vadai Selection – fermented lentil soft dumplings, deep-fried to give a crisp outside; Lamb Puffs £4.75, baked puff pastry stuffed with spicy lamb masala and vegetables, served with chutney ' My mum Trudi (born in India) used to make these. She filled them with spicy minced lamb and pea curry (Mattar Keema) and she called them Curry Puffs. I used to take them to boarding school!' Ed); Chicken Samosa £4.75, lightly spiced chicken and potato filling in filo pastry, served with tomato chutney. Main courses include Moru Kachiathu – sweet mangoes and green bananas cooked in yoghurt with green chillies, ginger and fresh curry leaves, Beet Cheera Pachadi – fresh beetroot and spinach in a yoghurt with roasted coconut, mustard seeds and curry leaves, and the house signature dish Rasa Kayi (minced vegetables, ginger, garlic and fennel seed). Varutharacha Kozhy Curry £7.95, chicken curry, dry roasted coriander, grated coconut, dried red chillies, fresh curry leaves and

tomatoes (eat with boiled rice); Malabar Erachi Chaaru £7.95, aromatic lamb, turmeric, red chillies and onion (this dish is great eaten with a Paratha); Kappayum Meenum £12.50, king fish in sauce of onions, chillies, turmeric, ginger, served with a plate of steamed cassava. During the evening all main courses are served on the traditional banana leaf (see page 58). Prices are a bit higher than N16. Like its sister restaurants, the place is very tiny with seating on two floors packed into the narrow rooms. It does two full sessions every night, plus a full weekday lunch trade. So book and go early. Service 12.5%. Hours: 12-3 not Sun / 6-11. Branches: Rasa, N16 Rasa Express NW1 & N16, Rasa Newcastle and next entry. www.rasarestaurants.com

RASA SAMUDRA　　　　A-LIST

5 Charlotte Street, W1T 1RE　　020 7637 0222

Outside it has the same blackcurrant-yoghurt-pink paintwork as all Rasas are the same colour; this is Das' house colour and he loves it. Lovely hanging baskets burst with red flowers. Inside wooden carvings hang on pretty Wedgwood blue walls. Dining is on two floors, and the regulars tells me they prefer quieter, more spacious upstairs. If you wish to understand Keralan food, all Rasas are encyclopedic in the subject. The menu includes many of Rasa's signature vegetarian dishes (see previous entry). But here Das also uniquely specialises in Keralan fish and seafood (Samudra means 'of the sea'). Menu Snapshot: Achappam £4, a flower shaped snack made of rice flour and coconut, black sesame and cumin. Pappadavadai £4, popadums dipped in a light batter of rice flour, cumin and sesame, fried to give them extra crunch and crackle! and numerous delicious chutneys are a meal in themselves including the remarkable Meen Achar fish pickle) and Konju Achar (prawn pickle). Samudra Rasam £5.95, made from prawns, crab, mussel and squid cooked with tomato, onion and black pepper in the sauce of traditional red rice essence (a hearty soup!); Konju Varuthathu £7.50, king prawns marinated in a spice paste of chillies and onions then fried and served with salad (a light lunch time meal); CCP Vadai £4.50, crunchy deep-fried patties made of mixed lentil, cashew nuts and fresh spinach laced with fresh curry leaves, ginger and green chillies; Nair Dosa £6.50, a rice and black gram flour pancake filled with a mixture of potatoes, beetroot, carrot, onion and ginger served with sambar and coconut chutney (this dish is one of our favourites and can be quite filling); Varutharacha Meen Curry £11.50, Tilapia fish with a sauce made with roasted coconut, red chillies, tomatoes and ; Pachakari Thoran £5.25, crunchy vegetables, tempered with mustard seed, cashew nuts, curry leaves and coconut (an absolute must, a lovely light dish) and leaving the best for last, the pudding! Banana Dosa £3.50, tiny pancakes are made from bananas, plain flour and cardamom, delicious! We

get reports of curt service at Rasa and indeed had experience of it ourselves. And expect to pay above average prices. Main courses £7-£15. Set meals (both highly spoken of) c£24 (veg), c£32 (seafood). Several private dining rooms for hire. Tube: Tot Ct Rd and Goodge St. Serv: 12.5% . Hours: 12-3, not Sun /6-11 daily. Branches, see above. www.rasarestaurants.com

RASA EXPRESS TAKEAWAY

5 Rathbone Street, W1T 1NQ   020 7637 0222

NW1, was so successful at serving busy office workers inexpensive lunchtime, tasty spicy treats, that a sister takeaway was called for. The menu is the same. See Rasa Express NW1 for details. Limited hours: 12, 3 Mon-Fri

RED FORT   A-LIST

77 Dean Street, Soho, W1   020 7437 2525

This venue is in the hands of the very capable Amin Ali. He has already built his name by securing Camden Council grants to open restaurants, which at the time achieved much acclaim such as the Last Days of the Raj and Lal Qila. They were co-operatives in that the work force shared in the work and the profits. But Ali had more ambitious ideas, and his Red Fort opened in 1987 claiming it was it was the first to offer the real cooking of India. This is not the case, of course, (see Veeraswamy and Gaylord, W1 and Rajdoot, B'm'); but a lot of people believed it. At first it was nothing more than curryhouse food, although it was done well. Then Amin got his ace card in the form of chef Mohammed Rais, a Delhi-trained master chef par excellence. Next came a controversial fire which destroyed this iconic venue. Rias went off to the Darbar, SW6 and the Fort lay dormant. Eventually a £2m rebuild took place and the Red Fort reopened in late 2002 to a fanfare of publicity, something Amin is adept at. The exterior is modernised but still recognisable. Inside 85 seats reside in a modernist Mughal setting with sand-coloured walls, Indian trimmings, slate floor with a red path, dotted with mosaics leading you to the back where water drizzles down the wall. Nearby, Tandoors are in view (behind glass). The drama continues in the toilets, where no expense has been spared. Neither has it backstage where there is a space-age, rarely-found air-conditioned kitchen. Rias returned to the fold and brought back his expertise in Dum Pukht cuisine. Rias mastered Dum under the legendary Lucknowi Chef Qereshi, the Exec at Delhi's Mughal Sheraton Hotel Dum Pukht restaurant. His specialities include starters such as Galauti Kebab – the smoothest patties of minced lamb and spices. Teetar Gilafi Kebab – spiced roasted minced partridge or Monkfish Tikka – chunks of monkfish smoked with ginger. For main course, the Dum Pukht cognoscenti go for Dum ki bater (quail in a creamy yoghurt, almond and cashew nut sauce) or Aromatic lamb shank or any of Rais' Birianis, each

cooked in a sealed pot: Avadhi Gosht Biriyani – Rais' 300 year old family recipe of lamb and rice. Samudari Biriyani – scallops, squid, prawns and rice. Subz Biriyani – moist basmati rice, vegetables and spices. Other dishes include Mahi Anaari, succulent king prawns with saffron sauce; Bhuni Duck, in a dry sauce; Lamb chops marinated in pomegranate juice. The restaurant has plenty of focus and charisma, just like its owner. *'The food is really superb, service good and the whole lunch a very enjoyable experience. I did notice the the menu is very small but I am sure all diners would be delighted with anything they choose.'* DC. The restaurant has plenty of focus and charisma, just like its owner. The venue's basement never worked well in its previous incarnation. But it does now in the form of Akbar a 'sexy' bar, seating 75 which can be used before or after dining upstairs or for lighter meals. Natural stone floors, with luxurious rugs, leather armchairs and low tables a an eclectic mixture of art and sculpture and an extensive list serves everything including Indian-style cocktails which runs to 1am. DJ Th-Sat eves. Table d'hote lunch and pre-theatre specials from c£18 for 3 courses. Dress smt cas. Service 12.5%. 12-2.15 Mon-Fri; 5.45-11 Mon-Sat; 6-10 Sun. www.redfort.co.uk

YOU SAY OK

You may get a discount of you show them this Guide.

W1: PICCADILLY: RAJ TANDOORI 72 Berwick Street, W1 ~ 020 7437 2897. Est 1969 by Abdon Noor. Show Mhim this Guide and you may get a discount. Hours: 12-2.30 / 5.30-12.

REGENT TANDOORI 16 Denman Street, W1 ~ 020 7434 1134. Good for a fix at sensible prices. Lunch and dinner daily.

TASTE OF MUGHAL 29 Great Windmill Street, W1 020 7439 8044. Long-standing 50-seater which *'never varies after all these years of visits.'* RW. Takeaway: 10% disc. Hours: 12-11.45.

SOHO SPICE   TOP 100

124 Wardour Street, W1F 0TY   020 7434 0808

Owner by chef Kuldeep Singh, Asraf Rahman and Dinesh Mody who jointly run Shaftesbury Avenue's Mela WC1 and Chowki W1. The menu features an extensive and intricate range of kebabs which change on a daily basis and are cooked in the show kitchen. Raminder Malhotra, Executive chef says he takes inspiration from chefs with royal pedigree including Tundee Main, a prominent craftsman of the 19th century. Chef Raminder highlights the fine line in the art of kebab-making, 'What differentiates a great kebab from an indifferent roast is that it should be crisp on the outside and soft and succulent on the inside. He also offers his signature 'hook kebab', a leaf-wrapped meat attached by hooks linked to one another and cooked in the tandoor. Other menu examples include steamed sea bass with raw mango, topped with kokum and coconut-tempered shrimps, wrapped in banana leaf; and Tandoori pheasant breast marinated with orange rind, roasted cumin and rock salt. The late night basement

bar/ night club opened in 2005. The combination of rich and warm colours, together with retro furniture, results in a contemporary room that features dark wood walls and plush roomy red leather banquettes. These double up as booths, ideal for groups or parties. An archway leading from the edge of the bar leads towards the DJ booth and dance floor, illuminated by disco lights. The range of drinks include speciality cocktails produced by Head Bartender Francis Lama and his team. Bar snacks are served until 3am, include kebabs, tawa grilled halibut steak, lobster barbecue, plain or flavoured naans and squid with pepper, garlic, tomato and ground spices. So far so good, but hear this: *'Went with a party of 10 people – an old colleague's leaving-do in fact. This meant we were not offered the a la carte menu but were each given a choice of 4 set menus from which to choose. There seemed plenty of variety but such choices are generally simple for me – I went for the only vegetarian menu which from memory, I think was no. 4.!! The food was very good, including an excellent paneer starter. For all of the set menus the main courses were presented as a Thali, so smallish amounts of 5 or 6 different dishes. Each dish was unique enough that no-one was bored and the overall feedback was excellent. I can certainly confirm that the vegetarian dishes were well spiced, not oily though maybe just one of them could have done with a little more chilli heat? The baskets of naan breads, the tarka dhal and the rice were all excellent. The only criticism I have regards the service. When our party arrived we were presented with the four set menus. When the starters were bought to our table, the waiter asked "who ordered menu no. 4". I put my hand up and was presented with a Shami Kebab, amongst other meaty items! A couple of us remarked that the waiter had got his numbering wrong but he was absolutely insistent that he was right, and was actually insistent well beyond the point of rudeness!! He would not accept that, because I'm a vegetarian, I simply would not have ordered a menu containing a Shami Kebab for example! We had to call the original waiter to bring the set menus back to our table so we could show to him he had a mistake. This caused an argument between the waiters but no apology to our party. So again we see good food being somewhat tainted by poor service, otherwise it would have been a really good experience. Whether or not it should be Top 100 is matter of some doubt to me but I would try it again.'* AG. Sadly it's becoming a common problem Andy – a once-loved venus not being zealously cared-for by its ambitious management so the servants rule. Sadly we're getting this similar report about other venues in the same group. Won't delist this time but reports please.

TAMARIND   A-LIST

20 Queen Street, W1   020 7629 3561

Opened in 1994, This Guide gave it Best Newcomer Award in 1995, 97, Best Indian, 1998-9 and and best Chef 1999-2000 becoming the only Indian restaurant to be so awarded It won its first Michelin star in 2001 which it continues to retain. General Manager Rajesh Suri (formerly with Red Fort and Veeraswamy) joined in 1998 and is in no small part responsible for this success. Atol Kotchar was the original chef, and when he left in 2002 (to open Benares, W1), Sous chef Alfred Prasad (ex Delhi Sheraton and Veeraswamy) took on the mantle of Head Chef. He graduated from the Institute of Hotel Management, Madras in 1993 and completed his advanced chef training at the Maurya Sheraton in Delhi, working at the legendary 'Bukhara' and 'Dum-Pukht' restaurants then to the Madras Chola Sheraton where he was Executive Chef at 'Dukshin'-one of India's premier south Indian restaurants. Alfred finally moved to London in June 1999 where he worked as Sous Chef at 'Veeraswamy'. The design by Charles Leon includes the Tamarind logo running through it. The staircase gleams with hand-blown crystals. The restaurant is one big well-spaced room with 26 tables that seats up to 90. The preconceived notion of being unable to match Indian food and wine is dismantled here with the help of an experienced sommelier, who assists the customers in choosing the right drink. He in turn is assisted with a choice of 140 different wines, mainly from France, and the New World. Prices range from £15 to £1500 per bottle. Rajesh says, *'Over the years we have learned to change 2-3 different wines each month. Every fortnight we have a wine tasting for the staff. We have a really good sommelier, so the customers can trust his judgement'.* Prasad's menu combines new dishes and old Tamarind favourites At the open-view kitchen you can watch Tandoor and kebab-making. Menu Snapshot: Starters: Saag Aloo Tikki, spiced potato cakes with a spinach filling, served with tamarind chutney, Tandoori Subzi, grilled broccoli and paneer in spicy marinade, Murgh ka Chat, smoked chicken salad with red onions and peppers in a spiced avocado dressing. interesting mains include: Seafood Moilee, scallops, squid, mussels and king fish in a mild coconut sauce, £16.50, Lamb Chettinad, cooked with Chettinad spices, £16.50 and Bhuna Achari Khargosh, rabbit cooked with pickling spices. *'Our benchmark dal Makhni, low-cooked black lentils was perfect. Romali Roti was handkerchief-thin and soft.'* DBAC *' I had been looking forward to visiting this restaurant for many years. The occasion was full of surprises. First was their failing to give us the 'tasting menus' when they showed us to our tables. I had to ask if they offered tasting menus on Friday evenings and then, when they did bring them to us, they forgot the vegetarian version – next surprise. Once we had all the menus the waiter took our order for aperitifs and we were suitably impressed by his probing for which exact brand of gin and/or vodka each of*

TAMARIND

**20 Queen Street
Mayfair, London
WIJ 5PR
T: 020 7629 3561
F: 020 7499 5034**
www.tamarindrestaurant.com

Cobra Good
Curry Guide
Best UK Indian
Restaurant
2007/8

us preferred. When they arrived, they had been filled to the brim with tonic! Now I ran a pub for 3 years, not aimed at the same end of the social ladder as Tamarind, and even I know you never pre-fill a vodka or gin and tonic! – another surprise. The implication I'm afraid is that the tonic is either dispensed from a siphon or a large bottle, neither of which is suitable for Tamarind. The restaurant does need to look at this in my opinion. However, it is the quality of the food where Tamarind really shines. The Bhel Puri was superb as was the paneer starter. What happened next, however, was more surprising. When I ordered a tasting menu at Zaika, each course was bought to us individually and the constituent elements and regional origins of each dish explained in detail. Genuine care was taken that we appreciated every single course. At Tamarind, all the remaining dishes were bought together as a Thali, with no fanfare, no explanation and I'm afraid, precious little care. It did very little justice to the £48 price tag that sits with the vegetarian tasting menu. This is not to decry the food – it was exquisite. It included the most sublime naan bread, stuffed with cheese yet incredibly light and melt-in-the-mouth, that I have ever tasted. The remaining dishes were varied, beautifully spiced and there was certainly enough that we were never going to finish what was bought to us. Our colleagues were equally impressed with their meat-based dishes; it really is very difficulty to criticise the sheer quality of the food that is offered. I do genuinely wish however, that I can say the same of the service. Maybe they were distracted by the (reported but un-witnessed) presence of Tom Cruise and Katie Holmes but I'm not sure I believe this. I quite simply think they need to focus a little more on the customer and treat dining here as a full-on experience if the price tag is to be justified. I'm afraid it did not come close to Zaika in this respect.' AG. Clearly not the night the Mich inspector came, or is it true that it's only decor they care about? Despite these short-comings, Tamarind remains on our **A-LIST**. Main courses £15-£30. 2 cs set lunch £18, 3 cs £20. 2 cs set meal (6-7pm) £23. Service : 12.5%. Delivery. Hours: 12-3 Mon-Fri; -2.30 / 6-10.30. See Imli W1.
www.tamarindrestaurant.com

VEERASWAMY
OUTSTANDING RESTAURANT AWARD

99 Regent Street, W1   020 7734 1401

2006 marked the 80th birthday of this venerable institution and owners Ranjit Mathrani, Namita and Camellia Panjabi, the trio behind Chutney Mary, Amaya and Masala Zone marked the occasion by transforming the already gorgeous venue into a truly stunning ninth decade. As they put it 'the restaurant now reflects the glamour and glory it exuded in the 1920s'. But this is not 20s décor it is strictly 21st century. Mind you the pedigree is never forgotten. Established in 1926 and for many years, Britain's only Indian restaurant, its founders were an.Indian princess and her husband, the great grandson of an English General in the Bengal Army. Customers included Edward, Prince of Wales, King

Gustav of Sweden, Pandit Nehru, Indira Gandhi, Charlie Chaplin, King Hussein of Jordan, and Marlon Brando. You will notice picture of the rich and famous devotees of Indian food, whose rendezvous it has always been. Most definitely not the former, but decidedly the latter, one customer was also my mother, who saved up here nurse's money for an occasional visit in the 1930s to satisfy the fix she had acquired in the Raj. The entrance then as now is on the aptly-named Swallow Street. Go up the stairs one floor or take the lift. As you enter the main room, the wall-to-wall picture windows at first dominates with their great view of Regent Street. But you are soon spellbound with the interior. The builders were instructed to put back the original ceiling height and it is now a high ten feet and painted, sparkley silver countered by the dark wooden floor, handmade Moghul floral-design carpets and Indian black granite speckled with gold. On one wall, vividly coloured turbans remind one of the Indian Maharajas who once

frequented the restaurant. Century-old Kalighat-style Bengali paintings adorn the restaurant. The tiled mirror wall (at the cute booth called the honeymoon table) is a good idea but who broke some of the tiles? The lighting combines primary-coloured glass shades redolent of handis, exorbitant chandeliers, and LCD lighting colour-changing the fretwork screens. The short menu includes classics from throughout India and contemporary creations produced by a brigade of specialists from different Indian regions. Items from bhel, to dosas and lamb shank to lobster from Hyderabad to Chowpatti beach, and Goa to Delhi. This is not to everyone's liking, since it's far removed from curry house stuff and it's in the higher price range. Caveats issued, let me now tell you why this restaurant is so high in our estimation. We have always found the starters to be par-excellence, sometimes delectable, sometimes transcendent and the protein dishes too. On our recent visit we had Raj Kachori (a giant pani-puri filled with dahi and bhel street food, quite divine and much better than its description in the menu) and green vegetable kebab. Our mains were a delectable Lamb Biriani with a smooth pink Mirchi Salan sauce (chilli curry – delicious but very mild) and Syrian chicken stew, pink sauce again, but spicier and quite outstanding. We

had Sukhe Aloo potatoes, great and green Romali Roti (food colouring) disappointing. Menu Snapshot: Nizami Murgh, from the Royal kitchens of Hyderabad, chicken breast and koftas with pine nuts, lemon and rose petal; Begum Bahar, a homestyle Lucknow chicken korma with saffron; Sholay Chicken Tikka, smoked chicken with garam masala cooked in the tandoor; Mussels Moilee, fresh mussels in an aromatic ginger sauce; Malabar Lobster Curry, with fresh turmeric and unripe mango. Desserts at the Panjabi establishments have always been way above average, partly because they are made on site and not bought in. I am indebted to Sejal Sukhadwala, whose Time Out Indian restaurant reports are always perceptive and very witty, and who wrote of US food writer Jeffrey Steingarten, *'he once memorably described Indian desserts as tasting of face cream., but here the own-made kala jaam (semolina and milk dumplings in rose-scented syrup) and rasgollas (poached paneer dumplings) were fabulous.'* I can add to that: for it was at Veeraswamy that I first had hot Gulab Jamun, flambéed in Cognac. Some face cream! One more thing: the wine list is an exemplary selection. Mr Mathrani is a connoisseur, and it shows. If ever there were a time to convert from beer to wine, this is it. As for price: it's not always out of reach. True a meal for two will be c£80 + booze. But the 3 course set lunch is just £17, and there are good-value set dinners too: 5.30-6.30pm and 10.30-11.30pm, £16.50 two courses Upstairs the Palmer room (named after the founder) takes 36 seated and 60 standing. When we started the Curry Club in 1982, we used this room to hold our monthly meetings. It was then rather tatty. Not now: it is transformed with more turbans and is invitingly laid out for dinner for 18. And there are a number of framed prints up there which deserve attention. Our £89 meal was too much for us and what we couldn't manage was willingly packed to take away, and would have made the cost more bearable to get two meals out of it. Sadly when we unpacked next day they had failed to pack the main courses and out much anticipated dinner went out of the window. If you phone in to book, beware the unnecessarily endless recorded message, and when you do press 3 to reserve, you may have to listen to an entire Brandenburg concerto before anyone answers you. Service 12.5%. Hours: 12-2.15; 2.30 Sat & Sun / 5.30-10.30 ; Sun closed. See page 1.   www.realindianfood.com

WOODLANDS   TOP 100

77 Marylebone Lane, W1   020 7436 3862

A branch of Mr Sood's well-liked, small chain of southern Indian vegetarian restaurants. See SW1 branch for details.

DURBAR

24 Hereford Road

(off Westbourne Grove)

London

W2 4AA

020 7727 1947
020 7727 5995

www.durbartandoori.co.uk

top 100

Established 1956

London W2
Bayswater, Edgware Road, Paddington, Westbourne Grove

BOMBAY PALACE   TOP 100

2 Hyde Park, 50 Connaught Street, W2 2AA
020 7258 3507

In the late 1970s, Mr SS Chatwell was a successful Indian restaurateur in Ethiopia. Then a regime-change left him fearing for his life. He packed his bags and left for the USA. Luckily he'd packed his many bags full of dollars, and I mean FULL. I know because I met him in NY and he told me. It was not long before he opened Bombay Palace London opened in 1983. The 135-seater is: *'Top notch restaurant, impeccably appointed in bright and airy single room. Smart polite and efficient staff. Real tablecloths and napkins. Engaging if not extensive menu offering mostly North Indian dishes. Complimentary Popadums and small tubs of sauces. Very nice starter of Bombay Tiffin Vegetarian c£9 - a selection of Aloo Tikka, Aloo Paratha, Onion Bhajia, Bhel Puri and Samosa – all distinctively different and very tasty, served with lettuce leaves and sliced giant radish. Balouchi Raan c£16 - outstanding, exquisite, beautifully tender cut of lamb leg, partially sliced of the bone. Had been marinated and slow cooked, with a hint of char - fabulous, subtle, varied flavours, a little sauce. Peshwari Naan £2.50 - light, fluffy, aromatic and tasty with a smattering of nuts and fruits. However, service charge rather steep at 15% and automatically added.'* RW. Menu Snapshot: Bombay Fish Curry c£10, king fish fillets simmered in a spicy curry sauce with mustard and turmeric; Murgh Kaleji Masala £6, chicken livers sautéed with onion, tomato, cumin and coriander; Anarkali Chaat £4.60, fresh pomegranate seeds, goats cheese, watercress, grapefruit and walnuts; Dahi Batata Puri £4.50, crisp lentil puffs with tangy mixture of bean sprout and coriander, finished with hung yoghurt, mint and tamarind chutney; Batak Pepper Fry £10, duck with roasted onions, crushed peppercorns, lemon and bell pepper. Service 15%. Cover charge £1 Takeaway: 10% discount. Hours: 12-2.45; 3 Sun / 6-11.30; 11 Sun. Branches: Beverly Hills, Budapest, Houston, Kuala Lumpur, Mississauga, Montreal, New York, Toronto, Washington DC . www.bombaypalace.co.uk

YOU SAY OK
You may get a discount of you show them this Guide.

W2: CONNOISSEURS INDIAN 8 Norfolk Place, W2 1 LQ ~ 020 7402 3299. 46-seater. *'Excellent value, good quality, nicely presented and very filling.'* Del: 5m. Hours: 12-2.30 / 6-12.

W2: GANGES 101 Praed Street, W2 ~ 020 7723 4096 It's been with us since our first Guide. 12-2.30/5.30-11.

NOOR JAHAN 2 26 Sussex Place, W2 ~ 020 7402 2332. MD Aziz Ahmed's 90-seater on two floors opened in 2002. Av with wine £30 pp. 12-2.30/6-11.30.

SITARA 228, Edgware Rd, W2 ~ 020 7723 1101. Indian /Arabic entertainment, on dance floor to 6am.. Av with wine £50. Hours: 5.30 to late Mon-Fri; from 6 Sat. Closed Sun

DURBAR   TOP 100

24 Hereford Road, W2   020 7727 1947

Opened when time began in 1956, by Shaimur Rahman Syed. Seats 60 diners – wicker chairs, arches, plants, Indian art, brass coffee-pots. Specials include: Chicken Xacuti, very hot with dry chilli and coconut and Chicken Silla, shredded chicken tikka. Good-value are the Thali set-meals from £8.95; Southern Indian recipe for Kholopur Chicken – very hot with chilli, ginger and lime;Mughlai Badami Chicken steam cooked in a delicate bland of spice with pistachio & cashew nut sauce 6.95; Nihari Lamb shank marinated with yoghurt, garlic & ginger. Slow cooked with wild lemon £7.95; Chicken Malaber Mango and coconut milk with mustard seeds & jeera sauce £6.95; Lime Chicken With onion, coconut milk, lime juice, lemongrass, chilli and ground spice £6.95; Lamb or Chicken Tikka Masala Tikka morsels in exotic masala sauce. Mild spice £6.95; Gosth Hindustani Lamb with Roasted spice, garlic, ginger & ground almonds £6.95. There is a good range of veg dishes and 13 varieties of bread are baked daily in the Tandoor. Tandoori fish and meat dishes are cooked in true northwest Indian style. Biriani, Parsi, Kashmiri and Thali set meals, from £14.95 all give the diner a chance to sample a wide variety of dishes influenced by regional home cooking. Co-owner Chef Shamin Syed (pictured

here) won the International Chef of the Year Contest in Feb. 2000. He says of his winning dish – Oriental Chicken (diced chicken cooked with onions, yoghurt, tomato, ground almond, and coconut in hint of spice cream sauce, served sizzling £7.95)

'it's been on the menu for over 30 years'. What more can we say about one of London's most stable and experienced venues Well there is a bit more. RCF says *'it's one of our regular haunts. Whenever we go it is without fail packed full of Indians and Arabs. That says quality.'* Takeaway: 10% discount. Hours: 12-2.30 (not Fri) / 5.30-11.30 daily, including bank holidays. www.durbartandoori.co.uk See previous page.
Branch: Greenford Tandoori, Ruislip Road East, Greenford, Mddx.

CURRY PALACE   NEW ENTRANT

36 Queensway, Bayswater   020 7243 8992

Situated opposite HSBC Bank, alternate red and white is the colour scheme here, including walls and smart leather chairs, white tablecloths, red napkins and white china. Colourful art hangs in the main restaurants (there is a very nice al-fresco dining area, complete with linen covered tables and proper chairs, not those horridly uncomfortable metal café-things, that you see just everywhere!). Altogether a clean, modern and traditional establishment. Menu Snapshot: Onion Bhajia £2.75; Reshmi Kebab £3.75 - boneless chicken marinated in yoghurt and mild spices, baked on tandoor; Tandoori Mixed Grill £11.95 - tandoori chicken, chicken and lamb tikka, sheekh kebab, tandoori king prawn and naan bread, served with house chutney and salad; Butter Chicken - chicken fillet tossed in butter, cultured yoghurt, cream and curry sauce; Chicken Balti Balti £8.45, served with rice or bread; Paneer Makhni £4.95. Nearest Tube: Queensway. Hours: 12-11.30, Fri & Sat to 12. Sunday Special Dinner - starter, main, side with rice or bread £11.95 - good deal!   currypalaceuk.com

GINGER   A-LIST

115 Westbourne Gr, W2 4UP   020 7908 1990

Bangladesh's top chef, Albert Gomes was Exec at Dhaka's five-star Sonargoan Hotel when we met him there in 1996, and were stunned by his cooking. He was frankly surprised at our enthusiasm, under the impression that the UK's 7,000+ Bangladeshi-owned restaurants would offer their own food. We urged him to get a posting in London, and put Bangladeshi cooking on the UK map. And he did. Firstly with a short festival at the Red Fort, then hooray, in a permanent position at the new Ginger, in 2001, and he brought his chef son. His style is upmarket home-cooking, and at Ginger he was given an upmarket new venue (modern wood floor, cyan chairs and white walls). I'd have preferred a more upmarket location, but it's there, and we should rejoice. Bangla cooking (see page 55) majors on fish, the bonier the better, shrimps, and a wealth of fresh vegetables, many only recently seen in the UK. Banglas love sweet, bitter, sour and hot. Curries are generally thinner than we get at the curryhouse, and beef, chicken, mutton are eaten on the bone. That said, the Brits are not yet ready for bones or bitter or very sweet desserts, and Gomes uses fish like Bekti, a favourite Bengali fish, which is relatively bone-free, with firm, white flesh. Even so the menu produces unfamiliar dishes, starters such as Bekti Macher Kebab, tandoor-baked. Gomes develops this further with Stuffed Squid, yoghurt-marinated squid stuffed with the same tandoori Bekti, both £4.50. Singara is the Bangla Samosa, using spiced vegetables stuffed into short-pastry, and made into a pyramid shape. Pyazi, the Bangla bhaji, their favourite street snack, both £2.95. Katti Kebab Calcutta's favourite

snack, shredded pieces of spicy roasted leg of lamb served in a whole wheat wrap, £3.95. Mains do include CTM and it's done well (and yes it IS available in Sylhet's Polash hotel, no 100 on the menu!. But, please, try something new. Kashi Bhuna is a boneless goat curry, spiced hot, Kacchi Biriyani, delicately flavoured, aromatic Moghul lamb Biriyani with dried plums and flaked almonds, Papaya Gosht, aromatically spiced lamb cooked with green papaya, all £7.95. Dab Chingri is made by mother-in-laws when the son-in-law visits, using king prawns, cooked with fresh coconut milk, cardamom and a bit of saffron then served in a tender green coconut, £11.95. Surmai Macher Biriyani, unique to Bengalis – fish Biriyani, £8.95. Raj Ash Kalia, a Bengali stir-fry of duck, capsicum and onions, lightly spiced. Moni Puri Prawns, a classic dish from the moni puri tribes people of Bangladesh, which consists of juicy king prawns cooked with ginger and light spices in a mellow sauce, £13.50. Bangladeshi vegetables appear on the menu when in season. Look out for chichinga, potol, kakrol, karela, doodi, mooli, lau, and more appearing in expertly cooked classics such as Pumpkin Bhaji, fried red pumpkin in a mild sweet and spicy taste, Green Banana Curry, fried plantain in a thick sauce, Baingan Borta, puréed smoked aubergine with ginger and garlic, Potoler Dolma, a Hindu dish from West Bengal, small gourd-like vegetables stuffed with paneer and golden sultana, Lau Dal, moong lentils and white pumpkin. No Bangladeshi meal is complete without their beloved bitter tastes. Shukto combines karela (bitter gourd) with aubergine, potato, green papaya, carrot, sweet potato, green banana and mooli cooked with a little bit of milk. All around a fiver each, and you can do no better than choose an all-veg meal at Ginger. Desserts are equally classical: Mishti Doi, a sweetened set yoghurt resembling shrikand, and Payesh, a jaggery-flavoured rice pudding. This is the breakthrough the UK has been waiting for. Our 7,000 Bangladeshi restaurateurs must take note. We the critics and gourmets have been saying it to you long enough; it's time to stop being complacent by coining it by doling out curryhouse pastiche. You may be right; middle England isn't ready for you to throw out the lucrative CTM/Korma/Vindaloo baby with the bath water. but if you want your industry to be taken seriously, it's time to see why Ginger much deserves our Best Bangladeshi Award. Takeaway 20% Discount. Hours: 5.-11.

JAMUNA

38A Southwick St, Paddington, W2
                                020 7723 5056

50-seater opened in 2005. The deco: bare wooden flooring, blond wood furniture, yellow and mustard walls and soft lighting. Chef, Jasbinder Singh Oberoi, India-trained he worked in London's Cinnamon Club and Mint Leaf. Starters like Spinach Cake served with homemade tomato and raisin chutney £5.50 and

Samundri Tikka £7, made with corn-fed chicken marinated with orange zest, chilli and honey and Murgh Bemisa, £7, pan fried chicken cakes flavoured with garlic, basil & lemon leaf. Mains include Adraki Chaampen, Lamb cutlets from the tandoor, marinated in ginger, peppercorn, mint and yoghurt £24; Spinach and Cottage Cheese Dumpling, with garlic & served with tomato gravy £12; Baigan Bhartha, aubergine cooked in the clay oven with ginger, coriander & tomato £12 or Lobster with saffron and garlic £36. Rajasthani Venison, is marinated with Rajasthani spices in sesame and tamarind sauce. Freshly made desserts and a global selection of wine. Party room, seats 25. Service charge: 12.5%. 12-2.30 / 6-11 daily   www.jamuna.co.uk

MANDALAY BURMESE   A-LIST

444 Edgware Road, W2   020 7258 3696

This restaurant has the distinction of being the UK's only Burmese restaurant. Located at the moment in the unfashionable end of Edgware Road, it seats just 30 and is run by the Ally brothers, Dwight (front) and Gary (cooking) Burmese-born and Norwegian-educated. We say at the moment because we're told of plans afoot to relocate. Mum and Dad were on duty when I dropped in for lunch. She was busy cooking, and he busy chatting to a regular customer. I asked for a beer and got it at once, suitably cold, from the Fanta-packed cabinet, as much part of the décor as the oil-cloth table covers. This place is a must for foodies. It will never get a Michelin star, thank heavens – it is far too scruffy and in the wrong location! But for an utterly honest, non-rip-off, inexpensive, hardworking, sensibly operated,clean and simple gaff, this is it, above all reeking with care from top to bottom and sumptuous food. Burmese food is a cross between Chinese and Indian cuisine with a slight influence from Thai food. Rice and noodles are the most important staple foods. Fritters, soups, salads and main dishes such as stir-fry and curry dishes make up every day meal. Many interesting meat and seafood dishes and a variety of exotic vegetable dishes can be found in the cuisine. Ingredients such as garlic, turmeric, tamarind, coriander, mint, tamarind and chilli show the Indian influence; fish sauce, shrimp paste (which comes in a very strong smelly block, shaped rather like a small house brick, very dark brown in colour called blachan) dried shrimps, lemon grass and coconut milk., its Thai influence and soy sauce, noodles, rice flour and ginger, Chinese. Whoever is on duty will give good menu guidance. And here is a Snapshot from it: Popadoms (Papara) £1.20 with Prawn Crackers (Nga-Moak-Kyam) £1.90. For starters choose from three different Spring Rolls (Kaw Pyant Kyam), vegetable, shrimp and vegetable, or chicken and vegetable, all are £2.10 for a portion of two. Or from three different Samosas (Samusa), vegetable, egg and potato or minced chicken, all £2.10 for a very generous portion of four. A-Kyam: fritters from £2.30, Bean Sprout; Calabash; Leafy

Green; Shrimp and Bean Sprout; Shrimp and Vegetable. Salads (A-Thoat), feature strongly on the menu. I rather liked the Raw Papaya and Cucumber Salad at £3.10, delicious; Chicken and Cabbage Salad £4.50; Shrimp and Lettuce Salad £4.50. Soups (Hin-Cho) are eaten as a digestive (just like Thailand) and there are some interesting choices: Bottle Gourd Soup £2.90; Dozen Ingredients Soup (Sett-Na-Myo Hin-Cho) £2.90 (sounds intriguing!); Chicken, Shrimp and Lime Soup (Kyet-Tha Bazun Tanbaya) £2.90. Let's move onto the main course lamb, chicken and seafood dishes and my favourites are - Spicy Lamb Curry (Seit-Tha Hin) £6.50; Chicken with lemongrass (Kyet-Tha Zabalin) £5.90; Crispy Fried Fish in Season Sauce (Nga Kyam) £6.50. Noodle and Rices dishes are also very good like the Rice Noodles in Fish Soup (Mokhingar) £6.90; Noodles with Coconut and Chicken (Kyet-Tha Ohn-No Khauk-Swe) £6.50 and Spiced Rice with King Prawns (Bazun-Kya Dan-Bauk) £7.90. If you can manage a pudding, I recommend the Banana Fritters at £1.90, if you really can't manage another mouthful, take them home and eat for breakfast! Or Coconut Agar-Agar Jelly and Faluda (milk, ice cream, jelly and Rose syrup £2.90. Dad told me to try the Tea-leaf salad. It uses leaves he says are imported from Burma (I didn't ask how) which Mum had made that morning just for him. I protested saying I couldn't eat his lunch. He said *'no worries she's made enough for an army.'* It consisted of fried moong lentils with the texture of rice crispies, loads of chilli (great) something fishy and salad and tea leaves. Amazing!. *'We started with Shrimp and Vegetable Spring Rolls and Egg and Potato Samosas £2.10 served on a single plate in anticipation (correctly) of them being shared, accompanied by bowls of chilli, tamarind and soy – delicious. Lamb with Ginger £5.50, extremely tender lamb, in a thick, tasty sauce with right amount of ginger. Chicken Curry with Tomatoes – spicy tomato based thin curry sauce akin to Thai curries. Noodles Coconut and Chicken £5.90, a heap of soft and crispy noodles with plenty of chicken intermixed, all in coconut juices. Vegetable Rice, Chinese style with texture. All dishes were excellent, each tasting very distinct, fresh, lively and agreeably flavoursome. Wonderful food, value tremendous. Highly recommended.'* MW. That was MW's first visit. Here's what he has to say three years on, now as a regular: *'Had one of my regular visits last week. As always, wonderful food. It's certainly my sort of place, and as it's always good there's little to add'.* MW. Licensed. Despite being inexpensive, they sensibly take credit/debit cards. Essential to book evenings. Takeaway service. Babies and children welcome: with high chairs on offer. Hours: 12-2.30 / 6-10.30, Mon - Sat. Closed Sundays and bank holidays. Just round the corner is the Ally family's hotel, also called the Mandalay (per En-suite room double/twin inc breakfast.) - £59.00.   mandalayway.com

URBAN TURBAN   NEW ENTRANT

98 Westbourne Grove, W2   020 7243 4200

When we were first informed by Chef Vineet Bhatia, thatt wants to offer: *'something more affordable, which could be franchised nation-wide in the form of "street food eateries", similar to those I grew up with in Mumbai'*, we were surprised but pleased. Surprised, because he chose his Rasoi (see SW3) for its tiny number of seats (38) specifically, he said, so that he could concentrate on cooking at house-party levels not on mass-production. Despite the seat number being unviable (you need min 60 to make profits) Vineet made not only profits but a much-loved, Mich-starred success, where booking a place is harder than getting a donation to Children-in-Need out of Robert Mugabe. Surprised too, because he isn't the first at the street-food / fast-food / or that irritating new name, 'tapas'. In 1990 Britain's first attempt to pioneer a chain of 'Indian-fast-food-outlets' opened on this very street. US-financed Nine Spice Diners opened to much trumpeting at 115 Westbourne Grove in late 1990 with plans to open 10 more outlets in that year with national franchising to follow. They failed in the same time-scale. Reason: wrong street, too much local competition, service too slow. One or two other aspirant franchisers have also come and gone since then. But low-cost, 'fast-food' concept(s) will happen, with or without franchising. In the last decade London's Masala Zone and Tiffin Bites are well under way with proven track records, and other 'names' (eg Yogesh) are opening their own one-off venues with the same aspirations. We are pleased, because Vineet, despite being bowled over with success is great company; his wife Rashima works 24/7 with him – that curious logo is her work; he cooks sensationally and it would be great to make Vineet quality food available to the masses. So what does he need? Location. location location is needed for nation-wide ambitions and is hard to achieve even with a deep purse But Urban Turban is a catchy name and the Grove a catchy place for trendy 20-something Notting Hillies whom, after a slurp the gym and a workout at nearby Caffé Nero and Starbucks and disenchanted with no-booze, rude Khan's, are the target customers of a place like this for a quick refuel: so location OK. Set over two floors, with private dining downstairs, the dinig room is big with high ceilings, mirrors, brown walls, small shiny black tables, joss sticks, sex-in-the-city bar, downlighters and a piercing sound-system louder than the Stones had at their freebie Hyde Park concert in the 70s, (it was 1500 watts) which of course makes conversation nigh-on impossible. This doesn't remind me of any Mumbai street-food joint I know, and I've been going there since it was called Bombay! Next service: Sadly we are not in receipt of great reviews here. Its staff are weak on la poilitesse (now becoming the norm) and seem prone to attacks of amnesia. *'They forgot half of my order then told me it was my*

fault' RL. And so to the menu: first those 'tapas items', include Chicken Lollipops, minced chicken ball on a stick; Battered Tilapia Goujons; mini Keema Mattar Samosas (mince and green pea); Spiced Crab Cakes; Chicken Chaat, lettuce with a morsel of chopped chicken and sweet and sour chutney; Queen Scallops gratinated and flavoured with mustard seeds and coriander. Some items are served in dainty paper cones. Note the items such as lamb Seekh Kebabs with rosemary or 'home-smoked' honey and mustard tandoori salmon with cucumber-dill raitha or masala red chicken with onion relish and you'll detect Vineet's penchant for fusion and sugar in many dips and sauces. A house speciality is the good-fun hot 'volcanic-rock' grill-platter upon which you cook raw spiced fish, meat and chicken at your table. Mains include a well-crafted Lamb Biriyani, an average tasting CTM and Baingan Bharta (aubergine) which actually tastes deliciously smokey as it should do but which is tedious to cook so hard to find. Now to the caveats: the menu states that *'dishes are served as they are prepared, with no formal sequence!'*. Masala Zone pioneered that. It keeps costs (and time) down because the chef brigade just gets on with cooking their own specialities; and the waiters serve what is ready; neither party has to deliver your order in one serving. But it irritates those not used to it. *'Helpings small, prices high (av £40pp with drink) and service slow.'* JGS Service: 12.5%. Hours 10am-mdnt; - 5 Sun. www.urbanturban.uk.com

London W4   Chiswick

WOODLANDS   TOP 100

12 High Road, W4   020 7994 9333

A branch of Mr Sood's well-liked, venerable small chain of southern Indian vegetarian restaurants. See SW1 branch for details. Party room seats 40. Two pavement tables. Service charge: 12.5% Hours: 12-2.45 / 6-10.45.

London W5   Ealing

MONTY'S NEPALESE CUISINE
BEST UK NEPALESE

There are enough Monty's in Ealing to form a Gurkha regiment. Three Nepalese chefs Hari Thapa, Bisnu Karki and Mahanta Shrestha, set up originally in the incredibly popular Ealing Broadway venue (now closed) in 1980. They relocated to South Ealing. Since then, the original group split, but they all still use the original name, logos, spin, menu and they all have Nepalese cooks. So because we have as many raving reports about any of the four venues, what we say is that all the Monty's do all the formula curries (which they cook well). And they all have a Nepalese specials list with items such as: Kathmandu Dal £4.50, lentils with ginger, onion, green

chillies, tomatoes and cumin; Aloo Bodi, £4.50, potato with black-eye beans; Chicken Dilkhoosh £10, chicken breast in a creamy sauce with rice and mushrooms to mention just three. Our advice is that you go for the Nepalese items. *'Monty's provides excellent value for money and are a haven of quality cuisine, exquisite Nepalese spicing and caring service.'* AIE. Take your pick of which Monty's you prefer, and frankly any one is as good as any other. Here they are:

MONTY'S NEPALESE CUISINE

4 Broadway Centre, 11 High Street, W5
         020 8579 4646

Young blood Dipender (Bishnu's son) converted an Italian restaurant next to the Post Office and Club Boulevard in 2000, and refurbished it to be the most spacious, and most modern Monty's. It's a light and airy restaurant with wicker furniture, layers of fresh linen and attentive, smiley waiters. *'We are named after Sir Montgomery'*, he says, but doesn't expand on this elusive explanation. Hours: 12-3 / 6-12. (to 11 Mon). Branch: Monty's, W13. See page 41.www.montys-restaurant.com

MONTY'S NEPALESE CUISINE

1 The Mall, Broadway, W5   020 8567 5802

Mahanta Shrestha took on this 68-seater venue, 'Monty's came from my name, Mahanta', he says. Details, see above. Hours: 12-3 / 6-12. Branch, Monty's 53 Fife Rd, Kingston. Run by Kishore Shrestha.

MONTY'S NEPALESE CUISINE

224 South Ealing Road, W5   020 8-560 2619

The reincarnation of the first Ealing Monty's opened here years ago. Still going strong with Hari Thapa in charge. *'The name Monty's,' he says, 'is a tribute to Field Marshal Lord Montgomery, of WWll Romell and Tobruck fame, and many Gurkhas fought under him.'* Hours: 12-3 / 6-12. Details, see above.

YOU SAY OK

You may get a discount of you show them this Guide.

W4: ANAPURNA Chiswick High Road. *'They seem to put a little extra effort into everything - I found most other curry in Chiswick fairly bland'.* Jon R.

W5: ZAYKA INDIAN CUISINE 8 South Ealing Road, W5 ~ 020 8569 7278. Opened in 1990 Sunday e-a-m-a-y-l. Hours: 12-2.30; 3 /6-11.30; 12 Fri & Sat.

ZEERA, 34 Hanger Lane, W5 3HU ~ 020 8997 0210. *'Always excellent. My girlfriend is veggy and she gives it a thumbs up too and it is very friendly.'* JR.

London W6   Hammersmith

We used to refer to King Street as 'Curry Alley', because it had so many curry houses, but new restaurants with excellent pedigrees have changed the scene remarkably. We have awarded our Top categories to no less than five restaurants here.

AGNI   TOP 100

160 King Street, W6   020 8846 9191

Agni is the Hindu fire God whose qualities include a 'burning passion'. Two men had that passion – to open their own restaurant, after slogging out out for others. Gowtham Karingi cheffed at Delhi's Bukhara, Zaika and was Veeraswamy Head Chef and Neeraj Mittra, managed Chutney Mary, Café Lazeez and Zaika. They achieved their dream in 2005. Agni's USP is that for the less money, you can get Indian West End food at suburban prices –food as good as it gets. As for Agni's spin about Ayurveda, it is poo-pooed by many Indians, and it can even can put some potential diners off trying the venue. They wrongly expect a kind of happy-hippy commune, joss sticks and mantra-singing. Agni is far from that, the tiny restaurant (45-seats on two floors) is very minimalist with pinky-peach walls, bare boards and the chairs and tables as spartan as those you find at the GCSE exam hall, though doubtless costing oodles more. But we don't come to eat the furniture, besides the cognoscenti prefer the marginally quieter upstairs, with its on-view kitchen. So does Agni live up to more of their spin, viz 'Great tasting food, exotic presentations, friendly-efficient service, comfortable surroundings and no-frill prices'?. Answers, yes, yes, yes, no (those chairs!) and yes. The welcome from the waiters in smart red-tunics is indeed spot-on and informative. The whole menu is imaginative and in some parts original, yet true to India, and as you'd expect, very good indeed. Here are some Snapshots: Papri Chaat £2.95, crisp whole-wheat biscuits dipped in yoghurt, with potatoes, chickpeas, tamarind and herb chutney; Maro Bhajiya £3.50, a Gujarati snack of slivered vegetables in a bishop's weed spiked gram flour batter.; Mumbai Bhel £3.25, snack of puffed rice, bombay mix, peanuts, potato, salad, fresh lime & chutneys; Chicken Tikka £4.50, 3 flavours, green herb, red spices and malai (cream & herbed yoghurt); Chicken 65 £3.75, south India's current favourite bar-snack, spicy-marinated chicken wings, with coriander, cumin, red spices, star anise, golden fried; Calamari Vepudu £4.50, crisp-fried calamari coated with black onion seeds and rice flour, served with a chilli chutney . Mains include Kolhapuri Chicken £7.50, a curry from Kolhapur near Mumbai with ginger, garlic, red chilli, coriander and coconut; Seafood Moilee £8.50, from Kerala's coast, with salmon, prawn, squid, mussels, coconut milk, flavoured with curry leaf, stem ginger, turmeric and lime. Several Thalis

are on offer from £7.50 and the Hyderabadi Biriyani is a which derives its name from the Persian word "Birian" meaning (Basmati) rice fried with rose petals, saffron, vetivier, cardamon and sweet spices before adding layers of Chicken or Lamb or Vegetables, or Prawns and slow-cooking in a sealed pot, also from £7.50. The desserts all £3 are truly imaginative, and why not Try home-made "Paan" Kulfi, made from fresh betel leaf kulfi with fennel, betel nut, dill seeds, melon seeds, rose petals and coriander, or the super-coloured Beetroot Halwa, slow-cooked with butter ghee, jaggery and cardamom. Or there's Red Chilli Ice Cream, 'not at all spicy ... just naughty', the menu says! or Rose Petal & Pepper Kulfi £3. Finally we give Gowtham and Neeraj top marks for an informative website. It carries the usual info, plus Gowtham's and Neeraj's 'Cooking Portal' where they offer their recipes, cooking techniques, and lessons 'cheats and kitchen speak', encouraging 'members' to blog. I love the fun and random bits of information and I simply cannot resist passing one bit on to you. Clicking the button for more information on 'Tandoori', we *learn the following astonishing fact: 'On July 2, 1995, the Indian politician Sushil Sharma was accused of murdering his wife, chopping up her body and burning the remains in a restaurant's tandoor oven. This grisly episode came to be known as the Tandoor Murder case. A court found the accused guilty on November 7, 2003, and he was sentenced to death.'* Something to contemplate when enjoying your mixed platter Joking aside this is a seriously good restaurant reflecting in all departments the passion which' Agni' Hours: Delivery Deservedly enters our TOP 100. Hours: 12 -2.30 / 6-11 Mon-Fri; 4-11 Sat; 12-10.30 Sun. www.agnirestaurant.com

GREEN CHILLI   TOP 100

220, King Street, W6   020 8748 0111

Business partners Head Chef Rajender Kumar, ex Maurya Sheraton Delhi's and Dubai's Kwality Hotel, G.M. and business partner Amit Dua ex Indian Taj and Oberoi 5 star hotels and Arif Khan, ex Baylis House, Slough opened Green Chilli in 2006. Light hues and 70 high-backed leather seats airily grace the venue. The cooking is mostly Punjabi with some specials from around India and a little innovation. Menu Snapshot: Kurkure Mushroom £3.95 Chef's original, fresh button mushrooms, deep-fried with a stuffing of fruity vegetable pickle and paneer. Mixed Pakora £4.25 shredded potatoes, spinach and onions, spiced with fennel, coriander and ginger, deep fried and served on a bed of sago popadums. Butter chicken £6.50, on-the-bone chicken, marinated in butter and yoghurt roasted in a tandoor; Lamb chops £6.50 , soaked overnight in dark rum marinade, spiced with crushed garlic, pounded chillies, cloves, coriander, mustard and yoghurt, cooked over live charcoal; Chicken Duck Shaslik £10.50, marinated overnight in a spicy yoghurt marinade,

skewered with onion, courgettes, tomatoes and peppers. Main course dishes: Vegetable kofta £5, vegetable dumplings served in rich curry gravy. Dal Makhani Side £4, Main Dish, £6, black lentils, slow -cooked overnight on a resting tandoor and finished with home-made butter. Kori Gassi Chicken £7.25,on-the-bone in a thin, spicy curry flavoured with roasted and ground red chillies, coriander seeds, pepper corns, cumin, coconut and garlic, finished with tamarind pulp. Laal Maas £7.50, lamb shanks cooked in hot Rajasthani masala. Bombay Fish Curry £8, simmered with doodhi (gourds), pounded cumin, coriander and aniseed finished with a tang of tamarind. Jumbo Pepper Masala £10 prawns stir fried with curry leaves, roasted moong lentils, freshly crushed black peppercorns, onions and bell peppers, topped with grated coconut. Breads include Romali Roti £2.25, whole wheat very thin bread made from unleavened dough. The desserts list is conventionally Indian: Ras Malai £3.25, Gulab Jamun with Ice cream £4, Maal pua with rabri £4, and Gajar ka Halwa £3.50. Hours: 12-3 / 6-12 Mon - Sat; 12-3 / 6-11.30 Sun.   www.greenchilliltd.co.uk=

INDIAN ZING
AWARDED BEST BOUTIQUE RESTAURANT

236 King Street, W6 0RF   020 8748 5959

Another stunner with an Indian Chef patron on this celebrated road, Indian Zing opened in 2005, but it nearly folded. Manoj Vasaikar wanted to pilot Indian Air Force jets but he failed the tests and catering college was close to his home and there he discovered he had talent as a chef. He cut his teeth at Taj and Oberoi Hotel's celebrated kandahar restaurant. In 1990 the Panjabi sisters were head-hunting chefs for their upcoming venture, Chutney Mary. Manoj became a chef de partie there, then deputy head chef then head chef at Veeraswamy. *'I learnt a lot from the two sisters'*, admits Manoj *'they are very astute in the intricacies of spicing and selecting quality ingredients.'* After a decade, like so many other Indian chefs, Manoj decided to branch out on his own opening – India 2000 in Esher, Surrey, it didn't last, nor did his other venture which followed in 2002 – Just India, SW14. But the seeds were sown, and public and critics alike loved his style. Perseverance and self-belief led to his third venture, Indian Zing. *'For the first three months of opening'*, states Manoj, *'I was losing money and almost regretted launching another restaurant. But then the reviews started to come out and I was bowled over, not only by them, but also the public reaction. I was just getting packed out and that's still happening to this day.'* Manoj is a Maharashtran, hailing from its capital Mumbai, where the food is mild and delicately spiced. The food at the restaurant is just that whilst being inventive, fresh and healthy. *'Im a great believer in taking ingredients from anywhere and using them for indian cooking. I don't think there should be any barriers so long as the strength of the*

saucing and the right balance of spicing are there in the food. *I also like simplicity, being able to talk to customers and gradually take my restaurant to a new level each year.'* You start with a free amuse-bouche of roast pumpkin, swede and parsnip rasam.Try melt-in-the-mouth green peppercorn Malai Tikka with cheese, or Vasaikar's signature Vegetable Bhanvala, a flat bhaji-style snack of onion and spices steamed and then griddled. Mains include Mevaari Chicken in a sauce of spinach, fenugreek and dill; Khyber Pass Raan made with lamb shank, poppy seeds, ginger, onion and spices; Monkfish Tikka, marinated in a green masala of coriander and mint, griddled in a clay oven, served with a tamarind relish; Tandoori Artichoke and Paneer, in a cashewnut and tomato sauce; Ghatti Lamb, from the Sahyadri Ranges with herbs and black pepper; Malvani Lamb Curry, from coastal Maharashtra using black pepper and dried coconut. In Indian Zing's decor, the ethos is comfort and quality, with a simple and elegant finish. The restaurant was designed on the principles of Hindu mythology: Vastu Shastra. Vastu means 'house' or dwelling place and its traditions create a harmony between the five elements of earth, sky, fire, water and air in the environment. Indian Zing has all the ingredients of a successful restaurant. Great service, inventive food, and relaxed atmosphere. This is somewhere I would visit for a light Indian lunch or for a relaxed evening with friends. Future plans: introducing an Ayurvedic Doctor to help customers choose the 'right' food for their unique body make up and regular food festivals. Hours: 12-2.30 / 6-1030. Branch Indian Zest, Sunbury Middx. See pages 38 & 39. www.indianzing.co.uk

SAGAR   TOP 100

157 King Street, W6   020 8741 8563

It is a pleasure to see the first South Indian in Hammersmith thriving. And you can tell it is because it is now open all day. Sagar and the other 'new' boys on the street are a pointer to the way things are heading. The public are tiring of formulaic curryhouse food and once they taste the real thing, there is no going back. Let us hope King Street is the forerunner to such superb venues nationwide. Sagar's small interior is modern with the right amount of south Indian knickknacks. Owner: S Sharmielan cooks food from Udipi, a small coastal town, north of Mangalore in the south-western state of Karnataka, celebrated for Bramin temples and cuisine. Masala Dosa originated here. By the sixth century AD, they were being made as temple feedings for thousands of worshippers. Udipi dosas are made from a thin batter cooked very thin and crisp in Karnataka and thick and small in Tamil Nadu. Also on the menu are Rasam, Sambar, Uppuma, Uthappam. Curries include Kootu, a typical Madrassi dish as found in the local homes, where it is slow-cooked in a mud pot over wood fire. It's a hot and sour curry, containing gourd, chilli, tamarind, sesame and coconut. Traditionally it's served with

Kazhani meaning 'rice-washed water'. Kootu is traditionally served with it. Try Bakabhat, a yoghurt-based rice, or Lemon rice, with cashews and curry leaves. The menu is a glossary in itself. Two temple puddings traditionally served to the public (by the thousands) at festival time are Payasam, made with vermicelli, sugar, condensed milk and cashews and Sheer,a wheat-based pudding with ghee, raisins and nuts. The staff are ever-helpful if you need menu translations. Hours: 12-11. Branch: Twickenham, Middlesex.

SHILPA   NEW ENTRANT

206 King Street, W6 0RA   020 8741 3127

2006 saw the second south Indian opening on this well endowed street and it has a good pedigree, being in the ownership of H.K.Haridas, London's most experienced Keralan restaurateur (see branches below). We are entering this restaurant because Haridas can do a great job, but we wonder whether we should. *The chef has come directly from the Taj hotel group, and the menu is mostly Keralan, with a few token north Indian dishes – quite why chicken tikka masala was felt to be necessary is beyond me. The room is a fairly narrow rectangle, with one set of tables on each side. Decor is a little eccentric, with sparkly blue lights and a couple of plasma screens showing Bollywood films. Popadums were ordinary but with more imaginative chutneys than usual: a slightly grainy but tasty coconut chutney, an over-sweet beetroot chutney as well as conventional mango chutney and a mint and yoghurt dip. A starter of Mysore Potato was not as good as the version at Rasa as it had less interesting spicing, but it had pleasant texture and a reasonably crisp exterior. Malai Murgh Tikka was tender, marinated with cheese and could have done with a little longer in the tandoor, but was certainly pleasant. At this point we waited, waited some more, and kept waiting. We ended up stacking the dirty plates at the end of our table since the waiter showed no inclination to do so, and even this action brought no response (there were all of three tables occupied at this point in the restaurant, and two waiters). The waiter was probably thinking: "hey this is a good wheeze, maybe if I keep on like this they'll bring the dishes from the kitchen as well and then I can just have a nap". Main courses were a mixed bag. Kingfish in a coconut masala was seriously overcooked, and although the coconut was decent the fish was virtually inedible. Prawns, by contrast, were just fine, nicely cooked with a tomato-based spicy sauce . Aloo Mattur went the other way, with badly undercooked potatoes in a rather bland sauce with hardly any peas. On the other hand okra, which is easy to screw up, here was quite good, a little less firm than I would have liked but by no means slimy. Naan was good, supple in texture with a little garlic flavour. Plain rice was fine). Service was absolutely dismal. [More bad service at a branch. Ed]. 'We had two courses, and this took almost two hours to serve on a night when a total of three other tables were in use. Two waiters managed to spend most of their time chatting to each other at*

the far end of the restaurant, virtually ignoring the diners. When we pointed out the problem with the (virtually untouched) king fish dish, the dish was taken away but was left on the bill. It is a long time since I have encountered service this inept. This is a shame since elements of the cooking showed ability, though two techmical errors is rather scary. Objectively I can just about score the cooking, but this could be so much better with a little more effort in both front of house and kitchen.' AH. AndyHayler.com Review

TANDOORI NIGHTS   TOP 100

319 King Street, W6   020 8741 4328

Mr Modi Udin's venue is one of the longest-standing on Curry King Street. It is pure Bangladeshi curryhouse and Modi is proud of that. He as friendly as they come, as are AB Choudhury, and his staff made the more confident with chef Mabul Miah's food. Fully licensed and air-conditioned. *'Extremely well laid out and furnished restaurant on the busy King Street. Seating for 100 with several discreet areas. Very attentive, efficient and knowledgeable staff. Succulent pieces of Tandoori Chicken with those small crispy cinders that you get on the best cooked meat. Equally enjoyable and freshly cooked Seek Kebab with just the right balance of heat and spice. Cool and fresh Cucumber Raitha with a subtle sour bite. Exceptional Roghan Josh with tender chunks of lamb in an exquisite and quite the best sauce I have had to date. Mould of aromatic, al dente Pullao and a soft, fluffy Nan. Very enjoyable.'* RW. Specialities: Bataire Masala £9.95, two quails barbecued and cooked in sauce. Sunday Buffet: £10, families welcome, concessions for children. *'Deservedly TOP 100.'* SO. Hours: 12-3 / 6-12. Branch: Twickenham, Middx.

YOU SAY OK

You may get a discount of you show them this Guide.

W6: LIGHT OF NEPAL 268 King Street, W6 ~ 020 8748 3586. Est 1979 by Jaya K Tamang & KC Druba with mostly curryhouse favourite items. Hours: 12-2.30/6-11.

HAWALI 357, King Street, W6 ~ 020 8748 7408. *'Excellent. Friendly staff, fronted by ebullient owner. Lamb Kalia £6.95 - brilliant, light sauce, almost Thai-style, loads of spring onions, ginger, garlic, suffusion of tender pieces of lamb with oodles of taste. Chum Chum Chicken £4.95, marinated chicken breast, stuffed with special chutney, barbecued in tandoor. Great glass of Lassi too!'* RW.

● **WE HEAR** Atul Kotchhar, Mayfair's Benares chef, is considering opening a fast-food outlet in Westfield, the new Shepherd's Bush mega-shopping mall. If he does, reports please.

London W8   Kensington, Notting Hill

MALABAR   TOP 100

27 Uxbridge Street, W8   020 7727 8800

Jo, Sophie and Tony Chalmers' and Anil Bis's three-floor 56-seat Malabar has quietly gone about its business since 1983. and it is a Notting Hill fixture, largely enjoyed by its clutch of locals. It is not expensive, and the care is comfortable and assured, from the cooking to the service. Despite its name, with dishes like Murgh Makhni, butter chicken, Gosht Masala – plenty of fresh mint, 'both c£8, and delicious. Five Lentil Dhall – less convincing, more spices needed. the food is more north Indian than south. Chilli Bhutta starter £4, a take on sweetcorn, is unusual. A likeable restaurant with food quite different in spicing and presentation. I wish this were in my home town, Berlin.' BH. Remains secure in our TOP 100. Hours: 12-2.45 / 6-11.30 Mon-Sat; 1-2.45, 6-10.45 Sun. Closed one week in Aug.

UTSAV

17 Kensington High St, W8   020 7368 0022

Entrepreneur owner of Malabar Junction, WC2, Ashok Modi launched Utsav, meaning 'festival' in 2003. It has 150 seats on two floors, almost opposite the Royal Garden Hotel. Architects Astore Harrison have designed contemporary decor, outside (striking glass, and blues, and a cute use of the first floor bay window. Inside an attractive wooden bar, white walls, creative lighting, theming blues and blondes. The food by chef Gowtham Karingi, ex Zaika sous chef (see next entry) is pan-Asian, a bit from here and a bit from there. Ok if the chefs understand regional spicing immaculately, and that they can get difficult ingredients. We felt perhaps the Goan Prawn Balchao lacked that sourness only achieved from toddy vinegar, while Kashmiri chilli would have helped the Roghanjosh. And there were too many squiggly dots and squirls (a Ziaka trick, passée in our opinion). That said, the Tirangi Chicken Tikka, marinated in saffron, cheese and coriander, was masterly. The Chicken Varutha in tamarind, red chilli, shallots, curry leaves & tomato sauce had spot on south Indian tastes, as did the fine Dosa and chutneys. The Paneer was fresh and juicy. Service charge 12.5%. Hours: 11.30-3 daily / 6-11 Mon - Thurs; 11.30 Fri & Sat; 10.30 Sunday.

ZAIKA   A-LIST

1 Kensington High Street, W8   020 7795 6533

This was Claudio Pulze and Raj Sharma (owners of SW1's celebrated Al Duca and Fiore Italian restaurants) was their first Indian venture (with Vineet) before the now-closed Deya. Set in a former bank, which bestows on it carved high ceilings and double height windows,

with their crimson swag curtains. The interior is elegant with ivory and buff paint scheme and wood panelling. Seats have various coloured backs. Delhi-born Sanjay Dwivedi is probably the brightest star to have qualified as a chef via the celebrated Ealing's Thames Valley Catering College's Asian course. At first he practised his continental skills, but his Indian roots soon came to the fore and he joined Zaika when it first opened in 1999 as Vineet's deputy. After a short secondment to open Deya W1, he returned to Zaika as head chef when Vineet departed to open his own venue (Rasoi Vineet Bhatia). Head Barman Davide Farchica residing in his 'Bedouin-style' 25-seat cocktail bar has cocktails from £7 to £36 and if you think that's expensive, how about the Louis Roederer "Cristal" 1989 champagne at £700.00, which makes an n/v glass at £12.50, or a glass of house white wine at £5.50 seem inexpensive!, which are just three of the items on Luigi Gaudino's constantly changing wine list. *This was my debut trip here and a business lunch, a colleague and me entertaining (for want of a better word!) three clients. The service was faultless throughout our meal and I don't recall ever seeing a wine list quite like it – quite intimidating to those of us more at home with beer and whisky! Thankfully my colleague was on hand to wade through the options and whatever it was he did choose was fantastic. But it is the food at Zaika that is the real star of the show. I have for some time had my eye on the Jugalbandi Vegetarian Tasting Menu, my colleague choosing the omnivorous 6-course Jugalbandi Tasting Menu (both c £40 per head) consisting of 1) scallop; 2) duck kebab;3) seabass with 'dosa' potatoes served with 'sambhar'- lentil and vegetable sauce; 4) Spiced wild mushroom rice, mini popadum & tomato 'makhni' ice cream; 5) Roghan Josh cooked in a rich onion & tomato sauce served with saffron rice; 6) Kulfi [with 5 glasses of different wines c£60]. Our three clients all chose a la carte, which made us look incredibly greedy but never mind, I wasn't going to miss this opportunity! In addition to these, Zaika also served an appetiser beforehand, making it one of the most filling meals I have ever had! My meal consisted of: Paneer Platter, Aloo Chat, Samosa, Mains: Khumbi Tamatri Khichidi, Subzi Ki Thali with Utthapam, and pud: Reshmi Mithai. I can say little more than every single course was absolutely superb, in terms of appearance, texture and taste. As we were with people who had ordered a la carte, it sometimes felt that our tasting meals were served a little slowly, bit it seems churlish to mention this given the quality and quantity of food. If I was to pick out one dish from the vegetarian menu however, it would have to be the Utta Pam, though admittedly I am a sucker for anything southern Indian! My colleague was equally complimentary about the omnivorous menu by the way. Two of the clients chose Biriyani, one vegetable and one chicken. I have to say I have never seen it served the way it was at Zaika, which was just rice with the vegetables/chicken mixed-in and no sauce, but they both said it was exceptionally good and there was certainly an awful lot of it! Suffice to say Zaika was excellent in pretty much every way and certainly worthy of the many accolades it has received since it opened. For the group of five of us the total bill came to a little under* £200, *which was good value for what we had. I would be looking forward to going again, but I'm afraid I have Tamarind in my sights for the next spot of client entertainment.'* AG. A la carte Food prices range from c£6.50 to £10 for starters and c£13 to £23 for main courses. The pre-theatre dinner (6 - 6.30) is a reasonable £16 for two Courses and £18 for three. Dwivedi's continental hand and his time with Vineet shows through with flavours and ingredients which are not Indian. Ingredients such as rosemary, basil and olive oil are distinctively European and do not sit easily on my Indian palette. That said Zaika is a well-oiled, competent venue, usefully placed for the Albert Hall and the Royal Lancaster Hotel. Service 12.5%. Hours: Lunch: 12-2.45, Sun - Fri / 6.30-10.45, Mon - Sat; 9.45 Sun. www.zaika-restaurant.co.uk

London W11 Holland Park

BOMBAY BICYCLE CLUB   NEW TOP 100

Holland Park, 128 Holland Park Av, W11 4UE
020 7727 7335

Today's BBCs are open to all who love Indian food. It has grown to three restaurants and 15 on-line delivery

outlets which all have in common a great logo of a turbaned Raj-style waiter holding a serving dish while riding a penny farthing. Decor, like at Rasa, has a penchant for pink and is *'extremely pretty.'* RL.
Hours: 7-11. Restaurant branches: Hampstead, Holland Park. Del: Battersea, Chiswick, City, East Dulwich , Friern Barnet, Fulham, Greenwich, Islington, Little Venice, Putney, Tooting, Surbiton, West Hampstead, Wimbledon and Weybridge. See pic left and rear cover. www.thebombaybicycleclub.co.uk

London W13 West Ealing

LACUNA   TOP 100

1-4 Culmington Pde, 123 Uxbridge Rd, W13
020 8579 9992

You cannot miss the huge frontage, decorated with individually planted conifers in square wooden tubs.

And you should not miss going in to this 120-seater restaurant with its stylishly decorations in pastel shades, with arches and ceiling fans. Established in 1984 by Sunil Lamba, (with relations to London's Gaylord) and it's been in this Guide since then, serving competent north Indian formula food. It's built up a large local following, and in its time it's seen so many new Indian restaurants come and go in Ealing, and even now it stands out above the 25 or so competitors, a chupatti-throw away. Laguna Special Butter Chicken £5.95 is the most popular dish. Service 10%. Sun. 12-12. www.lagunarestaurant.com Branch: Mr Lamba is proud of his outside catering department, and what a party with a difference it will make when you use the service. at Laguna Banquet Hall, North Acton Road, NW10.

MONTY'S TANDOORI

54 Northfields Avenue, W13　　020 8566 5364

'My curryholic daughter moved to Ealing and sussed Monty's out pretty quickly and invited me their on my previous visit. Lovely decor, swift service, fresh salad and yoghurt dip. Pops and picks were served while we ordered and this immediately relaxed us for a pleasant evening. Spicing and quality subtle and superb. We were stuffed, enough left for a meal for two in the freezer. Why black ceilings in the toilet? ' AIE. 'Highly recommended.' SO.). Hours: 12-3/6-12. Branch: Monty's, Broadway Centre, W5. (and more menu details).

YOU SAY OK

You may get a discount of you show them this Guide.

WI3: CARDAMOM INDIA 86 Northfields Ave, West Ealing, W13 ~ 020 8840 1634. Opened 2003 by Shipu, Shaikh and Chef Khan. Hours: 12-2.30/5.30-11.30.

WI4: AL'INDIENNE 197 North End Road, Olympia W14 ~ 020 7610 2020. Owner MJ.Arshad and Chef Raja give a *'good smiling welcome and excellent food in abundance.'* JL. Hours: 5.30-12. Sunday buffet: 5-1130.

London WC

Area: West End
Postcodes WC1, WC2
Population: 165,000

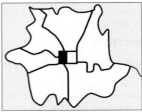

See page 72 for key to this map.

London WC1　　　　　　　　Holborn

HASON RAJA　　　　　　　　A-LIST

84 Southampton Row, WC1　　020 7242 3377

This 150-seat Holborn restaurant is named after a 19th century Bangladeshi poet-playboy who led a life full of drama, colour and romance. Established in 2003 its owner Rafu Miah (pictured with customer Ricky Gervais), has put his 30 years industry experience into creating an venue with elegant surroundings, adorned with immaculate suede Italian furniture and fresh flowers, an exotic feel, which complements its theatrical inspiration. The menu is Indian and Bangladeshi. Signature dishes include the Satkora Mangsho, a traditional Bangladeshi dish of diced shank of lamb cooked with wild Bangladeshi lemons; Anari Chaamp, tawa grilled lamb in a star anise and pomegranate sauce; the innovative Goose Ki Parchy, french goose in an aniseed and poppy seed blueberry sauce and the chef's special recipe Garlic Murgh Tawa, tender chicken cooked with tomatoes and green peppers with a touch of ginger and garlic. The vegetarian options are equally appetising with Tandoori Phool, roasted broccoli with

olives and crushed peppers and Kumbeki Sheek Kebabs, an outstanding dish of mushrooms, yam and paneer with mixed spices. Service is spot-on at affordable prices. If your favourite dish doesn't appear on the menu then the they'll ensure that it is prepared for you. Nominated as Best UK Bangladeshi restaurant by this Guide. Private room 20 plus another area in the basement for overflow or special functions. Lunch: 12 dish buffet for just £10. Hours:12-11.30.   www.hasonraja.co.uk

MALABAR JUNCTION

107 Great Russell St, WC1   020 7580 5230

Owned by Ashok Modi it specialises in Keralan cuisine. Decor: light, bright and airy restaurant with Victorian-styled glass skylight giving good light. Bamboo chairs, palm trees in polished brass pots, original paintings, a marble fountain and smiling Keralan waiters complete the scene. Meat and chicken is eaten by most of the population in south India; being expensive, it's mainly on festivals and weddings. Fish is loved on the coastal and river districts. Starters: Lamb Cutlets, £5, patties of spicy minced lamb, bread crumbed and fried, served with tomato sauce and salad, King Prawn Fry £8.50, with ginger, garlic, spices and sliced coconut, Malabar Chicken £8.50 with coconut, curry leaves, garlic and mustard, Spinach Vadai £3 fried crunchy doughnut of Chana dal, green chillies, onion, ginger, curry leaves and fresh spinach served with chutneys. And if you have any room left Banana Leaf Cake £4, rice with sweet filling of coconut, banana and jaggery wrapped in banana leaf and steamed – divine. The bar and further dining facilities are downstairs. '*We love this place so after a visit to the British museum, we couldn't wait for lunch there. But we found a dullness in the food, a lack of love in it, which disappointed. Bad day; bad time or what?*' DBAC. '*The waiter managed to knock one glass of gin and tonic over the table and carpet and seemed to have forgotten that we had ordered a starter. Overall a good meal and enjoyed the informal atmosphere, but the food was nothing particularly out of the ordinary.*' Cannon DY. Hours: bar: 11-11, except Sun: 12-10.30; Restaurant: 12-3/6-11.30.

RASA MARICHAM

1 Kings Cross Road, WC1   0871 0757217

Located in the 405-room Holiday Inn which opened a 160-seater 'Indian' at this venue in 1998. It had Goan chefs and lasted a year or two. It reopened as a branch of the Original Lahore Kebab House, serving really gutsy carnivorous Pakistani food. That lasted a couple of years. For its third incarnation, it has turned to the Keralan Rasa restaurant group to make it work. Maricham means black pepper, and pepper, particularly Keralan pepper is India's king of spices, her biggest spice export. This major spice was the heat-giver before chillies arrived from Brazil in the 16th century. Keralan food had been developed centuries before Christ, and

pepper was and still is a big player in recipes. Take Mulligatawny. It literally means 'pepper water'. Das's spin told us that the menu would be 'showcasing' black pepper'. Pepper, the menu tells '*is used to cure digestive problems such as wind, constipation, nausea and diarrhoea.*' Hmm! Just what we need to read before eating. But if it hasn't got you on the run (to the exit), stay. On a recent visit the service was very friendly and helpful, despite being given the impression that the restaurant, which was all-but empty, had closed. (It was just 9.50pm). We had the pops and pickles trays, then Potato Bonda, three balls of mashed potato dipped in chickpea flour batter and deep-fried (best dish we chose). Nair Masala Dosa was limp not crisp, Sambar, rather too thick but plenty of drumsticks, Rasam not bad. Varutharacha Kozhy Curry chicken with coconut, dried red chillies, curry leaves and tomatoes, not as good as Quilon's and Appam, a crisp, spongy rice pancake, which was rather thick and lacked finesse. The venue lacks atmosphere, reminding one of many an Indian hotel restaurant, which would not matter except for the fact that the food, in gargantuan portions, was just ordinary, as if the chefs are just going through the motions, though inexpensive at £40 inc wine for 2. Other menu items are detailed on the N16 branch. 4 course non veg meal, £20. Vegetarian £15.00. Service: 12%. Hours; 12.30-2.30 / 6-10.30. Branches: See Rasa London N16. Great website: www.rasarestaurants.com

London WC2 Aldwych, Covent Garden

YOU SAY OK

You may get a discount of you show them this Guide.

WC2: BHATTI 37 Great Queen Street, WC2 ~ 020 7405 5222. Owned since by 1990 by N. Ruparel. Seats 95 in 2 rooms. Del: £25 min, 4m. Hours: 12-2.45; 2 Sun / 5.30-11.45; 10.30 Sun.

INDIA CLUB   A-LIST

143 The Strand, WC2   020 7836 0650

On the basis that if it ain't broke, don't fix it (something this venue totally believes in) we can't better these comments, so here they are again. '*Previously we had visited during the week, so was quieter on Saturday lunch. Warm welcome. Soon settled with an excellent bottle of chilled white wine which we had managed to extricate from 'the lady down stairs!'* [Doris: Ed] '*We were offered and accepted the set meal £11 a head, pointing out that one of our number was vegetarian. This included Popadums – excellent with chutneys and pickles. Chilli Bhajias, Onion Bhajias, Masala Dosa and Tandoori Chicken. After a pause Lamb and Chicken Curry, Dall, Aubergine, Mixed Vegetable Potato and Chickpea, rice – plenty! Really too much for even us .. but all hot, fresh and tasty. Only one waiter, even when four other tables were occupied, but he was very cheery with repeated assurances that he would bring anything else we required! Not sure about the repainted walls, glad about the retained pictures and ancient stair carpet!*' GM. '*What can you say about The India Club.*

The same unsmiling welcome greets you – the head waiter being the same misery who served us on our last visit. Neither the ladies nor the gents had lights, there was still no Lassi (there never is!), the chutney and onion salad were both served piled up in saucers, there was no attempt at presentation but the food was sublime and what value for money with the quantities just right.' G&MP. And what's left to say about this much-loved venue? Plenty: 'Hi, I would like to add some comments of my own which may be of interest to you and your readers. I first came across this restaurant in the early 1970s when I worked for the London offices of an Indian newspaper chain in Carmelite Street, London. The India Club was a regular haunt of the Indian journalists based in London and home to an institution called 'the India League' an organisation that promoted Indian business and cultural interests in Britain. I first dined there at a reception held for the Indian statesman Krishma Menon a contemporary of Jaharwal Nehru the first prime minister of Independent India. On crossing the threshold again in 2004 was just like being in a timewarp; everything seemed to be the same. Up the steps past the hotel reception desk called 'The Hotel Strand Continental'. The manager of the Hotel in the 1970s had I seem to recall managed to install almost his entire family who occupied half a dozen rooms at one time. It turned out that he had been fleecing the place for years before someone actually checked the books and sacked him. I peeked into the same bar and the same lounge and then walked up the same stairs to the same restaurant. When I first went there all those years ago no-one could ever remember a time when the lift was in use. It had worked once apparently but the management had forgotten to renew the guarantee and the parts were all out of date, even in the 1970s. The woman at the bar has to be called Doris and has been there since forever. There used to be a legendary eastern european woman called Christine who waited at tables in the restaurant. I first took my fiancée to eat there in the early 1980s and it hadn't changed in ten years and I suppose I had got used to the slow service and taken the luke warm food for granted but my fiancee was very keen on hot food and trying to impress her I asked Christine if she would mind heating it up a bit. Christine gave me a look of daggers and said 'I try' and emerged ten minutes later 'wiz warmed plates - okay is better?' [for what it's worth. Indians prefer lukewarm food because they eat with their fingers, and they say it tastes better,! Ed.]

'It made absolutely no difference of course but then I wasn't personally that bothered. Returning in 2004 I noted the same pictures on the wall; one of Krishma Menon, one of Gandhi, one of the Indian poet Tagore and the same funny cubist paintings that must have once been daring but just look very dated now. The food though is very basic and totally different to the average fare you can expect at the curryhouse. When I say basic I don't mean to be insulting to the chef as this is high praise indeed. Try the Masala Dosai that come with coconut sauce – out of this world. As you rightly say probably not the place to take someone you are trying to impress. It worked for me though as my fiancée became my wife and we have been married for nearly twenty two years so it can't have been that bad. I used to regularly dine there in the 1970s and early

1980s with a couple of work colleagues but some people will undoubtedly be put off by the funny decor and the almost stand-offish nature of the waiters. They don't keep you waiting for that long but don't go over the top in trying to please you either like they do in your average high street tandoori. Oh by the way did I mention that the fire escape out the back that can be seen from the rear dining room and men's toilet windows which is also 'just the same?' BB. If you really want to know what the average Indian eating dive is like, this is it. Decor, presentation, smiling and saying please and thank you are not what matters: Cooking super food and getting your order to your table at affordable prices, is what matters. Not a Michelin-star formula (M's loss), so virtually devoid of posers and high on our A-LIST. Although it is unlicensed, you can buy Cobra, wine etc on the premises, or you can BYO no corkage charge. Hours: 12-2.30 / 6-10.50; closed Sun.

MASALA ZONE   A-LIST

48 Floral Street, Covent Garden WC2E 9DA
020 7379 0101

Summer 2007 saw the launch of this branch located opposite the now-disused old stage door and tall scene-dock doors of the Royal Opera House. For aficionados of opera, ballet and decent Indian food, this branch

cannot be better placed. In fact, we had a backstage tour of the House in the morning, popped in to Masala Zone for lunch and enjoyed all our usual Bombay Street snacks, went back to the House for a show and returned to Masala Zone in the evening for a Thali dinner before going home! It's a large restaurant, seating 200, but it doesn't feel like a barn, due to the clever location of the kitchen, which is in the middle of the main dining room. A bright and colourful display of Indian puppets hanging from the ceilings make for a interesting alternative on decoration, but I wouldn't like to have to dust them!. There is a no booking policy, you just turn up, sit and eat. If it is full, you never have to wait long, as a table will become empty soon. We have only ever waited a maximum of 5 minutes. Hours: 12-11; 1230-1130 Sun. For full menu description and list of branches, see Masala Zone, W1. www.masalazone.com

MELA   TOP 100

152 Shaftesbury Av, WC2H 8HL   020 7836 8635

When ex-Soho Spice chef Kuldeep Singh, with Sanjay Singh Sighat and Surinder Kumar Mehra (all Taj-trained chefs) opened Mela (meaning 'festival') in 2000, they pioneered an original idea to capture a vast potential lunch trade, always illusive at the Indian restaurant. Instead of sandwiches, choose naan, roomali, paratha, roti, puri and bhatura, appam, uttapams (served with coconut chutney), or dosa with a topping (filling) choice of as many curries as you can imagine, dozens of them. 2 for a simple choice to £5 for a Gourmet Snack Lunch. It was an instant success. The restaurant is open all day but it changes atmosphere in the evening, becoming more relaxed. Clean lines of white washed walls, large seemless mirrors and a few embroidered cushion covers, from Orissa. Square terracotta floor tiles, plastic wood-effect tables (sounds horrid but not), simple wooden chairs upholstered in spicy coloured fabric. The menu describes itself as *'Indian Cuisine – Country Style'*, which we interpret as Indian home-cooking. Kuldeep says *"ingredients here in England are much better than back home. This is a chef's paradise."* And he proves it with dishes such as Bater Khada Masala, marinated quails roasted in a spicy mango masala, and Malabari Seafood Stew, mixed seafood with turnip, cauliflower, coconut milk and coriander *'I decided to start with Gosht Utthapams – fluffy rice pancakes topped with diced, chargrilled lamb, onion, pepper, freshly grated coconut and served with minty coconut chutney. A monogrammed square plate arrived with the* promised two pancakes and a small salad of carrot, beetroot, cucumber and green leaves tossed in a lightly spiced dressing – delicious. Pat decided on a Raj Kachauri, mini puries stuffed with seasoned potato, chick peas, onion and topped with mint and tamarind chutneys. What arrived was one large stuffed puri, in a bowl, which looked as impressive as it tasted. Mains were Khatta Khargosh, curried rabbit and Kori Gassi, chicken on the bone in a thin, spicy curry flavoured with chilli, spices, coconut tamarind. We accompanied our dishes with Plain Rice £1.95, Romali Roti – better than the offering at Benares – and Mirch Baingan Ka Salan, baby aubergines in peanut-flavoured yoghurt gravy, which never arrived and I decided not to remind them. Mela is a lovely restaurant, with cheerful waiters, serving lovely Indian food.*' DBAC. This is echoed by HC: *'Charming and authoritative person in charge. Whole place was running well. Food, again outstandingly good, definitely a very good restaurant – amazing menu.'* HC. Hours: 12-11.30; 10.30pm Sunday.

MOTI MAHAL   A-LIST

45 Great Queen Street, WC   020 7240 9329

It opened in 2005 with a remarkable pedigree, the story of which which I will share with you. The tandoor, the ancient clay oven, and its offspring tikka, meaning 'a little piece', had been an unintentionally well-kept secret in its place of origin, the rugged, inhospitable, mountainous area of Pakistan/Afghanistan for centuries, When Kundan Lal Gujral opened Moti Mahal to serve tandoori dishes in 1920 in Peshawar it was the only such restaurant in the world. Then in 1947 along came partition, the separation of one nation into the states of India and Pakistan. One of the unforeseen effects of partition was the fleeing of population who being of the 'wrong' religion feared persecution. Hindus fled from what became Pakistan into India and vice-versa. One such Hindu political refugee, that restaurant owner, fled from Peshawar taking his tandoors with him. In 1948 he established Moti Mahal in Daryaganj, Delhi making it not only India's first tandoori restaurant, but one of India's very few restaurants of any kind. It remained the place to go for decades. I was taken there in 1984 by a Delhi friend of mine, who remarked, *'Visiting Delhi and not eating at Moti Mahal is like going to Agra and not seeing the Taj Mahal'*. Tandoori in Britain was in its infancy at that time, and I can truly say I had never tasted Tandoori items as good as there. So successful were they that Moti Mahal embarked on the franchising route and now have over 30 franchise Motis, many in Delhi and they are looking for more franchisees all over India. So Moti Mahal finally opened in London under the ownership of the founder's grandson. Monish Gujral. You will be forgiven for finding it hard to find. Its signage is tiny and high up and the full-length, full-height glowing window display of bottles looks like an extension of the pub next door, but it is the Moti. The 85-seat restaurant spans two floors. Guests can join the bustling ground floor bar

and dining area. The main interior is raw-stone-walled, while natural linen and cotton cloths and upholstery give the Indian feel. Dark heat-treated oak floors are offset against the orange silk wall hangings. The copper-backed open kitchen is busy with chefs at their the tandoors. Candle lanterns lead you downstairs to a more intimate dining room and another bar where 80 different whiskeys are displayed on illuminated glass shelves. Moti selected Anuirudh Arora, formerly at Oberoi's Hotel Udavilas then sous chef at Benares. His menu reflects a wee bit of new-wave but it remains true to the original Moti with the meats of the Northwest Frontier high on the agenda. Moti claim to have invented the Tandoori Chicken, Murgh Makhani (Butter Chicken) and the famous Dal Makhani. They did not (the Moghuls did] but they do these dishes to perfection. As you might expect, their Tandoori dishes feature large and include Murgh ka Soola (grilled supreme of chicken with cracked pepper and dill), Ajwain Aur Pilli Mirch Ki Machhi (organic salmon in carom seeds, yellow chillies and yoghurt) and venison kebab. Appetisers include dishes such as Sagar Rattan (scallops tossed with tamarind and baby tomatoes and pan fried crab cakes) and Shammi Sheekapur (ground lamb kebab from the erstwhile kitchens of Awadh – lamb patties filled with yoghurt, mint and onion) and Pan-fried cakes of corn, spinach and lentils. Main course dishes include Kadal Muthu Mappas (mussels, squid and monkfish simmered in coconut and curry leaf), which can be had with variety of accompaniments. '*We tried to go in through a closed door, which didn't help, but once inside found a light, airy , modern restaurant. The service overall was friendly and welcoming, though one could easily feel that the female maitre d' was a little overbearing. To see the chefs in their open-kitchen preparing the breads, kebabs etc and using the tandoor was fascinating. The food was outstanding. Our starters included wonderful tandoori -baked stuffed new potatoes which were so delicate and soft you wondered whether they were potatoes at all! The main courses however were the stars of the show, particularly the paneer simmered in a rich, tomato sauce. The mixed vegetable curry was very dry, beautifully spiced and contained almost no sauce at all; a welcome change as vegetable curries can often be all sauce and nothing else! The black lentil Dal Makhani provided a bit more moisture. We had mint paratha, which was just sublime and gave everything an unusually refreshing edge!! Just fantastic food. The coup de grace however, was the outstanding malt whisky menu. As one would expect from a restaurant like this, the prices were approx double what they really should be, but the range was superb. I had an 18 year old Caol Ila at 46%. Beautiful. Meal with wine and service charge: around £45pp. A wonderful experience.*' AG. We were pleased to give them our BEST NEWCOMER AWARD last time. And despite an unpleasant phone call from an abusive manager, Sebastian that we were in effect, crooks for invoicing him for an ad he had forgotten he had ordered, we still keep in them in our A-List. Hours: 12-3/530-11.30; Closed Sun.   www.motimahal-uk.com

PUNJAB   A-LIST

80 Neal Street, WC2   020 7836 9787

The Punjab opened in 1947 in Aldgate and moved to its present site in 1951, making it the oldest UK Punjabi restaurant. For its entire life it has been in the capable hands of just two men, the late founder and now his son Sital Singh Maan. The venue has several areas. Some prefer the rear room with its more modern looks. Others prefer the side room which seems to retain its Indian looks. The Punjab was one of the original pioneers of the curry formula. Only here it is done as it has always been done, and as it should be. The result is unlike the newer Bangladeshi clones, and is probably what old farts think they remember when they say '*curry isn't like it used to be*'. CT is a bit suspicious if the redec; '*the wooden tree is quite striking. Seems not to have weakened the food.*' CT. The food is meat-orientated, spicy, savoury and very tasty. Specialities: Anari Gosht £8, pomegranate and lamb, Benaam Macchi Tarkari £8, nameless fish curry, Acharri Murgha £8.50, pickled chicken. Also try the Vegetable Koofta £5, diced pumpkin with spices and herbs made into balls. '*Chicken Methia – beautifully flavoured and chicken was real quality. Linda had Chicken Tikka flambéed with brandy at the table – spectacular.*' MG. Regulars have their own club, the 'Punjabbers'. Service 10%. Hours: 12-3/6-11.30; 10.30 Sun.   www.punjab.co.uk

YOU SAY OK
You may get a discount of you show them this Guide.

WC2: SITAR BALTI 149 The Strand, WC2 ~ 020 7836 3730. '*Now opens at 5.30 so we can get to the theatre without a rush. Prices higher than av, but food warrants.*' D&HC.

ST MARTIN'S SPICE 92, St Martin's La, WC2 ~ 020 7379 9355. '*One of our guests has always been very anti-Indian restaurant. Luckily it passed with flying colours. Service efficient and friendly, all the food very good and prices are reasonable. £116 for 4 inc two bottles of wine and liqueurs.*' HC. T/a: 10% disc, £10 min. Delivery: 5m, £10 min. Hours: 5.30-1.30, 12 Fri & Sat.

TANDOORI NIGHTS 35 Great Queen Street, WC2 ~ 020 7831 2558. Owner Mrs Yasmeen Rashid opened here 1993. Service 12.5%. Lunch and dinner, daily.

TAILPIECE

We've received many reports about rude, inefficient, forgetful, 'don't-care' service. Marina O'Loughlin, eloquently wrote this about Urban Turban, W2 in Metro 27.02.08 '*I wonder if the waiting staff have been taking lessons from legendary (read rude) Khan's across the road. When we're not being ignored by harried floor waiters, we're being condescended to by a manager who seems to fondly imagine himself somewhere more elitist than this is supposed to be. He's living in his own private Groucho Club, permanently accessorised by an invisible velvet rope.*' [Khan's W2 has been delisted from this Guide at the request of their PR woman objected to us mentioning their rude behaviour, despite us giving them a TOP 100 listing. Denial or what?]

ENGLAND

The entries in this Guide are recorded in alphabetical order: first the county then, within that, the town, then the restaurant. With the demise of Avon, we now start with Bedfordshire, the first town we record is Arlesey, and its first restaurant is Raj Villa, and so on. Our last English county is Yorkshire West, in which Shipley is the last entered English town (on page 308).

BEDFORDSHIRE

Area: East of England.
Population: 600,000
Adjacent Counties:
Bucks, Cambs,
Herts and
Northants.

Bedford

BLUE GINGER   NEW ENTRANT

116, Bedford Road, Kempston   01234 856 800

Blonde wooden floors, alternate white and paprika coloured walls, cream leather high back chairs, white linen place settings, abstract art on walls. Menu Snapshot: Mass Biran £4.50, fillets of fish spiced and cooked on a chargrill; Ostrich Tikka £5.50, Chicken Momo £3.50, shredded chicken cooked with medium spices, wrapped in a puri; Jalshah Duck, £10 - breast of duck, medium hot masala; Broccoli Bhaji £3; Saag Naan £1.80. *'We're regulars. Owner and staff always welcoming and the loos spotless. Decor is modern and the chairs are comfortable. The restaurant is small. The food is always freshly cooked, tasty and nicely presented. Portions are such that we never get beyond starters (to share) and mains. A good restaurant, one we do recommend to friends.'* S&MR. Takeaway: 10% disc, £10 min. Hours: 12-2(resvn only)/5.30-11.30.

CHOUDHURY'S OPEN KITCHEN

2 The Broadway, Bedford   01234 356162

'We have travelled quite extensively in India and Sri Lanka and Indian restaurants in the south of England and we have come to the conclusion that Choudhury's is best.'It's the largest restaurant in Beds and has been beautifully refurbished. It has a new menu with some tasty new and exciting dishes including fish. You can watch your meals being prepared hence the new name.' PE.

SAAGAR   NEW ENTRANT

71, Tavistock Street, Bedford   01234 400026

'The food is brilliant, King Prawn Korma and Salty Lassi is my favourite. The staff are all charming and extremely attentive - nothing is too much trouble and the food is great.' SF. email your reservation to: saagarindian@hotmail.co.uk

Luton

ALANKAR

276 Dunstable Road, Luton   01582 455189

'Took advice from the Guide and was very impressed. Looked, from outside rather peculiar for a curry house. However, the food was of excellent standard. Reminded me of Madhu's, Southall. Not quite as good but the menu was vast. Had Kebabs and Lamb Chops, all came sizzling. Fish Masala very enjoyable. I must also say the spicy Popadums were the best I've had, full of flavour. Well worth a mention, would go again without a doubt. Nearly forgot, they served a beautiful dish called Begun Bortha, which is mashed aubergine. It was wonderful, trust me'. LH.

YOU SAY OK
You may get a discount if you show them this Guide.

ARLESEY: RAJ VILLA 27 High Street, Arlesey ~ 01462 835145. 70-seater owned by Akthar Ali since 1996. Branches: Raj Gat, Bedford St, Ampthill, and Raj Moni, Upper Street, London, N1.

BEDFORD:

ALAMIN TANDOORI 51 Tavistock St. ~ 01234 330066. Gulzar Miah's 42-seater. Hours: 12-2 / 6-12; 12.30 Sat.

GULSHAN 69 Tavistock St, Bedford ~ 01234 355544. Owners: Mrs BK Nijjer and Pakistani food by Chef Shanu Miah. *'Try Lamb Sharab, lamb tikka in cream and almond liqueur'* BB. Hours: 12-2 / 6-1.

MEAH TANDOORI 102 Park Street, Luton 01582 454504. *'Delightful.'* DS. *'Very impressed with the personal service and the splendid Chicken Shashlick.'* AW. *'A good restaurant'.* TK.

BERKSHIRE

Area: South East England
(west of London)
Population: 816,000
Adjacent Counties:
Hants, Surrey, Middx,
Oxon, Wilts

Cookham

MALIK'S   TOP   100

Royal Exchange, High St   01628 520085

Set in a former country pub, complete with clinging ivy,

and olde beams, this restaurant takes its name from Malik Ahmed, who, with partner Mujibur Rahman, runs front of house. He promises to give you food cooked to the highest standards, along with good wines, elegant surroundings and a wealth of atmosphere. And from reports received, he does it. Sun buffet lunch e-a-m-a-y-l Adult - c£11 Child - c£8. Super banquet (evenings) £18.95 per head (minimum of four) as follows:: Murgh Satta (Chicken with ginger and mushroom), Murgh Tikka Masala (chicken) Chingri Saag (King Prawn with spinach), Lamb Pasanda (Very mild lamb) Accompanied by Bengali Vegetable and Rice, Peshwari & Plain. Hours: 12-2.30 / 6-12. Branch: 14 Oakend Way, Gerrards Cross, Bucks. www.maliks.co.uk

YOU SAY OK
You may get a discount if you show them this Guide.

CAVERSHAM: THE GURKHA INN 64 George Street. ~ 0118 948 3974. Popular 42-seater. Car park nearby. Del: 3m £12 min. Hours: 12.30-2.30/6-11.30.

CROWTHORNE: VILLAGE TANDOORI 204 Dukes Ride. ~ 01344 780118

HUNGERFORD: MOONLIGHT 43 High St. ~ 01488 685252

ETON: GOLDEN CURRY 46 High St. ~ 01753 863961. *'Still there and very good.'* BT.

READING: GULSHAN TANDOORI Wokingham Rd ~ 0118 966 799799. *'Owner Mr Raja always eager to hear our views with a view to improve. Our answer is always same, food is nice - keep it that way.'* HBR. *'The best in Indian Cuisine.'* SSJ.

Eton

TIGER GARDEN

47 High Street, Eton	01752 866310

Situated in 'The Cockpit', built in 1420, where Charles II was a spectator. Note the stocks outside for ancient punishment. Menu Snapshot: Dhal Pakora £3.50 – lentils mashed with onion, coriander, battered and fried. Enda Bhunjon £4.95 – spiced egg halves in aromatic onion sauce. Mass Biran £15.95 – boal fish steak, pan fried with green chillies. T/a: 15% disc. Hours: 12-2.30 / 6-11. Branches: West Street, Marlow. 01628 482211. Tiger Cub: 29 Station Rd, Marlow. 01628 482020. www.tigergarden.co.uk

Reading

KATHMANDU KITCHEN

59, Whitley St, Reading	0118 986 4000

This 90 seater opened in 2001 and changed ownership to Nikul Patel in 2005, after which we received several favourable reports on Manager Navib Thapa's service and Chef Purja's food. True it has only a few Nepalese dishes on the otherwise standard menu. Try the Momo, or special Noodles, or the underrated Shak-Sukha, a Nepalese mince dish. Our our Indian friends like the place. *'It fairly recently changed hands and you can see a great deal of improvements in the service at this big restaurant. You will notice that the restaurant is getting fuller every week. By contrast, the owner, Nikul Patel, is a young chap and he is equally dedicated to this new business, enthusiastic and eager to improve. Although he appears new in the business and in the area, with his talent, he is learning the ropes pretty quickly. You see constant improvement inside and outside and a great deal of improvement in the taste of food with the same chef working there. I wrongly judged him first by his lower prices but then realised that he has to do that, being right in the middle of the most deprived ward in this country! We all admire the food, service and personal touch at this restaurants and would like to recommend you to feature it in your Guide.'* HBR. Good Gimmick: If you live within 3m, and spend £80 or more (max 4 diners) you get a chauffeur service. Hours: 11-2.30 / 5 -11.

SPICE OVEN

4 Church Street, Caversham	0118 948 1000

Fully Licensed. Air conditioned. *'Very impressed by quality of decor, feeling of spacious seating. Service very friendly and prompt. Waiters' uniforms modern, tasteful. Number of starters comparatively small compared to many restaurants, but quality very high. The 2004 GUIDE describes food, spicy and not for the faint hearted - certainly true. Started with Chicken Tikka Malai - flavour absolutely heavenly! Flavours of Chicken Tikka Biriani, Chicken Ajwaini, Dal Kabila, Pullau Rice and Roti - intense, bursting into a play of sensations across the taste buds, a well planned melody. Minor complaint, Biriani overpowering cardamom.'* R&NT. *'The food tends to be on the spicy side and not for the faint hearted. The restaurant is large, luxurious with wood carved fittings. The Taj-trained Indian chef produces authentic regional food. The prices reasonable. One of the best. A great addition to the Reading curry scene.'* GP. Hours: 12-2.30 / 6-11.

STANDARD NEPALESE

141 Caversham Rd, Reading	0118 959 0093

Established 1980. Seats 140. 8 parking places at front. Pond and fountain as centrepiece. Nepalese specials include Kathmandu Aloo. *'Three of us descended on this very spacious restaurant at 6pm on a Wednesday evening; by 8pm it was packed and queuing! Delicious spicy hot carrot chutney. Chicken tikka cooked in a specially prepared mild tomato sauce was out of this world. Chicken shashlick was brilliant. Absolutely nothing standard about this restaurant.'* MB. T/a: 10% disc. Free del, 10m. Hours: 12-2.30 / 6-11.

Slough

BAYLIS HOUSE   TOP 100

Stoke Poges Lane, Slough	01753 555555

Club Baylis opened in 2003 and 'It should definitely be

in the guide.' S.O. Agreed, Steve, and since you kindly came in on one of our cookery courses The Curry Club holds there, it gives us both the chance to tell all. Baylis pronounced Bay-lees is an exciting new venue. Actually the main house is quite old. Set in a five acre garden, it was built in 1697 by Sir Christopher Wren. It lay derelict for decades until it was bought in 2002 ago by an enterprising team. At once they restored the house and built a huge modern conference and banqueting suite which can hold more than 400 guests alongside. This marriage of old and new is striking and exciting. Alongside is a 16-bed hotel with en-suite bedrooms, and there is also a restaurant and bar, called Club Baylis, open to all. But the beauty of Baylis is that it is Indian-owned, Indian-managed and has Indian chefs led by Ashwani (Ash) Kumar. The venue handles a large number of Indian weddings, but more than that, it is a perfect venue for The Curry Club's Residential Cookery Courses. But that's another story.' SO. goes on: '*It is a bit cheeky to put this in as a review as the only time I have visited Baylis was during Pat's excellent curry course here. Shame on me for not going back with a big capital S! As the course progressed the manager and chefs became more and more fascinated with what Pat and Dominique were doing, and ended up inviting all of the participants to visit the kitchens of this fine complex. The banqueting kitchen makes you feel like you have just stepped onto the set for 'Land of the Giants'; the pilot lights on the gas burners alone being more powerful than my own stove – nuke setting! Head chef Ash took time out from preparing 400 covers for a wedding that night and 40 covers for the restaurant's busy Sat lunchtime. He not only proudly showed us around, he prepared some stunning dishes right in front of our eyes. On the evidence of the dishes that we tried in his kitchen, I fully expect that this restaurant will figure prominently in future guides. Particular favourites tasted were his Monk Fish Moullee (cooked in Coconut Cream, Pepper and Curry Leaves), the Bombay Potatoes, Chicken Methi and Spiced Pan Seared Salmon, but all of the dishes (rustled up effortlessly in front of our eyes) were superb (as of course were the banquets lovingly prepared by Pat and Dominique's own fair hands!). Overall opinion – excellent, would definitely recommend and I really must make the effort to return.' S.O.* We can endorse this. The food is gloriously cooked by Ash and his brigade of Indian chefs. Service is like you get at 7-star Indian hotels – discrete yet attentive and very accurate. Menu Snapshot: Tandoori Mixed Grill £10, king prawn included, but Naan Bread must be ordered separately; Goan Style Gilthead Bream £8, the whole fish cooked in the tandoor; Hara Chana Kebab £5, chickpeas, potatoes, spinach and garlic tempered patties – delicious!; Phal Dari Kebab 5, minced banana cake; Chicken Tikka Lababdar £6.50, onion, tomatoes, fenugreek; Prawn Moullee c£11, coconut curry sauce; Paneer Taka Tak £5.50, stir-fried cheese, red onion, peppers, chilli; Dal Makhani c£5 - black lentils in tomatoes and garlic (*yum yum!!'* DBAC). One of our Indian reporters sums it up: '*I regularly visit here and there is no doubt that this restaurant*

has maintained its level of service with the ever-excellent food quality as good as we experienced at the opening.' HBR. Bar Menu: small portions (and prices!) of snacks including: Cocktail Samosas £2.95; Vegetable Pakora £2.95; Malai Kebab c£5; Prawn Chilli £4.50 - wrapped in filo pastry. Hours: Lunch Buffet: 12-3, Mon-Fri, £12.95. Dinner, 6 - 10.30. Sun Dinner Buffet: 12-3 / 7-11, adult £7.95 and children £5.00. www.baylishouse.co.uk

BARN TANDOORI

Salt Hill Park, Bath Rd, Slough   01753 523183

It's in a rather grand, ex-cricket pavilion in the middle of nowhere – well, a park, actually, and next to the tennis courts. Taken over in 1996 by Messrs Mehbub, Rahman, Alam and Kandakar. Serves formula curries. '*I've revisited this excellent Indian restaurant in the park twice with large business parties at very short notice. The staff copes admirably, delivering many different orders at the same time, maintaining high-quality cuisine with superb service.'* TE. '*Masala dosa was a great mixture of vegetables in a pancake. Chicken dhansak was tasty with an excellent balance of spices and chillies with the lentils. Worth a return visit.'* RH.

HAVELI   NEW ENTRANT

93, Stoke Poges La Slough SL1 3NJ
01753 820300

This is the kind of restaurant that never blows its own trumpet yet is packed with Asians who adore good food at good prices, a la carte or self-served from the buffet. It has a banqueting suite that seats up to 500. The venue is adorned with antiques from India and the chefs prepare Northern Indian or Punjabi, Chinese and European cuisine. www.havelirestaurant.com

SKYWAYS HOTEL AND BRASSERIE

19 London Road, Slough   01753 522286

Skyways is a family-run hotel offering an excellent 'home from home' service with lovely warm rooms, satellite television, and full English breakfast. All at half the price of the larger hotels around Slough. Nothing unusual in that, you say, but what about the restaurant Says TE: '*It has retained the same Nepalese chefs and waiters whose excellent cuisine and efficient service put Skyways 'on the map. New manager is Ram Panwar, from the Cookham Tandoori, who has a long track record of success in cooking and managing tandoori cuisine. Revamped menu offers a wider variety of dishes and 'special dinners'.* TE. '*I stayed here and enjoyed an excellent meal at a reasonable cost. Chicken Patia was excellent, generous naan breads and free pickles and popadums. I would recommend this hotel and restaurant to curryholic business travellers and regular diners.'* RA.

Suningdale

TIGER'S PAD   TOP 100

3 Station Parade, London Rd   01344 621215

Richard Green's Tiger's Pad is set in expensive, minimalist, open-plan decor with satisfying tables. They have Indian chefs, led by Chef Ajoy Sachdev and it is great to find the real delicious thing, rather than another formula curry house. We get many satisfied reports on the place, for example AF has consistently commented the likes of: *'Gets better and better. They continually refine and change their menu. Sikadari Badi Lamb is out of this world. I'm convinced it is the "find of the decade".'* AF. DBAC says: *'it is a gem of a place and the sort of pad anyone would wish to find as their local.'* And then we got this poignant note from Alan: *'We moved to the curry desert of Devon from Berkshire and can find no equal to the Tiger's Pad in Sunningdale, a great exponent of the skills of cooking great Indian food.'* Sun Buffet £10.95 from 12-5.

Thatcham

KAILASA

35 High Street, Thatcham   01635 862228

'There are some restaurants which give you a good feeling as soon as you walk in - the Kailasa is one. Inviting eatery with white wood tables, royal blue napkins and fan shaped wall hangings - flock wallpaper enthusiasts would probably have a fit! Chefs Specials include: Boal Kofta, Sabji Bangla, Shatcora Gost, Sylheti Akni, Chingri Anana. Tandoori Chicken - seriously tender and seriously large. Excellent King Prawn Puree - juicy, tender, well spiced beasties. Chingri Ananas - chicken with pineapple, served in half a shell, with loads of fresh coriander - delicious. Sylheti Akni - kind of mixed meat biryani with a proper vegetable curry. A special mention to Sag Bhajee, obviously made from fresh spinach - a really nice change. Nan and Popadums were, respectively, light, moist and warm, non-greasy. All in all a very pleasant lunch.' S&ZM.

Theale

CAFE BLUE COBRA   TOP 100

20 High Street, Theale   0118 930 4040

Blue Cobra pioneered a dual menu restaurant serving Thai and Bangladeshi cuisine under one roof in 1999 Abssar Waess. The first-timer is struck by the coolness and fresh cleanliness of the decor. The bar area, with its marble and cane furnishings, seats 30. It leads on to the main dining area, whose 60 ormolu seats are designed to evoke airy oriental verandas. The light walls are a regularly changing 'gallery', home to the works of local professional artists. Cuisine is under Ana Austin leads

two separate chef teams. Diners can order one cuisine or the other or they can mix and match. *'I generally prefer to stick with one cuisine, so I often make two visits in a week, having Indian one day and Thai the next.'* RL There is a wide range of Bangladeshi and Bengali dishes, some of which will be familiar to the curry aficionado. Delights include Shingara 2 veg & Ponir Pastries; Garlic Calamari Served with herbs tossed on sweet potato or Skewered Chicken Pakora Battered and deep fried; Onion Bhajee Deep fried, chopped onion cluster. Mains include Grilled Duck Breast Tandoori Tikka Masala with sweet peppers and Skewered Vegetables Grilled. Thai Appetisers include Siam Delight (a selection including): Thai Prawn Toast (4), Deep Fried Tiger Prawns (4), Veg Springroll (2) and Spicy Chicken Niblets (4) all for £9.85. Thai Mains include: Chicken Curry Green Style, Duck Pad King Stir Fry and Prawn Pad King Stir Fry. *'What a dilemma - should I choose from the Indian menu or to select from the Thai Food was sensational, unique and exquisitely presented, very different to the average formulation curries. Playing contemporary blues music made a nice change.'* SO. Hours: 12-2.30 / 6-11. Closed Sun. www.cafebluecobra.co.uk

Twyford

HAWELI   TOP 100

15 Church Street, Twyford   0118 932 0939

Raj Sattar runs a very good establishment as is recorded by our reporters. *'Further to my last report on the Haweli, of Twyford. They have stopped using artificial colourants, which is wonderful. Back to good natural flavours and colours. Nicki and I have had several T/as since and the food has been very good. Business is absolutely booming - I have never seen it so busy! Must be the success to be reaped from being entered in the GUIDE. A couple of weeks ago we had our young nieces over for 5 days and treated them to a meal from Haweli. The youngest (only 9!) came with me to collect the order and the staff treated her like a little princess - which she is, of course. She was much impressed! Last night I tried something a little different - Khulnar King Prawn... baby lobsters barbecued in the shell then served delicately spiced with herbs in a Bangladeshi style sauce. Very nice. I must get the nieces over at Easter so that I can take them there for a meal out'.* RT. And again: *'The food and service was impeccable as always. I telephoned for a collection as my wife wasn't feeling up to going out. We ordered a Chicken Tikka Biriani c£10, a Murgh Mowchak c£8, a Pullao Rice, a portion of Niramish c£3 and a Plain Naan £1.75. The telephone manner was very friendly (I think they are beginning to remember me) and the food was ready when I arrived. The friendly greeting at the door made me feel like a sultan! The meal was carried to the door for me and contained two Popadums and a rose for my wife. The food was excellent as usual. This restaurant is really blossoming more each month - well worth a visit.'* RT. Menu Snapshot: Reshmi Kebab c£3- minced lamb burger

spiced and cooking in butter served with a fried egg; Sulimoni Kebab £3.50 - authentic Bengali kebabs served with melted cheese; Aloo Bora c£5 - potato cake made with mashed potatoes, seasoned with mint and ginger, served with tamarind sauce; Lamb Pasanda c£8 - cooked in yoghurt, cream, ground almonds, fragrant spices and red wine; Tandoori Mixed Grill c£11 - Tandoori Chicken, Chicken and Lamb Tikka, Sheek kebab, King Prawn and Naan bread, all Balti dishes include a Naan. T/a: 15% disc. Del: 5m. Hours: 12-2.30 / 5.30-11.30. www.hawelitwyford.co.uk

Windsor

MANGO LOUNGE   NEW TO OUR A-LIST

9 Datchet Rd, Windsor, SL4 1QB   01753 855576

It's opposite Windsor Castle, and near the Theatre Royal and the stations. Parking is tough. Decor is modern and

exciting. The first floor meeting / dining room holds 25. The secret weapon is is chef Ashwani Kumar from Baylis, Slough, as are his backers. He is one of the best Indian chefs in the UK, and further more he is one of a rare breed – he just loves cooking and he gets on with the job without blowing his own trumpet. (others please note). Starters: Slow-roasted cumin, spinach, and sultana and feta cheese samosa, £4.50; Chicken thigh tikka with green spice and mustard £5.50; Star anise smoked lamb neck cutlets & chops, marinated and served with spiced onions £5.50. The Platter of assorted starters (for two) £14.95 of King prawns, chicken tikka and lamb cutlets includes golden purse, Thai fish cake, Tandoori salmonshows that there are Thai items on the menu. Vegetarian version is £9.50. Main Courses include Lamb Rogan Josh, £9.50. Baby lamb simmered slowly, intensive flavour with black cardamom and clove; Saag

chicken/lamb £9.50, Chef's special cooked with spinach and garlic; Royal chicken korma, stuffed fillet of chicken, cashewnut, saffron infusion, £11.50; Spinach and goat cheese kofta £7.50, Stuffed with green raisins, holy basil and redwine jus; Thai chicken green curry £10.50, with aubergine, bamboo shoots, lime leaves and sweet basil; King prawn moilee £12.50. King prawns cooked in a coconut and curry leaf sauce. Desserts include warm spiced organic chocolate mousse with ginger & cinnamon kulfi £4.50; Poached pears, fruit compote and dressed with organic chocolate sauce £5.50 and Cardamom-flavoured pannacotta with pistachio ice cream £4.5. And you can sluice that down with 100ml of Muscadel or Muscat de Beaumes de Venise, £6.50. The wine list is equally thoughtful, with prices from£15 to £55. Tucked into the reds list amongst international classics are two of interest: Shiraz, Sula 2007 India £25.00, Indian full-bodied wine said to *'go well with rich food'* and Austrian Blauer Zwiegelt, Pfaffl 2006 £31.00 described as *'a lovely little wine with stewed cherries'*. Windsor has 110 restaurants, of which most are mediocre troughs for tourists. Mango Lounge will find itself full of them, hence its all day hours. We doubt that few will realise how good the place is. But you will, so reports please. Welcome to our TOP 100. Service 10%. Hours: 12 - 11. www.mangoloungewindsor.co.uk

YOU SAY OK

Good formula houses where you may get a discount if you show them this Guide.

TWYFORD: THE MITA'S 37 London Rd. ~ 0118 934 4599. M.Quayyum & Chef Shilu Miah's 38-seater opened in 1994. T/a: 15% disc. Car Park . Hours: 12-2.30/6-11.

WINDSOR: RED ROSE, SHARMIN & VICEROY PREMIER are *'Still there and very good.'* BT

WOKINGHAM: ROYAL INDIAN TANDOORI 72 Peach Street, Wokingham ~ 0118 978 0179. 70-seater est 1978 by T Ali. T/a 15% disc. Hours: 12-3/6-12.

Wokingham

SULTAN BALTI PALACE

7 Market Place, Wokingham   0118 977 4397

In the middle of the pretty old town, upstairs, low ceilings, black beams, white washed walls, several small dining rooms make for an intimate and upmarket dining experience. Downstairs is modern, cafe -style, with its own menu, for light snacks while out shopping or between office meetings. Good Pakistani cooking. Branch Originasia, Richmond, Surrey.

BRISTOL

Area:
South West England
Population: 410,000
Adjacent Counties:
Glos, Soms

Bristol Centre
Consists of BS1, BS2

KATHMANDU

Colston Tower Colston St Bristol, BS1
0117 929 4455

Ashok Mali's family-run 100 seater opened in 2003.
Menu snapshot: Nepalese Kancha Mali's repertoire:
Kancha Kukhura Special. Tandoori chicken cooked in
Nepalese spices; Chhoyla Lamb cooked on charcoal with
ginger and garlic and served in a 'hot' sizzler; Chicken
or Lamb Kritipur, with whole spices in the curry; Sea
Bass Nani, fillets cooked in a creamy Nepalese sauce,
served with butter beans and asparagus; Chicken or
Lamb Natapole, with tomato, coriander and ghee; Duck
Makalu, strips of duck breast cooked with coriander,
peppers and onions – truly Nepalese style. *'We visited the
Kathmandu on many occasions – our girls living in Bristol at
that time recommended it. We went there for the top quality
and beautifully prepared Indian dishes and have always
appreciated the friendly welcome provided by Ashok and his
team. Ashok suggested we try his Nepalese specialities. Boy, are
we glad we glad we did! The above dishes plus Vegetable Tikka
Masala, preceded by a wonderfully spiced platter of chicken,
lamb, beef and different spiced kebabs to get us started was
right up there with the very best food we have enjoyed, ever. If
we compare this with your current Best Nepalese, the Gurkha
Square in Fleet, Hampshire (another very good restaurant, by
the way), the Kathmandu would win hands down! We're not
surprised therefore to see that the Kathmandu is fast
establishing itself as one of the finest curry restaurants in the*

South West.' DS. Your editors visited with Janis Leibart
long-time a backing singer with Michael Bolton. OK –
explanation: she bought a number of my cookbooks and
we got a freebie to the show at the Colston Hall, which
was GRRREAT by the way. Anyway in return we hosted
her to a pre-show curry and since the Kathmandu is
almost opposite the stage door, we went there to find
most of the crew and musicians were already trunking in!
Set Lunch c£8, Set dinner from £14.50. Hours: 12-2 /
5.45-11; 12 Sat; 10.30 Sun. www.kathmandu-curry.com

MYRISTICA
NEW ENTRANT & NEW TO OUR TOP 100

14 King Street, Bristol, BS1 4EF
0117 927 2277

Myristica was opened a listed building by brothers Amit
and Tosh Lakhani in 2006. Myristica can be translated as
nutmeg or spice - but the whole experience is said to be
'with passion from India'. The chefs under Bhaskar
Cokkalineam ex Taj and Mela, are on show cooking the
curry sauces to order and naan breads and tandoori
dishes straight from the oven. They also do Masala Dosa
- a south Indian speciality of paper thin rice flour
pancakes filled with chicken, prawns or vegetables. A
fresh seafood counter offers a marinated selection of fish
that customers can choose and request the chefs to cook
as they like. For example, pick the marinated prawns on
display and have them served as a starter, in a mixed

salad, with your favourite curry sauce, or just as they are! a plasma screen in the window gives passers-by a taste of the action! Menu snapshot: Organic Black Cod, fillet marinated with crushed chilli flakes, dry coriander, chopped ginger, garlic, garam masala and chargrilled; Tandoori Chicken, Nyama-style classic grilled chicken marinated in traditional spices perfumed with mustard oil. Very popular within the Indian community in East Africa; Achari Venison in a delicate pickling marinade, cooked in tandoor served with potato & spinach mash; Roghan-e-Resham, supreme of chicken flavoured with cumin and rock salt, skewered with cubes of onion and peppers; Guinea Fowl Stir Fry, a stir fried boneless breast with dry red chillies, roasted spices, shallots and curry leaves; Vermicelli Mysore Chicken' cooked with roasted coriander, chillies, curry leaves served on bed of India's favourite seasoned thin rice pasta. (£9.50-£13). Desserts include Chocolate Samosas, deep-fried filo pastry filled with chocolate dipped sponge & shredded pista served with ice cream and Shrikhand, made with cream, milk, saffron, nutmeg, and crushed pistachios. House speciality! There is a private dining room with a large table. Jaldi Jaldi platter £5.95 Main courses of the day accompanied by vegetable side dishes, pullao rice, naan bread and mixed salad, available weekday lunch. Avg. Cost Per Head: £27.00. Hours: 12- 2.00 Mon-Fri / 5.30-11.15; 10 Sun. Welcome to our Top 100. www.myristica.co.uk

RAJDOOT

2 Unite House, Frogmore Street, Bristol, BS1 5NA   0117 926 8033

Established in 1966 by Indian architect Des Sarda and now is owned by V. Pathak and managed by Biju Mulavarikkal. It pioneered the upmarket look at Indian restaurants with its attractive, very Indian decorations eg: beaten copper tables in the bar area and bronze statues. The new ownership seems to have brought a stability in food quality over the last 2 years. Here is a Menu Snapshot: of Chef Bharat Bhusan's offerings: Paneer Tikka c£4 - cubes of Indian cheese marinated with yoghurt and spices served with onions and capsicums; Makhan Chicken c£10 - tikka cut from chicken supreme, simmered with butter, yoghurt, onions and puréed tomatoes, flavoured with cinnamon, cloves and a touch of fresh cream; Bombay Aloo Jeera £4.50 - potatoes tossed in cumin, ginger and garlic; Onion Kulcha £2.70 - bread stuffed with onions and herbs. We no longer get complaints that it was insipid. Hours: 12-2.15/6-11.30. Branches: Manchester, B'ham, Dublin & Fuengirola, Spain. www.rajdoot.co.uk

OH CALCUTTA!

216 Cheltenham Rd, BS16   0117 924 0458

The 52-seater is a partnership between Simon Perry, his brother Matthew and Jullu Miah, who is also head chef. It's is influenced by the contemporary styles and vibrant colours of Barcelona. Built-in lighting in the seats and an exposed a/c unit, create a freshness throughout the restaurant. An 8ft x 4ft projection screen shows 'visual music', playing chilled lounge sounds with random arty images giving customers an added dimension. Trained in the Midlands and specialising in Bengali cuisine, Jullu has drawn up a menu of some of Bengal's favourite dishes. Each order is cooked fresh upon request, using small amounts of oil, bearing in mind how important healthy cuisine is to consumers. The venue ensures that they are able to give their customers time and offer a good dose of friendly service, just like in Spain. T/a 20% disc 6-7 & 10-11, 10% 7-10. Hours: 6-11.30. www.ohcalcutta.co.uk

YOU SAY OK - BRISTOL
You may get a discount if you show them this Guide.

BRISTOL CENTRAL: CHILLI'S TANDOORI 39 Park St, Bristol, BS1 5NH Avg cost pp Lunch: £8.00, Dinner: £18.00

OLD INDIA 34 St Nicholas Street, Stock Exchange Buildings, Bristol, BS1 1TG Avg cost pp Lunch: £15.00, Dinner: £28.00

VICEROY 28 Park Street, Clifton, Bristol, BS1 5JA

BRISTOL NW: CHURKAS TANDOORI 403 Gloucester Road, Horfield, BS7 ~ 0117 942 2898 46-seater with some Nepalese dishes. Hours: 12-2 / 6-12.30.

ONE STOP THALI CAFÉ 12 York Road, Montpelier, Bristol, BS6 5QE

BALTI HUT 1 Upper Byron Place, Clifton, Bristol, BS8 1JY. In a basement vault.

BRUNEL RAJ 7 Waterloo Street, Bristol, BS8 4BT

RAJPOOT 52 Upper Belgrave Road, Bristol, BS8 2XP

BS9: WESTBURY-ON-TRYM: BRITISH RAJ 1 Passage Road, BS9 ~ 0117 950 0493. Respected in the area.

BUCKINGHAMSHIRE

Area: South East England
(west of London)
Population: 700,000.
Adjacent Counties:
Beds, Herts,
Middx,
Northants, Oxon

Amersham

LEMON GRASS

17 Hill Avenue, Amersham   01494 433380

Golam Sarwar opened this 38 seater in 2005. Its name might make you think Thai not Indian, but in fact it is a regular curry house with all the favourites. It is BYO making it attractive, price-wise. Some of chef Islam's specials have curious names too: Flamingo is not, presumably, that pink bird (though it might make a great alternative name for CTM), it is chicken or lamb cooked with herbs, yoghurt and, yes, lemon grass!. Juliet Roman sounds like a Shakespearean TV police series, but is in fact Chicken Tikka with minced meat, capsicum, tomato and saffron, both c£10. Chicken Sandeman is not to do with wallpaper, it is Tikka cooked with garlic, yoghurt, cheese and mushrooms, etc at £7.95. Good fun, eh. Hours: 5-11.

YOU SAY OK
You may get a discount if you show them this Guide.

AMERSHAM: SANTHI 16 Hill Ave, Amersham ~ 01494 432621. 90-seater established by Rashid Miah and Chef Shotul Miah in 1992. Hours: 12-2.30/6-10.45. www.santhirestaurant.co.uk

ASTON CLINTON: SHAAD, 132 London Rd ~ 01296 630399. Opened in 2004 in a former pub with large conservatory at rear and car park. *'Clean toilets.'* CL. T/a: 20% disc £15 min. Sun Buffet: 12-3 - £9 adult, £5 child. Banquet Night: £10.95 Th. Hours: 12-2.30/5.30- 11.30.

AYLESBURY: THE CHADNIS 43 High Street, Waddesdon ~ 01296 651255. 70-seater est 1999 by Mr Shah. *'All super, couldn't be faulted. Plenty of staff; service attentive.'* DL. Hours: 12-2.30 / 6-11; 11.30 Fri & Sat.

BOURNE END: ALY'S TANDOORI, HEART IN HAND, Cores End Rd, Bourne End ~ 01628 531112 Mohammed Hussain's 70- seater est 1999 in former pub, with a pretty front 'awning' and hanging baskets. Hours: 12-3/6-11.30. Sun: 1-1.

Beaconsfield

SPICE MERCHANT   NEW ENTRANT

33 London End, HP9 2HW   01494 675474

This is the flagship of a four-venue group established in 1994 by Bashir Islam and his wife Aysha. Alfresco dining is fun in a garden complete with waterfall and a pond spanned by a wooden bridge. Group chef is Vijay Anand. Menu Snapshot: Starters: Bataki Nazrana, Tandoori duck & cumin tempered potatoes, wrapped in filo pastry, served with spiced red onion & mango chutney; Murgh Nazakat, succulent skewered chicken delicately flavoured with garlic and nutmeg; Chat Masala, tangy masala sauce cooked with chicken or potato or chana (chickpeas); Salmon Tikka, fillets of salmon ,marinated with dill, fennel, ginger and honey. Mains: Sikendari Badi Lamb, shank of lamb marinated with herbs and spices then roasted in the oven; Dum Ka Murg. Baked flattened chicken breasts stuffed with a mixture of spinach and cheese. Served with cumin and coriander tempered mashed potatoes; Sunehri Jalpari, Pan fried sea bass, marinated in lime and mustard, crusted with gramflour and served with kadhai mixed vegetables; Chettinad, (chicken or lamb), marinated with freshly ground coriander, pepper and red chilli, finished with coconut milk. Avg Price: £43.00. Hours: 12-2.30 / 6-11. Branches: Cookham, Henley-on-Thames, Uxbridge. www.spicemerchantgroup.com

COOKHAM: SPICE MERCHANT NEW ENTRANT
High Street, SL6 9S. ~ 01628 522584. Est 1983 as Cookham Tandoori in a 500 year old building, with low ceilings and original beams, all of which contribute to a cosy and intimate atmosphere. Menu and details, see above.

Buckingham

HOUSE OF SPICE

19 Fort End, Haddenham   01844 299100

Situated in a former public house, nicely appointed with good ambience, very good quality food and service. Varied menu showcasing some interesting new dishes. *'Offers a varied menu, showcasing some interesting new dishes alongside some old favourites. Nicely appointed with good ambience. Very good quality food and service during each visit. Didn't disappoint this time either. Benchmark dishes passed with flying colours along with some new offerings. Overall opinion: very good. Would return.'* SO. Hours: 12-2.30 / 6-11.30. Branch: Chinnor Indian, 59, Lower Rd, Chinnor, Oxon.

DIPALEE TANDOORI   RE-ENTRANT

18 Castle St, Buckingham. MK18 1BP

'It's superb and I highly recommend that you pay it a visit! The staff are extremely friendly and helpful and the food is

delicious (with a long list of awards) and extremely reasonably priced AND they have Kingfisher on tap! I am a very satisfied, regular customer. 'PT

High Wycombe

CURRY CENTRE

83 Easton Street	01494 535529

'Haven't visited for a while as I'm not often in the right place at the right time so to speak. Consequently, when an opportunity to meet up with some business colleagues presented itself, I decided to stick my neck out in the hope that it was still as good as it was last time that I visited. I'm pleased to say that my two colleagues and myself were not disappointed. The Tandoori Chicken was excellent, with perfectly cooked, succulent chicken, which was beautifully spiced with just the right amount of heat. For main course I had Lamb Achari that was also very good with nicely spiced lamb in a very tangy Indian Chutney sauce. My colleagues also seemed to fare very well with Chicken Tikka and a mild creamy chicken dish, which I've forgotten the name of. Also on the menu were a number of new and different dishes that I have not seen before including a mango and chicken dish for which they won an award. I can't lay my hands on the T/a menu at the moment but I'll send you more details if I come across it! Service was also good and the staff were all very friendly. Prices also seemed very reasonable for this area. Overall opinion – very good and will come back to try some of those other ! SO.

Milton Keynes

(Includes Bletchley, Stony Stratford, Woburn Sands and Wolverton)

JAIPUR   BEST IN UK AWARD

599 Grafton Gate E, MK	01908 669796

This is the Guide's third consecutive BEST IN UK AWARD given outside London and despite there being deserving cases in London, no one, not in London, the UK and India for that matter, desrves it more than MK's Japiur and its owner Ahad. He has built his name in MK, with a series of successful restaurants, with the help of his equally successful brothers. Here's the background: Known only by his surname, Ahad had a dream to construct a new fantastic new restaurant, in white marble – a Taj Mahal complete with dome. We all have dreams; few of us realise them. He spent years planning and once he decided to proceed he took a financial risk the like of which is no dream ... nightmare rather. Even his banks were dubious. But Ahad started to build. MK's residents thought he was building a mosque, which Ahad thought hilarious, as he is firmly a restaurateur. It was opened in 2004. We believe the resulting free-standing restaurant is unique in the world. The inside is just as plush and it cost Ahad a cool £4m. 'You can spot

the Jaipur from some distance away, it really does stand out. Through double glass doors is a large circular reception. A young man takes coats, umbrellas etc. Photographs and awards adorn the walls, a sweeping staircase or a lift takes you upstairs to Ahad's new Thai restaurant, the story of which appears below. There is a sign on the restaurant door, which politely requests smart dress, no trainers or jeans. (Hooray for that). A grand, well-stocked bar, is located on your right and is for drinks service only. If you have arrived early or are waiting for a table, you on the side of the main eating arena, behind very beautiful and high, turquoise glass screens. The dining area has been divided into three spaces. The main area is encircled by more turquoise screens, which in turn encircle a lavish, four-faced, three-tiered waterfall, made from beaten copper cubes. Sparkly glass coins, in different hues of blue share the tiers with fresh orchids. The walls of the other two dining spaces have huge, tasteful, hand-painted murals of Maharajas in howdahs on elephants. Menu Snapshots: Dahi Papdi Chat £3.50 - tangy mix of flour-crisped, potatoes, chickpeas tossed with yoghurt and tamarind sauce. Squid and Avocado Salad £4.95, served on a bed of sliced mango. King Prawn Puri c£8, sweet'n'sour spiced prawns rolled into a spinach flavoured bread. Sula Salmon c£8, smoked Rajasthani speciality, marinated with honey and dill leaves. Dum ki Nalli c£10, delicately spiced Avadh's lambshank. Lal Mas £7.95, lamb cooked with red chilli. Ahad has a huge following of sophisticated diners, who love it. As last time, we've had loads of reports about the Jaipur and there isn't a bad one amongst them. Indeed have had more delighted reports about the Jaipur than almost any other restaurant. Here is the pick of them, from a one-liner to an essay: *'One of my favourites'* RAC. *'Truly outstanding. The Swordfish tikka starter was superb and the second time I visited and asked why it was no longer on the menu they said no problem and made it especially for me. That is the quality of service you get here. The Lamb shank was tender, falling off the bone and the spices it was cooked in were sensational. You may have guessed; I like this place.'* SO. So much so that Steve went back: *'Two more great evenings at this excellent restaurant, creating a further four new converts to this fine establishment. It's good to see that the consistently high standards are being maintained. During the first visit with a colleague from Australia, we enjoyed the excellent Kashmiri Rogon Gosht and Tandoori Swordfish amongst others. During*

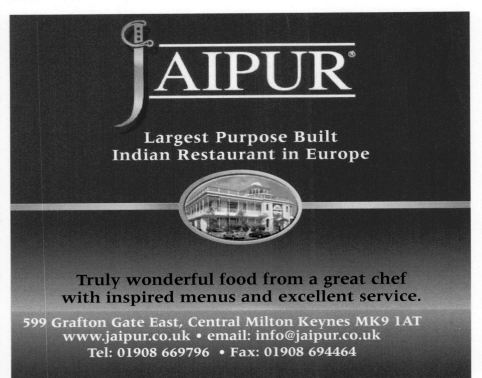
the most recent visit with a party of four, we tried the Tandoori Sea Bass which was very succulent, perfectly cooked and with a very delicate and flavoursome, but complimentary spicing; Chicken Korai does what it says on the tin!i - an excellent example of this old favourite. Chicken Paneer had very delicate spices but without any single one dominating; excellent texture to the cheese (firm but not rubbery). Vegetable Kebabs were also much enjoyed. Overall opinion – Excellent, would continue to recommend. Shame they no longer seem to do the Tandoori swordfish but even so, as Arnie so eloquently put it I will be back!' S.O. 'Hi Pat, Looking forward to your new good curry guide, take old copy where ever we go. Tried at least 35 restaurants from it. Our favourite is Jaipur in Milton Keynes. We stay in the Hilton for the weekend and always visit the Jaipur Sat night. A place to dress up for.' DV-W. 'I have visited this restaurant on many occasions and aside from the outstanding quality of the food, the other most noteworthy element of this establishment I would like emphasis is its consistency. The ambience of this restaurant and service is also spot on. It is probably my most visited restaurant; whilst by no means the closest to home (it takes between 45 minutes and one hour to get there). The reason that I keep coming back is that the quality of the food is outstanding and it has never let me down. I have taken friends, clients and overseas visitors there on numerous occasions and it has always consistently been exceptional. On one particular visit, I took along a friend who was visiting from Australia. He had originally lived in the UK and has been visiting Indian restaurants for as long as I have. He mentioned to me that he had always been intrigued by the dish called Kurzi lamb. Since this is marinated whole leg of lamb, it needs to be ordered at least 24 hours in advance which meant that neither of us had tried it before. Despite the fact that the only date we could all meet up was a Sun – Reeder (maitre d') arranged for their own version of this legendary dish to be served to us alongside the normal Sun buffet. The buffet itself was excellent, including their wonderful Tandoori Swordfish, but the lamb was truly outstanding. Our party consisted of four adults and four children and everybody went home very satisfied. On another occasion Jaipur kindly hosted a farewell event for a colleague and good friend of mine, catering for around ten, including a number of important clients. Needless to say there were a number of new Jaipur converts that day. Overall – an excellent top quality restaurant! They'll have to change the locks of the door is they want to stop me coming back! I will continue to recommend it.' BP. T/a: 10% disc. Sun Family Buffet: 12 to 4 – £12 adult, £6 child. Hours: 12-11.30 (10.30 Sun). Snacks and beverages only between 3pm and 5pm, except Sun www.jaipur.co.uk. See also inside front cover.

LA HIND

502 Elder Gate, Station Sq, MK   01908 675948

MK is well endowed with Indian restaurants, and you would imagine that La Hind, formerly Mr Ahad's Jaipur, now run by Suhel Ahmed, would be as full as it was in its Jaipur days. But it is, well almost. It is a fairly standard menu, with Duck appearing here and there. Specials include Duck Tikka Jalfrezi. Sun Buffet: £8 adult, £5children, 12-4. Hours: 12-2.30, not Fri/ 5.30-11.30; 12-11 Sun.   www.la-hind.com

JALORI   TOP 100

23 High St, Woburn, MK   01908 281239

M.A. Hai (Ahad's brother – see Jaipur, above) is known to all simply as Hai, and like his brother he is a very successful restaurateur. He established the the 80-seater Jalori in 1994. It's bigger than it looks, and has a loyal following that includes Johnny Dankworth and Cleo Lane. It is really pretty inside and out as the picture overleaf an on page 200 show. Chef Abdul Quayam prepares food that is *'First class.'* BG. Starters include Kebab-e-Aloo Palak £4, a crisp rissole of potato and spinach served with sweet & sour sauce. Spicy Tandoori Wrap £4, barbecued spicy sweet and sour chicken served in a pocket of thin Indian bread. Some mains: Elaichi Duckling c£10, roasted duck breast cooked with spices, dried apricot, pepper, tomato and fresh herbs. Chicken or Lamb Peri Peri £7.50, chicken or spring lamb cubes, spiced with peri peri sauce,(chilli) and finished with Sun-dried tomatoes. One English dish roosts uneasily on the menu: Roast Chicken with chips peas and mushrooms. £8.50. Hai still hasn't got rid!. If your diners don't like Indian food, why are they there? You do not often find Indian Desserts at Indian restaurants (no demand they

tell us) but at the Jalori you will get Gulab jaman £3.50, small cake-like fried spheres in sweet syrup and Rasmali, ditto, not fried, in a milky sauce with pistachio nuts, both £3.50. They are divine ! Try them, or else it will be 'no demand!' *'I'd like to tell you how much we always enjoy eating at Jalori. Mr Hai and his staff are always very welcoming, the restaurant is always immaculate and popular with other diners. They have a wide range of choices, all well described on the menu and although there is always something we haven't tried before, the Onion Bhajees always get my vote as the best I've ever tasted. We do try other Indian restaurants, but the Jalori is the one we keep coming back to.'* M. A. Licensed but, unusually you may BYO, corkage charge £2. Every restaurant should do that. Indeed the Jalori deserves its TOP 100 rating for that alone, but it also deserves it for Hai's attention to detail and care. Min charge £15 per person, but no service or cover charges, and the prices are reasonable. Hours: 12-2.30 / 6-11.30. (Sun e-a-m-a-y-l buffet till 3pm, c£10). www.jalori.co.uk

MOGHUL PALACE   TOP 100

7 St Paul's Court, High St, Stony Stratford, MK
01908 566577

'It's an old monastery school where monks once beat knowledge into the sons of local gentry.' says LT. Now the local curryholic gentry beat a path through its Gothic arch, complete with wrought-iron gate, beyond which stands the imposing clerestoric building. Owners Monowar Hussain and Anfor Ali greet you and, given a chance, will tell you how much you spent in 1994 converting this Victorian former cigar-factory-cum-orphanage-cum-school into their 100-seater Palace. And impressed

ORCHID LOUNGE AT JAIPUR
BEST UK ORIENTAL ASAIN RESTAURANT

599 Grafton Gate East, MK   01908 669811

It has been a long time coming. Even before Ahad opened his Jaipur (see earlier), he had plans to turn the first floor into a Thai restaurant. I remember walking over the empty space with him. '*What do you think*', he asked, something he does to everyone. Well now it has opened and it is a sumptuous, astonishing venue, not bettered by anything in the west end. The cooks and waiting staff are Thai and the food is authentic and served beautifully. We have had several reports which cannot fault the place. *'Situated upstairs in the excellent Jaipur restaurant in Milton Keynes, this restaurant oozes class from the moment you get through the door. The interior is exquisite and the ambience was excellent, a bright and airy outlook with access to balconies which boasted 'stunning' (I quote) views of Milton Keynes. The waiters / waitresses also looked the part, being dressed in regional costumes, and there was a lady playing traditional dulcimer as you entered.'* SO. Menu Snapshot: Orchid Lounge Mixed Starters 14.95, A selection of Spring Rolls, BBQ Chicken Wings, Chicken Satays, Prawn Toasts and Fish Cakes. (for two people), Hoy-Ob (Mussels) 9.95 Steamed mussels with chillies, sweet basil and lemongrass; served with traditional Thai chilli dressing. Salads Yam Neua Yang 10.95 Spicy grilled beef salad with vegetables and chilli dressing. Tom Yam Goong, 6.95T raditional spicy prawn soup with mushrooms, lemongrass, chillies and lime juice, garnished with chopped coriander. Curries: Panang: Neua, Gai, Ped Lychee 8.95, Choice of beef, chicken or duck (lychee) in smooth Panang curry flavoured with coconut milkand Kaffirlime leaves. Vegatable Dishes: Phad Hed Gratium 5.25 Stir-fried seasonal mushrooms with garlic sauce. Phad Phak Ruam-Mit 5.25 Assorted vegetables with oyster sauce. Gaeng Gra-Ree Tofu Lae Phak 8.25 Yellow curry with fresh tofu and vegetables in coconut milk In fact we are so happy with all that Ahad has achieved with this venue that we have made it the unique Award of Best Oriental Asian Restaurant and that includes Malaysian, Thai, Indonesian, Burmese and Japanese. Hours: 12-2.30/5.30-11.30; 10.30 Sunday. See page 60. www.orchid-lounge.com

you will be, with the spacious reception area with its armchairs and comfortable sofas where you wait to be seated, and the scale, height, tiled floor, stonework and wood panels of the dining room. Be nice to the gargoyles, they're there to ward off bad vibes! And wonder what the monks would think of the menu offering all the familiar curry items. *'Original wood panelling still in place, very high domed ceiling over half of restaurant - with mock stars in the deep blue sky and a mural copying Michael Angelo's Sistine chapel ceiling at the non-smoking end, which is raised up two or three steps. Food superb. - delicious, but no salad which I thought a bit mean, however, contents of the thin pancake included lots of coriander, sauce and prawns of course. Regretted choosing Chicken Tikka Bhuna when I saw my companion's Chicken Shashlik, which he said was the best ever, anywhere. Service good and friendly - I'll go again.'* MS. *'we perused the menu in the lounge, where the conversation ranged from church to curry.'* DL. T/a: 10% disc. Hours: 12-2 / 6-11; 12-10 Sun (all day Sun Buffet, £9.95. www.moghulpalace.co.uk

THE SILK ROAD

151 Grafton Gate E, MK	01908 200522

This is first venture of owners, Adbus Samad, who also lectures on Pan-Asian food at Birmingham City College and Subhojit Chakravarty, who is also Head Chef, who trained as a chef in Calcutta then worked in top 5 Star hotels, including Delhi's Orchid. The menu is largely Indian regional cuisine, rather than curryhouse, and there is a hint of fusion in some dishes. The menu is described as 'contemporary in style yet maintaining the traditions of authentic Indian cooking'. Presentation is in the plated style rather than served in a pot or karahi. Many diners dislike this style, because it determines your portion size and it makes sharing difficult – a technique done at a number of trendy London westend Indian restaurants. Some menu snapshots: Rajasthani laal maas £7.95, lamb braised with aromatic spices, chilli, ginger and garlic. Chennai ka Chettinaad, £7.95, a south Indian chicken curry fried with spices, crushed peppercorns and curry leaves. Thai Red Curry (Gaeng Phet) flavoured with bamboo shoots, coconut cream, lime leaves and fresh chillies, chicken / beef £7.95 king prawns c£10. Malaysian spicy king Prawns £12.95 King prawns simmered in coconut milk, lemongrass, chillies and roasted mustard with cucumber and mange tout. Lamb Shank Masaman £12.95, Thai-style Lamb Shanks cooked with coconut milk, roasted peanuts, lemon grass, cassia bark, hint of fish sauce and cardamom pods. Vegetable dishes can each be ordered as a side dish £3.50, or a main course £5.95. Notable are Punjabi Chole: chick peas cooked traditionally like a north Indian-style with yoghurt and special Chana Masala and Dhal Panchmel, a mixture of five different lentils cooked slowly in a pot and then tampered with whole cumin. Indian Banquet £14.95 pp (min 2) and Oriental Banquet £15.95 pp (min 4). Hours: 12-2.15 / 6-11. All day Sun Buffet 12-9.30. Reports please. wwwthesilkroadrestaurants.co.uk

Newport Pagnell

MYSORE   TOP 100

101 High St, Newport Pagnell, MK	01908 216426

Another high-standard goodie from the Ahad stable, this one operated by brother M Abdul Odud. *'The dining room, cleverly housed within two cottages, seats 98, yet provides a number of secluded areas, which 'give a good feeling of privacy'* HG. *'We were unsure of arrangements and numbers for a special charity dinner, so Mr Odud gave us a selection from the menu at a fixed price. Lamb Dhansak with Sag, Mixed Raitha, Pullao Rice and Paratha, all very good. The complete meal and decor (small corners and niches, then a large area with skylight, a bit colonial and glorious at full moon) to be recommended.'* BG. *'Colleague prefers the Mysore*

to Jaipur. He had Chingri Puri – KP's served in a thick sauce on thin deep-fried bread. I had, Jhinga Puri – KP's in a sweet and sour sauce, served on a puffed bread. Both went down a treat. Followed by Chicken Zallander, Chicken Delight, Vegetable Pullao, Bhindi and Naan. I have to admit that it was better than the Jaipur, which is not exactly a slouch in the curry stakes. I guess when you are choosing between very good restaurants, personal taste has to come into it and I like the cosy feel of the Mysore. I have been to the Jaipur and had just about the best meal I have had, but it is a bit formal. I like places that are more laid back and the Mysore is that' MW. T/a:10% disc. Hours: 12-2.30 / 6-11.30.

Princess Risborough

COCO TAMARIND

Aylesbury Rd, Askett	01844 343111

Situated in a former pub, this classy restaurant seems to have got it right. The decor is modern and stylish with elegant, high backed chairs, white tablecloths, recessed spotlights in the ceiling and a pretty blue teardrop-shaped oil lamp and a rose bowl containing a contemporary flower on each table. There is a wooden display cabinet at the far end of this 70-seater restaurant, housing traditional Indian -themed ornaments including wooden elephant bookends, spice collages and a pestle and mortar. The effect is finished off with solid, nicely weighted cutlery next to large, square, white 'welcome plates' which remain on the table during popadums. *'Service was fairly efficient, attentive and friendly. The wine list was of modest size but with a thoughtful range to suit most pockets. Food was beautifully presented and of excellent quality with many new dishes sitting happily alongside old favourites. Prices were on the high side but then so was the quality. Portion size was excellent for the starters but then of a similar size for the main courses (I know what you're thinking but they have a policy of not serving starters on their own!). Starters: Scallops Masala £8, Salmon Tikka, £8, Vegetable Pakora c£5: with delicious red onion, tomato, mango and sweet chilli chutney, Murg Chat, £5.25 and King Prawn Puree, £8 were all excellent. Main courses: It was great to see a range of different fish options: Tandoori Monk Fish, £16 was truly delicious as was the Goan Fish Curry £13, cooked with curry leaves, pepper and coconut milk. The Sea bass was also good but lacked any real wow factor. Chicken Pathia £8 was very hot but tasty; Flattened Chicken with Spinach and Cheese was sweet, spicy, well balanced and delicious. Another interesting item was whole Lamb Shank, deliciously spiced but again a little on the hot side. Dal Samba (lentils with vegetables) was also excellent with perfectly cooked al denté vegetables, served here as a main course. Service was overall very good for a full and busy Sat evening, taking around 3 hours to serve our large family party of 9 with drinks, popadums, starters and main courses. There was an oversight on the main courses, which could have spoilt the evening for one member of our party had there not been such a good selection of alternatives amongst the rest of the*

party. The incident was dealt with very professionally though and to our satisfaction. Overall opinion: very good, would definitely return and would recommend for those who would like to try some different Indian dishes and are prepared to pay more for the quality.' SO. Hours: 12 -2.30 / 6 -11.

YOU SAY OK
You may get a discount if you show them this Guide.

PRINCESS RISBOROUGH: JAFLONG 16 Duke Street ~ 01844 274443. *'Reasonably priced, very friendly, welcoming staff. Best in the immediate local area.'* SO.

WINSLOW: MAHABHARAT 25 Market Square ~ 01296 713611. 44-seater est 1979, taken over by Nurul Islam 1990. T/a: 15% disc. Hours: 6-11.30; 12 Sat.

Stokenchurch

MOWCHAK PUB & RESTAURANT

Wycombe Road   01494 485005

Good because it's a proper pub serving English real ales, (and everything else a traditional pub serves) and the restaurant does good quality formula curries. *'It's a dream for a CAMRA lover and Curryholic, and we find it worth travelling a long distance at least weekly, just for this delightful combination'.* RL. *'Have enjoyed this establishment on a number of occasions. Bland exterior of pub belies excellent restaurant - clean, bustling and modern in style, everything nicely presented. A rare pleasure to sample fairly well-kept English ales such as Fullers London Pride and Adnams in the same building. Very tasty chutneys, particularly good mango, are presented in attractive wooden dishes. Prawn Puri – excellent execution, one of my benchmarks. Chicken Tikka - flavour a bit sweet and mild for my taste. Lamb Korai – possibly the best I have tasted, a lot of fennel and cardamom – loved it! Vegetarian Thai – quality but quite pricey. Chicken Balti – spicy, tangy with large pieces of chicken, very good.'* SO.

Wendover

RAJ

23 Aylesbury Rd, Wendover   01296 622567

A 300-year-old listed building in a beautiful old street, in a picture-postcard town. Exposed beams, with walled partitions, dividing the 60 seats into almost separate rooms, creating agreeable ambience and comfort. *'Busy Fri evening but still service very good with a bit of joyful banter with the staff. Chicken Zafrani , good, Chicken Pathia , very tasty. One of our party changed order to Chicken Tikka once seeing one arrive on next table ; never seen one like it and wonderful flavour! Light and fluffy Nan breads. Very enjoyable experience in a 'not too cramped' atmosphere.'* JH. *'Very tasty, high quality, formula curries with good service. A little cramped. Still serves their famous Balti curry in a bucket! I have been there on a couple of occasions now and look forward to my next visit.'* SO.

CAMBRIDGESHIRE

Area: East of England
Population: 750,000
Adjacent Counties:
Beds, Essex, Herts,
Rutland, Lincs,
Norfolk,
Northants,
Suffolk

Cambridge

CAFE NAZ   A-LIST

47 Castle Street, CB3 0AH   01223 363666

One of the very successful restaurants in the bright, well-run chain. It is in our A-LIST as Nominated Best Bangladeshi and Winner Best Chef Award. *'One of the best meals that I have had.'* JP. Party room 30 Del: 2m £12. Hours: 12-3 / 6-12. Menu details and branches at Cafe Naz, Brick Lane London, E1 and Cardiff. www.cafenaz.co.uk

YOU SAY OK
You may get a discount if you show them this Guide.

CAMBRIDGE: GOLDEN CURRY 111 Mill Road, Cambridge ~ 01223 329432.

GULSHAN 106 Regent Street Cambridge ~ 01223 302330. *'Polite staff - handshakes by five of the staff! The flavours overlapped.'* DW

INDIA HOUSE 31 Newnham Rd, Cambridge ~ 01223 461661

PIPASHA 529 Newmarket Rd ~ 01223 577786. Mngr: Abdul Hye's 60-seater in 2 rooms. Del: £2.50 ch, 3m £10 min. Hours: 12-2 / 5.30-11.30; 11 Sun. www.Pipasha-restaurant.co.uk

KOHINOOR 74 Mill Road, Cambridge ~ 01223 323639. Used by generations of dons and students.

TAJ TANDOORI 64 Cherry Hinton Rd ~ 01223 248063

ELY: SURMA TANDOORI 78 Broad Street, Ely ~ 01353 662281

PETERBOROUGH: BOMBAY BRASSERIE 52 Broadway ~ 01733 565606

INDIA GATE 9 Fitzwilliam St, P'brough ~ 01733 34616
TAJ MAHAL 37 Lincoln Rd, P'brough ~ 01733 348840
ST NEOTS: JONONI 12 High St, St Neots ~ 01480 219626

Wisbech

MOGHUL

13A North Street, PE13 1NP   01945 466228

'We visit this newly refurbished restaurant every Friday night and have done for the last six years. Everything is clean and welcoming! There is always a very friendly welcome. Every table is laid and complete with fresh flowers. Menu is quite extensive – but they will cook things that are not on the menu and will offer "new" dishes. We've watched them advise those who have never visited a curry house before. Portions are generous and service is with a smile and a quip. Food quality is always good. There is quiet background music and comfortable seating, including for those waiting for T/as. We have a lot of curry houses to choose from in the King's Lynn and Wisbech area but always return to the Moghul. They cope well with large parties and still look after the individuals on their own. Toilets are clean and well looked after. We recommend the Moghul to everyone !' JRF

CHESHIRE

Area: North West
Population: 1 million
Adjacent Counties:
Clwyd, Derbs,
Greater Man,
Mers, Shrops, Staffs

Chester

EURO ASIA   NEW ENTRANT

Unit 1, Ethos Plaza, City Road   01244 315946

An Indian and Mediterranean restaurant. *'Nicely decorated, well lit pleasant restaurant. Staff attentive but not over the top. Had to wait for a table on an empty Friday lunchtime, (while the waiter finished vacuuming at 12.45pm). Chicken Tikka Shorish Special £7.50 - with crushed mustard seeds and ginger, hot sauce - new one to me - had a two chilli rating, mediu, against Madras with three chillis, but boy it had a lovely spice kick. Good portion served absolutely piping hot. Excellent. Rice nice and fluffy, chapatti hot and moist but a little on the large side...' that's not a valid complaint, is it Dave! '...decent meal, nothing to write home about, maybe I'm being spoilt by the Mumtaz and International in Bradford.'* DB. Special Lunch menu: £8, choose from five starters, five mains (all chicken), rice, bread, followed by coffee or tea. Hours: 12-3/ 5 - late.

RUAN ORCHID THAI

14 Lower Bridge St Chester   01244 400661

'I have a weakness for lunch time curries. Quality of food magnificent. First and second visit, had Chicken Curry with Kaffir lime leaves, and after a lengthy discussion on merits of hot and Thai hot - settled on hot. First mouthful was sublime, like having the whole of the Rio Carnival dancing on my tongue. Flavours were exquisite, tamarind coming through - superb. In the end even my little toe was sweating, but what a great meal. Had the same dish on my next visit - again brilliant. Chicken in Hot Thick Curry and Beef in Red Thai Curry also magnificent. Producing some of the best curries I have ever eaten, flavours shine through.' DB.

YOU SAY OK
You may get a discount if you show them this Guide.

CHESTER: GATE OF INDIA   25 City Road, Chester ~ 01244 327131. 64-seater in 2 rooms, est 1973. Moinuddin Ahmed from from 1992. T/a menu states: *"Starters, side dishes and beverages will not be served unless accompanied with a main meal."* Stupid rule. Get rid or get pulled. T/a: 10% before 11. Hours: 6-2; 2.30. Sat, 1 Sun.

CREWE: EVENING SPICE Poolside, Madeley, Nr Crewe ~ 01782 750088 Est 1998 in a former pub. Prop Nasir Miah with chef GA Choudhury. T/a: 20% disc. Hours: 5-10.30, Mon closed, except Bank Hols. www.eveningspice.co.uk

Ellesmere Port, Wirral

The Wirral is neither a town nor a county and until 1965 was part of Cheshire. Since then the northern part (a small, digit-like, curry-rich peninsula between the rivers Mersey and Dee) has been part of Merseyside. Ellesmere Port remains in south Wirral but is in Cheshire. See also Merseyside.

MUJIB

Viscount Hotel, Whitby Rd, Ellesmere Port
0151 357 1676

Chef Proprietor Nazrul Ali has created a fusion menu laid out in 22 sections, with unique dishes such as Chittagong crab salad served with garlic croutes and mango dressing, organic vegetarian dishes, Atkins dietary dishes and classics like Korma, Madras and Vindaloo. *'I wish to recommend a new Indian restaurant - the Mujib - which is aiming to 'beat the Birmingham balti of the fusion of the North'. With restaurants in Harrogate, and now Ellesmere Port, Cheshire, the Mujib specialises in 'Indian fusion'. Proprietor chef Nazrul Ali has cooked Indian, French Provençal, Italian, Oriental and Thai cuisine and it shows on the menu. The dish Joi Yorkshire, created by Ali, is typical mixing traditional English roast lamb and light spices with Yorkshire pudding and Bhuna sauce. Let your Curry Club members know about the unique experience that is the Mujib.'* KC. 12-2/5.30-11.30; 12 Fri-Sat; 1211 Sun. Branch: Harrogate. www.mujibrestaurants.co.uk

SHERE KHAN   NEW ENTRANT

26 Cheshire Oaks, Outlet Village, Ellesmere
Port. J10-M53   0151 355 5150

The company invested £175,000 on this venture, a 93-seat restaurant with 11 staff, where the MD say he is looking for total sales of £1.2m in the first year. Average spend £8 pp. *'An upmarket version of the Rusholme Kebab shops, modern furnishings, well lit and tidy. "A new concept on dining - Freshly prepared Indian food," I asked for Chicken Tikka with a Madras sauce, but they were unable to do it. The food arrived within two minutes, so is already prepared, waiting to be served. Opted for Chicken Jalfrezi, instead, served with Pullao Rice. Decent portion, tender chicken, very wet sauce, very few peppers or onion and only one chilli. Served in a bowl, around an island of rice. Whole experience lasted just 15 minutes. Cost is reasonable and OK for a quick fix.'* DB. See Shere Khan, Rusholme, Manchester, M14 for history etc.   sherekhan.com

THE TAJ OF AGRA FORT   TOP 100

1 Cambridge Rd, Ellesmere Pt   0151 355 1516

Spacious, clean and welcoming restaurant owned by Shams Uddin Ahmed. *'A couple of nice touches set it apart – the waiters, in their Agra Fort jackets, ask you how long you want between starters and main courses and give you the time requested, and slices of orange were delivered with the hot towels after the main course, whether desserts were ordered or not. Pepper stuffed with small pieces of tandoori chicken and lamb, as mentioned in the guide, was excellent. Paratha was one of the best I've had. A very good evening and I look forward to visiting again.'* OC. *'Heartily recommended.'* RW. *'We totally recommend this restaurant to you.'* MB and friends. *'Decor and service top drawer. Popadums – warm and crisp, lime pickle needed replenishment, garlic and ginger chutney (a new one to me) was excellent. Tikka melt in the mouth, Bhajia size of tennis ball. CTM – too red, Jalfrezi – drier than normal, both excellent. Naan warm and moist. Top rate.'* DB. Hours: 12-2 / 6-11.30 (Sat 12.30am). Sun buffet 1-11.30.

Northwich

BENGAL DYNASTY   A-LIST

Rear of Black Greyhound, Hall Lane,
Wincham, Northwich   01606 351597

The interior of this 150-seater is an absolute dream. with white walls, blonde floor boards, original hanging art and suspended lights over each table. Running down both sides of the restaurant, are comfortably upholstered, semicircular booths, encasing round tables, very stylish and enough space for six. Square tables, two lines of them, run parallel to the booths, giving great flexibility for dining. *'Impressed.'* DBAC. This is the third of a small chain of excellently managed restaurants. For more information see Bengal Dynasty, Deeside, Clwyd, Wales.

YOU SAY OK
You may get a discount if you show them this Guide.

MIDDLEWICH: SPICE GARDEN 338 Booth La. ~ 01606 841549. *'Strange location - you need a car to get there! Quite surprised to see a number of people eating at 5.45pm. Madras curry sauce thick and spicy. Service pleasant.'* DB.

SANDBACH: THE TASTE OF THE RAJ 11 High Street. ~ 01270 753752. Anam Islam's 38-seater.

UPTON *(Adjoined to north Chester, but is part of the Wirral).* **UPTON HALAL BALTI HOUSE** 167 Ford Rd ~ 0151 604 0166. Shofiul Miah's venture est 1996 is BYO, big and relatively cheap. Open daily except Tues, 5-11.30. Branch: Manzil, 73 Grange Rd East,

WINSFORD: KESAAN 23 Queen's Pde. ~ 01606 862940. 'Scruffy but excellent'. DB.

TARPORLEY: RED FOX   NEW ENTRANT Four Lane Ends, Tarporley. 01892 733152. Owner, AK Jilani's former public house, nicely decorated in white and orange, with heavy dark wood tables and chairs, upholstered in yellow and orange stripes and soft lighting.

Warrington

JAHAN

Chester Rd Walton Warrington   01925 86086

Previously 'The Ship Inn.' *'Just happened to be driving past, noticed this relatively new restaurant open for lunch. Out of the way for passing custom, so surprised to be joined by a group of twenty others. Nicely decorated, modern style, light and airy. Popadum, Onion Bhajia, Mango Chutney and Yoghurt arrived well presented, nice and fresh. Chicken Tikka Biriani - not the biggest portion, but sufficient with decent proportions of chicken, garnished with omelette, cucumber, tomatoes and served with a very healthy portion of curry sauce. Rice nice, fluffy with good flavour, curry sauce subtly spiced, curry sauce was rich with a kick, not quite hot enough. One of the best Birianis I've had over the last year. Service wasn't the best, but I'll give it another try.'* DB. Sun Buffet adult c£12, child £7. Secure parking. Hours: 12-2.30 / 5-11; 12-11 Sat & Sun.

CORNWALL

Area: West Country
Population: 525,000
Adjacent County:
Devon

These sort of comments we receive a lot about Cornwall: *'A currinary desert. Waiters all bored and disinterested, prices high, food average or worse.'* Is this because they are spoilt by desperate tourists?

Padstow

THE JOURNEYMAN

Mellingey Mill, St Issey	01841 540604

A while back chef Steve Lloyd said *'I just got fed up with not being able to get a decent curry after years of coming here on holiday from the midlands and so decided to do something about it'*. And he and his partner Christine Old opened this 20-seater in 2006. He cooks Thai, Chinese and traditional English cuisine in the middle of rural Cornwall. And of course he cooks Indian too *'your balti cooking book was the first curry recipe book I bought'*. Dr MO says *'First impressions: very friendly, cosy, tasteful decor, original features in keeping with the buildings original function as a watermill. Friendly welcome, homely, felt comfortable straightaway. Well presented and varied menu -*

including Beef Wellington. Good quantities, excellent Balti Jalfrezi - very tasty. Very impressed all round.' Dr MO. OK so it does English food. but in the curry desert of Cornwall, it makes a change not to be a Rick Stein fish operation. Oh and yes, the Balti should be good – I know the recipe!! – Ed. Starters from £4.25 - £6.75. Mains From £7.95 - £15.50. Large onsite car park. Two Bedroom Cottage available. Hours: 7-11.30 Tue - Sat.

YOU SAY OK
You may get a discount if you show them this Guide.

BODMIN: VIRAJ INDIAN CUISINE 50 High Bore Street ~ 01208 73480. *'Food surprisingly good. Prices average, portions ample, service good.'* MW.

PENZANCE: GANGES BALTI 18 Chapel St. ~ 01736 333002. *'A large restaurant. Huge chunks of chicken, the largest I've ever seen. Many different flavours in the meal, top quality stuff.'* GGP. *'Chicken Karahi, cooked with black pepper, attractive sour taste. Very prompt, efficient service.'* MP.

PENZANCE: TAJ MAHAL 63 Daniel Place Penzance. *'Excellent. Quantity generous. Service prompt and polite. We always enjoy visiting. Good quality food at reasonable prices.8/10'* G&MP.

ST AUSTELL: TAJ MAHAL 57 Victoria Rd, Mount Charles 01726 73716. Est 1985. *'Bhajias, crisp and tasty. CTM well-spiced, generous portions. Looking forward to visiting once more.'* N&JG. Hours: 5.30-1.30.

ST IVES: RUBY MURRIES TAKEAWAY 4b Chapel Street. ~ 01736 796002. T/a only. *'Punjabi cuisine. Have arrangement with pub up the road you can eat your T/a with a pint – an admirable arrangement.'* MW.

TRURO: GANGES St Clement St. ~ 01872 24253. Truro's first (1987) and biggest (100) owned by Mohammed Udin. *'Good sized portions, average prices.'* MW. T/a: 25% disc, min £10. Hours: 12-2.15 / 6-11.15; 11.45 Fri & Sat.

TRURO: SHANAZ 1 Edward St. ~ 01782 262700. Karim Uddin's popular Shanaz is in its 12th year. *'Our Truro favourite. Food extremely well done and well presented.'* GP.

Truro

GULSHAN

Fore Street, Probus, Truro	01872 882692

'Run by Alom Ali (from Chittagong) and his English wife Sue, ably assisted by son in kitchen and daughter in restaurant. A pleasant, airy restaurant, plain white walls. Marginally, above average prices, portions extremely generous. Good quality succulent, pieces of chicken. Service efficient and friendly. A nice little gem in the Cornish countryside.' MW. Alom and Sue also provide frozen curries to locals pubs, campsites etc. T/a: 10% disc. Hours: 5.30-11. Monday closed, except Bank Hols.

CUMBRIA
formerly Cumberland and
Westmoreland
Area: North West England
(Lake District)
Population: 496,000
Adjacent Counties:
Borders, D&G,
Durham,
Lancs, Yorks

Barrow-in-Furness

MITHALI

252 Dalton Road, Barrow	01229 432166

'Drove around town and discovered Mithali by accident. Wednesday night and parked right outside.' [Tony, you

always manage to park outside the door! how do you do it – Ed.] *'Met a man outside, carrying his T/a, said it was his regular haunt and the curries were very good. So, in we went! Two elderly waiters seemed to know all their regular diners. (Show them this Guide and you may get a disc). 'Mushroom Pakora - dipped in a light besan batter, slightly spiced, then deep-fried -very, very good. Sheek Kebab - OK. Mithali Special Curry - lamb and chicken in hot sauce with huge lightly battered (unshelled) King Prawn on top eaten with Nan bread - couldn't fault it. A little on the expensive side, but we came away extolling the virtues of the place.'* T&MH.

Carlisle

DHAKA TANDOORI

London Rd, Carleton, Carlisle 01228 523855

Off at J42 of the M6 and you'll find A Harid's 100-seater smart, upmarket restaurant. Est in 1995, the 100-seater has car parking for 100 at rear and a new large front conservatory. *'Comfortable seating and pleasant decor. Good, friendly service. Large portions of lovely food reasonably priced. Much better than motorway services!'* IB. *'Consistently good. Try Chef M Ali's Kebab Kyberi, diced chicken in mild spices with fresh tomatoes, onions, served sizzling in iron karahi.'* AY. Show them this Guide and you may get a disc. Del: £12 min. Hours: 12-2 / 6-12.

TEZA   NEW ENTRANT

4a, English Gate Plaza, Botchergate, Carlisle
                                         01228 525222

Contemporary restaurant, full name Teza Indian Canteen and Bar. Uncluttered, clean lines, decorated with white walls, spot lighting, dark veneer floors and bar, tubular steel chairs with leather seat and back (you know, those iconic German designs from the 1930's) no tablecloths, white linen napkins. Fantastic cocktail bar. Extensive wine list and Illy coffee. Head chef, Sanjay Mohakud's Menu Snapshot: Chicken Malai Tikka £3.50; Punjabi Chilli Chicken Tikka £3.95; Salmon Tikka £4.95 - cubes of salmon marinated in English mustard, honey and cream cheese, grilled; Aloo Tikka £3.95 - pan fried patties of mash potato filled with green peas, served warm, topped with yoghurt tamarind and mint chutney; Chicken Chettinad £7.95 (one of my favourites!) boneless chicken, South Indian spicy masala with black pepper and mace; Kerala Fish Curry £10.95 - cooked in fresh garlic and chilli sauce with caramelised onions; Lamb Shank Rogan Josh £11.95 - braised slowly in a chilli infused broth, flavoured with fennel and ginger powder, served with Vegetable Pullao; Mushroom and Jeera Rice £3.00; Alloo Kulcha £2.50. Thursday night: all you can eat buffet, £9.95 per person, from 5.30pm. Starters, main courses, rice, breads, side dishes and desserts.   www.teza.co.uk

Cockermouth

THE SPICE CLUB   NEW ENTRANT

25 Main Street, Cockermouth   01900 828288

www.thespiceclubcockermouth.co.uk

Six brothers set it up in 2006, with one, Abul 'Jimmy' Haidur as manager *'Recomended to me by a friend who drives miles to here for a takeaway. ignoring all his local curry houses. A very modern design in the spotlessly clean restaurant. Very nice welcome and good table settings very well laid out and a pleasure to sit at. Menu was very comprehensive with many stylish dishes as well as the usuals. Very nice easy to understand menu. Servis very good and professional. Background music, modern western played at a nice low volume. Very modern, nice decoration with good comfortable seats. Food was superb. I had Chicken Tikka 'Delight', a dish made with the addition of Cointreau (the Cointreau was a bit heavy and appeared to have been added at the end of cooking, careful if you are driving. This did not spoil the dish but it almost did) and CT Malayan for my partner was also very good. Good portions very well presented and attractive to look at. All served in white dishes/bowls and plates. Onion rice was very good and the Garlic and Cheese Naan was good. Toilets were emaculate.'* RE. T/a: 15% Disc. Hours: 12-2.0 / 5.30-11.30.   www.thespiceclubcockermouth.co.uk

Penrith

CAGNEYS TANDOORI

17 King Street, Penrith   01768 867503

'Took a welcome caravan week to Penrith on the edge of the Lake District to resample Cagneys. A very unusual restaurant with a wall separating the 'u' shape. Parking easy. Shown to a window table for four, which overlooked the main street of the town. Kingfisher and Bangla only came in bottles and expensive. Northumbrian Bitter (I'm a real ale man) was a reasonable £2.40 a pint. Please decor, service OK, waiters smiled. Garlic Mushroom Puri £3.35, coloured orange, not impressed. Sheek Kebab £3.50, Lamb Tikka £3.50, Fish Tikka £3.35, enjoyed by all. Chicken Jalfrezi £7.95 (my usual), OK, sliced chillies, hot. Monika had Karahi Gosht £7.95, tasty, large and flat pieces of exceptionally tender lamb. Plain Nan – superior.' T&MH. Half portions available for children. Hours: 12-2 and 5-11.30.

RAJINDA PRADESH

Centre Parks, Whinfell Forest Penrith

The spin says *'Nestled in a stunning landscape on the edge of the Lake District, it's a wildlife haven, home to one of the few remaining colonies of Red Squirrels'.* It is also home to Yang Chinese, Bella Italia, Cafe´Rouge and Rajinda Pradesh Indian and all are only open to resident holiday

makers. *'Rajinda is nicely decorated, light and airy, and has a lovely relaxed atmosphere. The food is excellent and there is even something on it that Jacs will eat. Pops and chuts excellent. Menu has changed since my last visit but there is plenty of variety. I ordered Kodi Vepudu, chicken marinated in spices and vinegar and deep fried, very like a spicy chicken tikka, excellent start to the meal. Jacs had the onion bhaji, crisp, light and moist. My main course was Chicken Chattinadu, chicken cooked in a tamarind sauce with 10 different spices, from South India. Again a good portion of chicken, plenty of sauce beautifully spiced. Pillau rice was light and fluffy. Jacs had the Methiwale Scallops, we asked for the sauce to come separately as Jacs wasn't sure whether she would like it. After deliberation with the chef she was told that yes they would do it that way but the flavours would be totally different. Huge portion of scallops arrived (at least 10) and a well spiced fenugreek sauce that surprisingly Jacs liked. Again the food in this restaurant never fails to impress and is up there in my top 5. It's a pity that we only visit once a year. The food for 2: £38.30, Drink: £11.20. TOTAL: £49.50'* DB.

TASTE OF BENGAL

60- Strickland Gate, Penrith   01768 891700

Established 1994. Fully licensed and air-conditioned. 'Sun night at 7.45pm: waiters not geared up for a rush, because two other parties arrived at the same time. Nice to see families with children enjoying a curry experience. Parking difficult, fairly good 'chippy' across the road. Drinks served promptly, but waited for starters. We shared a Mixed Kebab - not really big enough for two, too much for one. Friends ate Onion Bhajia £2.20 and Sheek Kebab £2.70, OK, enjoyed. Naga Curry Masala - based on a special Indian chilli'. (Actually, Tony, Naga is unique to Bangladesh and VERY hot, rather like a Scotch Bonnet - Pat loves them! Ed) Tony continues: 'I ate the chicken version, marvellous. Lamb Tikka Roghan Josh £6.50, lamb slightly chewy, but not gristly bits. Lamb Pathia £7.50, definitely the hottest dish between us, enjoyed it nevertheless. Chicken Tawa c£11, expensive, but Nan included, very impressed, very tasty, slices of chicken, served on griddle. Our friends, Julia and Peter, have a spoilt Jack Russell, they always take a couple of pieces of lamb or chicken back it him - but not today, they didn't. Highly recommended.' T&MH. Thursday Night: choice of starter and main course set meals for £10.95, including Popadums and Chutneys. T/a: 20% disc. Hours: 5-1; 11.30 Fri & Sat.

YOU SAY OK

You may get a discount if you show them this Guide.

COCKERMOUTH: TASTE OF INDIA 5 Hereford Ct, Main St ~ 01900 822880. F Rahman's Chef NI Khan's 60-seater in 2 rooms + 44-seat private room. *'Excellent flavours / use of spices.'* AY. Hours: 12-2.30 / 5.30-12. Branches: Red Fort, Keswick *'excellent meal.'* DH, and Emperor of India, Bowness.

KENDAL: FLAVOURS OF INDIA 20 Blackhall Rd, Kendal ~ 01539 722711. Yaor Miah's 95-seater.

PENRITH: CHUINI'S 19 King St, Penrith ~ 01768 866760. Hours: 5-12.

WHITEHAVEN: AKASH 3 Tangier St.~ 01946 691171 Owners Abdul Karim, MK Rayman and chef Nurul Hoque. T/a 20% disc. Hours: 12-2.30 / 6-12.

ALI TAJ 34 Tangier Street, Whitehaven 01946 693085. *'Long-est curryhouse gets better with age. Best in the area.'* RE.

DERBYSHIRE

Area: East Midlands
Population: 1m
Adjacent Counties:
Cheshire, Leics,
Greater Manchester,
Notts, Staffs, S Yorks

Allestree

EDEN GARDEN

Unit E1, Park Farm Centre   01332 558 555

'A good experience to share. A little hard to find being upstairs above a small shopping centre (free parking on the roof) and in a housing estate, so you're unlikely to just be passing and spot it on your journey. However, worth seeking out as there is a large bar area with lots of sofas so it's very relaxed. Good choice of drinks (Cobra and Kingfishers draught plus Singha, Tiger and others bottled, wine, champagne spirits etc). Restaurant is actually smaller than bar with only about 56 covers. Great decor and excellent staff, and the owner Sean (from Vancouver via Kenya and other places) very receptive to comments both good and otherwise! Definitely very good but needs to sharpen up a couple of things to be excellent (i.e. garnishes very plain with no imagination, paneer bought not made in house etc) otherwise, interesting menu with some unusual dishes and excellent balance of flavours. Not over oily (a big put-off in many restaurants) and they even have a 'healthy options' section on the menu. Endless list of nan breads and has even made Marmite nan for one customer – yuk!. A really good night and, despite being a little pricey and negative comments above, well worth investigating. Will be going back.' GC. Tapas menu, serving Tikkas, Kebabs, Bhajia and Samosas - delicious! *'The very best, you could taste all the different spices. Relaxed atmosphere.'* L&ST. *'Impressed with the decor, friendly and well informed staff.'* AB & BJ. *'Friendly people, fantastic food with great service.'* M&PT. Menu Snapshot: Harin ke Khazna £13.95, grilled venison, pan fried, garlic, pepper, crushed tomatoes, bay leaves, methi, served with vegetables and rice - one of Lord Mountbatten's favourite dishes, while he was a viceroy; Mumbai Machli £12.95, monk fish, onions, garlic, ginger, tomatoes, whole red chillies, fresh lime leaves, served with rice; Zeera Has £12.95, strips of duck, stir-fried with potatoes, black cumin, curry leaves,

175

twist of orange and lime; Vegetable Makhani £7.95, cauliflower, courgette, aubergine, carrots, peas, turnip, capsicums, sultanas, almonds, pineapple, green chilli and fresh cream; Garlic Tomato Nan £2.30. *'Excellent food, wonderful staff and service. Presentation perfect, tops for ambience.'* JB & TN.. Hours: 5.30-11.

Castle Donnington

CURRY-2-NIGHT

43 Borough Street   01332 814455

'The service, although exceptionally polite and attentive, a little slower tonight, due to the arrival of a large party, twenty people. Chicken Tikka £2.80 - arrived hot and sizzling with a copious portion of onions. Far more tasty than the insipid offerings that is made at other establishments. Julie's Onion Bhajia £2.50 - was crisp and brown. Vegetable Roghan Josh £4.50 - did not disappoint and the Chicken Tikka Massala £7.80 (served with Pullao Rice) was pleasantly sweet. Has become a favourite. Recommended.' N&JG. *'All Tandoori Special Masala dishes, from £6.80, Karahi dishes, from £6.25 and House Specialities, from £7.80 are all served with Pulao Rice, making for good value meals. Balti Dishes, from £6.20, are served with a plain Naan Bread - delicious!'* N&JG. All Tandoori or Tikka Masala dishes are served with Pullao Rice and range in price from £7.80 for chicken to c£10 for king prawns. Curry sauce extra £2.50. T/a: 10% disc, £10 min. Del: £10 min, 5m. Hours: 5.30-11.30; 12 Fri & Sat.

INDIAN BLUES

7 Corporation St, Chesterfield   01246 557505

'Colleagues had praised it. Fairly busy, bar with a handful of drinkers looking as though they had no intention of moving to a table. Usual versions of everything,;not a modern style menu. The candle on the table was lit when we asked but blown out when the food arrived! Brinjal Bhajee, disappointing, very undercooked, all other dishes good. Nan, excellent, light, crisp and well charred underneath. Food was very good, very reasonable and we really enjoyed the meal.' hc. *'Recommended by 'locals'. Despite not booking, were shown to an excellent window table, offered drinks and popadums straight away - fresh and excellent. Very good and hot Shami Kebab. Chicken Pasanda - enjoyed. Mama Halimas Biriani £9 (lamb tikka, chicken tikka, king prawn served with chilli and tomatoes, hot and spicy) - served on a silver platter, really excellent, hot, spicy - fabulous! (garnished with enough salad to feed a platoon.) Not exceptional service.'* DL. *'You are immediately struck by the 'accuracy' of this restaurant's name when you enter and are faced with the striking red walls! Mixed Kebab starters very good as was Tandoori Trout. Prawn Puree was slightly odd though with a creamy coconut Korma style sauce, although I think this dish seems to be popular in this region (see also Kaash, Chesterfield). Service was good. Overall opinion – very good, would recommend and return here.'* SO.

YOU SAY OK
You may get a discount if you show them this Guide.

ALFRETON: NEW BENGAL 3 King St. ~ 01773 831620. Owner F Ahmed. Hours: 6-12; 1 Sat.

BURTON-ON-TRENT: SPICE OF ASIA 99 Station St. ~ 01283 517799. *'Food high quality served by v. obliging staff, clean table layout, quality cloths changed between courses.. BYO, no corkage, hygienic toilets.'* BM. T/a: 15% disc. Del: 5m £10 min. Hours: 5.30-12; 12.30 Fri & Sat.

BUXTON: INDIAN PALACE 5 Cavendish Circus. ~ 01298 77260. Hours: 5-1130

BUXTON: TAJ MAHAL 35 High St ~ 01298 78388. 'As Buxton is the highest town in England, is Koyes Ahmed's the highest curryhouse?' RW.

CHESTERFIELD: GULAB 207 Chatsworth Rd, Brampton 01246 204612. R Miah's & A Rahman's 40-seater. Hours: 6-11.45; 12.45 Fri & Sat.

CHESTERFIELD: KAASH 375 Sheffield Rd, Whittington Moor. ~ 01246 261655. *'Almost next door to the excellent Derby Tup pub. Ambience and service good: including an immediate, no-nonsense swap for a dish that I had wrongly ordered and didn't like (there were two very different Prawn Purees on the menu). A pigeon could have figured this out faster than I did (see Indian Blues above)! The quality of the food was also very good including the Karai Gosht and the Balti Chicken Rezala. Overall opinion – very good and would visit again.'* SO.

Derby

ANOKI   TOP 100

129 London Road Derby   01332 292888

Upstairs restaurant in 'The Old Picture Hall', with a marvellous barrel-vaulted ceiling and modern chandeliers, though the only nebulous link to its cinema origin is the playing of Bollywood musicals on the end wall plasma screen. Head Chef: Rakesh Kumar's Menu Snapshot: Paneer kebab £5.95, packed with fresh mint, nuts, spices and lightly barbequed; Achari Aubergines £5.50/£8.95, fresh aubergines in a spiced tomato sauce; Dahl Makhani £5.50/£8.95; Shahi Chicken £11.95 - chicken breast seethed slowly in a blend of herbs, cashew nuts and cream; Salmon Dil Tikka £14.95 - fresh fillets, lightly marinated and barbecued, served with mixed green salad and Makhani sauce. *'A cut above your average curry house with expensive designer furniture and turbanned waiters of the old school. Limited menu but plenty of tempt the curryholic. Starched tablecloths and napkins. Petals adorn the stairs up to the dining room. Marvellously equipped toilets, where hands are dried on individually laundered and rolled white linen towels - top notch stuff. Pops and chuts appeared automatically. Stunning starter: Hot Garlic Kofta £6.95, perfectly cooked mince with a mouthwatering combination of garlic, herbs, spices and just the right amount of chilli to ad some zing, served with a tangy sauce. Exquisite! The Haandi £14.95, was outstanding, served in a Haandi pot, no cloying stewiness, rather an aromatic fusion of quality meat and a well thought out blend of spices. Perfectly accompanied by a light and fluffy Naan covered with plenty of fresh garlic £3.50. tremendous value for money. Very highly recommended and worth missing the train for!'* RW. *'Uses high quality tableware*

and crockery which would not look out of place in any Michelin star establishment. Enter and ascend the stairs, where you are warmly welcomed by your host in traditional dress. Luxurious and very tasteful surroundings, very comfortable high backed chairs with beautifully decorated tables including white linen. On the rear wall, Bollywood movies are projected, but this is not disturbing. Complimentary Popadums are served, neatly cut into triangles, with a selection of pickles. Menu quite limited, but varied enough, daily specials add variety. Thoroughly enjoyed starters of Paneer Kebab – excellent; Prawn Puri - best I've tasted. Lamb Haandi, Dal Makhani, Pullao Rice and Nan - perfect presentation and exceptional taste. Extensive but pricey wine list. A TOP 100 restaurant.' D&VH. Agreed. Hours: 5.30-11.30.   www.anoki.co.uk

SHALIMAR   NEW ENTRANT

2 Midland Road, Derby	01332 366745

'What a fantastic find! A delightful well appointed near to the Midland Hotel and railway station in Derby. Although, only 6pm, on a Saturday night, the Shalimar was nearly full. The Chicken Tikka Masala £8.95 (inc: Pullao Rice) was a large, well flavoured dish and the Mixed Vegetable Roghan Josh £4.95 - was equally generous. Best of all though was the Cheese Naan £2.50. This venue is an equal in service and quality to the nearby Anoki.' N&JG. Well, that's a challenge, Nick! What do you think? Del: £10 min. Secure parking with CCTV. Hours: 5.30-12; 2am Fri & Sa. theshalimarrestaurant.co.uk

YOU SAY OK :
You may get a discount if you show them this Guide.

DERBY:

ABID TANDOORI 7 Curzon St. ~ 01332 293712. Mohammed Ilyas' 90-seater serves Pakistani and Kashmiri curries. 'Delicious and generous as always. Service always quick and the waiters helpful. BYO, £2.50 a cork.' NH. Hours: 5.30-3. Branches: Abid, Matlock. (see below) Abid Balti, Causley Rd, Alfreton.

CINNAMON NEW ENTRANT 140 Nottingham Rd, Spondon, DE21 7NP ~ 0845 345 1723. Opened 2007. Reports please. Hours: 5.30-11.30; 12 Fri & Sat.

MARSALA ART NEW ENTRANT 6 Midland Rd, DE1 2SN ~ 01332 292629. 'Modern decor and waiters in Indian costumes. Starter: Galoti Seekh Kebab, £5.15, far from the usual blandness and three rather than the usual two. Main Course: Masala Chooza, £11, well spiced, generous; Sabzi Masala, 5.35, ditto. Total with pops and a pint: £30.05, well worth the outlay.' JP.

MOGUL 43 Green La, Derby. 01332 203303 70-seater. 'Pleasant and friendly. Cracking blend of spices with a real zing!' RW. Hours 6 -late

SHABUZ BAGAN 80 Osmaston Rd, Derby. ~ 01332 296887. 'Very friendly' GAM.

RIPLEY: SHEEZAN II 11 Church St. ~ 01773 747472. 42-seater. Pakistani curries. Chef N Hussain & mngr M Sharif since 1983. Hours: 6-12; 1 Fri & Sat.

Glossop

BULL'S HEAD ALE & CURRY HOUSE

102 Church S, Old Glossop	01457 853291

There are other curry-serving pubs in this Guide, but this one is in CAMRA's Good Beer Guide and now in ours. This marriage made in heaven is a first. Old Glossop is a village in the Peaks at the foot of the Penines. The Bull's Head was built in 1604, with stone floors, low beams and open log fire. 390 years later publicans Thea and Steve Hakes moved in and brought with them curry chef, Fais Ahmed. A full curryhouse menu is served evenings only. No Juke box or gaming machines. Specials board. T/a: 10% disc. Hours: 5.30-10.30 (4-10 Sun).

WE SAY NO

SHAH JAHAN 1 Awsworth Rd, Ilkeston. *'Did you write this review on <www.qualityfoodonline.com>?'* J.L Ritchie. This is part of it (all sic): *'excellent place to dine or have a celerbration. The most fineist The most finiest Environment. Me and my family and friends spend many occations in the Shah Jahan The best Indian curry house in England I've ever been. --- I am a member of the the good curry guide and I have tryed 387 Indian restaurants in England. Review Created by Pat Chapmen (sic)'* Pat answers. No I did not write that review. I would never gush like that and I own the Good Curry Guide furthermore though I am more than capable of creating my own spelling mistakes, it's unlikely I'd mispell my name – I presume they are referring to me. It's so badly written that it's obvious the restaurant wrote it. It's my major problem with the internet – unauthorised endorsements attributed to me. This one is a pack of lies. If you must go here don't blame me if you hate it. JPR said: *'It was pretty bad, all 3 curries were the same colour and taste as they used a base slop consisting mostly of ghee.'*

Matlock Bath

ABID TANDOORI

129 Dale Road, Matlock Bath   01629 57400

Mohammed Bashir's 70-seater is in this delightful Peak District spa town, nestling on the River Derwent, with its many pleasant walks and even a cable car to take you to the top of the cliffs. Just the thing to work up an appetite for Chef Maroof's Pakistani and Kashmiri cooking. *'The Lamb Bhuna was huge and excellent. The rice was a little al dente and the Sag Aloo was a disappointment. Massive menu.'* AGR. Del: £20 minimum, 5m. Hours: 6 - 12 (1am Fri & Sat). Branches: Abid, Derby. (see above) Abid Balti, Causley Lane, Alfreton.

DEVON

Area: West Country
Population: 1,105,000
Adjacent Counties:
Cornwall,
Dorset, Somerset

Holsworthy

BAY OF BENGAL   NEW ENTRANT

2 Fry Street, Holsworthy   01409 25410

Local curryholic Rachel Brooks opened her 40-seater in

2001 with chefs Salal Uddin and Prodip Shen and young head waiter Kamal. *'It's comfortable in unremarkable surroundings, apart from a large fish tank along the back wall. The menu lists all the usual suspects. The Chicken Chat starter was very salty, but the waiter - either by acute hearing or some foreknowledge - asked if it was too salty and whipped it away to be changed when I confirmed it was. The next one wasn't quite so bad, and reasonably tasty without being anything other than average, but lacked the sharp tanginess of Chat. 3 round Onion Bhajias were stodgy and not particularly appetising. Despite never seeing a 'Dhansak Pathia' before, I resisted and ordered Chicken Tikka Pathia' OK, fairly hot, although not the thick dark brown dryish gravy associated with the dish (in fact the opposite - fairly thin light brown sauce). Tandoori Chicken was not particularly 'moreish' - rather greasy with a taste neither of us could quite define, and seemed grilled rather than tandooried. Mixed Vegetable etc. were pretty run of the mill. Portions and prices were average, service efficient and friendly. It was a January Saturday and we were the only ones there and one del run during the couple of hours we were there. It's surprising they managed to keep going if such sparse business is the norm. But I hope they do, as despite the unexciting nature of the food, the town deserves an alternative to pub grub and fish & chips.'* MW.

Ilfracombe

RAJAH   TOP 100

5 Portland Street, Ilfracombe, EX34 9NL
01271 863499

Sadly, founder Ralph Wild passed away this year and our condolences to his wife Janet and son James, who conniues the business head chef (a role he has had for some time). *'We stumbled across what can only be described as a piece of curry heaven. Welcomed you into atmospheric surroundings via a very comprehensive and reasonably priced menu. Good ambience and helpful waiting staff. Tantalising smell of orders being prepared was almost too much to bear, but in no way prepared for the cuisine placed in front of us, nothing short of perfect. Having eaten our way through half the meal, we ordered another Nan. This was speedily placed in front of us and just as speedily demolished. Shame we found*

this piece of heaven on our last day in Ilfracombe. Wish they could post their curries to Hull.' M&JR. *'I and my wife, first went there in 1993 and found it a pleasant, friendly restaurant with attentive and knowledgeable staff. We have visited it once or twice a year most years between then and now, albeit sometimes for T/as as my young son wouldn't sit still long enough to risk it. Both T/a and restaurant meals take a while to be prepared they are worth the wait. However, I have tried Chicken Dopiaza and Lamb Rogan Josh and both are different to the 'traditional' fare found where we live in Sutton Coldfield. That said these interpretations are nice in their own way, but do not expect lots of tomatoes in the Rogan Josh. The meat in all the dishes is nice and tender. On our last visit we tried some ribs as starters, unusual for an Indian restaurant. These were I think in a honey based sauce I can't remember exactly. They were delicious and there was a lot of them. The menu is short but includes some dishes not found where we are. The décor of the restaurant lends extra charm and the restaurant when busy seems cosy, comfortable and relaxing, never overcrowded. The standards have remained high on each visit. Finally I must mention the Peshwari Naan, the best I have had.'* RGC. Mr Chapman (RGC above. and no relation) has put his finger on why some people like this restaurant while a few seem less keen. Put simply it is NOT curryhouse food. For example, there should not be tomatoes or red peppers in the authentic, aromatic Roghan Josh. The dish originated in Moghul Kashmir before such ingredients were 'discovered' in the Americas.

YOU SAY OK
You may get a discount if you show them this Guide.

BOVEY TRACEY: SPICE BAAZAAR 38 Fore St. 01626 835125. *'I guess it's pretty well bog-standard, but round here it's gold dust'* TR. Hours: 6-11.30.

EXETER: GANDHI 7 New North Rd. ~ 01392 272119. *'Remains reliable; friendly staff, tasty food.'* CS.

EXETER: JAMUNA 9 Market Street, Eyemouth ~ 01890 751007 .40-seater est 2006 by Humyune Khan. T/a: 10% disc. Hours: 12-2 / 5-11.30.

EXETER: GANGES 156 Fore St, Exeter. ~ 01392 272630. *'Excellent starter Scallops Masala - something I have not seen before. The remainder of the meal was also good.'* JAP.

EXETER: TAJ MAHAL 50 Queen St, Exeter ~ 01392 258129. *'Sun eve: I expected to find it empty. It was in fact busy, and to their credit, I was found a table - and more importantly wasn't rushed. The meal was very good, the side dish of raita which was genuinely dry and very tasty.'* JAP.

ILFRACOMBE: BOMBAY PALACE 36 Green Close Rd. ~ 01271 862010. 60-seater owned by R.Miah and family. Specialities: duck, salmon items and Nargis Kebab, meat, wrapped around hard boiled egg. Del: 2m £15 min. T/a: 10% disc. Hours: 5.30 - 11; 11.30 Sat. Branches: Barnstaple and Exeter.

ILFRACOMBE TANDOORI 14 High St Ilfracombe. 01271 866822. Est 1987. Head Chef: Jamal Miah. Birthday Parties enjoy a comp cake. Min Ch: c£11. Hours: 6-11. www.ilfracombetandoori.co.uk

NEWTON ABBOT: PASSAGE TO INDIA 137 Queen St. 01626 688443.

EASTERN EYE 120 Queen St ~ 01626 352364. Est

1990. *'When complimented on the food, the waiter replied, "It's Indian!" mimicking Sanjeev Baskar from Goodness Gracious Me! It was a good evening.'* SO. Del:4m £2 . Hours: 12-2 / 5.30 - 11.30; -12 Fri & Sat.

RAJ BELASH 41 Wolborough St. ~ 01626 332057. *'A few Nepalese dishes. The food was good'* JAP. Sun Buffet: 12.30-8, £8 adult, £5 child. Hours: 12-2.30, not Fri & Sat / 6-11.30; 12 Fri & Sat.

Penzance

TAJ MAHAL

63, Daniel Place, Penzance	01736 366630

'A little gem, hard to find, tucked away in a side street off the seafront. We had visited here once about 8 years ago but had never been able to find it again in several more visits here. Some unusual choices and a wide range of fish dishes; quality outstanding; quantity more than adequate Decor contemporary. Understated but effective lighting Service prompt, polite if deferential. Comfort: stylish, comfortable chairs, some partitioning, although rather close together. Starters: Lamb Tikka well marinated, very tasty. Best I've ever tasted. Taj Mahal Mixed Special (Sheek Kebab, Onion Bhaji and Chicken Tikka) all well marinated, deliciously light, well presented and tasty. Main Course: Aman Bujin £7.35 (Chicken Tikka cooked with almond, coconut and mango in a sweet honey sauce. This was well marinated and very sweet and korma like.) Lamb Tikka Marichi £7.35 sizzling hot, very spicy and well marinated. Side Dish: Matar Paneer £2.60 OK but nothing to write home about. Accompaniments: Pullau Rice £2 very nice; Peshwari Nan £2.20 a doughy and no syrup; Drinks 1 pint Kingfisher £3.20 and Sparkling Water £1.70 Bill: £32.30 Tip £3 Total £35.30 Mark: 8/10.' G&MP.

Plymouth

JAIPUR PALACE

144 Vauxhall Street, Barbican	01752 668711

Syed Wahid's air-conditioned and licensed restaurant, seats 70 diners in two rooms. Menu Snapshot: Chicken Pakoras £3 - fried with lentils and green chilli; Chicken Laflong £6.10 - barbecued chicken, Satkora (Indian citrus fruit); Egg Bhuna £3.50; Coconut Rice £2.50. T/a: 20% disc. Del: 4m £10 min. Hours: 12-2, not Fri & Sat / 5.30-12. Sister to Jaipur Palace in the Barbican. The menu the same, but the prices are not. Branch: Meghna T/a, Fore Street, Ivybridge, 01752 698138

Sidmouth

CINNAMON TREE   NEW ENTRANT

2 Radway Place, Vicarage Road, Sidmouth	01395 514190

Opened in 2006. *'Well worthy of inclusion, especially since*

good curries are hard to find in Devon. It was busy and lively when we visited. Staff seem proud of what they do. All the dishes we tried were excellent. Menu features a lot of duck as well as all the usual dishes. I hope this helps you with the next guide edition, which I find invaluable.' NC. Hours: 12-2/6-11.30.

Torquay

MAHA-BHARAT

52 Torwood St, Torquay   01803-215541

'In the three years, that we have lived in the curry-free-zone that is south Devon, we have tried some 25 restaurants from Plymouth to Teignmouth to Paignton to Torquay. Sometimes we have stuck with a particular restaurant for 3 or 4 months, only to find that the chef leaves and it all goes downhill. We have eaten some of the worst curries ever cooked and we've eaten some pretty good (but never great) curries. You have to understand that we moved here from Berkshire and regularly ate at Madhu's Brilliant, Bombay Brasserie, Madhuban in Liss, Viceroy-of India in Virginia Water and Tiger's Pad in Sunningdale - all great exponents of Indian food. But now we have found an oasis. It's plain ugly to look at from the outside. I was surprised to find that inside it's great. The staff are wonderful. They remember my name after only 3 visits. But the food - oh the food is wonderful. We went there last weekend with a group of 9. The waiter looked after the children (3 x 5 year olds - entertaining them with the HUGE fishtank) while we revelled in dhansaks, vindaloos, jalfrezis and bhunas with wonderful naans & parathas. Then the kids were served a terrific (unspiced) chicken tikka which they all thought was very grown up. All in all a tremendous restaurant with a great chef and staff that recognise what customers are all about. Up there with the best and after trawling through dozens & dozens of restaurants in South Devon I'm pleased to report that there IS somewhere where it is worth eating Indian food in this part of the world.' AR. *'PS: ... just don't be put off by the outside decor! I was ~ BIG mistake!'*

SAJNIZ

487 Christchurch Rd, Boscombe   01202 391391

'Situated on a corner premises, Sajniz is long and spacious. It is newly opened and well appointed. The refurbishment is

impressive and puts the customer at ease. The furniture is elegant and comfortable and there's plenty of space in a lengthy restaurant with a classy bar. The menu has all your favourites and some new things to try. The following are all worth a try at c£9.50: Sajniz Oriental Express, sliced chicken tikka and egg noodles is medium curry and very acceptable; Their Bonnani Chicken, chicken breast with slices peppers, mushrooms and chillies is hot and racy; Asary Lamb is lamb and pickle curry has oomph and good edge and Taal Chicken mixed masala and buna styles to give a warm but mild curry. From the high street standards their Butter Chicken, Dhansak and Ceylon are worth considering and are nor ferociously hot. Sensible variety of vegetable side dishes including Kala Bajee (kidney beans). Be warned, Nan at Sajniuz comes the size of medium blanket and will easily do for two people. They do Banquet Nights on Tuesday and Wednesday and a really fine set meal for two c£22, four £44 and six £56. Service is genial and welcoming if a bit slow the night we were there. Very busy at weekends. All told an experience that will make you feel thoroughly spoiled. You feel trouble is taken to please.' RG.

Seaton

RAJPOOT

41 Harbour Road, Seaton   01297 22223

Fully licensed and air conditioned. *'The lights of the Rajdoot, shining like a beacon through the mist and rain, in this quiet, little town. Warm welcome from proprietor brothers Mizzen and Azziz. Comfortable restaurant. I don't know what we did without them!'* JB. Hours: 12-2 / 6-11.

DORSET

Area: South West
Population: 705,000
Adjacent Counties:
Devon, Hants,
Soms, Wilts

YOU SAY OK
You may get a discount if you show them this Guide

BOURNEMOUTH: ANGLO INDIAN 223 Old Christchurch Rd ~ 01202 312132. Owner Runu Miah. T/a: 15% disc. Min Ch: £8. Hours: 6-12.

MUMTAZ 736 Christchurch Rd, Boscombe E, Bournemouth ~ 0120 393 323

CHRISTCHURCH: STARLIGHT 54 Bargates ~ 01202 484111. Owners Ian Clasper and Abdul Hai. 12-2/6-12.

Poole

THE GATE OF INDIA

54 Commercial Rd, Lr Parkstone, Poole
01202 717061

Messrs Choudhurys 80-seater in 2 rooms, est 1993. '*The very posh Poole Yacht Club is not far away and their membership is noticeable here. Poole Hospital medics frequent it. Spacious (free in the evening) parking at the rear. Each visit is a delight. Long may they prosper.*' RG. And here is Bob's update: '*It has recently undergone a redec and come up bright and smiling with some fine new additions to their already extensive menu, e.g: Asari Chicken / Lamb, sweet and sour curry, meat is marinated in herbs, yoghurt and delicate spices and cooked mixed with chutney and garnished with coriander; Naga Curried Chicken / Lamb, for the Old Sweats (it's one of the Vindaloo Brigade). The meat is marinated in herbs, yoghurt and various spices and then cooked with tomatoes, garnished with coriander and naga chilli; Shatkora Curry Chicken / Lamb cooked with tomatoes, onions, capsicums, green chillis, spices and the citric vegetable, Shatkora to produce a fairly hot curry; Chom Chom Chicken / Lamb meat is marinated in herbs, yoghurt and spices and cooked with ground almonds, capsicums, honey and fresh cream. At the next table was a convivial group, obvious strangers to the area, all having a splendid time and exclaiming on their good fortune at landing up at such a splendid eatery. I asked how they had lighted at The Gate of India, be told they'd ordered a taxi at their hotel and asked the driver where they should for a really good curry. "He didn't think twice. And here we are...." And you can't say fairer than that.*' RG. T/a: 10% disc. Hours: 12-2.30 / 6-12.

SAMMY'S

193 Bournemouth Rd, Lr Parkstone, Poole
01202-749760

'*Sammy's previously trading as the Royal Lahore, offers an enjoyable night out with memorable food. The service, menu and cooking are of a very high standard. But there's much more to it all than that. We visited during the Easter holiday and the place was packed to the ceiling. It was noticeable how many family parties there were; all with children – all having a great old time. This was clearly Sammy's policy, encouraging family visits, parties and children. It pays dividends. The staff are vociferous, jolly, vigorous, helpful, charming and attentive. Lights out for the cake with candles! Enthusiastic choruses of "Happy Birthday to You" with three hearty cheers! This is more than a meal. It is a night out. The menu is very fine and all dishes are cooked to order as you watch them at the grills and ovens with the occasional exciting flare-up (all safely behind glass). Among tasty starters Champ Gosh (marinated lamb chops) £3.80;Chicken Wings £3.00; Liver and Kidney £3.90. There's a goodish selection of standard curry dishes. Chef's Specials include a simply sparkling Chilli Chicken (or* Lamb or Prawn) laced with dynamic green chillies £6.90; a rich and subtle Tawa Chicken £6.90 and delicious Methi Lamb (or Chicken of Prawn) £6.90. A good range of Masala dishes. and Tandoori main dishes with a Tandoori Mixed Grill as a main dish comes to table at £8.90. A selection of Birianis at £7.50 and Vegetable side dishes include a splendid Muttar Paneer £5.50 and Mixed Bindhi and Karela (okra and bitter gourd) £3.50. Sammy's is to be especially commended for having a well appointed disabled toilet and although the high doorstep makes wheelchair access a bit problematic, they'll all lend a hand to get you aboard and spoil you rotten when you're settled in. Sammy himself circulates among his guests and makes you feel so much more than just a paying customer. Free del. Very highly recommended. Not to be missed.*' RG. Sammy has branch in adjacent Ashley Rd, Poole.

POOLE: MOONLIGHT 9 Moor Rd, Broadstone ~ 01202 605234. A.Malik's reliable house where might give you a disc if you show him this Guide.

POOLE: TAJ MAHAL 2 38 High St, Poole ~ 01202 677315. '*A large group of us proved no problem to the staff on a busy Sat night. Lots of duck speciality dishes. Well worth the visit.*' SO.

SHERBORNE: RAJPOOT House of Steps, Half Moon St ~ 01935 81245. Shatkora and fish dishes here.

WEYMOUTH: BALTI HOUSE 24 Commercial Rd ~ 01305 766347. '*Always a staff welcome you. Tables laid with fresh flowers. Food always excellent. Recommended.*' LD.

Wareham

GURKHA

Sandford Rd, Sandford, BH20 7A 01929 556959

Opened 2006, it is Nepalese owned and run, but offers a range of Chinese, Thai and Malaysian as well as Indian and Nepalese dishes. Although it does have an a-la -carte menu, the main theme is an buffet at reasonable prices. '*Seats 100+ in pleasant, comfortable surroundings, with modern-style wooden flooring and a bar at one side. More importantly, the buffet counter offered a good selection about 30 items including two soups, three different rice, noodles and popadums. In addition there were various vegetable garnishes, pickles and sauces. What's more, the trays were not full so as to gradually get cold and congealed during the evening, but were regularly topped up by small amounts being continuously cooked by several chefs in the open kitchen behind. As I made a total pig of myself I can't recall everything I managed to sample, but I do recall that it was all very good indeed. I had to rest my stomach on the table in exhaustion. It was all delicious.*' mw. It offers set meals from at £12 - £14 for two and up to £40 for four persons. The dishes may vary according to which cooks are on duty but the range is useful. The evening we ate there was a choice of Kashmiri style curries, Chinese and Thai dishes. Between us we had Gurkha chicken, Gurkha lamb curries together with Gurkha aloo, saag aloo and Chinese sweet and sour pork. The curries were mild to

moderately tasty but very pleasant. The sweet and sour pork was simply off the peg Chinese and no messing. There was a choice of plain boiled, fried or the usual pillau rice. The vegetable samosas were not well filled and not crisp. There was a good choice of Chinese and Thai dishes, too. We were there quite early on a weekday evening and – a good sign -- the place was very busy. It was mercifully free from pretentious twerps knitting their way through Oriental food with chopsticks. The staff is charming and helpful and the service faultless. The premises are fairly large and there is a disabled toilet. It has good parking. They have an extensive take away menu (with a lot of Indian curries!) and will prepare your favourite dishes on request if they are not listed on the menu, provided you give them – useful to know.' RG. *'PS: Your new Guide is a cracker! Many thanks.'*

DURHAM

Known as County Durham
Area: North East
Population: 875,000
Adjacent Counties:
Cumbria,
Northumberland,
Tyne & Wear,
N Yorkshire

YOU SAY OK
You may get a discount if you show them this Guide.

BISHOP AUCKLAND: THE KING'S BALTI   187 Newgate St. 01388 604222 Owned by Mohammed Boshir Ali Hussan. Chutneys and Pickles 50p a portion or £3 a jar – brilliant idea! Hours: 5-12; 11.30 Sun.

CHESTER-LE-STREET: GOLDEN GATE TANDOORI   11 South Burns Rd ~ 0191 388 2906. 45-seater est 1993. Ample parking in front. House specials: Kaleeya Beef or Chicken, hot cooked with roast potatoes, marinated in yoghurt. Sylhet Beef or Chicken, strongly spiced, dry with eggs and tomatoes. Takeaway: 10% disc. Del: 6m £10min. Hours: 12-2 / 6-12.

DARLINGTON: GARDEN OF INDIA   43-44 Bondgate, DL3 7JJ - 0871 714037. Hours: 12-2.30/6-11.30; 12 Sat.

REEMA   18 Coniscliffe Rd , Darlington. ~ 0871 7141346

SHAPLA   192 Northgate ~ 01325 468920. Established in 1980, SA Khan's 80-seat restaurant is *'Brilliant.'* PJ. *'Excellent.'* DMC. *'Enough to feed a small elephant'* SS. Hours: 12-2 (not Fri) / 6-12.

SPICE GARDEN   112 Parkgate, Darlington. ~0871 7141557

Barnard Castle

BENGAL MERCHANT   NEW ENTRANT

7 The Bank,Barnard Castle DL12 8PH
                                        01833 630700

Chad and Mufti Choudhury bought Bailie's restaurant. The Grade II-listed property (which dates from the mid-

18th century) is close to the landmark Butter Market in the middle of the main street of the village that is renowned for its public school and ruined 12th-century castle. It offers a bar a dining in three interconnecting rooms for 44 guests, and a rear timber-decked patio for alfresco dining. *'Second visit to this restaurant that opened in 2008 (plus numerous takeaways). There is already a good Indian restaurant in the town, Spice Island, but the Merchant is equally as good regarding quality of food – delicious. The staff are even more friendly and attentive, giving occasional free side-dishes and taking care of you. The Merchant wins hands down as regards comfort and décor. In the other restaurant, everyone sits in two table rows like a school canteen all facing wall-length smoked mirrors so it feels like you are hemmed in on top of each other. Not good when they often seem to have children in on an evening. The Bengal Merchant is more comfortable, roomy and relaxed and you can have private conversations as you are not sat on top of other people.'* GD. Hours: 6-12

Durham

CAPITAL   NEW ENTRANT

69, Claypath, DH1 1QT   0191 386 8803

Opened 2007 by Mohammed S Miah on the premises of an auction house. Chef Syed Islam has spring lamb, duck and fish dishes are on his menu. *'Good quality of food – delicious. The staff are friendly and attentive. But everyone sits in two table rows like a school canteen all facing wall-length smoked mirrors so it feels like you are hemmed in on top of each other. Not good when they often seem to have children in on an evening.'* GD. Hours: 6- 11.30.   Branch: Spice Lounge Durham.

SHAHEENS INDIAN BISTRO,

48 North Bailey, Durham City   0191 386 0960

'Bright and lively restaurant, pleasantly sited in an old post office on one of the side streets leading up towards the cathedral and castle. As you enter you can't miss the large painting of the Taj Mahal along the right hand wall and the backlit plastic vines, which peep through a wooden latticework

suspended just below the ceiling. Sounds awful I know but actually it's OK! King Prawn Puri £5.90, had a good balance between the tomato, herbs / spices and the acidity although it seemed a bit light on the prawns for that price! Mutton Tikka Masala Balti £9.20, was perhaps angling for the most number of Indian Dishes in one name, although as it included rice they could probably have got away with chucking a Biriani in the title somewhere! However, it had a good balance between the spices, the tomato and the rich ghee sauce. The Pullau Rice that accompanied this dish was very pleasantly aromatic and flavoursome. Service was OK. Overall opinion – slightly pricey but good, would recommend and return.' SO. Opens 6pm.

Stockton-on-Tees

MEMSAHIB'S

Boundary Cottage Farm, Inkerman, Tow Law
01388 731818

You can purchase a whole jar or pickle or chutney at £2.70 each – probably a good idea if you are eating in a large party of perhaps eight or more. T/a: 10% disc. Del: £10 minimum. Happy Nights: six course set meal £9.50, every Thurs & Sun. Stocks: Cobra and Kingfisher. Hours: 5.30-11, (11.30 Fri & Sat). Branch: Monju Stanley DH9 7OG.

SPICE LOUNGE NEW ENTRANT

St Nicholas Cottage, Durham Market Place,
DH1 3NJ 0191 383 0927

Same ownership as Captital. This one opened first in 2005 in the old market hall and it incorporates part of the listed wall. Decorated in slate grey and royal purple. Menu Snapshot: Xenuk £4.45 – mussels; Palak Pakora £3.45; Crab Bhaji on Puri £4.95; Chicken Biryani £8.80; Lamb Tikka Jalfrezi £7.95; Mushroom Pullao £2.95. Set meal for 2: £40. Hours: 6-12. spiceloungedurham.com

ESSEX

Area: Home Counties,
(east of London)
Population: 1,640,000
Adjacent Counties:
Cambs, Herts, Kent,
London, Suffolk

'GL' denotes those former Essex suburbs absorbed by Greater London in 1965.

Chelmsford
(includes Great Baddow and Writtle)

ESSENCE INDIAN ON THE GREEN

30 The Green Writtle 01245 422228

You've guessed it, this huge 200-cover restaurant overlooks the village green, furthermore this is nth reincarnation of an Indian restaurant on this site. Essence has a contemporary interior with a soft neutral background enhanced with inviting pictures that reflect the history of Writtle and the essence of India. Pre-dinner drinks are on offer in the Piano Lounge, where diners can sit back and relax in comfortable leather sofas, sipping on a cocktail and view pictures of famous patrons of the restaurant's other branches that decorate the walls. Essence serves an extensive Indian & Bangladesh combined menu, with a large choice of intriguing fish dishes and chef specials that are put together by Head Chef Jahanger Hussain. Essence is the latest venture of the Essence Group, a family run business established in 1998 and owned by Sharife Ali, Tariq Ali, Abi Kabir, Farouk Ullah and Sam Uddin. They have three other sites - Chadwell Heath, Romford, Essex; Redhill, Surrey and Sedgley, West Midlands.

SURAYA TAKEAWAY NEW ENTRANT

159, Main Rd, Broomfield, Chelmsford
01245 442014

'This is a humble takeaway, but nothing else has ever come close. Bhajia are flat and to die for with Raitha. Chicken Tikka starter, succulent. Dal, hot and gorgeous. No over use of cardamom. Always hot and fresh, you can watch the chef and cooks preparing. Never a wrong item. The BEST still after nearly twenty years. Shame they do not have a restaurant.' JS. Menu Snapshot: Reshmi Kebab £2.60, minced lamb burger spiced and dressed with fried egg; Chicken Kebab £4, pieces of meat with salad sandwich in freshly made bread; Cheese Naan £1.80; Jal Murgi £6.80,

spiced spring chicken cooked with green chillies and tomatoes, served with Pullao Rice; Lamb Achari £4.90, tender slices of lamb cooked in sweet,sour and hot sauce; Lamb Kashmiri £4.10, mild curry prepared with banana and served in rich creamy sauce; Garlic Mushroom Bhajee £2.30, Chana Paneer £2.70. Free Onion Salad with every takeaway. Delivery: £12min, 4m. Hours: 5-11.30.   www.takeaways.net

YOU SAY OK

You may get a discount of you show them this Guide.

Basildon: Asia Spice 2 Adams Busn Centre 01268 5253527

BASILDON: TAMARIND TREE 1 Reading Road 01491 671555. Back in business after a fire.

BENFLEET: MAHARAJA 358 London Rd. Keith Vaz and Ed Miliband started the Tiffin Cup, where 100 UK curryhouses are entered by their local by MPs into a national curry cooking competition. Siraj Ali Maharaja was runner up in 2007. www.maharajagroup.co.uk

Photo: left to right: Keith Vaz (bending over) Bob Spink MP, Siraj Ali owner the Maharaja, Ainsley Harriott, Sanjay (behind), Rt Hon Ed Miliband MP and Cabinet Minister, Maharaja Chef Akmal Ali, and his winning dish below.

BRAINTREE: CURRY PALACE 28 Fairfield Road, Braintree ~ 01376 320083. 52 seater est 1975 by MA Noor. T/a: 10% disc. Hours: 5.30-11; closed Mon.

BURNHAM-ON-CROUCH: POLASH 169 Station Rd. 01621 782233. Owner Sheik Faruque Ahmed. Hours: 12-3/6-12. Branch: 86 West Rd, Shoeburyness, Essex. 01702 294721

CHELMSFORD: TAJ MAHAL 6 Baddow Rd ~ 01245 259618. Modern, trendy chrome and pale wood. Hours: 12-2.30 /5.30-12.

CLACTON-ON-SEA: EAST INDIA TAKEAWAY 182 Old Rd.~ 01255 427281. Manager: M.A Salam. Hours: 5-11.30; 12 Sat

EPPING: RAJ 75 High Street ~ 01992 572193. 40-seater owned by Mumin Ali & Chef Abdul Ali. Del: £10 min, 5m. Hours: 12-2.30/6-12.

Benfleet

MUMTAZ MAHAL

10 Essex Way, Benfleet   01268 751707

Abdur Rahid opened his two-floor 90-seater in 1977. His is a typical, friendly, competent curry house, the like of which we like to find wherever we are. It's on two floors, both of which have a cosy atmosphere. There's a large car park adjacent. Prices fair. The food is the normal menu with every variation you can think of for chicken, meat, prawns and vegetables. '*It's all done sumptuously*'. IDB. Hours: 12-2.30/6-12.

Colchester

SAGARMATHA GURKHA

2 St Botolphs Circus   01206 579438

Est 1999. Formerly called Oriental House. Seats 42. There are of course many if not all your old favourites on the menu, and done well too, as they are so often by Nepalese chefs. Specialities includtraditional Nepalese 'village' meal c£10, the most unusual dish being Shanjali Kukhura (chicken marinated in ginger, green chilli, herbs and spinach). Two large car parks with CCTV in front and rear. T/a: 10% disc. Del: £15, 5m. Hours: 12-2 / 5.30-11.30.

Gants Hill (GL)

KANCHANS   TOP 100

53 Perth Road, Gants Hill   020 8518 9282

'*Location, location, location*', they say. And it is almost on the roundabout, near the tube, with a huge plate glass window with large ornately carved wooden double door with brass studs. Unmissable. But is Gant's Hill in suburban Essex the right location. Only time will tell. Because this restaurant is a real cut above anything forms around. Inside it's a beautifully decorated restaurant, with creamy walls, crystal mirrors, Indian artefacts, lavish upholstery and place settings. Upstairs is a huge banqueting suit which is ideal for large family-and-friend parties. And does well for smaller Asian weddings. The owners have run a standard curryhouse down the road for years, but they decided to do the job properly. The chefs all Indian, cook authentic Punjabi Indian curries and accompaniments – everything wonderful from the spicy Lamb Knuckle to the Black Urid Dal. Definitely worthy of our top 100. Gants Hill is very lucky indeed. Parking at rear. Cover ch £1.50. Hours: 12-3 / 6-11.30.

Hockley

KERALAM

200 Main Rd, Hawkwell, Hockley   01702 207188

'*The only South Indian in the area. As good as those in Tooting and Kerala itself, which I know well. Dosas could not be bettered. Interesting vegetables like beetroot. Staff friendly, prices reasonable, well worth a detour.*' JAR. Menu extracts: Bhelpoori £2.50, poori, puffed rice crispies, potato, green chilli, sweet and sour sauces. Squid Fried, marinated squid served with salad Trivandrum style. Cashew Nut Pakoda, batter fried cashew nuts served with Date Chutney. Masala Dosa, rice and lentil pancake filled with potato and onion masala, served with Sambar and Coconut Chutney. Malabar Meen Moli , kingfish cooked with tomatoes, tamarind, onion, garlic, ginger and garnished with coconut milk and curry leaves. Kerala Erachi Olathiyathu, boneless pieces of lamb fried with fresh sliced coconut and herbs. Fully licensed. Del: £15, 3m. Hours: 5.30-11.30.

Ilford (GL)
(inc Goodmayes, Newbury Park and Seven Kings)

BOLLYWOOD GRILL   NEW ENTRANT

1, Scene Complex, 2, Cement Road, Ilford, IG1 1VP   020 8553 1130

The one-stop venue is a restaurant (2nd floor) , club and bowling alley. A very lovely restaurant, kind of Arabian decor, seating 120 people. Mixture of seating arrangement, choose from square tables for four with either dark leather, button backed, banquet seating or lovely paprika coloured leather sofas, which look far to comfortable for their own good. After a good meal, I don't think I would want to leave! Regulars love head chef, Satish Kumar's cooking, particularly the Pani Puri, Chicken Jalfrezi, Kadai Murg Karachiwala, Paneer Tikka and the bread basket. We hear it's exceptional. Reports please. Credit cards accepted. Hours: 12-2, Saturday lunch only and 6 -12.

CURRY SPECIAL   TOP 100

2 Greengate Pde, Horns Rd, Newbury Pk, Ilford   020 8518 3005

Family-run by GL and Paul Luther, Punjabi Kenyan Asians. They are related to the Southall Anands (see Brilliant and Madhu's, Southall, Middlesex), resulting in a different menu from that at the formula curry house. This is the real taste of the Punjab – savoury, powerful, delicious and satisfying, and as near to Punjabi home-food as you'll get in Britain. The family signature dishes are Karai Mexican Mixed Vegetables, and the renowned Butter Chicken, Jeera Chicken and Chilli Chicken. A full portion for four is £12-13. Half-portion £6.50-7. These are starters, and are huge. And the fun is to go in large parties and share each of these. That's the way the local Asians enjoy it, leaving lots of room and lots of choice for the main course. Clues to the Luthers' Kenyan background is also in the menu. Mogo Chips are fried cassava, £3 and Tilapia Masala is an African fish curry, starter £3, main £6.50.Try the Kenyan Tusker lager. '*Food brilliant, authentic and interesting. Service quite slow but well worth the wait. Definitely not run of the mill. Worth the TOP 100 status.*'SJ. Remains in our TOP 100. Hours: 12-2.30 Tue-Fri / 6-12 daily; closed Mon.

JALALABAD   TOP 100

247 Ilford Lane, Ilford   020 8478 1285

55-seater established in 1977 by Nazrul Islam (head chef) and Badrul Islam (manager). It serves 'good-as-they-get' formula curries. Diane says it all really: '*We*

went there on it's recommendation in the guide. Fantastic! Excellent food, lovely people and comfortable surroundings. Prices are inexpensive and they also provide a Del service. We haven't gone anywhere else since we discovered it. Absolutely deserves its place in the Top 100.' DA. Stays safely in our TOP 100. Del: £15 min, 3m. Hours: 12-2.30 / 6-12 (1am Fri & Sat). Branch: next entry. www.jcuisine.com

JALALABAD 2   TOP 100

992 Eastern Av, Newbury Park   0208 590 0000

[Yes the phone no is correct]. H Islam manages. Has attracted the likes of world embassy champion snooker player Ronnie O'Sullivan. *'My first impression was pleasant surprise. The décor was of high quality minimalism. I was greeted at the door by the waiter, who showed me to my seat, followed up by the menu. I was intrigued by the variety of the cuisine available, but could not make my mind up, so I was recommended the Chefs special Biriyani, £8 – succulent chicken, lamb, prawns and mushrooms, alongside the Peshwari chicken – cooked in an exotic sauce topped with onions and garlic garnished with fresh coriander. I also ordered a side order of Bombay Aloo (£2.50) a spiced potato, which dipped in the chef's special sauce tasted exquisite. I was particularly taken in by the Motka Kulfi dessert, £2.50 which came in an exclusive ceramic pot filled with highly luxurious rich saffron and pistachio flavoured ice cream topped with nuts. Bollywood music videos play on a large widescreen television to depict the exotic and carry on the theme of the Indian cuisine.'* FA. Del: £15 min, 4m. Hours: 6-11. Branch: previous entry. www.jcuisine.com

---

We need
your reports
and information.
Please use the form on
pages 339 & 340
or report online on
patchapman.co.uk

MOBEEN

80 Ilford Lane, Ilford   020 8553 9733

The owners of this chain of Pakistani caffs are strict Muslims, so BYO is not permitted and it's unlicensed. Go for darned good, inexpensive, value-for-money, Punjabi, Kebabs, tandoori items and curries of all sorts, selected from the counter, with specials varying from day to day. No credit cards. No smoking. Can be heaving with local Asians, who know you won't find better food, and which adds to a fab atmosphere. Being Punjabi, it's a bit short of vegetarian fodder. Hours: 11-10. Branches: Mobeen, 229 High Street N, E6; 222 Green St, E7; 725, High Rd, Leyton, E10.

SRI RATHICA

312 High Road, Ilford   020 8478 7272

65-seater. Raj Mohan Ramadass' restaurant specialises in Tamil Nadu cuisine – fabulous south Indian food – none of your curryhouse here. So our advise is not to ask for the kormas and the CTMs. Try things form this snapshot of what you can expect to eat: Thayir Vada £1.95 - fried doughnut made of black gram batter, ginger, onions, green chilli, curry leaves and cumin, then soaked in seasoned and tempered yoghurt; Cashew nut Pakoda £3.95, nuts dipped in spicy batter and deep-fried; Chicken 65 £4.95; Fried bone chicken marinated and fried, served with cucumber, onions and lemon; Mutton Mysore £6.95, with ginger, garlic, coriander leaves and red chillies; Rasam £1.95, hot pepper soup of tomatoes, tamarind and spices; Ghee Roast Masala Dosa £4.95, crisp pancake, roasted in butter, filled with potato masala, served with sambar (lentil curry) and chutneys; Utthapam £3.50, rice and lentil flour, topped with chopped, onions, green chillies, tomatoes, curry leaves and ginger, served with sambar and chutneys; Nandu Varuval £7.95; Fried crab curry; Vazhakkai Poriyal £3.25, green banana curry. Del: £15 min, 2m radius. T/a: 10% disc. Price Check: Popadum 50p, Chicken Chettinad £5.95, cooked with curry leaves and mustard seed, Pullao Rice £1.95. Hours: 12-3 / 6-11; 12 Sat. Branch: 57 Station Rd, Harrow. 020 8863 8822 www.srirathiga.co.uk.

SURUCHI

506 High Road, Ilford   020 8598 2020

Cuisine is a strange combination of: South Indian and Chinese. Specialists in vegetarian dishes, Indian style, including such favourites as: Bhel Puri £2.95, Masala Dosas £3.25, Onion Utthapam £3.25, Vada (2) with chutney and Sambar £2.50. If you prefer a little Chinese delicacy, try the Mogo Chilli Fry £3.50, Spicy Szechuan Noodles £3.50, Spinach and Bean Sprouts with dry chillies £3.50. All sounds great to me!! Service charg10%. T/a: 10% disc. Lunch Special: three courses £4.99 – good value. Hours: 12-3 / 6-12.

YOU SAY OK

You may get a discount of you show them this Guide.

DUNMOW: JALSA GHAR QUEEN VICTORIA 79 Stortford Rd ~ 01371 873330. Owner Iqbal Chowdhury opened in a pub (Queen Victoria) in 1998. Menu Snapshot: Crispy Sardines £4.50, marinated and shallow fried; Vegetable Roulade £3.50, spiced vegetables, rolled in Indian pastry. T/a: 10% disc, min £10. Hours: 12-2.30/6-11; 12-10.30 Sun. www:jalsaghar.co.uk

HALSTEAD: CURRY COTTAGE 73 Head St. ~ 01787 476271. Manager Forhad Hussain. Opened Dec 2006. Branch: Spice Zone Indian, 1c Head St, Halstead. 01787 479701.

HARLOW: ESSENCE OF INDIA 2 Hart Road, Old Harlow ~ 01279 441187. *'My husband has taken a liking to their side dish Aloo Bahar, potatoes and lentils'.* HS.

HEYBRIDGE: HEYBRIDGE TANDOORI 5 Bentalls Centre. ~ 01621 858566. Abdul Rofik, Abdul Hannan and Nazrul Islam's 70-seater. *'Four non-curry eaters have become converted.'* SJ. Del: £10 min, 3m. Hours: 12-2.30 / 6-11.30; 12 Sat.

HORNCHURCH: CINNAMON SPICE 10 Tadworth Pde, Elmpark. ~ 01708 478510. Owner Syed Ahmed. Service ch 10%. Del: £10 min, 3m. Hours: 5-12.

ILFORD:

ILFORD: HAWA BENGAL 530 High Rd, Seven Kings. 020 8599 9778. Mr Bashir Ullah is owner-chef, Mr Hudda Kabir runs the front. *'Staff very helpful; we've also been guinea-pigs trying new and tasty dishes not yet on the menu.'* AN. Hours: evenings only.

MASALA 910 910 Eastern Avenue Newbury Park Ilford IG2 7HZ 0845 345 1723. Serves authentic Punjabi Cuisine. 20% off collected orders. Hours: 12-2 / 6-12; Sun: 12:30-4 / 6.30-11.30

LEIGH-ON-SEA: MUGHAL DYNASTY 1585 London Rd, Leigh 01702 470373. Pretty, upmarket 68-seater from Nazram Uddin.

TAJ MAHAL 77 Leigh Road, Leigh 01702 711006. 70-seater, est 1973 and owned by manager Shams and chef Noor Uddin. Hours: 12-2.30 / 6-12.

ONGAR: VOJAN Epping Road, Ongar 01277 362293. Proprietor Jamal Uddin. Hours: 12-2.30 / 5.30-11; Fri & Sat 11.30; Sun Buffet: 1-10, £9.95 / £4.95 child. .

RAYLEIGH: SPICY TAKEAWAY 159 High Street, Rayleigh 01268 770769. 36 seater. Del: £10 min, 4m. Hours: 5.30-11.30; 12 Sat; 11 Sun.

ROMFORD (GL): ASIA SPICE 62 Victoria Road, Romford 01708 762623. 54-seater owned by Yeabor Ali since 1975. Branch: Rupali, South Woodham Ferrers, Essex.

UPMISTER: SPICE OF INDIA 2 The Broadway, Front Lane, Cranham, 01708 222045. ~ 56-seater opened in 1985, taken over in 2004 by the Noor family. Sadikul and Shaikul run the front while Abdul heads the kitchen. Shashlick Chicken Masala is his most popular dish. Hours: 12-2/6-12. Branch: Lee Raj Takeaway, SE12.

WESTCLIFF-ON-SEA: SHAGOOR Hamlet Court Rd. 01702 347461. *'Very large and beautifully decorated. Food good to excellent.'* AS. 'Highly commended' SS.

Shoeburyness

POLASH

84 West Road　　　　　　　　01702 293989

The Polash and its slightly younger branch have been in our Guide since we began, which makes them old friends to these pages. Manager SA Motin tells us his decor is 'wonderful, air-conditioned, with water fountain'. But there's a third Polash in the same ownership. Not in Essex, nor even Britain. It's in Sylhet,

Bangladesh, the town where so many of our curryhouse workers come from. Polash is the best hotel in town, which doesn't mean much. Their restaurant, the Shapnil, has an item on its 200-dish menu that amazed us when we visited. Item 95 is no less than CTM! It is the only place in the whole of Bangladesh where it is to be found. And, says owner Sheik Faruque Ahmed, *'it sells really well!!!'* His UK partner, M Khalique, agrees. *'The food was beautifully prepared, tasty and the right strength. Service excellent. Atmosphere relaxed and friendly. Despite the fact that the proprietor informed us that they did not give CC disc on a Sat, they gave us a disc of 10%.'* BP-D. min charge £10. Hours: 12-2.30/6-12; Sun 12-12. Branch: Polash, Burnham on Crouch.

Southend-on-Sea

KERALAM

28 Clifftown Road, Southend　　　01702 345072

Said it about Ilford and I'll say it here too. Treasure this one please Southend, especially as it is easy to find, being opposite Southend railway station.! It is another south Indian restaurant, and with it. Mr Sadique's vibrant fresh food breaks away from the curryhouse mould. Don't think that all South Indian food is vegetarian or fish dishes – not true – chicken and lamb feature very nicely. Menu Snapshot: Kappa and Meen Curry £3.95, cassava, herbs, spices, served with fish curry; Kaddka Porichathu £3.25; Fried mussels; Erachi Olathiyathu £5.95, lamb fried with fresh sliced coconut (one of Pat's favourites); Malabar Meen Biriyani £6.95, marinated Kingfish, onion, cashew nuts, sultanas, curry leaves and rice, served with coconut chutney, raita and salad; Avial £3.25, fresh vegetables cooked with coconut, yoghurt, cumin, curry leaves and spices; Kaipanga Varatiathu £3.25, curry leaves, mustard seeds, cumin, fennel, deep-fried bitter gourd and puréed fresh coconut; Pickle Tray is expensive at £2. I hope it contains some tasty home-made delicacies! The food is as good as ever.' JAR. Price Check: Popadum 50p, Cheera Chicken £5.25, Pullao Rice £1.75. Hours: 12-2.30/5.30-11.30; 11 Sun. Reports please.

DESI WAY TAKEAWAY　　　NEW ENTRANT

373, London Road, Westcliff　　01702 333414

Owner, Ruhul Shamsuddin says *'my father taught me the industry, but rather than opening a restaurant, I decided to launch a takeaway and opened Desi Way in 2005.'* It boasts leather sofas, a big plasma screen for Bollywood films, posters, flame-lighting, a delivery vehicle parked outside, which is a real rickshaw. The menu has dishes such as Bollywood Bad Boy! The talking point is the bank of five 10 inch LCD screens placed on the counter, which transmit live the cooking process from the kitchen to the customers right up to the point of packaging so that

customers can see how the food is prepared. *'I offer a complementary drink or kulfi if they have been waiting long. So the customers never get bored.* Perhaps the USP is the delivery transport fleet, which includes one of the subcontinent's and Thailand's icons, the tuk-tuk or put-put (pictured left) the motorised three-wheeler taxi which buzzes around like a dodgem. Though only comfortable for twpo passengers plus the driver, it is not uncommon to see six or even eight passengers on board! These vehicles are banned from entering the driveways of major Indian hotels and even city centres. But in Westcliff, it is a welcome, fun sight.

GLOUCESTERSHIRE

Area: South West
Population: 821,000
Adjacent Counties:
Bristol, Gwent,
Somerset,
Wilts

With the demise of Avon as a county in 1997, Gloucestershire has regained territory which was taken from it when Avon was formed in 1965.

YOU SAY OK
You may get a discount of you show them this Guide.

CHELTENHAM: CURRY CORNER 131 Fairview Rd. 01242 528449. Est 1977. Seats 40 in two Tudor-style rooms. T/a: 10% disc. Hours: 5.30-11.30.

INDIAN BRASSERIE 146 Bath Rd,.01242 231350. 56-seater , managed by A Rakib. *'Best in town – a nice atmosphere.'* CS. Branch: Dilraj Tandoori, Dursley.

CHELTENHAM: KASHMIR 1 Albion St. 01242 524288. Abdul Rauf's modern and stylish family restaurant. T/a: 10% disc. Hours: 12-2/6-12.

DURSLEY: DILRAJ 37 Long Lane, Dursley 01453 543472. Standard menu. *'Delicious, ample portions, very relaxed and friendly. Excellent'* IB.

Cheltenham

JOY   NEW ENTRANT

9, Montpellier Cresc. GL50 1US 01242 522888

'Tidy restaurant, nicely decorated, reasonably spacious. Service a bit hurried as they squeezed us in 10 minutes before closing. Menu interesting with main dishes only being served as lamb and chicken, only four fish dishes on whole menu. Popadoms OK with usual array of chutneys. I ordered Onion Bhajia - three golf balls, moist and nicely spiced. Chicken Tikka, Pullao Rice, plain Madras Sauce - large portion of chicken (ten pieces), small portion of rice, large portion of sauce. So, in all, too much tikka, not enough rice and a gallon of sauce. Despite these portion anomalies, food excellent. As gang of five, ordered far too much food, can't remember what others had, but all said how good the food was. £117 (£15 drinks) for five.' DB.

188

Gloucester

BABURCHI

42 Bristol Road, Gloucester	01452 300615

Formerly The Paradise. *'The menu is certainly very similar to what it was previously and it's still my favourite in Gloucester.'* CS. *'Better than ever (following a fire). Wide range of meals, service is good and prices reasonable eg: Onion Bhajia , CTM. I enjoy vegetarian meals on occasions and the menu has a Special Vegetarian Dishes section. Particularly like the Vegetable Jeera. Well worth a visit.'* DT.

SAFFRON   NEW ENTRANT

72, Bristol Road, GL1 5SD	01454 411102

'Welcoming restaurant amongst an enclave of eateries to the south of the city centre with a friendly feel and smiling and youthful staff. 52 diners can be accommodated in a well furnished interior, comfy seats and pleasant decor. Decent menu with all the favourites plus specials. Reshmi Kebab £2.95, lovely, juicy, tasty meat, well spiced and topped with light and fluffy omelette, served with deep yellow sauce and crisp salad. Superb Begum Bahar £6.95, rich satisfying dish of quality lamb and juicy tikka in thick sauce, bountiful in onions - very satisfying. Special Naan £2.70, a little odd, being essentially a good Keema Naan, moist and light with a pleasant filling, then with slices of Chicken Tikka draped on top covered with melted (and pongy) grated cheese. The overall effect was OK, but on reflection I wish I'd had a Garlic Naan. Tarka Dal £2.50 - was quite superb, nicely fluid, perfect balance of ingredients correctly assembled. A thoroughly enjoyable dish and unreservedly recommended.' RW. Credit and debit cards accepted. Delivery: £10min. Takeaway: 10% discount, £10min. Hours: 12-2 / 5-12.

Newent

NEWENT TAKEAWAY

34 Broad Street, Newent	01531 822748

'Murgh Jalahle Jeera Gosht, Chicken Tikka Paneer, all three very good, the Murgh sweet and hot, Jeera smokey and meaty, the Tikka a strange but successful use of cheese in an Indian sauce. We'd have loved to try more! One of the best T/as we've had. Decent sized portions, rice average, but flavours were the great attraction.' RB. Hours: 5-11.30; 12. Sat

Tewkesbury

RAJSHAHI

121 High Street, Tewkesbury	01684 273727

'From strength to strength, that's how the Rajshahi has grown. Reputation with local, business visitors, tourists and boat

people (the rivers Severn and Avon join at Tewkesbury) make it necessary to book to ensure a table. Warm, fresh Popadums and tangy pickles. were washed down with draught Cobra, followed by lovely Meat Samosas, Chicken Tikka Roghan Josh, Sag Aloo, Pullao Rice and Nan. The Pistachio Kulfi was beautifully present, delicious and not rock hard as is often the case.'* TE. T/a: 10% disc. Hours: 6-12; 12.30 Fri & Sat.

Thornbury

MOGHULS BRASSERIE

8 High Street, Thornbury	01454 416187

'Converted Inn, wood panelling, low beams. Waiters very smart, food formula curry house. Tasty Sheek Kebab, Ayr-Biran – colleague had to contend with bones. King Prawn Dhansak, nicely sauced, prawns overcooked. Service OK.' MS. Hours: 12-2 / 6-11.30.

MUMTAZ INDIAN

7 St Mary's Centre, Thornbury	01454 411764

The Mumtaz is on two levels. The downstairs seating area and small bar are for T/a customers and perusal of the menu. The restaurant is upstairs. *'Menu not too extensive, but food extremely good and large portions. Clean European-style decor and music! Very helpful staff and friendly. Would go back.'* WW. KB was less enthusiastic about the decor and other reports talk of standard curries of generous proportions. AE-J found the Phal too hot on one occasion and too mild on another, although his fiancée *'loves the Kormas'*. *'Good'* G & MP. Evenings only.

HAMPSHIRE

Area: South
Population: (5th largest) 1,664,000
Adjacent Counties: Berks, Dorset, Surrey, Sussex, Wilts

Aldershot

JOHNNIE GURKHAS

186 Victoria Road, Aldershot	01252 328773

'Glad to see the restaurant is still as seedy as ever, although it's not quite so easy to accept since the prices are now as much as anywhere else. Mint sauce is excellent. Famous Dil Kusa Nan – an enormous bread topped with cherries and coconut.' pd. *'Food is very plentiful, beautifully cooked and spiced and nothing was left!'* JW.

YOU SAY OK

You may get a discount of you show them this Guide.

ALRESFORD: SHAPLA 60 West Street, Alresford 01962 732134. *'A group of retired officers of The Royal Hampshire Regiment, who are addicted to curries, meet once a year as members of The Vindaloo Club (15 of us).'* JK. *'In our Top 5'.* RP.

ALTON: ALTON TANDOORI 7 Normandy St. 01420 82154. M Shahid's 48-seater. *'Food was excellent. We were very impressed.'* JW. Hours: 6-11.15.

ALTON, FOUR MARKS: SAFFRON 8 Oak Green Pde, Winchester Rd, Four Marks, Alton 01420 561872. T/a: 10% min order £10. Hours: 12-2.30/5.30-11.30; 12 Fri & Sat.

ANDOVER:

THE CHILLIES, NEW ENTRANT 10 Winchester Road, Andover, SP10 2EA 01264 339211. *'Considerably better than the Asia, Salisbury which has made the last two Curry Guides.'* CG.

ANDOVER, LUDCERSHALL: MUCHAL 33 Andover Rd. 01264 790463 *'A visit to the Mughal is deeply reassuring. Some things have not yielded to the modish and the silly, but have stuck to good old fashioned ways of doing things very well.'* RG.

PINK OLIVE NEW ENTRANT: Weyhill Rd, Weyhill, Andover, SP11 0PP ~ 01264 772356. Owner Taj Uddin offers his family recipes with modern fusion. Set in a grand old English building its modern interior features wild pink decor. Seating 112, people, the contemporary Indian restaurant is split into three main areas. Head Chef Sufian Khan cooks signature dishes such as Tandoori Sea Bass and Lamb Xacuti. www.pinkoliverestaurant.com

BASINCSTOKE: KASHMIR 4 Church Street 01256 842112. *'Can understand why we keep returning.'* HC. Hours: 12-2.30 (closed Sun lunch .) / 6-12.

EMSWORTH: TASTE OF INDIA 45 High Street. 01243 376 669. Tufail Ahmed took over this tiny 28-seater in 2003. Hours: 12-2 / 5.30-11.20; 12 Sat.

Andover:

SHAHI RAJ   NEW ENTRANT

4a Winchester Street, Andover, SP10 2EA
                                01264 355210.

'And while I'm on, I'm surprised to see that this one has mysteriously escaped comment in your Guide. It prides itself on its traditional curry house formula, and we are fortunate to have it as our local. It has provided consistently excellent and mouth-watering Indian fare since the wonderful hostess Rahela Khanom took it over in 1996, and has huge following of local enthusiasts. In particular, the Chicken Tikka is beautifully spiced, tender and succulent. This has tended to be my benchmark, because restaurants that can get this right consistently are pretty rare, and if they can do this right then you don't have to worry too much about their ability to do the rest! Now that's not all, of course. Rahela has been adding additional speciality dishes such as the Sylheti Targ Murghi, a delightful combination of marinated chicken, fresh aubergine, gently sweet sauce with roasted onions and peppers, topped off with a garlic condiment. Try also her Jhinga Rani and Chicken or Lamb Omriti. In summary, this is a classic curry restaurant, but with a wide and delicious selection of additional speciality dishes. Thanks for listening! DS.

Basingstoke

BENCAL BRASSERIE

4 Winchester Street.   01256 473795

Fully licensed and air-conditioned. *'It is a year since we've been here. It has new chairs, very attractive, tall-backed cream leather which makes the restaurant look much more up-to-date and upmarket. It is time they changed the menus to match. The staff also look as though they have been told to smarten up, now in very white shirts with black bow ties and black brasserie style aprons. Food is as good as ever, in fact we thought the meal was really outstanding. Service, as usual, lets the restaurant down. There is a large notice on the door claiming that they have been nominated or actually awarded a good service prize...'* Did they buy it? *'...certainly very friendly, but so unprofessional. Wine was not as described on menu, brought to table opened, not presented for approval or tasting and each glass was picked up and filled. Onion Bhajia - very good flavour, more onion than batter, not stodgy like some. Prawn Patia - not served on bread, but wrapped in large fried, light pancake, filling was wonderful. King Prawn tandoori - excellent. Chicken Shashlik Chop Makhani - a dish that started as a shashlik but removed from skewer and served in a very spicy sauce - fantastic. Chingri Jhol - large king prawns in medium sauce - lovely. Mushroom Rice - a bit mean on the mushroom this time. Brinjal Bhajee - excellent.'* HC. *'A favourite.'* CG. T/a: 15% disc, £10 min.
www.bengalbrasserie.co.uk

Fareham

CAFE TUSK

24 West Street Fareham   01329 235511

An interesting formula - the Indian Buffet - seating 176. Several display islands, each containing piping hot Indian food: starters, curries from the very mildest Korma through to Vindaloo, and a chill island with dessertys. Generous portions are assured, as you quite simply help yourself from 50 lunch and 60 dinner dishes. Prices: Lunch: £6.99, Mon- Fri, £8.50, Sat, Sun & Bank Hols. Dinner: £12.99, Sun- Thur; £13.99 - Fri & Sat Discounts for children. Obviously no t/a or del. Hours: 12-3; 4 Sat & Sun/ 5.30-11.30; 11 Sun. www.cafetusk.co.uk

Farnborough

CURKHA PALACE

78 Farnborough Road.   01252 51155

The home of the Gurkhas, Church Crookham, is no

longer. And huge numbers of Britain's favourite warriors are being disbanded, throwing the baby out with the bath water, we think. One legacy, fortunately for curry-lovers, is the relatively high number of Nepalese restaurants.Hours: 12-2.30/6-11. Branch: Gurkha Palace, Liphook, Hants.

Fleet

GOLDEN TRIANGLE

196, Fleet Road, Fleet   01252 616352

Formerly Rajput. Apparently closed, due to several reason, some being EHO fines of £3000, subsidence and structual problems. It has now be rebuilt and has opened in this incarnation. 'Seats 100 downstairs and the upstairs banqueting hall, seats 200. We started with the customary crisp and freshly cooked Pops and *delicious Chutneys. Prawn Lababdar - superb flavours with Special Fried Rice and Cauliflower Bhajee. Lamb and Seafood Biiryani, with plain rice and Sag Bhajee, declared as excellent. Cobra was £9.50 for three large bottles.Slightly more expensive than the average curry house, but is worth it for the high standard to food. The chef can be seen preparing in the central part of the restaurant. Our only criticism, the manager, head waiter, chef and waiters kept coming to ask us if we were enjoying our food, which was irksome...better that, than being totally ignored! Now rates as our favourite.'* JW.

GURKHA SQUARE   TOP 100

327 Fleet Road, Fleet   01252 810286

Of the several Nepalese restaurants in the area, reports received place this one at the top. And it is actually patronised by Nepalese. This 67-seater, owned by AB Gurung, managed by Om Gurung, is as good as you'll find. *'Rather twee and overrated.'* MG. *'Delighted to see the Gurkha Square in the TOP 100. My wife and I can certainly back this up. Perhaps slightly on the pricey side, but superb value for money. We particularly like the Mis-Mas, and the rice and naan are quite excellent.'* DT. *'Comfortable, polite service, excellent food.'* GR. Del: 3m. Hours: 12-2.30 / 6-11.30

WE THE RESTAURANT

333 Fleet Road, Fleet   01252 628889

Sammi Choudhury opened this curiously-named Indian/Thai restaurant in 2003. The design is by top Bangladeshi architect Enamul Karim Nirjhar with modern, clean decor, waterfalls and coi-carp pools targeted at the top end of the market, as its prices show. Sammi's claim to fame was the night Prince William booked for 40 army chums from nearby Sandhurst for their pre-passing-out blow-out. Sammi revealed to this publication that Wills ate CTM and ordered seconds, and that he drank Jack Daniels and Coke. Flushed with success Sammi placed an ad in the local rag proclaiming

that *'you too can eat the same food as heir two to the throne at £19.95'*. The menu(s) are comprehensive and here's a Snapshot: Indian starters: Shark Bhuna £ 12.95, cooked in a spicy thick sauce; Indian Tantaliser £5.50, including Lamb Tikka, Chicken Tikka, Chithol Kofta and Vegetable Kofta; Mains: King Prawn Roshney £ 14.95, cooked with garlic, green chilli, tomato, green peppers and onion and Chicken / Lamb Satkora £ 10.95, with a citric vegetable from Eastern Bangladesh. Thai starters: Prawn Crackers £ 2.95; Pak Tod £ 5.50, deep-fried mixed vegetables in a light batter, served with a sweet chilli dip. Tom Yum Kai £ 5.95, Chicken soup cooked in a herb broth with mushrooms, lime leaves, lemon grass, galangal, fresh chilli and coriander. Thai Main: Red Duck Curry £ 10.95, cooked in a Thai red curry sauce, coconut milk, and kaffir lime leaves. The wine list is remarkable. House whites and reds start at £10.95 but the Lafite Rothschild, vintage unknown, sells at £399.95, as does Louis Roederer Cristal champagne, billed as the 'ultimate'. Personally I put Krug into that position, but this is a curry Guide and if you can afford it you , go for it. Hours 12-2.30 / 6-11. www.wetherestaurant.co.uk

YOU SAY OK

You may get a discount of you show them this Guide.

FARNBOROUGH: POPADOMS 33 Medway Drive, Cove 01252 376869. Sanjiv Singh's 36-seater Nepalese. Bikash Devkota is mngr. Del: £8 min. Hours: 6-10.30.

BENGAL LOUNGE NEW ENTRANT: 1 The Street, Wrecclesham, Farnham 01252 713222. Est in the former Cricketers Pub in 2006. They promise Bangladeshi food which differs from traditional Indian eg: Maas Biran starter, fish appetizer and Main: Lamb Mishti khodu, cooked with butternut squash, a traditional Bengali home dish. *'Service very slow.'* JW. Reports please. Hours: 12-2/6-11.30. Branch: Benares, Farnham. www.bengallounge.co.uk

FARNHAM: DARJEELING 25, South Street, GU9 7QU 01252 714322. *Refurbished and now very smart and modern. Wooden and carpeted floors, turmeric and cream walls, spot lighting, high back leather chairs and the front, plate glass window, looks out toward the church - lovely! Has been enlarged, but the service is not as good as it was, although the food is still very good.'* JW.

FLEET: GULSHAN INDIAN 264 Fleet Road, Fleet 01252 615910. *'Consistently good. Fleet's oldest Indian est 1978. We regularly use it for takeaway, and the Gulshan Special is my favourite.'* JW.

GOSPORT: PRINCE OF INDIA 3 Marina Bldgs, Stoke Rd, 023 9271 1272. Del: £12 min 3m. Hours: 5- 12; 1 Fri & Sat.

GRAYSHOTT: GURKHA DURBAR 30 Headley Rd, Grayshott 01428 605 855. *'In our Top 5'.* RP.

HORNDEAN: INDIAN COTTAGE 4 The Square, Horndean 023 9259 1408. 48-seater est 1978, Anwar Miah from 1996. *'Well worth a visit. Will go back again.'* DL. Hours: 12-2.30/6-12.

Hamble

CINNAMON BAY

4 High Street, Hamble   023 8045 2285

'Clean, modern decor, beautiful table linen, very different menu. Great place.' BF. Specialities include Batak Biran Jalfrezi £11.50, boneless duck with fresh green chillies.

Ayre Mass Jalfrezi £8.95, fillet of Ayre in hot spicy sauce. Mahaan Shabji Kashmir £5.95, vegetables soaked in butter, cooked in creamy sauce with tropical fruits. Khasi Amchor £8.95, charcoal roasted lamb tikka, sweet, creamy yoghurt sauce, with mango slices. Expensive Chutney Tray at £1.50 – you could buy a whole jar for that! Takeaway: 20% disc. Hours: 5.30-12.

Hook

HOOK TANDOORI

1 Fairholme Pde, Station Rd   01256 764844

Syed Ahmed established the venue in 1985 and is an old friend of the guide. All the old favourites and a large section of house specialities, which at first glance seem expensive, BUT, Special Pullao Rice is included. Also, beef curries are available, including: Handi - medium spices; Shatkora - Bangladeshi lemon and Pathori - thin slices, hot - all £9.95 including rice. T/a: 10% disc. Price Check: Popadum 50p, CTM £9.95 (inc Pullao Rice), Pullao Rice £2.25. Hours: 12-2.30/6-11.30;10.45 Sun.

Liss

MADHUBAN   TOP 100

94 Station Road, Liss   01730 893363

There is probably no better success story than the Madhuban's. It opened its door in 1987 in the village of Liss which had been occupied long before Lyss Abbas status was granted in 900AD by King Alfred to the Nunna Mynstre in Winchester. Its church, St Peters was founded at that time and stands today The immediate population is some 1300 souls. The choice of location for the restaurant was a matter of chance. Its owner, Ludoe Miah, who with his late father, established themselves as chefs and managers in curryhouses in the 1960s, simply wanted a new site and did not much mind where it was. Under the circumstances this may have been ill-judged. How could an Indian restaurant survive with such a small footfall, with only 30 seats? Furthermore it has been done by self-financing, albeit enhanced by extracting bank loans from pessimistic bank managers. But survive it did, and within 15 years it had expanded first to 70 seats then to 86. Against all the odds the Madhuban was so successful that turned away many customers, particularly at weekends, which created allows a competitor curry restaurant to open in the village. But even this did not solve the Madhuban's 'problems', if such a phenomenon can be called a problem. In 2008 it expanded again with a complete rebuild to 130 seats. The building was gutted, and for the first time became one area. A new kitchen was built alongside. The original plate-glass windows reveal an inviting bar and waiting area. Now with help from Lodue's brothers Bedar, Didar and Dodo and some

experienced waiters, you will not find better customer care anywhere. Customers names are remembered as old friends. Such is the success that despite doing two sittings and 100 takeaways, it often still cannot fit in all diners at the weekend, so book early. The eight-page menu epitomises the Madhuban's attention to detail. It is illustrated in full colour and fully describes all the dishes. There are 22 starters, 7 items from the tandoor, plus 5 naans. There is an ample choice of old favourites, and they are all done well. '*Given the extensive menu, it took some time to make any choices.*' HC. '*Highly rated – long may it remain.*' J&JM. '*It's is my local; have just got back from there in fact. Hussiani Kebab followed by Dhaba Gosht, Bhindi Bhajee and their superb Pilau. In our Top 5'.* RP. One more thing: Prices here are among the cheapest in the area. This helps its appeal, but there is much more to it than that. It is the epitome of a good house. Hours: 12-2.30 / 5.30-11.30. www.madhubanrestaurant.co.uk They also own Honey Garden, Madhuban Curry Sauces. www.madhuban.co.uk

Portsmouth

BLUE COBRA

87 London Rd, North End   023 9266 5000

Opened 2006 as a 200 seater on two floors. Menu Snapshots: Zhal Naga (very hot chillies) Chicken or Lamb £6.95, from the Sylhet region, cooked with fresh Bangladeshi Naga chilli - hot!; Chicken Shahee £7.95, lightly spiced, tandoor, mint, garnished with grated cheese, served with salad on sizzler; Kanchi Chops £3.95 / £7.95, tandoor marinated lamb chops, served with salad on sizzler; Masalas Chips £1.80; Moglai Poratha £1.50, flaky thick fried Indian bread with a spicy omelette. *'Everything totally excellent. Decor, ambience, food presentation, service fine quality of dishes. They will do very well providing they can make the most of available parking spaces in the area.'* CF. T/a: 10% disc. Del: £15 min. Hours: 12-12.

SAFFRON

1 Kingston Rd, Portsmouth   023 9277 9797

Sayed Khan's fully licensed, air-conditioned is modern modern and huge restaurant, (though it doesn't look it - clever seating!) seating over 200 diners, in two rooms, both with bars. Pat and I have eaten here, when the upstairs room was completely packed out with Portsmouth Football team and supporters. I am not a fan of football at all and didn't use this opportunity to get autographs. Back to the Saffron - food nicely presented and promptly served, by young but experienced waiters. The owner is a charismatic man, who has a very friendly and loyal following. Popular dishes includChicken Aloo Jhool and Chicken Shakuti. Menu Snapshots: Swordfish Bhuna £9.95; Kodu Goosth £8.95 - lamb, pumpkin, garlic, ginger, green chilli and coriander leaves; Chicken Raj Naga £8.95 - sliced chicken tikka, sauce made with Bangladeshi Naga chilli - hot!. min ch £8. Hours: 12-2.30 / 6-12.

STAR OF ASIA

6 Market Way, Portsmouth   023 9283 7906

Opposite the old Tricorn car park, is this great little 40-seater restaurant, with a gorgeous sapphire blue, shiny terracotta tiles and blue mosaic front. Est 1992 by Abdul Mothen, who manages while Chef Gian Uddin cooks. *'Far enough away from the circuit drinking area. Hot and crispy Popadums. Excellent Rashmi with large portion of succulent kebab, topped with fluffy and tender omelette. Tandoori Chicken beautifully tender. Lovely Meat Bhuna and tangy Chicken Dhansak. Late generally means 1am, though when I left at 2.30am people were still arriving!'* RW. Hours: 12-2.15 (Fri closed) / 6 to late; Sat & Sun 12pm to late.

Southampton

CAFÉ MUMBAI   TOP 100

Lower Banister Rd, Bedford Pl, Southampton, 023 8063 0006

A truly stunning venue, which opened in 2006 and offers fine Indian cuisine for up to 200 diners. There is a bar with an Indian 'Tapas' menu. An informal buffet on the ground floor and a la carte dining on the first floor, overlooking the restaurant below and open style 'theatre' kitchens. 'Not located in the best area of Southampton. The surrounding streets house pubs and night clubs, which attract (on opening night) large groups of harmless, parading, howling Uni students, fortunately off somewhere else. The building used to be a wine warehouse. It is clear that a lot of money has been spent remodelling and decorating this impressive establishment. A well lit and full height plate glass window, let the uninvited see their 'beautiful people' (S'ton Footballers and 'wags' etc) sip champagne and rub shoulders with other dignitaries - including Pat and me!! Sally Taylor, from BBC South Today News, was in the upstairs gallery, wearing a pair of ill fitting, pale pink jeans, which should have seen the charity shop many moons ago (she looked as scruffy as me!), filming with the crew. I don't know if she stayed to eat, if she didn't she missed a treat. During the very busy and noisy reception, we were told to be seated, as the speeches were about to commence. I elbowed the 'wags' out of the way and bagged a table in full view of the theatre kitchen. Pat was announced as, the *'Egon Ronay of Indian Restaurants'* - flattery indeed and gave a speech. Following Pat, a dreadful comedian, apparently a local, didn't entertain with his toilet humour, everyone looked suitable embarrassed. And then to finish off, the Mayor, who in usual 'mayoral-style', wittered on about nothing. I was reminded of a similar long Mayor's speech at another launch party many years ago, at which real comedian Frank Carson made a speech. He summed up the Mayor's speech by saying, *'Thank you, Lord Mayor for shortening the winter!'* What do restaurants get mayor in for opening day? I have yet to find one who likes curry! Wines were poured and an assortment of starter platters were served. The kitchen brigade of an impressive ten chefs, is led by Uday Seth, in an on-view kitchen. All are highly trained and from five star Indian hotels, so no curry house stuff here. All the food was delicious and included: Fish Amritsari £5.25, gramflour battered-fried fish; Chestnut-Chard Pakora £3.75, water chestnut and crunchy chard pakoras; Chicken Shaslik £4.50; Aloo Tikki £3.95, griddle fried potato patties stuffed with gingered green peas; Shikhampuri Kebab £4.95, baby lamb cooked with cinnamon, cardamom, Bengal gram, minced, packed with yoghurt cheese, mint and onions, a delicacy from Hyderabad, all served with wonderful chutneys - Imli; Podina; Mango and Cachumber. Saint's

Manager (can't remember his name and wouldn't recognise him if he walked past me in the street) was surrounded by his cronies! He cautiously bit off a piece of chicken tikka, as if not a fan of Indian cuisine. Well, that's OK, I'm not a fan of football!' dbac. Menu Snapshot: pepper Crab £5.95, soft shell crabs with garlic and black pepper with ginger and green mango sauce; Potli Samosa £3.50 , savoury chicken mince stuffed in crusty pastry, deep-fried and served with tamarind chutney; Masala Vada £3.50, coarsely ground lentils blended with fennel, ginger and green chillies, deep-fried; Machali Neelgiri £11.95, monkfish simmered in a green herb curry of coconut, chillies, coriander and roasted spices; Murgh Tikka lababdar £8.5 , chicken tikkas in creamy tomato-based onion gravy, flavoured with grated ginger and an abundance of fresh coriander; Dhungaar ka Saag Gosht £10.95, sliced lamb chargrilled, smoked and tossed with spinach and garlic; Bhindi do Pyaza £6.50, green okras sautéed with onions, tomatoes and a touch of spice; Pudhina Paratha £2.50, mint flavoured bread. Another high quality curry venue for Southampton.Hours: 12-2.30 / 5.30-11 Mon-Tue; 12-11 Wed-Sun.   www.cafe-mumbai.co.uk

KUTI'S BRASSERIE   A-LIST

37 Oxford St, Southampton   023 8022 1585

It's hard to miss Kuti's purple exterior used since they first opened in 1985 on London Road. and their relocation in 1994. Owner Mr Kuti has financed a recent major refurbishment includes hand-painted designs straight onto the walls, using a central theme of lotus flowers contrasted by silver finishing. The reception area is now styled as a lounge with a Bedouin feel again in a myriad of colours, while retaining the original purple as the core shade. Kuti's serves Bangladeshi and Indian cuisine and there is a Head Chef for each region. Romis Miah, who has been at Kuti's for 20 years is in charge of the Bangladeshi cuisine while India-trained Kamal Kishore formerly at Delhi's Hyatt Regency, heads the Indian cooking specialities. Menu Snapshots: good fish dishes, including: ayre, sea bass, sole and trout; also a good selection of popular curry house dishes made with beef; Bonhoor Delight, diced venison, served with a rich orange-flavoured Grand Marnier-based sauce. £8.95, Paneer Shashlik £4.50, cubes of cottage cheese, green chilli, ginger and coriander; Kerala Chicken £7.95, coconut, chilli; Lobia Dhal £5.95, black eyed peas, onions and tomato. We have had a lot of correspondence on this, and here is some of it. *This upmarket establishment features a doorkeeper in traditional dress, novel presentation of mixed warm and crisp popadums in a basket, and a varied menu that is proud of Bangladeshi / Sylheti cuisine and meats not regularly encountered such as Venison, Duck and Beef. The 'Beef Bangla' is very tender and almost melts in the mouth. Expect to pay £20 per head for popadums, slightly adventurous main course, and a large Cobra.'* GR. *'The quality of the food has been excellent. On my most recent visit, very much enjoyed Bonhoor Tikka, tandoor marinated venison, served with a delicious sauce. I like the signature dishes. Tandoori Quail, particularly noteworthy. Service can vary, from slow during very busy periods to slightly over-pushy on the alcohol front, but generally good quality. Unconditionally recommended.'* SO. *'In our Top 5'.* RP. Fully licensed and air-conditioned. Daily Buffet lunch: £8.50, dinner £14.50. T/a: 10% disc. Hours: 12-2.30/ 6-12.

Kuti's Royal Thai Pier opens in 2008 in Southampton offering Thai Cuisine. Branches: Kuti's Noorani - Fair Oak, 465 The Square, Fair Oak, Eastleigh, SO50 7AJ ~ 023 8060 1901; Kuti's Kohinoor - Portswood   2 The Broadway, Portswood, Southampton, SO17 2WE ~ 023 8058 2770. www.kutis.co.uk

POPPADUM EXPRESS   TOP 100

48 Oxford St. Southampton   023 8063 2444

This 140-seater is M.Ed. Amaze Khan's second outlet, whose theme is a combination of traditionalist cuisine and modernist decor with a signature maroon colour The bar staff, who boast that there isn't a cocktail that they can't do, also offer tea, coffee, smoothies and fruit juices. The choice of name sounding more like a crisp fast-food outlet perhaps does not give potential diners the real feel of the cuisine. Khan's USP is his on-view kitchens containing no less than seven different cooking units used in India for thousands of years such as Murghi (open fire grill), Tawa (griddle), Shami Tawa (walled griddle), Kadhai (wok), Lagan (steam pot) Shilajit Stone (special stones from Hyderabad, with aphrodisiac properties) and of course the Tandoor. All of this is managed by a team of highly trained Indian chefs, led by Ishtyak Ahmed. Born in the culinary heartland of Awadh (Lucknow) he learned his trade from the legendary chefs Ustad Abdullah Khan and Ustad Zaiki the was exec at Lucknow's Taj Mahal Hotel. Ram Kishore also from Lucknow is sweet maker. Ahmed uses different sauces to give every dish a completely different taste and texture and the open-plan kitchen allows diners to watch the chefs in action. The menu travels around India's different regions as well as including favourites like Chicken Tikka Masala and chef's specials like Lamb Mughlai. Main courses start at £7.95 and a selection from the more hearty set-menus are priced £15.95 upwards. Take away and Del service. Branch: Popadum Express 40 Woburn Place, Russell Square, London WC1.   www.poppadomexpress.co.uk

P.O.S.H.

1 Queensway, Southampton   023 8022 6377

Established 1991. Upstairs to find inviting armchairs in a comfortable lounge. Go through to a huge nautically-themed restaurant, seating 150 diners, with bar, grand piano, band stand and a dance floor - quite a place. AFAQ: what does P.O.S.H mean . And Port-Out Starboard- Home! And what did that mean In the old days when ships were the main transports to India, the experienced travellers chose their cabins to be 'POSH' to avoid the hot sunshine flooding through the porthole. Menu Snapshots: Paneer Tikka £4.95, curd cheese, flavoured with ginger, garlic, coriander and lime juice; Honey Glazed Salmon Tikka £5.95; King Prawn Toast £5.95, round of toast, smothered in an olive and anchovy butter, topped with garlic and chilli stir-fried king prawn; Duck with Mushroom in Red Wine £5.95, duck, onions and mushrooms sautéed in rich creamy sauce. *'It is well decorated though its size gives it an empty feel. The dodgy middle-of-the-road music being played as you were seated did not bode well, although the restaurant itself did have quite a good ambience. Service was average to poor. The food is variable. I have eaten there and been very pleased, swordfish and salmon tikka starters, and other times it has been very average. The Baked Sea Bass was very delicate and succulent and the Sea Bass in Red Wine was also very pleasant, rich and spicy. Duck Bhuna was tender with a very nice spice balance but was too salty. The Chatt, which was chickpeas in a pleasant, tangy sauce, had a nice heat and clean coriander leaf finish. Overall opinion – OK, with reservations but would probably give it another try'.* SO. Del: 3m, £15 min. Hours: 12-2 / 6-11. www.poshrestaurant.co.uk

TIFFIN CLUB   NEW ENTRANT

1 Oxford Street, Southampton   023 8023 3433

Miff, Shah, Rakib & Mufti opened this branch in 2007. Reports please. Hours: 12-2/6-11. For full details see The Tiffin Club, Winchester. .www.tiffinclub.co.uk.

YOU SAY OK

You may get a discount of you show them this Guide.

LYNDHURST: PASSAGE TO INDIA 3 Romsey Road, Lyndhurst 023 8028 2099. AA Kaysor offers venison and duck specials. T/a: 20% Hours: 12-2/6-11.30. www.passagetoindia-lyndhurst.com

SOUTHAMPTON: NATRAJ BALTI 3 Winchester St. 023 8036 6344. *'Veg Baltis very good; according to friends meat dishes excellent too. Was once a night club and there's dancing and live Indian music on Fri & Sats'* MD. Commended by SS. Hours: 12-2/ 6-11.30.

SOUTHAMPTON: MIRCHI 4 Bedford Place, Southampton 023 8033 8800. Smallish curry house that gets busy so book. Del: 3m, £10 min, eve only. T/a: 15% disc. Hours: 12-2; Not Fri/5-12. www.mirchitandoori.com

Southsea

BOMBAY BAY   TOP 100

Fort Cumberland Rd, Southsea Marina
023 9281 6066

In 2005, Southsea Marina handed the operation of its all-day bar and restaurant to the Pompey Gandhi Group (twelve brothers and cousins, surname Karim) based in Kingston Road and who already operated two other restaurants. Parking is usually sufficient. The exterior is rather utilitarian, and the actual restaurant is up a flight of stairs, above the Marina offices. The restaurant has a two-aspect panoramic view of the sea, the 'mainland' and Hayling Island. See previous page. After you have taken in the views, you notice the primrose yellow and burgundy walls with wall mounted seafaring artwork. The window seats, with their views are the most popular, especially in daylight. On a good day, the large outside terrace area with several steel table and chairs is a magnet, and a full service is available there. Even on a coldish day heaters make it a relaxing place to be. Exec chef Lahin Karim oversees the kitchens, and has aimed his menu at healthier food 'with less ghee and crunchy vegetables'. He also presents his food on rather smart white china plates. It has smart pale yellow and burgundy walls with muted modern seafaring artefacts. Menu snapshot: Starters, which come with a splendid salad include Mussels £45, stuffed with rice, served with garlic and coriander sauce; Bombay Missali: Chicken tikka, lamb tikka, sheek kebab and squid or Hush Tikka, duck fillets marinated in spices in orange flavoured sauce both £6. Mains include (all £9) Goan Chicken or Lamb Tikka, cooked with red goan chilli, garlic, green peppers, coriander, coconut milk and fine spices, fairly hot. Vegetable dishes (£3.20) include Broccoli Bhajee and Niramish. Set lunch menu between 12pm & 5 is good value at £7.95. And for Sun lunch they do a carvery roast with all the trimmings. They are usefully open all day (the only venue in the area to do this) mainly to offer a bar and snacks service for the marina boat owners, and anyone else who wants to avail themselves of this service. 12-11 Sun-Th; 3-12 Fri; 12-12 Sat and Bank Hols. www.bombaybay.co.uk

GOLDEN CURRY   TOP 100

16 Albert Road, Southsea   023 9282 0262

Some years ago, I was interviewed here, by the then local TV station Meridian, and I sampled many dishes from the korma to the phal. As a definition of the formula, they were spot on. Colours, aromas, tastes, textures, service and price – all done right by experienced 'old hands'. In fact the 52-seater has been owned by Salim Hussein (manager) and Razak Ali (head chef) since 1979, and has a justifiably loyal following. I am often

Golden Curry

16 Albert Road

Southsea

Hampshire

PO2 2SH

023 9282 0262

Top 100

sent letters & emails by people bemoaning the loss of taste these days compared with 'the good-old-days' Well here you find it, done as it used to be. One secret is that they cut no corners. Never mind that patronising phrase often overused by overpriced fancy restaurants: *'we use only the finest and freshest ingredients'* What else would you use? The worst and stalest ingredients Golden Curry don't need to say that because you can taste fresh and finest. Whole chickens, for example are pot-simmered in light spices, then boned and cooked off in your curry dish, with the resultant great flavour to match. (As opposed to tasteless pre-boned breast). It has a huge local following all of whom know the waiters by name, and vice-versa. It is common to see three generations at table, all of whom have been regulars almost since birth!. This is what a decent curryhouse is all about: a friendly home-from-home, where you get cared for with decent food, decent service and an unpretentious price tag which doesn't require a new mortgage. Menu extracts: Chicken Tikka Chilli Masala £7.05. Special Mixed Fried Rice £2.75, with prawns and cabbage, garnished with omelette. Vegetable Thali £7.30, Vegetable Bhajee, Brinjal Bhajee, Cauliflower Bhajee, Tarka Dal, Mushroom Bhajee, Nan and Pullao Rice – great value! *'An excellent restaurant which my husband and I go to for a "curry fix".* Salim is a wonderful host, greeting his clients with courtesy and friendliness, the waiters follow his lead. Ali runs a wonderfully efficient and clean kitchen.' C&CH. 'Excellent food and service. Our regular curry restaurant.' DKM. 'Staff always friendly and attentive. Extremely clean and cosy restaurant. Meals range from very good to superb! Good sized portions which are very filling.'* GB. *'An excellent restaurant. Received a nice welcome. Table, decor – clean and tidy. Meal was as I ordered it – HOT! I have been all over the country but it would be hard to beat this curry house.'* EC. PS: The locations is great if you have a night out at the gorgeous King's Theatre, next door, and they do a quick meal if they know your plans. Del free, 2m over £20 (under that £2.50 charge made). Hours: 12-1.30 Sun to Th / 5.30-12.30 Mon-Th; 5.30-12 Sun.

T & J MAHAL

39 Elm Grove, Southsea   023 9281 5824

A restaurant with two head chefs – Kalam Khan, specialises in Bengali and Goan cuisine and Joshim Ahmed, whose talents lie with authentic and contemporary cuisine. Superior formula curries served here, in this smart restaurant in Southsea, where there is quite a choice of eateries. Menu Snapshots: Achari Chingri £4.95 - tandoor cooked, tamarind flavoured tiger prawns; All Bora £3.25 - fried mashed potato, stuffed with mint, ginger, flaked almonds and spicy peas; Mixed Grill £7.95 includes a Nan. Hours: 5-12.

STUBBINGTON: STUBBINGTON TANDOORI 35a The Green, Stubbington, Nr Fareham   01329 664615. Mr Rahman's 40-seater. T/a: small disc. Del: £12 min, 4m. Hours: 5.30-12.

WATERLOOVILLE:

CINNAMON 258 London Rd 023 9223 0181. *'In our Top 5'.* RP.

INDIAN COTTAGE 51 London Rd, Cowplain 01705 269351. At Sheik Shab Uddin's tiny 30-seater Chef AH Khan's *'food is excellent and the staff always attentive'.* D&BR & L&AC. Hours: 12-2.30/5.30-12. Branches: Indian Cottage: Port Solent, Gunwharf Quays & Horndean.

PURE ZING 1 Purbrook Chase Precinct, Crookhorn Lane, Waterlooville 023 9224 0066. Hab Rahman's takeaway with places for dining in. Branch: Tamarind & Moonlight Express, Nutbourne, Sussex.

SHALIMAR 9 Hambledon Pde, Hambledon Rd, Waterlooville 023 9225 1565. 56-seater managed by Mujib. *'Does the simple things well. Friendly young staff who are both polite and efficient.'* GS. Hours: 12-2.30/5.30-11.30.

WINCHESTER: BALAKA 75 Stoney La. SO22 6EW   01962 859606. Ali Forid Miah's good formula curry house. Hours: Lunch and dinner, daily.

Wickham

KUTI'S OF WICKHAM   NEW ENTRANT

Star Corner, Fareham Rd.   01329 835353

A new venture from Kuti Miah managed by Joe, with good reports received. Starters £3-5 each, mains £7-13, desserts £5-8. Outside tables. Hours::12-2:30/6-12. *'One of our Top 5'.* RP. See Kuti's Southampton, Hants. www.kutis.co.uk

VATIKA   NEW ENTRANT

Wickham Vineyards, Botley Road, Shedfield, Southampton, SO32 2HL   01329 830405

The 40 acre vineyard, est 1984 by owners Gordon and Angela, has a well-equipped winery, set in a dramatic 200 year old barn whose old oak beams contrast with the high-tech stainless steel wine-making tanks. October sees the harvest in full swing. In April they bottle the wine of the previous vintage. The 7.5 acre nature reserve has woodland and a small carp lake where you can spot abundant wildlife including deers, great-spotted woodpeckers, sparrowhawks and many other birds. The elegant, spacious50 seater restaurant has large traditional beams and French doors opening out onto the terrace, with stunning views over the vineyard. Benares' backers are involved and plan to open here in July 2008, after we go to press. This means that Atul Kotchhar is overseeing the cuisine with Executive Chef Jitin Joshi in charge and manager Bernine Van Schoor. A rare and varied wine collection. Reports please. www.wickhamvineyard.co.uk www.vatikarestaurant.com Kotchhar's backers are also considering further openings, in Canary Wharf, and Westfield, the new Shepherd's Bush mega-shopping mall.

Winchester

TIFFIN CLUB   NEW ENTRANT

at the Westgate Inn, Romsey Rd, Winchester
01962 840804.

Miff, Shah, Rakib & Mufti are the owners. Miff is the chef and he likes Indian fusion and he likes telling you about himself and his food: *'I've built up a reputation for innovation, for pushing the boundaries of Indian cuisine – indeed for initiating the revolution of 'Fusion' cooking'*, so Atul, Vineet, Vivek, Chad et al must have copied him! That aside it is innovative, and for those who want it they do the conventional dishes, albeit *'with extra panache'* (sic) at £6.50 to £9.50. For the more adventurous we hear good things about Miff's fusion food. Menu Snapshot: Chilli Crab Cake, £5.95, Saffron-infused crab and potato cakes with a hint of coconut, dusted in gram flour; Stuffed Baby Squid, £5.95, squid with a herbal hot stuffing of prawns, chilli and coriander; Whitebait & Cachumba, £3.95, crisp whitebait served on a fiery salad bed; Mango & Pomegranate Lassi £2.50; Zyava Chicken, £7.95 based on the Mexican Molé where dark chocolate is fused with chilli to which Miff has added tangy tamarind giving the dish a complex favour and a slight bite. Kamala Chicken has a sweet zesty orange sauce with the delicacy of cinnamon, Barramundi fish steamed with saffron, lemongrass, ginger and honey while Monkfish Patrani is Miff's take on the Parsee favourite (pomfret) coated with a paste of green mango, chilli and coconut, wrapped in a banana leaf and steamed. The restaurant prides itself on using Hampshire meats for a small range of curries. Reports please. Hours: 12-2 / 6-11. Branch: 1 Oxford Street, Southampton, SO14 3DJ www.tiffinclub.co.uk.

HEREFORDSHIRE

Area: Welsh Border
Population: 220,000
Adjacent Counties:
Gwent, Powys,
Shrops,
Staffs,
Worcs

Gorsley

ROADMAKER INN GHURKHA
NEW ENTRANT

Gloucester Rd, Gorsley   01989 720352

'Owned and run by four ex-Ghurkha soldiers; it maintains a pub bar with the restaurant serving Nepalese cuisine in the evenings. We started with the Ghurkha Special (£10.95) which is was a very nice mixed grill and certainly enough for two. We also had Momo (£4.95), steamed lamb mince dumplings with a spicy tomato chutney, again very good. The main courses of Himalaya Chicken (£8.95) and Nepalese Lamb Curry (£9.95) were delicious and the children voted the Chicken Tikka Masala as the best they had ever tasted. The accompanying Naans (£2.00) were beautifully light. Well worth a visit.' MC. www.theroadmakerinn.co.uk

Hereford

KAMAL

82 Widemarsh St, Hereford   01432 278005

'A narrow-fronted and impressively named enterprise that fronts a surprisingly long and capacious curry house. Helpful and friendly staff. Menu contains usual suspects, plus specials. Real cloths and hand towels. Jangra Purr – unusual, almost spring roll, delightful chat style curry with salad and sweet sauce, enjoyable. Lamb Tikka Biriani – very good, well cooked, a shade greasy, boiled egg rather than usual omelette topping.

Lamb absolutely top quality, mouth watering. Recommended.' RW. 3 course Sun Lunch: £8. Del: £14 min. Hours: 12-2 / 5.30-12.

Kings Langley

CINNAMON LOUNGE   NEW ENTRANT

18, High St, WD4 8BH   **01923 263923**

Situated in a lovely old Englush building, apparently 500 years old. The front of the building has black beams and lovely herringbone bricks. The interior, which has been completely refurbished, still retaining its original inglenook fireplace, but not much else. Comfortable, high backed leather chairs, sit around tables which are cleanly laid with white linen, blue or red glass chargers and sleek cutlery. Suka - king prawn or duck, tamarind sauce, herbs and honey; Pitta Paneer Saag - cheese, spinach wrapped in puri; Chot Poti - chick peas, eggs, potatoes, tamarind sauce; Lamb E Kodu - with Bangladeshi green pumpkin; Sharabi - chicken or lamb slices, simmered in a mild buttery, red wine sauce, garnished with nuts. Hours: 6-11; 11.30 Fri & Sat. Sunday Buffet: 12-3. Branch: Cinnamon Lounge, London Colney, AL2 1LP.   www.cinnamon-lounge.co.uk

Kingston

HYDERABAD   NEW ENTRANT

57, Bridge St, Kingston, HR5 3DJ   **01544 231999**

'Run by brothers Eklim (very popular with the locals) and Shalim Khan, who experience is over 20 years, (their father ran a restaurant in Stourbridge). The family is originally from Khar Bari, Syhlet' I think virtually every Bangladeshi restaurant owner is from Syhlet, I am surprised their is anyone still left! (only joking! I've been there and can confirm that the population is thriving!). *'Worth the forty minute drive to eat there, service is excellent and so is the vegetarian food. Have tried various dishes including the Baked Bean Balti £3.95. Lamb Passanda £7.95 (including rice) is to die for. There can be a bit of a wait when they are full, but this is rural Heref'd – we go with the flow! Fantastic.'* SSL. Takeaway: 10% discount. Hours: 5.30-11.

Leominster

JALALABAD

33 Etnam St, Leominster   **01568 615656**

Well promoted by the ebullient owner-manager Kamal Uddin Owner-chef Abdul Mukith's food menu attracts regular praise from Leominster locals. *'Menu Conventional Quality Excellent Quantity Very generous Decor Obtrusive peacock feathers arranged around the wall - disturbing for some Service On the slow side Comfort Good, not too close seating Comments Starters: Popadums 50p x 2*

plus £1.20 chutney; Onion Bhaji £2.25 – taste good, texture fine; Tandoori Mix £3.95; Presentation good, slightly small portions. Main Course: Chicken Keema Mattar £6.95; Garlic Chicken £6.95. Mushroom Pullao Rice £2.15; Peshwari Nan £2.15. Drinks: Tiger x 2. Bill £31.40. Mark 8 / 10.' G&MP.

YOU SAY OK

You may get a discount of you show them this Guide.

BROMYARD: TASTE OF INDIA 22 High St. 01885 488668. *'Had a good meal in here.'* Hours: 12-2.30/5.30-11.30; closed Tues.

HEREFORD: KHAN'S Plough Inn, Canon Pyon, 01432 830577. *'In a pub! Excellent food at very reasonable prices – best in Hereford.'* PJM. No credit cards. Hours: 5.30-12.

HEREFORD: TASTE OF RAJ – NEW ENTRANT ,67 St Owenens St. 01432 351075. *'Policed by efficient, almost surly staff. Good menu to tempt the palate. Very enjoyable overall, definitely recommended.'* RW. T/a: 10% disc. Del: £14 min. Hours: 6-11.

ROSS-ON-WYE: OBILASH – NEW ENTRANT 19a Gloucester Rd. 01989 567860. Est 1985, Janu Miah's Obilash seats 40. Del: 3m, £25 min. T/a: 10% disc. Hours: 6-12.

ROSS-ON WYE: BENGAL LOUNGE – NEW ENTRANT 1 Copse Cross St, Ross. 01989 562803. *'Sizzler Mix starter, £3.75 enough for two. Signature dishes come in at £10.95.T/a: 10% disc.'* MC.

CAFE ZAM ZAM – NEW ENTRANT 23 High St, Ross, HR9 5BZ. 01989 764030 *'Very reasonably priced – house specials all at c£7. The mixed platter for two (starter £6.90, main £13.80) gives a nice variety of tastes to try; those who like a kick to their meals may enjoy the garlic chilli chicken. Staff are very welcoming. BYO allowed'* MC. *'In a different league.'* JC.

HERTFORDSHIRE

Area: Home Counties, (north of London)
Population: 1,042,000
Adjacent Counties: Beds, Bucks, Cambs, Essex, London

'GL' denotes those former Herts suburbs absorbed by Greater London in 1965.

Abbots Langley

FOREST OF INDIA

39 High Street   **01923 270077**

Established 1996. Owner AK Chowdhury runs this 120-seater. Menu Snapshot: Tandoori Pomfret £8; Tandoori Mixed Grill £8, including King Prawn and Naan bread – great!; Rupchanda Bhuna £7.95, lightly fried pomfret, medium sauce; Murgh Nawabi £7, marinated chicken, mushrooms, onions, tomatoes and brandy – fit the a King or even a Nawab! Del: 2m £12

min. T/a: 10% dis. Service 10%. Sun Buffet: 12-5, c£9 adult, £4.50 children, coffee and mints included. Thursday Banquet Night: c£10. Hours: 12-2.30 / 6-11.30. Branch: Sema, Whitcross St, WC1. www.forestofindia.co.uk

VICEROY OF INDIA   TOP 100

20 High St, Abbots Langley   01923 262163

Established in 1989 by Ronney Rahman. *'Food delicious, always fresh and elegantly presented. Waiters friendly and attentive.'* d&pm. *'Menu was full and standard with the unique addition of a number of hash (duck) dishes. Makhoni Hash – wonderfully flavourful, distinctive but mild spices in a cream and tomato sauce.'* RH. House specials: Makhoni Hash (mild) tandoori grilled duck, tossed in butter, cultured yoghurt, fresh cream and mild spices and Karahi Jhinga (hot), jumbo prawns cooked with a medium dry gravy, herbs, tomatoes, onions and green pepper, served from a iron karahi. Hours: 12-2.30/6-11.

YOU SAY OK
You may get a discount of you show them this Guide.

BARNET (CL): SHAPLA TANDOORI 37 High St. 020 8449 0046. SI Ahmed's smart 50 est 1981 is 'always very reliable, clean and cosy.' CT. Del: £1.50, 4m. Hours: 12-2.30/6-12.

BERKHAMSTED: AKASH 307 High St.   01442 862287. Owner Foysol Ahmed. *'Staff attentive without hovering.'* LB. Hours: 12-2.30/6-12.

CURRY GARDEN 29 High St, Berkhamsted 01442 877867. *'An old converted pub, lovely low beams and cosy booths. Very impressed. Will most definitely be back.'* SW.

BISHOPS STORTFORD: SHADONA High St.   01279 508149. *'Excellent cuisine and sharp service and we were all stuffed! Prices above average.'* AE. Hours: 12-2.30/6-11.

CHESHUNT: RAJ VOGUE 48 High St.   01992 641297. 82-seater est 1991 by Khalek Quazi. GR likes *'the Nawab Nargis, cooked with spicy minced chicken and fresh mint.'* T/a: 10% disc. Del: £15, 3m. Hours: 12-2.30; 2 Sun lunch buf £6.95./6-11.30; 11 Sun.

HATFIELD: PRINCE OF INDIA 10 Market Pl.   01707 265977. 48-seater est 1993, managed by SF Ali. *'Romantic and pleasant atmosphere.'* RL. Hours: 5.30-11.30.

HEMEL HEMPSTEAD: CHUTNEYS 79 Waterhouse St, Hemel 01442 243 595.   70-seater owned by Saber Khan. Menu unusuals: Noodles, with spicy minced meat, egg, ; Special Beef, tandooried fillet steak; Chilli and Coriander Naan. Del: 4m £15 min. Hours: 12-2 Sat & Sun. Sun lunch buffet £7.95 / 5.30-11.30.

HEMEL: GURU TANDOORI 5 Bridge St, 01442 254725. Owner SM Rahman. Chef S Uddin. 36 seats. MBS says he eats here twice a week for 25 years. Del: £15 min, 5m. Hours: 12-2.30/6-12. Branch: Guru, 630, Uxbridge Road, Hayes, Middx.

HITCHIN: INDIA BRASSERIE 36 Bancroft Rd, Hitchin 01462 433001. M Chowdhury's restaurant seats 32. *'The best in Hitchin.'* SW. Hours: 12-2.30 Tue-Thur/ 5.30-12; 1-11 Sun, buffet £7.95..

LETCHWORTH: CURRY GARDEN 71 Station Road 01462 682820. Chef owner Afiz Ullah's 72-seater has a *'huge friendly menu.'* MT. Hours: 12-2.30 / 6-12; 12-12 Sun, buffet 12-5.30. Branches (all named Curry Garden) at: Berkhamsted; Rickmansworth; Dunstable Beds; Hornchurch Essex.

SAGAR 48 The Broadway, Letchworth 01462 684952. Motiur Rahman's 'Trout Masala is one of the best.' LV. Service 10%. Lunch buffet, weekdays £5.50, Sun £5.95. Branches: Aashiana,

SAWBRIDGEWORTH: STAR OF INDIA 51 London 01279 726512. 70-seater in 2 rooms, est 1981 by Dilwa Jamal Ahmed. Free car park opposite. Specials includ Kurzi L or Chicken. T/a: 10% disc. Del: £12 min, 5m. Hours: 2/5.30-11.30.

TANDOORI NIGHT Knight St, Sawbridgeworth   0 722341. *'We had our wedding reception in this great restaurant* 'Hours: 12-2.30/6-11.30; 12 Fri & Sat.

Hemel Hempstead:

MOGUL

91 High St, Old Town, Hemel   01442 255

'I feel this is the best in Hemel – beautifully decorated always good food and service. Took two work colleagues two customers – all agreed the best meal! Chicken Rous Chicken Rezala and Mogul Special Masala – all fanta Side dishes and breads – all very good.' [and JH retur *'Phoned and collected within half an hour, all hot plus Popadums!'* [and JH keeps returning]: *'Busy Sat n party of nine. Table booked for 9.30; Sat down at 10pm. M courses at 10.45, no starters. Food as good as ever – well loa chicken and mushroom Rizato, thoroughly enjoyed by Only let down was Tandoori King Prawn looked great lacking in flavour. Bill at 12.20am. An enjoyable night too long! [and JH keeps returning]: 'Busy Thursday n Deep fried aubergines on the house to start absolutely gorg Roushini seemed a but rich. Mushroom Rizoti and Chi Gastoba – as good as ever!'* JH. T/a: 10% disc. Hours: 2.30 / 5.30-11.30; 12 Fri & Sat.

Kings Langley

KINGS LODGE HOTEL   NEW ENTRA

28 Bridge Rd, Hunton Bridge   0845 345 17

Kamal Chowdhury tells us that his hotel, bar restaurant, just 800m from J20 / M25 was built in 1 and used by King Charles 1st as a hunting lodge an

place to meet his lover Nell Gwyn. Note the date 1 and coat of arms on top of the open log fire in the lounge. Be that as it may, it has an original double-Continental Cuisine lunches & including Sunday Ro are by chef George Gryllis. Dinners are all-Indian Cui

MUMTAJ

Nominated best in the south

**115 London Road
St Albans,
Herts**

01727 858399

**Nominated Cobra
Good Curry Guide
Best in the South**

CHEZ MUMTAJ

Modern French-Asian Dining

**136 - 142 London Road
St Albans,
Herts**

01727 800033
Lunch
12 - 2.30 pm Mon to Sun

Dinner
6 pm - 11 Daily
Saffron Lounge: 6 - 11 pm

Email us
info@chezmumtaj.com

St Albans

CHEZ MUMTAJ
NEW ENTRANT NEW TO OUR TOP 100

136 London Rd, St Albans   01727 800033

Owner Chef Chad Radman trained at the Conrad Hilton Hotel School then worked for the Hyatt Regency Hotel, Houston, and the Hilton Group specialising in French, Indian, Malaysian, Thai and Mexican. Chez Mumtaj realises his dream to deliver a menu of 'Modern French-Asian cuisine' assisted by staff who have worked at Benares, Cinnamon Club and from the $1200-a-night Burj Al Arab hotel, Dubai. Chez Mumtaz, across the road from his Mumtaz was a former carpet warehouse, and Chad has spent a couple of million transfroming it into a very upmarket venue. Menu Snapshot: Starters: Mixed Meat Platter: Green-herbed duck breast, lamb chop, achari and chicken tikka with homemade chutneys; Chez Mumtaj Salad, green seasonal salad with cilantro, shaved mango, fresh pomegranate and papaya tossed with roasted cashew nuts, honey-mustard vinaigrette; Seared Foie Gras, with schezwan pepper-crush with lightly curried confit of cauliflower purée and hazelnut crumb oil; Soft Shell Crab, wild-catch blue-swimmer soft-shell crab in chilli and garlic tempura batter served with homemade ginger, prune, mango and fig marmalade. Mains: Seafood Biryani, dum phukt-style mixed seafood, saffron and rose water sealed in clay pot with puff pastry served with roasted cumin and cucumber boondi raita; Risotto, chargrilled freshwater king prawns, Devon crabmeat risotto with braised baby leeks, smoked aubergine caviar, basil and truffle cappuccino foam; Duck, seven-spice-dusted Barbary duck breast in sesame chilli ginger honey glaze with a stir fry of young vegetables, oriental rice, cassia & star anise apple and rhubarb compote; Guinea Fowl, classic homemade Thai mussaman curry, crushed peanuts, baby potatoes, pak-choi greens and wild mushroom rice; Spinach Dumpling, quenelles of spinach & sweet potato stuffed with goat's cheese served with chick pea cake, tomato fenugreek beurre blanc sauce and dill-saffron herbed rice. The Saffron bar (evenings only serves bar snacks, such as Chicken Tikka Burrito Wrap, chargrilled strips baby gem & cucumber with cumin tamarind mayo (pictured). Not everuone likes fusion, but if yopu do you will ot find it done better than by Chad at Chez Mumtaz. We welcome it to our TOP 100. 2 Course Lunch with coffee £14.95 or 3 Cs £16.95. Tasting Dinner Menu: £28.50 pp (Min 2). Service 12.5% Hours: 12-2.30 / 6-11. www.chezmumtaj.com Branch Mumtaz, see next entry and previous page..

MUMTAJ   A-LIST

115 London Road   01727 858399

Originally opened way back in 1962. Present owner, Muklasur Rahman Mojumder took over in 1983 and has established himself as a highly regarded source of Indian cuisine. Seats 44 diners in two rooms partitioned by an archway. The owner's son Chad Rahman now runs the place and we note his credentials in the previous entry. In 2002 he won the UK Curry Chef of the Year competition, run by the Chartered Institute of Environmental Health, and bless me he did it again in 2003, and again he won. St Albans ex MP Kerry Pollard loves the place but agreed with me that Chad is 'a brave man, and a brilliant chef'. '*I am lucky enough to travel widely on business, and never travel without your Guide. I aim to visit every TOP 100. I agree with all but one of those visited. Having visited many, many UK curryhouses in the UK, as well as in Brussels (ugh), Amsterdam (great), Stockholm (ugh), Riyadh (ummm), and the USA (hmmm), I am always pleased to get home to St Albans, and eat at my local, the Mumtaj.*' PFM. '*Smart, elegant restaurant just outside historic St Albans. Fairly small, intimate, air of refinement. Attentive and friendly service. Excellent Prawn Puri, really aromatic sauce, plenty of prawns, slightly crisp, oil-free puri. Lamb Nashilee 5, very good combination, robust spices, plenty of ginger, texture added by peppers and chillies, good cuts of gristle-free lamb, very enjoyable. Peshwari Nan, moist, well cooked, too much filling, sweet and delicious.*' RW. Del: 2m £15 min. Hours: 12-3 / 6-12. Branch: Chez Mumtaj (see previous entry).

Tring

OLIVE LIMES NEW ENTRANT

60 High St, HP23 5AG 01442 828444

Opened in October 2007, on the former Kristal Spice Restaurant. The owners are fast becoming part of Tring community, entering into the spirit of the apple festival, Christmas festival and even handing out tastings during the carols in the car park on Christmas Eve. Reports please.

YOU SAY OK
You may get a discount of you show them this Guide.

STEVENAGE: GATE OF INDIA 20 The Glebe, Chells Way. 01438 3176195. Abdul Salam's and Chef Arosh Ali's 57-seater in 4 rooms. Del: £10 min, 4m. Hours: 12-2.30/6-12.

WALTHAM CROSS: CAFÉ SPICE 63 High St. 01992 717546. Rezaul Huq Syed's 48- seater does Chicken Chauk, chicken in batter, breadcrumbs, deep-fried, served with mixed vegetables. Sun Buffet c£7. Del: 3m, £10 min. T/a: 10% disc. Hours:12.30-3.30 / 5.30-11; 11.30 Fri & Sat.

KENT

Area: South East
Population: 1,612,000
Adjacent Counties:
Essex, London,
Surrey, Sussex

'GL' denotes those former Kent suburbs absorbed by Greater London in 1965.

ZARIN   TOP 100

31 Bank Street, Ashford   01233 620511

You're on your way to/from the Channel Tunnel and you need a fix. Here's your answer. The former Curry Garden (a long-term entrant to this Guide) has achieved modernisation at its best. The frontage is inviting and you want to enter. In front of you is the bar area, immediately to your left the dining area. The modern interior is in shades of peach and terracotta, enhanced with tall black chairs and crisp white table linen. Asian-inspired art adorns the walls, but what draws your eye is the water feature at the end of the room. One highlight enjoyed by the regulars is the monthly Elvis Nights. But this is no ordinary Elvis. He's Asian with a stature more like Sammy Davis Junior than the King. But he performs with a zest that makes the evening unmissable. Lunch specials: Chicken Rasili: chicken cooked with broccoli and cashew nuts and served with pullao rice and salad. Vegee Noodlfresh seasonal vegetables cooked with noodles and served with salad. Wrap Chap Chicken: lightly spiced chicken mixed with fresh vegetables and noodles and wrapped in a chapatti. Hasin Chicken: succulent pieces of chicken cooked in light, medium hot spices; served with rice and salad. Chicken Rasili: chicken cooked with broccoli and cashew nuts and served with pullao rice and salad. Sun 18 dish e-a-m-a-y-l buffet £7.95, kids £4.95, 12 -10 Sun. T/a: 20% Disc. www.zarinrestaurant.co.uk

Bromley (GL)

CAFÉ EAST

123 Masons Hill, Bromley   020 8460 5452

Part of the Tamasha Group, owned by Shekor Tarat and Anil Deb, seats 76 diners. Brightly coloured menus, turquoise with orange for the food and fuchsia with orange for the wine list. Somebody has rather a 'Carry On' sense of humour with starters like Tossing the Kyber, (Scottish salmon marinated with ginger and garlic, flavoured with caraway and char-grilled on the tandoor), Hey Griddle, Griddle, (chicken cooked on the tava with green peppers, onions, tomatoes and fresh herbs), Goan, Goan, Gone! £10.95 (in a trice, these Goan prawns with a Portuguese influence – hot and spicy!), It's all Fenugreek to Me, (nuggets of soya delicately spiced with garam masala and cooked with fresh fenugreek), Kebab's your Uncle! £6.95 (potato, cauliflower and paneer chunks skewered with green peppers, onion and tomatoes, then popped in the tandoor to char grill, and, probably the worst joke of the lot, Grandma, we love you! ,(she may be plain, nutty or even highly scented, but we know you all love your nan). I can hear the groans [gro-naans] already! It's perhaps not the longest menu in the world, but there are some great dishes for everyone. Hours: 1-2.30 / 6-11. Sun brunch: three courses, £10 per person, live jazz band, 12-3. Branch: Tamasha, Bromley.

KOSTURI

18 Station Approach, Bromley   020 8462 8594

Kosturi seats 82 has lavender walls accented by strategically positioned spotlights installed in a hanging

wooden beam while long-shaded contemporary lighting hangs over the rest of the restaurant, adding to the natural light that pours in from the large glass window at the entrance. Bangladeshi chef Sarawar Uddin Khan has been with Kosturi since it first open in 2003. His menu ranges from Goa to Lucknow and Punjab for which he has picked up the Bromley's 'Best Curry Restaurant Award' in 2003 and 2005. Specialities include, Chicken Capasilla, chicken off-the-bone, cooked with crushed cashew nuts, almonds and green peppers; King Prawn Kornofuli, Bay of Bengal tiger king prawns tossed in butter and garlic and cooked in a special blend of herbs and curry leaves. The dish which won Khan his award is Juje Limu, chicken breast marinated in ginger/garlic paste, stuffed with paneer onion and fresh mint. Served with yogurt and lemon sauce it's only available on Fri & Sat, upon request. www.kosturi.co.uk

YOU SAY OK

You may get a discount of you show them this Guide.

ASHFORD: KENNINGTON TANDOORI 158 Faversham Rd, Kennington, Ashford ~ 01233 650 350. Chef Shofique Uddin's and Mohammed Miah's 38-seater. Del: 4m, £15 min. Hours 12-2.30, not Fri / 5.30-11; 11.30 Fri & Sat.

BARNEHURST (CL): JHAS TANDOORI 158c Mayplace Rd E, Barnehurst ~ 01322 555036. 50-seater est 1989 by the Jhas family – chef Kuldip, manager Robinder. T/a 10% disc. Hours: 6-11.30; 12 Fri & Sat; Sun closed.

BEXLEY, ALBANY PARK: RUCHI 56 Steynton Ave, Albany Pk ~ 020 8300 0200. Madan Prashar's 130-seater est 1986 – Starters: Punjabi Macchi, yoghurt marinated fish, gram flour, green chilli, ginger, deep-fried; Aloo Pappdi Chatt , chickpeas, potatoes, coriander leaves, mint, yoghurt, tamarind sauce on crispy bread,. T/a: 10% disc. Hours: 12- 2/6-11.30; 11 Sun.

BEXLEY: SACGOR 145 Blendon Road, Bexley ~ 020 8303 7549. Ali Uddin offers 'one of the most tasty Chicken Chats I've had for some time. Prawn Puri also unanimously approved. Certainly worth going to again.' MW. Hours: 12-2.30/6-11.30.

BIGGIN HILL: RAJ 187 Main Road, Biggin Hill ~ 01959 572459. 70-seater, managed by AM Crorie, decorated in an 'olde worlde' style. Del: £10 min, 3m. Hours: 12-2.30; 3.30 Sun/6-11.30; 12 Sat.

BROMLEY DOWNHAM: ROYAL GURKHA 419 Bromley Rd, BR1 4JP ~ 020 8461 4819. JP Gautam took over this 48-seater in 2006. *'Excellent food and service friendly.'* JB. *'Thoroughly enjoyable.'* E&PM. Del: 4m £10 min. Sun Buf c£8. Hours: 12-2.30/6-11.30; 12 Sat.

BROMLEY DOWNHAM: SURUCHI 466 Bromley Rd, ~ 020 8698 8626. Istab Uddin Ahmed's dishes include Tom Yum Soup c£3, the famous Thai soup with mushrooms, lemon grass and prawns; Goan Chingri Palok £4.25, king prawn, spices, wrapped with fresh spinach and deep-fried; Chicken 65 £2.75 - Hyderabadi style with green chillies and curry leaves. Del: 3m, £12 min. Sun. T/a: 10% disc. Hours: 5.30-12 daily / 12.30-3 Sun only, Buf: c£7 adults, £5 kids. www.suruchiindia.co.uk

Bromley

TAMASHA   A-LIST

131 Widmore Rd, Bromley   020 8460 3240

Established in 1993. Owner is Shekor Tarat. Attached to a small hotel, so if you need a decent curry followed by a bed for the night, now you know. Tamasha means *'something worth seeing'*. And it is! There is ample car parking, and you enter past a smartly saluting geezer, via an awning flanked by tub plants. Inside, there's a well-stocked bar. The dining room seats 120 in seven rooms, and is superbly decorated like a British Raj Club, with polo sticks and hats, black and white photos of polo teams, Maharajas and sumptuous banquets. Cane furniture with palms in copper planters. Head chef Rajinder Kumar cooks food from north and south India, Goa and Kashmir. Curry house formula, it certainly is not. Favourite starters include Bhajis (Pakoras), Kebabs and Tikka, and main courses Jalfrezi and Chicken Tikka Masala. Good they are, too. But a little exploring can yield some treasures: Chicken Nilgiri Tikka, boneless chicken marinated in spices, fresh coriander and mint, cooked in the tandoor. Goan Fish Curry, fish cooked in coconut and red chillies and garnished with fresh coriander leaves. Dum Pukht Gosht, marinated sliced baby lamb in a variety of spices and then steam-cooked in sealed earthenware, and Chicken Mirchi Wala, boneless chicken cooked in strongly spiced red chilli curry with potatoes, is popular, and Abrakebabra! so is the table magician who entertains the kids during Sun lunch buffet. *'Crowded right through the evening and booking in advance whatever the night is to be recommended. Real orchids on the tables and everything about it shouts quality. Many unusual and imaginative dishes. Chicken Nilgiri Tikka was an intriguing shade of green, caused by being marinated in mint and coriander, flavours came through as I ate. Fish Punjabi crisp and spicy, Aloo Tikki very tasty. Raan Jaipuri and Rara Gosht equally tender and delicious. The only thing that did not suit our taste was the Peshwari Naan which was very sweet and overloaded with ground almond, but no fruit. Portions ample, service efficient and polite (but not particularly friendly, not for welcoming doorman). Prices above average, but not excessive for quality of restaurant and location. Well deserves its TOP 100 status.'* MW. Menu Extracts: Malai Tikka, chicken marinated in cream cheese, cooked in tandoor, Aloo Tikki £3.95, minced potato burger, filled with lentils, served with mint and imli chutney, Aloo Pappri Chatt, chick peas, potatoes, coriander leaves, mint, yoghurt, imli sauce, crispy puri bread, Murgh Nawabi, chicken marinated in white wine, rich sauce of onion, tomato and saffron (sounds delicious!), Goan Chicken Xacuti, with coconut, Jhinga Tariwala, King prawns, spicy, tangy, red chillies, turmeric, bay leaves, Banarsi Dum Aloo, new potatoes stuffed with mint, cheese, tangy dry gravy. The annual Tamasha birthday party, held in Marquees on the grounds is amazing, and is one of Bromley's most-loved events, with unlimited food and drink , music and dancers, and a massive 600 guests. To get onto the invite list, you need to become one of Tamasha's regulars and go on their mailing list. Service charge 12.5%. 20 car parking spaces. Live jazz and blues on Sun, Mon, Tues eves. Sun lunch buffet with in-house magician. T/a: 10% disc. Hours: 12-2.30 / 6-11. www.tamasha.co.uk

ZANZIBAR

239 High Street, Bromley   020 8460 7130

Ebullient owner Ken Modi opened his Carioca in 1971 but changed its name because 'I got fed up with Karaoke requests'. The main room seats 50, its walls and ceiling decorated with coconut matting, giving the feeling of being in a fisherman's hut '– a very glamorous one' according to Mr Modi. The party room, which includes a mock Pullman railway carriage, seats 70. The menu contains the regular favourite tandooris, baltis, curries and accompaniments. *'After a morning shopping on a Sat, we headed to the Zanzibar for a lunchtime buffet. The food is on view from the outside, as it is displayed on a warming table in the window. This sounds awful but it's actually well done, the dishes, polished and spanking clean, the food, fresh. We were politely served our starters first: a fresh, crisp salad with flat Onion Bhajis and half a Nan with chutneys, raita and a Coconut Chutney which was incredible, with a slight hint of heat from its mustard seed. The service became very friendly and helpful when we were given huge warm bowls for the self-serve buffet. The dishes were explained to us: Chicken Tikka Masala (smoky flavour – great), Bhoona Gosht, Mild Chicken Curry, Meat Madras, Bombay Aloo (excellent – new potatoes), Cauliflower Bhajee, Dal Makhani, Brinjal Bhajee, Plain and Pullao Rice and Nan bread. After two visits to this array of food, I was stuffed and delighted. Good food from a clean, well-decorated restaurant.'* MPW. Hours: 12-2; 12.30-3.30 Sun / 6 -10.30; 6.30 Sun.

Chatham

COCO DINER   NEW ENTRANT

330 High Street, Chatham   01634 842489

'I often express myself a little jaded visiting restaurant after restaurant that offer the same old curryhouse dishes and yearning for something more authentic. I've found it in Chatham. This 55-seater opened in 2008 in what was a former pub and it is the only southern Indian in Kent. The décor is smart and modern, having lime green walls, plain dark wood flooring and dark wood tables and chairs, which are of good, solid quality, and a small bar. A couple of potted ferns add a bit of greenery, behind which are four comfortable easy chairs, for those waiting for their take-away A interesting feature is a coloured tiled tableau of Queen Victoria just inside the entrance, which I gather is antique and a protected feature. Menu Snapshot: Starters: Njandu Peera, crab meat sautéed with grated coconut, curry leaves and mustard seeds; Karveipullei Yera (tiger prawns deep-fried in a corn flour batter with chilli powder and curry leaves); Batata Bonda (potato balls laced with fresh ginger, coriander and black mustard seeds and then deep fried) and Ethekka Appam (plantain slices dipped in a rice batter a seasoned with sesame seeds and crisp fried). Mains: fish dishes – tiger prawns, sea bass, king fish, tilapia – duck, chicken, lamb and, of course, authentic southern Indian vegetable dishes. I was so overcome with discovering such a menu that I was in danger of over-ordering, but resisted with commendable restraint. We had a Karveipullei Yera and Batata Bonda to start, but couldn't resist having a Uthappam, rice pancake, rather like a pizza, with onion and tomato topping, each as well as you don't get them outside specialist South Indian restaurants. And they were all memorably delicious. The Uthappams were as described, and came with a pot of Sambar, a runny vegetable curry of lentils and exotic vegetables and coconut chutney. The Karveipulla comprised four tiger prawns, cooked as described above and attractively presented with a tangy pink sauce topping. For our main courses just we had to have a Masala Dosa (a favourite of my wife when she can get it), which was huge and came with a bowl of Sambar and coconut chutney. I had the Meen Vevichathu, curried king fish. Both were again delicious, the Dosa having plenty of lightly spiced potato filling, while the four small fish fillets were cooked in a tomato and onion sauce with fenugreek, tamarind and a couple of well-cooked chillis. This surrounded a little mound of steamed cassava. We also had some Puliyogare (rice cooked in tamarind juice, mustard seeds, curry leaves and peanuts), which came plated like a small sandcastle and had a delicious piquancy and nutty flavour. What more can I say? The dishes are not for those who like the fieriness of vindaloo, all have a more delicate balance of flavours, with coconut much in evidence, and a freshness about them that is often lacking in standard high street restaurants. Sadly it is in he rougher end of a fairly unprepossessing town, which may deter people.* Licensed. 12-3; 12.30-3.30 Sun / 6-11; -10 Sun. Closed Mon. www.cocodiner.co.uk

YOU SAY OK

You may get a discount of you show them this Guide.

CHATHAM: ACE OF SPICE Watling St, Chatham ~ 01634 578400. Owners Ali & Mukid Choudhury. Hours: 12-2.30/6-11. Branch: Lily Spice, A249 Detling Hill, Stockbury. 01795 844628.

CHATHAM: THE ROYAL 50 New Rd. 01634 827799. 40 seats in a former pub *'Overall good.'* MW. Del: £10 min, 4m. T/a: 10% disc, £20min. Hours: 12-2 not Fri /6-12.

CRAYFORD (GL): CHANDI SPICE 108 London Rd, Crayford, DA1 4BT ~ 01322 559191. 40-seater est 1997. T/a: 10% disc. Del: £10 min. Hours: 12-2.30/5.30-11.30; 12-11.30 Sun buffet.

FARNBOROUGH: VILLAGE CUISINE 145 High St. ~ 01689 860077. 40-seater, est 1991. Imaginative specials inc: Creamed Mussels – served in their half shells, lightly spiced with saffron cream sauce. Owner Fahim Maksud promises 10% disc if you book and if you show him this Guide when there. T/a: 10% disc. Del: £10 min, 4m. Hours: 12-2.30/5.30-10.30; Sun buffet 12-6.30.

FAVERSHAM: INDIAN ROYAl 16 East St. 01795 536033. 40-seater est 1991 in a Tudor-style building. Specials inc: Malai Kasa, cooked with coconut, almonds and chilli; Makhoni, cooked with mangoes. *'Friendly service. Sufficient portions with av prices.'* MW. Hours: 12-2.30/5-11.30. Sun Buffet 12-5 – £7.50 adult, £4 kids.

Darenth nr Dartford

GREEN SPICE

Green Street, Green Rd   01474 708855

Abdul Bari opened this restaurant in 2002 in a former

pub. The premises are large and it offers ample car parking space both in front and behind. It seats about 150 in comfortable surroundings – modern wooden flooring and colourful ceiling lights, and a well stocked bar all of which provide a pleasant ambience. The menu lists all the standards plus specials includFish Lazeem – Scottish salmon, medium sauce, orange zest; Kaleji Bakakara: liver, Bhuna style, hot and tangy; Silsila Chicken - marinated, cheddar cheese, mild and creamy sauce. *'Curiously,while there are only explanations of the ' chef's specials' the menu invites customers to ask a member of staff what other dishes are and asking a member of staff may not be very helpful. Service was businesslike and matter-of-fact – neither friendly nor unfriendly (for example there were no smiles when we arrived nor from any of the waiters who served us. Even old curry hands like me would have to ask for a description of starters such as Chicken Sorati, and what the main dish styles such as Khanza, Ahadi, Asanok, Amrenga or Lazeem have that is different from the many others. of the items we had, portions were very generous – too much really in the case of the starters. Prices were about average, but taking into account the size of the portions, very reasonable. Finishing touches were there – hot towels, mints and a 'customer comment form', which is always a good touch which suggested discussing any aspect of the food or service with 'The Store Manager'!? I would have no hesitation in returning, although I'd definitely give the Begun Biraan a miss!'* MW. T/a: 10% disc. Hours: 12-2.30; 3 Sun / 5.30-12; 11.30 Sun. Branch: Zara, Canterbury.

SHERE KHAN EXPRESS NEW ENTRANT

Bluewater Shopping Centre DA9 9ST
Greenhithe   01322 624113

Off the M25/A2. Indian fast food. See Shere Khan, Rusholme, Manchester for history, branches, etc.

Folkestone

GURKHA PALACE NEPALESE
TOP 100

97 Enbrook Valley, Folkestone   01303 257700

Kishore Sapkota is owner of this sixty seater, Nepalese restaurant. Menu Snapshot: Kalejo Bhutuwa £2.85, stir-fried chicken liver; Sinka Prawn £3.25, yoghurt marinated prawn; Fried and served on bamboo skewer; Tama Bodi £2.90, bamboo shoots, black eyebeans, potatoes; Chukauni £2.90 spicy potato salad with sesame seed; Staff Curry – Lamb £7.00; Momo £5.50,

warm chicken dumplings served with Nepalese spicy chutney. Stocks: Cobra & Gurkha beer. Do try the Nepalese specialities, we have many happy reports about them. Del: 3m £12 min. T/a: 10% disc. Hours: 11-2.30 / 6-11. www.gurkhapalace.co.uk

INDIA   TOP 100

1 The Old High St, Folkestone   01303 259155

We like the ebullient Mr Ali Ashraf who chose Folkestone to establish his 42 seat India in 1985. Being a French-trained Indian chef and speaking French too, perhaps he felt being close to France would be au fait. In some cases he combines French methods (cream, wine and brandy) with Indian spices to provide an original interpretation of his Indian dishes. *'Only subtle clues reveal that this restaurant is special; I can't help feeling they could be overlooked by a casual observer. The building fabric may be faded, but the table presentation and service was impeccable. My main basis for visiting the India was the Guide's recommendation on the basis of food, and I can confirm reports that this was notional. I had the Crab in White Wine for Entrees (£4.95) followed by Chicken Jalfrezi (£5.95) and Special Fried Rice (£2.75). I have never before experienced such exquisite flavours. Every morsel exploded with new surprises and made the experience one that you wished would never end. Anything you believe you know about curry is turned on its head and it was a truly culinary experience. I shall certainly be visiting again and can whole heartedly agree that this establishment deserves its listing in your top 100.'* DTH. *'Six of us ate there last Sat and it was excellent. My favourite Chicken Jalfrezi was superb. We paid less than £20 a head including Popadums, starters, main courses with vegetables, breads and drinks.'* BT. Hours: 12-2 / 6-10.30.

Halstead

BENGAL MANGROVE

London Road, Halstead   01959 534688

Of course, they serve CTM etc, but why not try some unusual dishes, eg: Chingri Tali Baja £4.50, tiger prawns seasoned in light spices, deep-fried in breadcrumbs; Crab Piri Piri £5, fiery red hot chillies, rice vinegar, spring onion and Goan spices; Mysore Bondi £3.50, mashed potato balls, ginger, curry leaves, black mustard seed, deep-fried – all starters are served with salad and homemade chutney. Badami Stuffed Murgh Masala £8.95, chicken stuffed with vegetables, cream, almonds and pistachio; Sathkari Gosht c£8, lamb, wild lemon, naga chilli, lemon leaf; Dahi Dover Sole c£13, pan-fried in yoghurt sauce; Salmon Tikka c£9; Vegetable Milijuli £4.95, baby potatoes, mange tout, stir-fried in garlic oil; Nilgiri Korma c£5, paneer, cabbage, beans, carrots, mint, sweet and mild sauce. *'Took my son who at eighteen, was already a confirmed curryholic. Food superb. Polite waiter. Drinks bill seemed a bit hefty, however, for the quality*

of restaurant and food, prices were reasonable. Manager gave me guided tour of conservatory area (70 seats). I'll be back in the near future.' CO. T/a: 25% disc.

CALCUTTA CLUB NEW TO OUR TOP 100

London Road, Polhill, Halstead TN14 7BG
01959 534 688

Over two centuries ago Calcutta's Park Street restaurants in the clubs served British officers of the Company and the Raj the very best of Indian cuisine. This Club is on the A224 between Halstead and Polhill.

Feast your eyes on this menu; it includes some absolute corkers! Snapshot: Pudina tikka £4.95, boneless chicken marinated in freshmint, coriander and cooked on bamboo skewer; Afghani Murgh Malai Tikka £4.95, fresh ginger, green chilli, black cumin, cardamom, cottage cheese; Jhinga Palak Pakora £4.95, deep-fried fritter, baby prawns, fresh spinach, gram flour, onion, spices; Utthapam £4.50, ground rice bread cooked on a flat iron griddle, green and yellow pepper, onions, tomatoes, served on banana leaf with fresh coconut sauce (delicious! one of my favourite breads); Victoria Prawn £12.50, seawater prawns marinated in dark rum, ground black cardamom, black cummin, dry ginger, yoghurt, cream, spring onion and tomato; Murgh Khandhari £8.95, boneless chicken, rich cashew nut, red onion gravy, tomato, fresh coriander and ginger; Kakori Kebab £8.50, finely minced lamb, saffron, rose petals

and cardamom; Dum Pukht £9.50, lamb escalope, half cooked in aromatic spices, flavoured, slow steamed in sealed earthenware pot; Kaju-Kismish Korma £8.50, tender lamb, ground almonds, raisins, cashew nuts, saffron; Bihar Mirchi Aloo £4.50, spicy baby potatoes, green chilli, black cummin; Avial £4.95, green vegetables, tamarind, ginger, coconut; Amritsari Masala Kulcha £2.50, bread stuffed with spic potatoes, currently our favourite! infact I made one last night and it was delicious (Tip: you need a tava to cook this bread properly, a frying pan makes it too greasy).Wonderful Indian desserts are on offer - Hilary, take note! Gajar ke Halwa £3.95, grated carrot, milk, khoya, sugar, served hot with dry fruits (I like this with vanilla ice-cream); Bengali Rassogulla £3.95, chaina balls, chutned mild and sugar syrup; Thandi Rasmalai £3.95, cottage cheese and thickened mild, served chilled with postachio and almonds. The Striped Elephant Bar, named after the venues logo, is ideal for pre and post dinner or luncheon drinks. The spacious and modern first floor conference suite accommodates 60, seated. It's air-conditioned and equipped with LCD projector, DVD and VHS player, remote controlled screen, cordless mike and high speed Wi-Fi internet access. Hours: 12-2.30, 4 Sun/6-11.30, from 7 Sun.   Welcome to our TOP 100. www.calcuttaclub.co.uk

Minster, Thanet

MINSTER TANDOORI NEW ENTRANT

1 High Street, Minster, Thanet   01843 822517

'This 50-seater est 1990, is modern-looking outside and in, with a light, airy and contemporary style. A good menu, in which all the usuals are enhanced but a number of different dishes. For example, Kakra Bhuna (minced crab with chopped garlic, spring onion and tomato), Tikka Salmon, and spiced Red Mullet amongst the fish selection, and some duck dishes amongst the others. Amongst the starters was Tandoori Chicken, which is surprisingly unusual (most restaurant just

Calcutta Club

*offer Chicken Tikka, but personally I prefer it on the bone).
Enquiry elicited that this was the wing/breast portion, so my
wife asked if she could have two of these instead of her more
usual ? Tandoori Chicken (1 breast and 1 leg portion), as she
prefers the breast section to the leg. I thought this may be a bit
cheeky, but it was absolutely no problem at all, and it was
delicious – well marinated and full flavoured. My Chicken
Tikka Jalfrezi was equally tasty, in a good, full-bodied hot
sauce that had the chillies cooked in it, as it should be, rather
than fresh chillies merely sprinkled on as some restaurants do
(and regular readers will know that this is something I am
often critical of). All other dishes – Vegetable Bhaji, Tarka
Dhal and accompaniments - of a good standard. Portions
about average, and while prices maybe marginally above the
average on some dishes, it's so marginal as to not really be
noticeable. Friendly and efficient service, and all in all a good
meal – which is no doubt why they were full.'* MW.

Rochester

SINGAPORA

51 High Street, Rochester   01634 842178

Dr and Mrs Shome's 150-seater spreads over three
floors, with tables in odd alcoves. Specialising in
Malaysian, Chinese, Indonesian, Thai and Japanese
cuisine. *'Cosy, but deceptively larger with upper floors and
basement. Aromatic Duck, shredded with sliced spring onions,
cucumber and plum sauce rolled in pancakes. Udang Roti,
King prawns on sesame toast – substantial flavour. Ayam
Penang, Malaysian dish, crispy chicken with ginger and
onions, tasty. Ayam Iblis, sliced chicken, chilli and ginger, very
tasty. Washed down with red house wine c£10, smooth and
excellent value. Portions a little on the small side. Efficient
and friendly service. Pleasant alternative.'* MW. Del.
Hours: 12-3 / 6-11; 11.30 Fri & Sat; 12-10.30 Sun.
Branch: 73, Brewer Street, Maidstone.

YOU SAY OK

You may get a discount of you show them this Guide.

GILLINGHAM: TWYDALL TANDOORI 50 Twydall Green. ~
01634 386110. S Rahman's curryhouse 'does some nice things eg
Lamb Albadami £6.50, mango, creamy, mild sauce' RL. . T/a:
10% disc. Hours: 12-2.30 not Fri / 5.30-11.30, 10 Sun

MAIDSTONE: BENGAL DINER 98 King St. ~ 01622 756094.
50-seater. Branch: Shamrat, Maidstone.

MARDEN: MARDEN TANDOORI Albion Rd.~ 01622 832184.
*'Lucky there are two Indian restaurants in such a small village, both
providing a good formula curry; makes for a difficult decision next time!'*
MW. Hours: 12 -2.30/6-11.

ROYAL 27 High Street, Marden ~ 01622 833224 . 65-seater in 2
rooms and 'good-weather' garden. *'Service friendly and efficient'.*
MW. Hours: 12 -2.30 / 6-11.

MINSTER, ISLE OF SHEPPEY: SHERAZ 10 High St.~ 01795
876987. *'Interior looks like a Kebab House. Friendly service. Punjabi
cooking surprisingly good. Nappali Chicken – good, hot, chillies. Dhal Samba
– tasty.'* MW. Del: £12 min, 3m. Hours: 11-11.30; 12 Fri & Sat.

ORPINGTON (GL): CURRY HOUSE 24 Station Sq, Petts Wood ~
01689 820671. Basth (Baz) Wahab runs this 42-seater. 'Food

good but atmosphere non-existent. Eventually won the waiters
round and managed a laugh and a little conversation.
Flavoursome fish tikka. Main dishes were well up to expectation.'
CC&GM. Hours: 12-3 (not Mon & Fri) and 6-12; closed Mon.

RAJ OF INDIA 4 Crescent Way, Green Street Green, Orpington
~ 01689 852170. 72 seater est 1987 by owner-manager Muzibur
Rahman. Hours: 12-2.30/6-12. Branches: Raj of India
Sheerness, Swanley and Sittingbourne; Raj Bari Sevenoaks;
Maharajah Bexley; Juboraj Brentwood, Essex.

RAMSGATE: RAMSGATE TANDOORI 17 Harbour S. ~ 01843
589134. 70-seater, owned by Rezaur Rahman, managed by Mrs
Rahman. Cooking by head chef Joyanti Mendas. Del: £10 min.
Hours: 12-2.30 / 6-12.

ROCHESTER: BENGAL BRASSERIE 356 High Street,
Rochester ~ 01634 841930. An old friend of this Guide.
www.bengalbrasserie.com

ROCHESTER: SHOZNA 153 Maidstone Rd. ~ 01634 847 847.
Owner Jamal Udin. Starters: Chicken Cutlet; Stuffed pepper
(meat or vegetable) c£4. Mains: Monchorian Chicken, chicken fillet,
mango, cream; Badami Chicken, roasted cashew, butter, medium
spices; Ultra-hot Naga Chicken or Lamb, all c£8. Hours: 12-2, resvn
only/5.30-12. Branch: Shozna, 18 High St, Stroud, Kent.

SANDWICH: INDIA VILLAGE 11 The Butchery. ~ 01304
611991. 'In the former fire station. Generous portions. Duck
curries on the very large menu.' SC.

SEVENOAKS: ASIA CUISINE 107 London Rd. ~ *01732 453153.*
'My local. Does a brilliant CTM and always friendly service.' KT. *'Nice
place, very cosy, love the Indian music. Portions more than ample and
prices just right.'* RL.

SPICE CLUB 57 High Street, Sevenoaks, TN13 1JF. 01732
456688. *'Very helpful staff smartly dressed in black,. Food outstanding.
Starters: Fish Pakora; Boal Malchi, very good. South Indian Garlic Chilli
Chicken, very popular. Sevenoak's best!'* KT. Hours: 12-2.30/6-11.30.

SIDCUP (GL): BLACKFEN BALTI 33 Wellington Pde, Blackfen
Rd. 020 8303 0013. A friendly, pleasant, 48-seater, owned by
Muzammil Ali since 1983.

SIDCUP (GL): OVAL BRASSERIE 49 The Oval, Sidcup ~ 020
8308 0274. Owned since 1988 by Anwar Miah with chef
Mohibur Rahman. Del: £10 min, 3m. Hours: 12-2.30/6-11.30;
12-11.30 Sun: buffet £7, £4 kids.

STOCKBURY: LILY SPICE A249 at Detling Hill, Stockbury ~
01795 844628. Ali and Mukid Choudhury opened in 2006 in a
former a Little Chef on the main route between Medway and
Maidstone. Plenty of free parking. Hours: 12-3/6-11. Branch:
Ace of Spice, Watling Street, Chatham, 01634 578400

SWANLEY: RAJ OF INDIA 23 High St. ~ 01322 613651. *'VG
and hot Chicken Vindaloo, Pullao Rice and Nan Bread - excellent meal,
just right.'* BP-D. Branch: Raj Bari, Sevenoaks, Kent and Alishan,
Tonbridge, Kent.

Strood

SHOZNA INDIAN CUISINE

28 High Street, Strood   01634 710701

Established in 1978. Taken over by J Ahmed in 1996.
Seats 38. Parking at rear for 50 cars. Chef Jamal Uddin
Ahmed was the 2003 runner-up winner of the Curry
Chef of the Year contest run by the CIEH, (Health
officer's institute) and the food is good. *'Does not look
much from the outside, inside pleasantly cosy. Relatively small,
seating 48. Custom made furniture, all good quality. Started
with my benchmark – Onion Bhajia. Four, small, round,
plenty of onion, crisp outside, moist inside, excellent. Bhari
Kebab – small pieces of kebab, spicy, rich sauce, extremely tasty,*

first class. Long debate over mains, chose Badami Chicken – delicious full bodied sauce, chopped cashew nuts, slightly herby. Dhansak – included Pullao Rice, well spiced lentil sauce. Smart, clean toilets. Portions just right, prices average. The car park is behind the restaurant, up a small alleyway, easy to miss. An excellent little restaurant, packed on a Thursday night.' MW. Naga Lamb £6 is garnished with incendiary Naga chillies so be warned! T/a: 10-15% disc. Hours: 12-1.30 / 5.30-12.

Tenterden

THE RAJA OF TENTERDEN

NEW ENTRANT

Biddenden Rd, St. Michaels   01233 851191

'Opened in 2004 in a former country pub a couple of miles north of Tenterden. A doorman in full traditional Indian costume greeted us as he opened the door to usher us in. I had pre-booked a table, but I began to wonder whether this restaurant was like others in failing to take reservations seriously as we were invited to take a seat in the bar/waiting area despite arriving dead on time. My concerns were unfounded, as within a minute of arriving we were led through the packed restaurant to our table. I was pleased we'd booked, as despite seating a generous 90 people, the place was packed. The restaurant is modern with wooden flooring, light coloured walls and low ceiling without being ostentatiously contemporary. The seating is comfortable with cutlery and tablecloths of good quality. The menu was also more exciting than the norm, as although it offered most of the standard dishes, there were very many different and enterprising dishes, including venison, duck, pheasant, scallops and mussel. Our starters: the wife's usual Onion Bhaji – five walnut sized, nicely spiced and crisp, and sufficiently agreeable (and petite!) for her to only offer a small sample and guard the rest jealously. My friend ordered Pitta Paneer Sag, spring-roll-shaped deep-fried puri giving a crisp outside yet soft inside. My Chicken Chat was more robustly spiced, with a good sharp tangy flavour. From this good start we moved onto even better things. My Lamb Xacuti (a Goan dish) was first class. Superb tender chunks of lamb were cooked in a dark, thick and very flavoursome sauce. I was also pleased that they had not overdone the coconut (as occasionally is the case) and it was absolutely delicious. My friend went for the Chicken Jalfrezi, which again was very good with the chillies properly cooked in to give it a hotness that set the tongue a tingling as you ate it rather than setting it on fire at the first mouthful. My wife went for Vegetable Bagan, an assortment of aubergine, broccoli, mushroom, peppers, onion, tomato and even some apple in large pieces, each barbecued to al dente perfection in a lightly spiced sauce. it was a shot in the dark as we were ordering vegetable side dishes, but the shot hit the bull's-eye. It was so wonderful, I could easily become a vegetarian. The veg side dishes were also excellent. If one had to find a criticism, the two dishes were slightly oily, but it's only nitpicking. As for the service, the waiters were all smartly dressed in uniform and busily engaged throughout the evening dealing with the large and full restaurant; efficient and attentive without being overbearing - and the owner, R.K.Raja, was always on hand to lend a hand in serving and have a friendly chat. Prices were surprisingly reasonable, particularly for the type of place it was. In fact, it really wasn't any more expensive that the average high street Indian restaurant, which came as a pleasant surprise. The portions were also quite sufficient. So often I try a new restaurant only to be disappointed, but not this time I'm happy to say, as all in all it was an excellent meal, with each dish having a differently distinct flavour. I only wish it was nearer to where I live.' MW. Branch: Mouchak St. Michaels.

Tunbridge Wells

JUNAHKI

NEW ENTRANT

63 St. Johns Rd, T' Wells   01892 615200

Junahki is a firefly, those amazing insects which light up in the dark. For Tun W it's a recent bright light in town with rather plain decor but good Indian food cooked by Indian chefs. Hours: 12-2.30 / 6-11.30. T/a: 20% disc. www.junahki.com

YOU SAY OK

You may get a discount of you show them this Guide.

TENTERDEN: BADSHA 10 West Cross. ~ 01580 765 151. AH Shuab's 70-seater serves an 'awful lot' (he says) of Jalfrezi and Mossalla. 'Have served stars' (he says) 'like The Drifters'. Wow! T/a: 10% disc. Hours: 12-2.30/6-11.30.

TONBRIDGE: ALISHAN 149 High St. ~ 01732 770 616.

TUNBRIDGE WELLS: RAJ PAVILLION 20 Grove Hill Rd TN1 1RZ ~ 01892 533 153. Jewel Zaman Manager.Pictured below.

TUNBRIDGE WELLS: KIRTHON 60 The Pantiles 01892 526633

WEST WICKHAM: BLUE GINGER 101High St. ~ 020 8777 4080. 'Staff, welcoming, knew what they were doing. Aloo Bora, particularly good and flavoursome. Spicy Bindi, hot and crispy. We''ll be back.' G&CM. T/a: 10% disc. Banquet Night: Weds £9.95. Sun lunch buffet £7.95.

West Kingsdown

RAJDANI

17, London Rd, W Kingsdown   01474 853501

Proprietor Suna Meah runs it with other members of the

family, including the chef. Good sized car parking; two ponds; a little decking-style bridge to cross over the ponds. Separate area for T/a. Visited for dinner. Ate plain pops with chutney tray. Onion Bhajia, Chicken Aliza (chicken pakora), Tandoori Prawn, Chicken Chat in puri with plenty of crispy salad main course, huge tandoori king prawns in a cashew nut korma sauce, chicken with cashew nut sauce – delicious chicken tava – spicy but not hot. Plain Nan – light, fluffy – all breads that came out of the kitchen were really good. Red rose on leaving; We were introduced to a couple who dine here six days every week, and on the seventh, they visit other Indian restaurants. There's loyalty. Hours: 12-2.30 / 6-11.30. www.rajdhani.net

Westerham

KINARA AT PITT'S COTTAGE

TOP 100

High St, Limpsfield Rd   01959 562125

This restaurant changed hands in March 2005 since when we have had mostly praising reports and one, a bit disappointed. *'We had been very excited by the prospect of having a Top 100 entry in our neck of the woods! We visited on a Sun at lunchtime. They offer a buffet at £9.95 per person, however we asked to order off the main menu and they reluctantly agreed to this request. Service thereafter was efficient and friendly. The bill for three was £57.00 including a service charge of 10%. Overall we felt that the surroundings and service were certainly above average but found the food slightly disappointing.'* Alex e-mail. But Rachel loves it. *'Thought you might like to know of a new Indian restaurant opened in Westerham, it used to be called Pitts Cottage, but has been taken over by a guy from Dublin'* Kushi Mohammed – Ed) *'who currently runs a place called "Kinara", he has opened a Kinara in Westerham and I would thoroughly recommend it....the food is fantastic'.* RB. Menu Snapshot: Tandoori Trout £3.50; Aloo Tikki £3.25 - deep-fried mashed potato cakes with garlic and ginger; Keema Aloo £8.50 - minced lamb simmered with potato, tomato, onion, chilli, ginger; Lamb Lobia £9.95 - lamb fillet, green beans, ginger, garlic, cream; Paneer Nan £2.50 - stuffed with cheese. T/a: 10% disc. Price Check: Popadum £1.25 a basket, CTM £7.25, Pullao Rice £2.20. Hours: 12-3 Fri to Sun; 6-11.30, daily. www.kinara.co.uk

TULSI   TOP 100

20 London Road, Westerham   01959 563397

Tulsi (biological name Ocimum Sanctum), is the sacred basil plant of India, where it is grown as a symbol of good luck and good health. Owned by Deb, it has a small waiting area with tables and chairs, and an extended, slightly elevated, well-decorated eating area, with a polished wooden floor. Walls covered by framed posters of Bollywood film stars. Ambience is good with very friendly staff, well-dressed in national costume. Chef Anil K Hazra cooks wonderfully innovative Indian cuisine – just how many like it. 'This was our first visit on a busy Sat night, but after a short wait we were seated. Service was excellent and the food delicious.' JB. Hours: 12-2.30; 3 Sun/6-11.30.

LANCASHIRE

Area: North West
Population: 1,434,000
Adjacent Counties:
Cumbs, Greater Man,
Mers, N Yorks,
W Yorks

Adlington

SHAPLA TAKEAWAY

178 Chorley Road, Adlington   01257 474630

'Shapla's chef and part-owner got Sharjus the reputation it had / has when he was the head chef back in the 1980s. Going there brings back the original Sharju experience that it seems to lack today. I travel at least twice a week to the Shapla by-passing several top restaurants on my 15m each way journey. Yours with good curry at heart'. AH.

SHARJU   TOP 100

Church Street, Adlington   01257 481894

Mohammad Ali Shaju's 144-seater is easily found on the A59. Its resemblance to a residential bungalow ceases on

entry. It is stylishly decorated with cream walls, ceiling and table linen, blue carpet, and 144 wicker chairs, in two dining rooms. Wooden fretwork screens give tables privacy. *'Modern, out of town restaurant, conservatory. Arrived at 6.45pm, as the large car park was filling up. A few moments wait before being ushered into conservatory, restaurant already full. Couldn't fault any of the dishes. Despite being busy, service was good, but indifferent. Not pressurised to leave, however it was all hands to the pump to get the table changed for the next sitting. We will return with our caravan, there is a site next door.'* T&MH. T/a: 20% disc. Hours: 12-2 / 5.30-11.30; 12 Fri & Sat; 1-11 Sun

SHERE KHAN   NEW ENTRANT

12 Eanam Old Rd, Eanam, Blackburn, BB1 5BY
01254 676797

A former garage opened in late 2007 as a 240-seat restaurant with rooftop car parking for diners. Shoaib Patel and partner John Saddique runs similar franchises in Birmingham. See Shere Khan, Rusholme, Manchester for history etc. sherekhan.com

YOU SAY OK
You might get a discount if you show them this Guide.
BLACKBURN: SHAJAN Longsight Road, Clayton-le-Dale, Mellor, Blackburn ~ 01254 813640
BURNLEY: SHALAMA 56 Church Street, Burnley ~ 01282 434403
CLITHEROE: DIL RAJ 7 Parsons Lane, ~ 01200 427224
FLEETWOOD: AL MINAr 26 Larkholme Parade ~ 01253 777787
HASLINGDEN: SUNAR GAW 16 Regent Street ~ 01204 364915
LANCASTER: BOMBAY 16 Jubilee Hs, China St. ~ 01524 844550

Greenhalgh

ASHIANA   NEW ENTRANT

Fleetwood Rd, (Just off J3 / M55), Greenhalgh
01253 836187

'*Again a lunch time and again the only diner. Waiter kept apologising that the meal was taking longer than expected due to a problem with the gas. I ordered Chicken Mossuman with a plain boiled rice and chapatti. Good portion of curry sauce with loads of vegetables and good amount of chicken. Nice and spicy. Fluffy rice and good chapatti. Excellent meal, this restaurant gets better with every visit. Food and Drink £12.50.*' DB

Longridge

VICTORIA'S INDIA   A-LIST

The Dog Inn, Market Place, Longrige, PR3 3RR
01772 785111

This is the story of entrepreneurship 'against the odds'. Tony and Carol Walters have done what so many say they wish to do: they have opened their 'dream'

restaurant. The reality has been more of a nightmare, with the battle grounds consisting of acquisition of premises, planning permissions, builders, budgets, overspends, personnel, work permits and officialdom in general. But the couple believe in doing things correctly, and they achieved their opening in 2005. Early on they consulted Pat, whose advice was to obtain a top manager and top chefs – something easier said than done. But more of that later. Walters himself said 'some thought, that we were mad to open an Indian restaurant in Longridge. However, we concluded, that with the right head chef, a good location and superior local produce, that we would have the correct elements for a good restaurant. Victoria's India is a unique name for an Indian restaurant. The name evolved from the building's architecture. It is a beautiful 1865 Victorian villa that was built by the Rev Booth, then Longridge vicar. The church opposite and the school behind in Chapel St are from the same period and have the same, design elements. Being within a conservation area, the couple wanted to keep the building substantially as it was. Now completely refurbished the building, is clean and modern, and I am pleased to report that original period features have indeed been restored and not replaced! Feel free to admire the tiled floor and the fire places. There are two dining areas, the larger is called the 'Albert' room and seats thirty diners, the smaller, the 'Victoria' room, seats twenty diners and is also available for private hire. A walled garden, which has an awning for those sunny and rainy days, seats a comfortable twelve diners. Long summer evenings can be enjoyed with cocktails or coffee and liqueurs (and perhaps a cigarette or two!). The owners engaged Didier Vincent as general manager, having worked in places as exalted as P&O's Aurora and Oriana as well as the QE2. As for the food, the early decision was that whatever was on the menu, it would be cooked authentically, and not in curryhouse style. The kitchen is tiny (something celebrity chefs couldn't cope with) requiring good organisation. It is led by chef, Bishal Rasaily, who earned his spurs at Delhi's Maurya Sheraton under chef qereshi (of Dum Pukht fame) and London's celebrated Chutney Mary (see SW 10). Their specials include: Tandoori Fish Salad £5.50,, grilled salmon chunks and fresh green salad; Aloo Pakora £2.90, potato wheels dipped in spiced gram flour batter, then golden-fried for crispness,

STOP PRESS: Within a couple of years from opening, Victoria's India outgrew the Manse so they moved in early 2009; just a couple of hundred yards, literally down the road (Berry Lane actually). And they have taken their unique name, 'Victoria's India' with them to a public house called The Dog Inn. It's an impressive free-standing building, and allows the owners the opportrnity to expand with new ideas. We need your reports and information. See pp 339 & 340 or report online online at patchapman.co.uk

garnished with coriander leaves; Chicken Malai Tikka £4/£9.90, a creamy kebab of boneless chicken breast, blended with cream and cheese then grilled in tandoor; Sheek Gilafi £4/£9.90, spiced ground lamb coated with diced bell peppers and onion, cooked on skewer in tandoor; Paneer Makhani - cottage cheese tossed in tomato, cream, cashew nut gravy and juliennes of ginger, garnished with cream; Kadhai £8.50, choice of chicken or lamb, stir-fried with finely chopped onion, ginger, garlic and green chilli, cooked in tomato juice, sautéed with bell pepper and finished with fenugreek leaves and kadhai masala; Royal Biriani £10.50, Basmati rice steamed with tender curried lamb or chicken, enhanced with saffron, aromatic spices, garnished with almonds, sultanas and an omelette, served with vegetable curry sauce. Sun Buffet Lunch: £6.95 adult, £3.95 for the younger curryholic. We have awarded Victoria's India the Most Welcome Newcomer Award against stiff competition from many London venues. Our reasoning is simple. Unlike so many London newcomers have almost unlimited budgets, resources and experts to achieve the job. The Walters did it on a shoestring, learning as they went, proving that it can be done. And what has been done for Indian cuisine is to bring London to Longridge, something that the whole of the north of England should take note of. Prices are within reach, and we hope Victoria's India becomes a serious destination for all devotees of Indian food. The website is unflashy and informative, and uniquely even lists it suppliers. I wish Victoria's India was my local. Lucky Longridge! Hours: 6-11.30 Tues to Sat, Last food orders: 10.30; 2-11. Sun/Bank Hol. (a la carte after 7). Mon closed. www.victoriasindia.co.uk

Lytham St Annes

BILASH BALTI

19 St Andrews Rd, St Annes   01253 780001

'*I'm a regular and it is my favourite. It was the first to introduce Balti dishes in the Fylde and every other restaurant copies what they do. The food is excellent and the staff are very friendly and polite. Owner ,Mr Hoque and his sons run the place. I would give this restaurant 10 out of 10 - it's that good.*' AC. Menu Snapshot: Fish Pakora £7.75, served with salad and Gobi Bhajee; Makhon Chicken £6.50, diced tandoori chicken, butter, tomato, cream; Kashmiri Korma King Prawn £8, with dried fruit. Hours: 12-2 Sat-Thurs/6-12; 12.30 Sat.

MOGHUL

12 Orchard Rd, St Annes   01253 712114

'*I'm not usually prone to putting finger to keyboard but I feel I must share with you my recent experience at the above restaurant. My wife and I are, as you so well put it in your own words "curryholics" and on our annual pilgrimage to the west*

coast for rest and recuperation we enquired as to the whereabouts of a good curry restaurant, the hotelier pointed us in the direction of the town centre and the Moghul. On entering the establishment it was obvious from the outset that this was no ordinary place; from the decor down to the service it oozed class. We were greeted by Mr Ali a most convivial host, within minutes of our unannounced arrival we were seated, drinks ordered and the menu brought to us. The list of dishes presented to us was mind-boggling and some of which I confess have never heard of before, I enquired into one dish – Achari Gosht (pickle-based lamb) which I wanted to try. Without any prompting and for no extra charge Mr Ali asked his chef to prepare us a sample dish. It was exquisite. I shall not say what we finally ordered but just to say it was prepared and presented beautifully. Mr Chapman please pass this onto your loyal readers as a must-go -to venue you will not be disappointed.' GW.

Preston

SAGAR PREMIER

Clayton Brook Rd, Bamber Bridge, Preston
                                          01772 620200

'*Chatting to regular customers, some of whom had driven over from Yorkshire!, their enthusiasm for Sagar quality continues to be very high. Interior still looks fresh and classy, a credit to the meticulous housekeeping and hygiene. Waiters know what their customers' favourite drinks are, so they are served by the time they walk through the door. Our meal of fresh Popadums and pickles, Meat Samosas (on par with Depa Tandoori, London), Mixed Kebabs, best quality chicken breast and lamb in aromatic sauces, Dupiaza, Madras with piquant Pullao Rice and Sag Aloo were all generous portions and absolutely delicious. With several rounds of Cobra, the price was very competitive. Sagar's swift and efficient service, makes for a very relaxing meal.*' TE. N&JG like it too. Menu Snapshot: Macchi Malai, fish curry, garlic, tomato, green chilli, crab meatballs, mustard and spices; South Indian Murghi, off the bone tandoori chicken, mincemeat, coriander leaves; Exotic Salmon, black pepper, cinnamon, spring onion and garlic; Tomato Rice; Garlic and Coriander Paratha. T/a: 10% disc. Hours: 12-2 / 6-11.30; 1-11.30 Sat & Sun.

NABIS RESTAURANT   NEW ENTRANT

East Lancashire Road, Windle, St Helens,
WA10 6QY   01744 751352

Sohail and Khalid Nabis opened here in 2006. Their father had established now-closed ventures in the area over the previous 30 years. It has '*plush furnishings, split-level dining, open kitchen and plasma screen. The menu changes monthly and you can expect a choice of imaginative Indian dishes, including lobster.*'JT. Hours: 12-2 Th & Fri only / 5.30-10 Mon-Th; 10.30 Fri & Sat; 3- 9.30 Sun. www.nabisrestaurant.co.uk

LEICESTERSHIRE

Area: East Midlands
Population: 912,000
Adjacent Counties:
Derbs, Lincs,
Northants,
Notts, Rutland,
Staffs, Warks

Leicester

Leicester is home to a good number of Gujaratis from India. In addition, many of its Asian community settled there in the 1970s when they became exiled from Africa, specifically Kenya and Uganda, where they had lived for generations, having been taken there as clerks and semiskilled plantation labour by the British. Most contemporary Leicester Asians have little concept of the Indian subcontinent, few having ever visited it, but you would not know this from the quality of the food, particularly in the cheap and cheerful cafés, snack bars and sweet shops all over town. The first curry house, the Taj Mahal, opened in 1961 and is still there! I dined there that year, and when I asked for chilli pickle the anxious owner appeared and spent half an hour counselling me against eating hot food! (To no avail, I might add!) Now there are over 80 'Indian' restaurants on our database which, in a city of around 300,000 population, is a ratio of one 'Indian' restaurant per 3,750 people, making Leicester our second most densely curry-housed city in the UK (see Bradford, West Yorkshire).

Leicester, Belgrave Road

Paul Motley describes Leicester's 'Little India':

'Belgrave Road, just north of the city, is Leicester's golden curry mile. As well as containing a great selection of authentic, real Indian restaurants both vegetarian and non-vegetarian, Belgrave Road and the surrounding area offers an insight into Indian shopping for jewellery, fashion, cookware, food and spices plus much more all at bargain prices. Suns seems to be a real family day out for the family unit of three generations together without attitude, something we seem to have lost these past years. Leicester has one of the highest percentages of Asian population in any town or city in the UK with a forecast that the majority of its population will be of ethnic origin by 2011. Leicester is quoted as an outstanding example of diversity and ethnic plurality and is internationally heralded as a model of community and cohesion. All this reflects in the diversity of the food offered

around the Belgrave/Melton Road Area of the city. You could be forgiven if you thought that you had miraculously been transported to somewhere in India and some may even feel a little intimidated by the fact the English faces are very few and far between, however the populous are very far from intimidating in fact by contrast the atmosphere is far far friendlier than the majority of town centres plus service in the many family run shops and business establishments really is second to none. By the way should each November, Leicester is renowned for attracting over 600,000 visitors for this important event, which is incidentally the highest number in the world outside of India.' PM.

BOBBY'S GUJARATI VEGETARIAN

154 Belgrave Road   0116 266 2448

Atul Lakhani (aka Bobby) owns a restaurant with two advantages – a license and very reasonably priced food, so it's ever-popular with a cafeteria-type atmosphere. Mostly Gujarati food, which is light and slightly sweet. You pay (credit cards taken) at the till. Hours: 11-10.30.

CURRY FEVER   A-LIST

139 Belgrave Road   0116 266 2941

Established in 1978 by Anil Anand (head chef) and Sunil Anand (manager). They are related to the Brilliant and Madhu's Brilliant of Southall, Middlesex. The food is Punjabi, cooked just as they eat it at home. House specialities, which show the owners' Kenyan background, include: Jeera Chicken £15, one of their signature dishes, a must-eat, fabulous whole chicken briskly fried with cumin seeds and powder; Pili Pili Chicken £15, whole chicken, hot and spicy sauce, another must -eat; Mogo Shashlick £5, skewered cassava, onion, capsicum; Machusi Lamb £8, Kenyan style lamb, fenugreek sauce. Previously we gave it our BEST IN THE MIDLANDS Award. Though this time the award has moved elsewhere, it is an award which lasts for ever. *'Curry Fever – still the best in Leicester'* CM. T/a: 10% disc. Service: 10%. Min Ch: £10. Hours: 12-2 Tues to Sat / 6-11.20; 12 Sat. Monday closed.

FRIENDS TANDOORI   TOP 100

41 Belgrave Rd, Leicester   0116 266 8809

Manjit Pabla's sophisticated and stylish restaurant serving superior (scrummy!) curries. Do book your table for the weekend, you will not be disappointed. Menu Snapshot: (all between £5 & £7): Lussani Kebab, chicken marinated in fresh garlic and roasted in the tandoor; Kali Mirch Ka Kabab, chicken rolled and marinated in cream and crushed peppercorns; Masaledar Champaan, tender lamb chops marinated in a ginger-masala base with yoghurt and grilled in the tandoor; Malai Kofta , mashed vegetables, deep-fried and cooking

in a creamy sauce; Bhartha £6.25, roasted, smoked aubergines mashed and cooked with peas and fresh tomatoes. A traditional Punjabi dish with a smoky flavour; Daal Panch-Rattani , a combination of five lentils tempered with cumin, garlic, onions and tomatoes. Desserts: (all c£3): Gulab Jamun, homemade, served hot or cold with ice cream, lovely; Ras Malai, reduced milk shaped into discs and poached gently in full-fat milk, garnished with pistachios and saffron, wonderful. Don't forget to linger over the wine list, it really is an informative selection from all around the world. T/a: 20% disc. Hours: 12-2.30 /6-11.30; closed Sun. www.friendstandoori.co.uk

SAYONARA THALI

49 Belgrave Rd, Leicester   0116 266 5888

'*This strictly Gujarati vegetarian restaurant is a must. It is not large (c 40 seats) nor is it plush but neither are the prices, it offers good vegetarian food at realistic prices in fact a Thali consisting of many different dishes, dhals, pickles plus bread and rice starts at a meagre c£7 which if I remember correctly includes a sweet or savoury Lassi The other dishes on the menu give a choice of Southern Indian cuisine such as stuffed dosa , Idli both being served with Sambar and traditional coconut chutney. Other choices include Northern vegetable both wet and dry dishes of exotic vegetables, lentils and legumes plus the Gujarati speciality Kudhi (aka Kari) a yoghurt and gram flour based dish and not forgetting the Mumbai (Bombay) snack foods and a selection of breads from various regions. We found that the ground floor was completely packed, we apprehensively made our way upstairs. I say apprehensively because I have often found that a floor away from the main hubub and eye of the management is often out-of-sight-and-out-of-mind plus it can sometimes lack atmosphere. This was not the case, although at first we were alone two other groups followed us up within a matter of minutes and a member of staff was promptly available to offer us a menu and take our order when ready. There were four in our party and we decided to order a selection of which we could all take a quarter from each dish. Palak Paneer was delicately spiced and probably the best I have tasted, Navarattan (nine vegetables) Korma was aromatic, Baigan & Aloo Karai of which both vegetables being cooked until just al denté and presented in a rich spicy gravy, Sweetcorn Masala a simple vegetable but attractively cooked plus a humble traditional soupy Massoor Dhal plus pickles. We estimated just one portion of rice would be ample as we were ordering a mixture of chapattis and bhaturas, the latter being a deep fried semi leavened bread which I have very rarely encountered outside of this city and I must say this Northern Indian bread was far superior to those we were served in Southern India but then again I suppose that's quite logical. I never usually refer to cost when reviewing a restaurant, I strongly believe your palette should judge a meal not your purse. This occasion is an notion as I do think that the cost of just over £10 per person including a nominal amount of drink was exceedingly good value for money and a nice conclusion to an interesting day out and to*

my wife's amazement I didn't return home to Northampton this time with yet another cast-iron karai to add to my collection nor a stainless steel spice storage container (my wife is of the opinion that I think more of my Indian cooking utensils than I do of her. I do strongly protest as I love them both the same).' PR. Hmmm, Paul, but do the pots love you She must be wonderful.

SHARMILEE VEGETARIAN

71 Belgrave Rd, Leicester   0116 261 0503

Opened way back in 1973 by Gosai brothers (manager, LK Goswami), this is a two-part venue. The sweet mart serves a rich assortments of Indian sweets, and such delightful items as Vegetable Samosas, Pakoras and Dahi Vadia, from 9.30am-9pm daily, not Mondays. The licensed restaurant is upmarket and vegetarian, decorated with marble pillars in shades of brown and dusky blue marble-effect walls, high-backed black chairs, white table linen. Tasty starters of Pani Puri, crispy puris served with spicy sauce, chickpeas and onion. Chanabateta, chickpeas and potatoes in a tamarind sauce garnished with onions. South Indian specialities: Masala Dosa, thin crispy pancake filled with potato and onion, Idli Sambar, flat pulse balls, both served with Sambar and coconut chutney. T/a 10% disc promised if you show them this Guide. Hours: 12-2.30 / 6-9.30; 12-9 Sat. closed Mon not bank hols.

Elsewhere in Leicester

CURRY HOUSE

64 London Rd, Leicester   0116 255 0688

Brick arches give this double fronted restaurant a clean and smart look. Originally opened in 1985 and taken over in 1997 by Mr Nisar Kolia, who is also the head chef. This is a family business, as Iqbal Kolia is front of house manager. Menu Snapshot: Karahi Wings £6.50, cooked in thick spicy sauce; Panir Tikka Sizzling, curd Indian cheese marinated in spices and cooked with peppers, onions, tomatoes in tandoor, served with salad; Navrattan Kurma both c£6, nine varieties of vegetables, served in a mild creamy sauce; Mattar Pilaw Rice £2, peas and rice. Student disc: 10%. Hours: 6 -11.45; 12 Sat; 11.30 Sun. www.the-curry-house.co.uk

EK MAYA   TOP 100

28 Dysart Way, Leicester   0116 262 1118

Kaycee Patel spent two years creating Ek Maya from a former warehouse to Leicester's biggest restaurant. It even boasts its own car park. Spread across two-floors, it has a 150-seats and room for 300 to stand. Downstairs is a 50-cover bar, while upstairs beyond the balcony there is a private dining area, complete with a lounge for

100 people. The adjoining Champagne room is the ideal chill area for private parties of up to 70. a There is even a retail area stocking a range of traditional artefacts, spices, books and crockery. The warm, earthy-hued colour scheme is very Mediterranean, while the rawness of the dark wood tables is reminiscent of Africa. Design inspiration from India dominates. There are the traditional gypsy paintings produced by special tribes in Rajasthan. Imprinted onto the hardwood tables in Sanskrit calligraphy is the charming old Indian adage, 'Daane daane pe likha hai, kaane wale ka naam'', ('the diner's name is written on every morsel of food'). A huge cover on the ceiling has yantras and symmetrical tantric shapes painted in raw reds and browns, complementing the light/dark mix of the oak floor. Even the food reflects the multicultural theme; Indian merges with the Mediterranean in dishes like Spicy Calamari Rings and Couscous with Tandoori Salad along with dishes and ingredients popular in Africa, such as Phaldari Plantain Kofta and Mogo Chips. A selection of traditional Indian food is also on offer, like the special Paneer Galouti Kebab, along with a special range of Ayurvedic dishes catering to different body types and taste combinations. As a restaurant clearly without conventions, there is no head chef. The four main chefs (one curry specialist, one desserts, one tandoori and one to oversee) are from five-star restaurants in India and their open-plan kitchen allows customers to see them in action. www.ekmaya.com

HALLI

153 Granby St, Leicester   0116 255 4667

Owner Jaimon Thomas opened his 90-seater South Indian vegetarian restaurant in 2006. He hails from an Udipi village (Halli) in Karnataka. The wonderful thing about this style of food is that many of these small dishes are served complete with their own condiments, making every dish almost a course in it's own right. South Indian food is perfect for the diner who does not eat wheat; dishes are made from rice, which is, of course, the main staple of the region. On a visit to South India, you will see rice fields growing everywhere. Menu Snapshot: (all items £3 - £5): Idli, gently steamed rice and lentil cake, served with Sambar and chutney; Upma, semolina cooked with nuts, green chillies and ginger served with coconut chutney; Udding vade, golden fried lentil doughnuts, fluffy in the middle and crispy on the outside; Kajoo Pakoda, cashew nuts quick fried in a crunchy batter with aromatic spices; Gulla Podi £2.99, four pieces of aubergine puffs fried in a thin, seasoned batter; Masala Dosa, rice and lentil pancake filled with traditional fillings of seasoned potatoes, onion and peas, Masala Dosa is their most popular dish, Your Editors always order this delicacy – absolutely delicious!; Beetroot Sasami, Udipi Brahmin dish, beetroot cooked in yoghurt with green chilli, curry leaves and mustard seed. Puds: Jaggery Dosa, golden pancake smothered

with warm cane sugar £3; Shavige Paysas £2, made from milk, vermicelli, sugar and cardamom pod. T/a: 20% disc. Hours: 12-2 / 6-11. www.hallirestaurant.com

KHYBER

116 Melton Rd, Leicester   0116 266 4842

The 40-seater Khyber opened in 1984 and still under the same ownership of Ashok Raval, who is also the head chef. *'It is cosy and immaculately clean with a substantial following among the affluent end of the Leicester Asian business community. After so much of the plodding, ghee-flooded rubbish pedalled in too many restaurants around the country, the Khyber's food is a delight and an altogether more subtle experience than the food presented in the other establishments you list in the area that supply meat-based dishes. The chief chef is Ashok while the front of the house is supervised by Ashok's younger brother Dinesh. The food is simply outstanding and, many of the loyal clientele would agree, is rightly regarded among the cognoscenti as the best in the city. It is a little more expensive than its rivals, but genuine lovers of good food do not begrudge paying. So please, please honour them with a visit next time you are in town and I would absolutely, 100 per cent, guarantee that you will not be disappointed.'* JR. His specials include: Lamb Chop Curry £8.50; Chicken Staff Curry £7; Chilli King Prawns £13, mild, sweet and sour, fried in crispy batter and cooked with spring onions, fresh sliced garlic, black pepper, mild chillies and soy sauce; Special Naan, stuffed with vegetables, coconut and nuts. Hours: 12-2 / 6.30-11.30. Sun closed. www.khybertandoorirestaurant.co.uk

NAMASTE

65 Hinkley Rd, Leicester   0116 254 1778

Partners, DK Dey (manager) and R Paul opened their fifty-four seater restaurant in 1994. Show a copy of this Guide to manager Mr Dey and you will receive a free starter. Regulars will be treated to a complimentary drink after their meal. Chef Aziz says that his Mossalla and Pasanda dishes are most popular, however please try his Balti Special Menu, all served with choice of either Boiled Rice, Pullao Rice, Naan or Tandoori Roti. However, if you are celebrating, how about the Royal Kurzi Lamb for four persons c£60, which includes all the business AND a complimentary bottle of wine. T/a: 10% disc. Sun Special Lunch: c£6. Hours: 12-2, Thur-Sun / 5.30-12; 1 Sat; 12-2 Sun.

POPADUMS INDIAN

330 Welford Rd, Leicester   0116 244 8888

Opened April 2005 by owner/manager Abdul Giash. House Specials include: Mixed Karahi £10, Tandoori Chicken, Chicken and Lamb Tikka, Sheek Kebab cooked in a sauce, served in a 'souk'; Genghis Said £6, barbecued chicken and spiced minced meat cooked with

peppers, onions and tomatoes, served in spicy sauce; Aloo Gosht £6, potatoes and lamb cooked in a medium or hot sauce; Cheese and Chilli Naan £2. Those who spend £20 or above on their T/a are rewarded with a bottle of wine. Sun Buffet Lunch: £6 adults, £6 children. Del: 5m. min £8. Hours: 6-11.30; from 12 Sun.

RAITHA'S

23 Leicester Rd, Kibworth Harcourt,
Leicester   0116 279 2323

During December 2004, Prakash Raithatha opened the cutely named Raitha's restaurant. Smart white building, with black timbers decorating the facade. The builders have been in and have built a very pretty raised terrace area, so you may sit outside, weather permitting – and nibble on your bhajias. Specials include: Chicken Achari £8, spicy dish cooked with cumin and limes; Honey Chilli Chicken £5; Mussels £6; Sizzling Fish Platter £7 for one or £11 for two; Mushroom and Tomato Naan £2.45. T/a: 10% disc. Del: 6m. Hours: 6-11.30; 12 Sat. www.raithas.co.uk

THE ROYAL LEICESTER

Lockerbie Walk, Rushey Mead, Leicester

No phone because it's a pub and you can't book. *'It was Rob the accountant's stag night and rather than embark on the usual rowdy drunken night out with boys which per se ends with the groom being tied to the railings with his trousers flying from the nearest object, he had elected to go for an authentic Indian meal with his work colleagues which he perceived to be a safer option.'* Has this got anything to do with a Restaurant Guide of high repute, Paul? Ed. *'Five of us found our way to an Indian pub called The Royal Leicester, which serves good earthy authentic Indian food. From the outside it was a seventies building, the interior of which had escaped any attempt to drag it into the new millennium. Please regard this as an observation rather than a criticism because the place exuded character and warmth absent in modern, trendy wine-bar which seem to be the fashion at present. After choosing a Formica table we ordered drinks from the bar. The waiter politely enquired to our Gujarati colleagues whether the chilli heat should be toned down a little for his English friends, a considerate thought which was declined. We chose to have two large sizzling platters as appetisers and when I say large I mean large, these consisted of various meat and chicken kebabs without an E-number in sight plus chilli-fried mogo chips, a chilli relish, a simple raita and a basic salad. All the chicken kebabs were moist well spiced and the seekh kebabs of a good texture and full of subtle flavour. The mogo made a good contrast to the meat selection and was something a little different than the norm. For mains we had King Prawn Masala, delicately spiced and cooked for just right. Methi Meat was full bodied with tender lamb chunks together the pungent green methi leaves, Chicken Masala which was delightful. The side dishes were also superb; Palak Paneer had generous chunks of soft paneer which had soaked* up the flavour of the gravy and the spinach was not over pureed which is so often the case. The new kid on the block to me was a dish called Ondo, potatoes with split mung dhal in a well-balanced spicy gravy, the dish I was assured is of Gujarati origin. I definitely would return there again and will, the genuinely friendly and obliging staff plus the relaxed warm atmosphere of the place also enhanced the evening in general. Rob enjoyed his chosen stag night, his food and is now a happily married man.'* PM.

TAJ MAHAL

12 Highfield St, Leicester   0116 254 0328

Ali Ashraf, established his 100-seater way back in 1961, long before the Gujarati population arrived. To say it is in old hands and safe hands is an understatement. It's Leicester's first and oldest and is does the traditional curryhouse formula, which when done well, makes a change from time to time. Anyway, it has a following now stretching over four generations and it was here that I was given the chilli-heat warning *(see intro to Leicester above)*. Min Ch: £15. Del: 3m, £15 min. Hours: 12-2 / 6-12; 1 Sat.

YOU SAY OK
You might get a discount if you show them this Guide.

LUTTERWORTH: EXOTIC SPICE 4 Church Street, Lutterworth ~ 01455 203000. 60-seater opened by Rafiqur Rahman in 2002 with Chef T Ali. Hours: 6-12.

MARKET HARBOROUGH: RYHANS ESSENCE OF SPICE TAKEAWAY 30 Coventry Rd ~ 01858 419039. T/a only, specials inc: Mussels & Squid. *'We enjoy your smiling faces'* Mr&Mrs W. Del: 5m. Hours: 5-11.

Market Harborough

SHACORIKA

16 St Marys Road   01858 464644

Owning manager, Ala Uddin, opened his seventy seater in March 1980. Decorated in shades of pink with gold detail and Moghul arches. Menu Snapshot: (all £6 - £9): Machali Aloo, flakes of Bengali fish wrapped in mashed potato and spices; Runner Bean and Mushroom Curry, Beef Al Amin, hot with cucumber and omelette; Tandoori Mixed Grill, lamb, chicken, prawn and king prawn grilled on charcoal in clay oven and served with salad and Naan; Onion and Garlic Naan £3. PM's opinion could describe 90% of the restaurants in this Guide: *The menu displayed some 200 heat-graded dishes. Effort was made somewhat to portray different regional foods such as Lamb Kovalam but its description bore no resemblance to any south Indian dish I know of. I decided to go for a very unadventurous Lamb Roghon Josh (in standard gravy with addition of fresh tomatoes to differentiate it from what would have been a lamb curry) with Tarka Dhal (presentable), Bombay Potatoes (in ample gravy with no spice additions to perk them up) and Sag Paneer (individually cooked) with*

rice and chapattis (leaving a lot to be desired). Whilst there was nothing outstanding about any of the dishes, they were all exactly as expected – the type that seduced me years ago into my passion for spicy dishes. The restaurant did not promise a menu authentically cooked by Grandma Patel and served exactly what the sign said over the door. It did not need to compete with upmarket establishments because there are none in the town and for early on a Monday evening it was extremely well patronised.' PM. Credit cards OK, but no cheques. Hours: 12-2/6-11.30. . www.shagorika.com

LINCOLNSHIRE

Area: East Midlands
Population: 988,000
Adjacent Counties:
Cambs, Leics,
Norfolk, Notts,
E & S Yorks

YOU SAY OK LINCS I OF 2
You might get a discount if you show them this Guide.

BOSTON: BOMBAY BRASSERIE 53 west st. PE21 8QN *'a good quality meal "out in the sticks"on banquet night with 5 courses for £8.90. mark 8/10.'* G&MP.

BOSTON: ROSE OF BENGAL 67 West St. ~ 01205 363355

BOSTON: STAR OF INDIA 110 West St.~ 01205 360558

BOURNE: SHALIMAR BALTI HOUSE 8 Abbey Rd. ~ 01778 393959

GRANTHAM: BOMBAY BRASSERIE 11 London Road, Grantham ~ 01476 576096

GRIMSBY: SPICE OF LIFE 8 Wellowgate. ~ 01472 357476

LINCOLN: PASSAGE TO INDIA 435 High St. ~ 01522 526166. Chef prop Gulzar Hussain's 75-seater in 2 rooms. Del: 5m, £10 min. min Ch: £10. Set Lunch: £7, Set Dinner: £10.12-2/5-12.

LINCOLN: RAJ 7a St Marys Street, Lincoln ~ 01522 536109

Lincoln

MACH BAR AND RESTAURANT

Weagby Road East,   North Greetwell, Lincoln
01522 754488

It's located just outside the historic city of Lincoln. Says owner Mavinder Gosal *'As new restaurateurs, we wanted to give our first restaurant a personal touch, so we chose the first two letters of our names, Mav and Charlotte, to create MaCh'* Menu Snapshot: Breaded Khumbi. mushrooms stuffed with spiced vegetables, coated in golden breadcrumbs; Chicken Nambali Tandoori breast chicken, garnished with delicious mozzarella cheese., Salmon Pakora marinated, coated in a spicy batter & deep fried, served with a fresh crispy salad. Punjabi Jhinga, King prawns

marinated in yoghurt, fresh coriander and mustard, cooked to perfection in the tandoor. Mixed Platter: chicken tikka, chicken wings, lamb chops and sheek kebabs. Ideal to share between 2. Mains include Shimla Pepper Chicken, cooked with sweet peppers in a spicy tomato based sauce; Goan Special, prepared with coconut milk and selection of spices to create a medium hot dish; Sajon Special. shredded tandoori chicken pot roasted with minced lamb, ginger, garlic & selected herbs & spices; Haash Tikka Sizzler. duck breast marinated and cooked in special spices, garnished with orange zest and Venison Special, served with a rich orange flavoured Grand Mariner based sauce. 24hr notice required for that one. All the favourites are also there. Hours: 6-11.   www.machrestaurant.co.uk

MALABAR JUNCTION   AT BARBICAN HOTEL

11 St Mary's St, Lincoln   01522 522277

Though the majority of south Indians are vegetarians (for economic reasons more than choice) when you do get Keralan meat and fish dishes, they are a refreshing change from the familiar dishes of north India. *'The meal was delicious, including Vegetable Korma, Lemon Rice, Mushroom Rice, Coconut Rice.'* NT. Menu Extracts: Ghee Roast Masala £6, crispy pancake roasted in purified butter, filled with potato masala, served with sambar and chutney; Spinach Vada £3.50, fried doughnut made of split black gram batter, ginger, onions, green chilli, curry leaves, cumin soaked in seasoned and tempered yoghurt; minced Lamb Cutlets £3.50, patties coated with breadcrumbs, served with tomato sauce and salad; Cashew Nut Pakora £2.50, cashew nuts dipped in spicy batter and fried; Lamb Chilli Fry £6.50, stir-fried lamb, mustard, red chilli, curry leaves, ginger, garlic, onion, tomato, garam masala and coriander leaves; Konju Kanava Masala £7, shrimps and squids cooked in thick gravy, flavoured with kokum. *'Yum yum!'* NT.

PLANET MASALA

Odeon Complex, Wigford Way, Brayford Wharf, Lincoln   01522 511511

'A totally different style of Indian eatery. Dishes are under titles such as Wrap and Run; Flame Grill and Masala Handi. You just choose what style of food you wish to eat, this is what you can expect: Wrap 1, Shai Grill Seekh Kebab £3.25, wrapped in a soft chapatti with salad and spicy sauce served with spicy chips; Flame 3, Whole Flame Grill Mirchi Mirchi Chicken, marinated in achaar masala, red chillies, lemon flame grilled, served with two spicy chips or two Naan breads. Masala 6, Jhinga Kharai £6.95, prawns cooked in masala and tomatoes served with Naan bread and spicy Saffron Rice. Children's meals: Masala Chicken Burger £3.95, served with chips, soft drink and ice cream. 'Delicious Spicy Masala Chips, I am sure they cook them in paprika. Onion Bhajia was far too hot and I had to leave most of it, though I did feed it to the birds.' lucky birds! 'Mixed Vegetable Curry delicious with the Pullao Rice.' NT.

Sleaford

AGRA and BOLLYWOOD LOUNGE

1 Pride Parkway, Enterprise Park, Sleaford
01529 414162

This huge restaurant, seating 110, opened in 1988 and was taken over in 1994 by Enus Karim, who is incidentally the Head Chef. His special include: Agra Capsicum Noorani, whole green pepper barbecued and then stuffed with tender chicken cooked with 'chat masala', scrumptious!; Akbhari £9, filleted pieces of chicken or lamb cooked in the tandoor and mixed with richly spiced minced lamb, mustard seeds, capsicum and topped with fresh coriander; Mango Delight £9, barbecued strips of chicken breast, cooked in a creamy, mild, rich sauce topped with ripe mango. He also has plans to build a thirty bedroom hotel with conference centre and casino. His 'Bollywood Lounge' opened last November, where customers can enjoy a pre-dinner drink or relax with coffee and brandies after their meal. The lounge is also available for private parties ie: 'Elvis goes to Bollywood', fabulous!! Menu Snapshot: Chingri Nisha £4, Bengal Tiger Prawn coated with sweet almond and coconut powder wrapped in a crispy pastry; Bengali Roast £3.50, quarter of chicken roasted and smothered in a lightly spiced onion and tomato sauce; all Balti dishes are served with Naan bread for that essential sauce scooping; Kurzi Lamb £35., served with salad, Egg Fried Rice, enough for two! Del: 20m, £10 min. T/a: 10% disc. Hours: 12-2 not Fri / 5.30-11.30, from 6 Sun. Branches: Agra 2, Ruskington, Lincs; Agra 3, Blyth, Notts and Choti, Lincoln.

INDIA GARDEN

19 Market Place, Sleaford   01529 302521

Menu Snapshot: Pili Pili Chicken £6.30, very hot with green chillies; Chicken or Lamb Deluxe £7.95, cooked with wine, almond, coconut, pistachio, fresh coriander and cream; Balti dishes all served with plain Naan Bread; Aloo Bagon £2.50, potato and aubergine; Chicken Pudina £5.15, medium with mint; Garlic Fried Rice £2.45; Butter Chapatti £1.10. Del: 3 m, £10 min. T/a: 10% disc. Stocks: Cobra, Kingfisher, Budweiser and Becks. Birthday Special Deal: four or more must dine then birthday girl/boy dines free! Price Check: Popadom 55p, CTM £6.10, Pullao Rice £2.10. Hours: 12-2, not Friday, and 5.30-11.30; 12 Fri & Sat.

Stamford

BOMBAY COTTAGE

52 Scotgate, Stamford   01780 480138

Established in 1994 by A Hussain and managed by H.

Rahman. Menu Snapshot: Fish Chutneywali £3.10, tasty fish kebab with spicy fresh mint, coriander and green chilli chutney; Royal Quails £3.95, whole quails marinated in crushed spices, grilled over clay oven; generous Tandoori Mixed Grill £10.50, tandoori chicken, chicken tikka, sheek kebab, lamb chop, king prawn, salad, BUT, Naan Bread not included. Del: 5 m, £15 min. T/a: 10% disc. Sun Buffet: £9.90 per person. Price Check: popadum 50p, CTM £6.90, Pullao Rice £1.90. Hours: 12-2, Sun to 3 / 6-11.30.

YOU SAY OK

You might get a discount if you show them this Guide.
STAMFORD: RAJ OF INDIA 2 All Saints St. 01780 753556
STAMFORD BALTI HUT 16 All Saints Place. ~ 01780 762013

MANCHESTER
(Greater)

Area: North West
Population:
Ranked UK 3rd
2,700,000
Adjacent Counties:
Cheshire, Lancashire,
Merseyside, Yorkshire

Greater Manchester was introduced as a county in 1965, though this was regarded as an imposition by many of its residents, who still refer to the counties that Greater Manchester gobbled up, e.g. parts of Lancashire and Cheshire. We have adhered strictly to the official current Greater Man territory for town locations in this Guide.

Altrincham
(inc Hale, Halebarns and Timperley)

BARINDA	TOP 100
134 Ashley Rd, Hale	0161 926 9185

First opened in 1982, taken over by Javed Akhtar in 1998. Seats 70. Standard range of Curries, Tandoori, Karahi and Balti dishes. *'If you are a stranger to an area, you are never sure what a suburb of a major conurbation is like. When I saw 'Hale' in the Guide, I thought that sounds like 'Sale' and is likely to be the same!! What I soon appreciated is that, to quote a colleague: "Hale is the poncey end of nicey – nicey Altrincham."'Having paid this area a visit, I can see what he means. It is a very designer -conscious part of the Cheshire set – loads of restaurants' Mercs and Beamers to*

match.' Well Mick, thanks a million. I'll forward the disgusted-of-Hales letters to you; that's Mick Wright of Bedfordshire. MW goes on: *'Anyway, I found the Barinda without any difficulty – almost opposite the station on Ashley Road. I started with Tandoori Chicken which has real melt in the mouth stuff, and then had Bengan Murghi – I love Brinjals in the Asian cuisine, and this was a very good chicken and aubergine dish.'* MW T/a: 10% disc. Del: £12 min, 3m. Hours: 5.30-12.

DILLI   TOP 100

60 Stamford New Rd, WA14 1EE   0161 929 7484

Dilli is the original name of modern India's Capital city, Delhi, India's gourmet capital. The Dilli restaurant delivers classic Indian Cuisine. It is also the first Ayurvedic restaurant in the north. Ayurveda, meaning life-knowledge uses traditional food ingredients which nourish specific parts of the body and counteract or prevent illness. Ayurvedic followers believe it relieve or prevent conditions like stress, heart disease, diabetes and asthma. It's a teaching that fries almonds to combat coughs, uses cinnamon to attack headaches, cloves to ease toothache, fennel to soothe sore throats, ginger for help with colds and arthritis, or garlic for blood pressure and rheumatism. Dilli is owned by chef-restaurateur Kuldeep Singh, onsite chef is Raminder Pal Singh Malhotra, assisted by Ravi Bajaj, Uday Kumar Seth and Mohammed Naeem. Softly-lit, intimate venue, decorated in neutral tones featuring intricate wooden wall-hangings which have been hand carved by skilled carpenters in Delhi. Seats 60

downstairs and 45 upstairs (which can be hired for private parties). Menu changes weekly, but specialities include: Murgh Handi Lazeez, chicken simmered in creamy yoghurt with garlic, cardamom, mace and saffron; Calamari Peri Peri, squid tossed with curry leaves, mustard seeds, peppercorns topped with seared King scallops. *'Uninspiring décor but neat and tidy. As usual it's a Friday lunch time and this restaurant is quite busy, I assume free from shoppers as parking is an absolute nightmare. This is not your usual standard curry house, out have gone the Madras, Vindaloos, Dhansaks etc to be replaced with dishes like Hari Mirch Ka Khargosh, rabbit with ginger and chilli and Thaaravuu Roast – Chetinad style pot-roasted duck with chillies and coconut mil). I ordered from the working lunch menu and they've done it again. It seems to be a growing trend among restaurants on the outskirts of Manchester to pile the food up on lunch menus. This one consisted of Batak Ka Samosa or Shikampuri Kebab followed by Methi Murgh or Murg Makhanwala accompanied by Naan (crisp but moist), Jeera Aloo very nice, Naan (crisp but moist). Rice (nice and fluffy). The Kebab consisting of two sausage shapes were tasty with a nice spicy kick, with a meagre salad garnish and a bland green chutney. The Makhanwala was tasty again with a nice spice kick but only four pieces of chicken. The service was pleasant and not over fussy however a couple of the ceramic serving bowls were chipped. Overall the food was good quality and well worth another visit for the a la carte menu. Negative points were the parking, chips in the bowls and a discretionary 10% service charge added to the bill. This is not mentioned on the lunch menu but hidden towards the back of the al a carte menu – a bit naughty. Food & drink & service £11.99'* DB. Service Ch: 12.5% discretionary. Hours: 12-11, 10 Sun. Branches: Mela and Chowki, London W1 and WC1. www.dilli.co.uk

SHERE KHAN   NEW ENTRANT

Hollins House, Cottesmore Grds, Hale Barns, Altrincham, WA15 8TS   0161 927 9400

See Shere Khan, Rusholme, Manchester for history, branches, etc.   sherekhan.com

Ashton-under-Lyne

INDIAN OCEAN   A-LIST

83 Stamford St East, Ashton   0161 343 3343

This is one of those rather rare establishments. It's a perfect curryhouse. It is the extraordinary level of care which we're talking about. Chef/Owner Nahim Aslam founded it in 1992. Seats 120. Large lounge with regular entertainment which attracts diners to stay and enjoy after dinner drinks. Hahim has introduced a new menu specialising on the dishes of the Punjab and Kashmir with some great British favourites. Gone are dishes like Vindaloo and much more subtle flavours have come in such as Chicken Gorkali an Indo-Chinese dish

with Chicken red and green peppers and special chilli sauce. He has come up with Lamb Hari Boti, delicately spiced and with a light mint to reflect the British love of mint with roast lamb. Chicken, fish and lamb Tandoor-barbecued platters are very popular. Another feature of the new menu is the daily special – a specially prepared dish, changed each day which Nahim describes as 'food my mother would prepare at home'. In other words it is prepared in a way that many Asian British families will eat when they are at home. The cooking techniques are very time consuming so are not often seen in the modern Indian restaurant. Having tried the idea as both a restaurant dish and T/a item, it proved so popular that it has become a permanent feature of the new menu. And to finish try the traditional Indian desserts such as Sheer korma and Pistachio Kheer. '*We are regulars, where the welcome is always warm and friendly. First impressions are good as it is an attractive, clean and well presented restaurant. Good menu, appetising food, served pleasantly. Recommended.*' PR. '*Have had a few parties here and have really been looked after.*' JW. An outdoor area called the Terrace has just opened. T/a ordering available online. Hours: 5-1; 12 Sat; 1-1 Sun.

Atherton, M46

FAR PAVILION   NEW ENTRANT

138, Bolton Rd, Atherton   01942 875077

'*My wife and I have been to a few restaurants in the Guide which brings me to tell you about one near the railway station in our small town situated between Bolton and Leigh. We both enjoy a good evening out together at our local Indian Restaurant. We have frequented this restaurant since 2001 which before none of us had been in an Indian Restaurant nor take away. The Restaurant is called The Far Pavilion, its on Bolton Road Atherton. Both my wife and I are on first name terms with the staff who are absolutely superb people. We do frequent other restaurants but have yet to dine in one better, the service appears to be better along with the menu, the personal touch like after dinner mints, Brandy and Bailey's, also there's the oranges and hot towels. Most of the previous mentioned are not standard with restaurants round here who appear to want your table for the next customers as soon as you have eaten. The food is so good and plentiful and the cobra on draught is a refreshing drink with any curry. The restaurant has won the best Restaurant in the area for 4 years running.*' DS.

Bolton

INDIA GATE   NEW ENTRANT

876 Bradshaw Rd, Turton, Bolton

'*Converted pub, seating c150 very comfortably, with excellent views (when it is not raining) of the West Pennines, about 4 m north east of Bolton. Service was excellent, and the selection extensive, with huge selection of starters and soups. the mixed kebab was excellent. We had 2 vegetarians with us and the choices were good, with Dom aloo notable (never come across it before). Also the king prawn zaffaroni (not a very indian name!) and lamb chef's specials were excellent. not normally a chicken fan. I tried the south indian chicken and this too was very good. Portions generous-and an (unsolicited) digestif on the house at the end finished off nicely. Bill for 4 with quite a few drinks-£95 - one of the best I have been to in the north. Not quite in Aagrah class, but not far below.*' SS.

YOU SAY OK
You might get a discount if you show them this Guide.

ASHTON: BLU SPICE NEW ENTRANT 160, Albans Ave, OL6 8TU ~ 0161 330 4900 '*Spread across three retail units in a housing estate.*' RW. Del: 3m, £10 min. Sun Buf: £9/£5. Hours: 5-11.30; to 1.30 Fri / 1-11 Sat & Sun.

ASHTON: TANDOORI TAKEAWAY NEW ENTRANT 72, Penny Meadows, Ashton under Lyne, OL6 6EL ~ 0161 217 0794. '*Open kitchen T/a just outside the town centre. Good overall.*' RW. Del: 3m, £10, min.T/a: 15% disc, £10 min. Hours: 12-10.

BOLTON: ANAZ TAKEAWAY 138 St Helens Rd. ~ 01204 660114

BOLTON: GREEN BENGAL 158 Darwen Rd, Bromley Cross, Bolton ~ 01204 304777. Est 2006 by Zia Choudhury.

BOLTON: HILAL TANDOORI 296 Chorley Old Road, Bolton 01204 842315

Bury

MALA   NEW ENTRANT

18 Holcombe Village, Ramsbottom, Bury, BL8 4LZ
                                                 01706 825702

'*We got a substantial takeaway and were not disappointed. Staff welcoming and friendly. It had a comfortable 'feel' to it and was reasonably smart in décor. We did not have to wait that long for our food and it was reasonably priced. I had a Vegetable Madras that was well spiced but was a little oily, as a Madras can tend to be in my experience. The vegetable content was fine, maybe a little too much potato for my liking. But overall it was fine. Jackie had a King Prawn Chilli Massala, which she said was good and certainly contained good sized, quality prawns. The naan bread was advertised as Bombay Bread, stuffed with cheese and chilli, which was a new one on me! It sounded great but was unfortunately tough and not at all light or fluffy. I have to say that the cheese and chilli in the naan were also virtually invisible, certainly to my taste buds! As a side dish we had a Matar Paneer, which was the strangest I've ever had! It was not entirely unpleasant but it*

was very sweet and 'gravy-like' in colour. The paneer was not melted in at all but stayed in solid triangles. Just odd really . Overall it was a perfectly good meal, just not anything to write home about. So I thought I would write to you instead.' AG.

Dukinfield

CHUTNEY MASSALA TAKEAWAY

1 The Square, Fir Tree Lane, Dukinfield SK16
0161 3030101

'Excellent T/a with multi-award winning chefs (real ones, not the 'pay and display' variety). Open kitchen, comfy chairs, comprehensive menu, good selection of fish dishes. Shami Kebab £2.50, outstanding, succulent, tasty patties, well spiced, herb laced mince, nice bite, served with simple salad, garlic yoghurt sauce. Lamb Tikka Achari £5, really good, lots of tender , moist lamb tikka, perfectly spiced, completely free of gristle, fairly dry sauce, piquant character, very nice on taste buds. Chapatis £1.20, acceptable – a bit dry. A freshen-up towel and mint provided in your carrier bag.' RW. Del: 3 m, £7.95 min. Menu Snapshot: Balti Peshwari Chicken Tikka £4.70, buttery sauce, almonds, raisins; King Prawn Bhangan £6.20, aubergines, tomatoes, green chillies, bay leaves, medium hot; Aloo Paratha £2. Hours: 4.30-11.20; 12 Fri & Sat.

Hyde

ALPANA   NEW ENTRANT

32, Market St, SK14 1AH   0161 368 3374

Fully Licensed. *'Latest incarnation had benefited from complete internal refurbishment that really cheered it up. Unusually, the decorators were aware of masking tape and the expression, 'cutting in,' so the paint work has none of the common curry house traits of being done by primary school children. Great young staff. Shiny vinyl seats and disposable tablecloths detract from overall impression. Reshmi Kebab £2.45, stunning, very succulent, well spiced patty, presented in a diaphanous bird's nest of egg rather than ubiquitous omelette, a masterpiece, wrapping gave wonderful mouth feel, topping of onion, delicious yoghurt sauce. Kabuli Lamb £6.20, exquisite curry, al dente Chana, top notch lamb, accompanied by cool lettuce salad, mint dressing, sculpted tomato. Flawless. Perfect light, fluffy Garlic Naan £1.70, stunning Tarka Dal £1.95. Fresh melon served afterwards. Very highly recommended.'* RW. All starters served with salad, mint sauce. All Special Tandoori Dishes served with salad, mint sauce, a choice of Naan or Pullao Rice and vegetable sauce. Hours: 5-11; 12.30 Fri & Sat / 4-11 Sun.

CLOVE

122 Market St, Hyde, SK14   0161 367 8209

'Only two shop fronts wide, appears amazingly spacious inside,

with light painted walls, chromium fittings, lots of light wood and a laminated floor. Very comfortable waiting area. Friendly staff, bare tables and paper serviettes. Lamb Chops Tikka £3.60, impeccable quality, the depth of penetration indicating a suitable length of marinade, spicing was excellent, pleasantly hot, matching the tender, juicy flesh perfectly. They cried out to be picked up and gnawed and I was happy to oblige, very satisfying, served with crisp salad and delicious tangy yoghurt sauce. Machli Rocha with Peshwari Pullao Rice £12.50, great presentation, white square plate, large fish steak and potatoes, very subtle spicing, earthy taste of fish, no bones, sauce superb, rice packed with flakes of various nuts and fruit. Tarka Dhal , brilliant, great texture. Highly recommended.' RW. T/a: 20% disc. Hours: 5.30-11; 11.20 Fri & Sat; 2.30-10.30 Sun.

GARLIC

43 Clarendon Place, Hyde   0161 368 4040

'Very smart, inviting 44-seat room. A large window through to the kitchen reveals a spotless and vibrant working area. Friendly and efficient staff, real tablecloths with standard menu. Very well presented food, even the Chutney Daba was served with a flourish to accompany two hot Popadums. Prawn Puri £2.20, smashing, managing the difficult task of being both flaky and soft. The prawn curry on top was a little lack lustre and didn't live up to the base. Lamb Tikka Biriani £6.20, utterly delicious, best I've had for many a year, perfect tasty rice with plenty of flawless meat. Tarka Dhal £2., great, positively pungent with garlic. A great all round experience.' RW. Del: £8 min. Menu Snapshot: Kebab Snack £3.50, sheek kebab on naan with salad and mint sauce, great! Hours: 5-11. CHEAP POPADOM!

YOU SAY OK MANCH 3 OF 9
You might get a discount if you show them this Guide.

DUKINFIELD: HERB & SPICE 99 Foundry Street, Dukinfield ~ 0161 343 5961. www.herbandspice

HYDE: CINNAMON TAKEAWAY NEW ENTRANT 18a Market Street, , SK14 1AY ~ 0161 368 4449 *'On site of burnt-down Megna. Large open plan kitchen, spotless, keen staff. Enjoyable meal.'* RW. Del: 3m, £10 min. Hours: 5-11, from 4 Sat, Sun & Bank Hols.

HYDE: FAIZAH NEW ENTRANT 32, Market St, SK14 1AH 0161 368 3374 *'A change of owners and name (from Alpana) 42-seater. Efficient, friendly staff. Recommended.'* RW. Hours: 5-11, from 3 Sun; to 12 Fri & Sat.

HYDE: SAFFRON TAKEAWAY 30 Manchester Road, Hyde ~ 0161 367 8600. *'Open kitchen with smart, enthusiastic staff. Highly recommended.'* RW. Hours: 5-11.30; from 4 Fri, Sat & Sun; to 12 Fri & Sat.

LEIGH: INDIAN GOURMET 239 Church La, Lowton, Leigh ~ 01942 727262. Smart modern restaurant, in shopping precinct. Hours: 5-11.

Manchester City

Manchester postcodes,

M1 to M45   Population: 433,000

For the purpose of this Guide, we have included M postcodes (M1-M45) in all our Manchester City entries. They are mostly inside the M60 ringroad. There is no geographical logic to our putting postcodes into numerical order. They are frankly a jumble. But it is the system which exists, and to help narrow things down, we have divided the city into Central, East, South, West and North, using major roads as our arbitrary boundaries. The city area is shown in white (below), while the remainder of GM is shown in lilac.

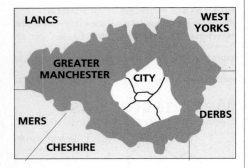

Manchester Central
M1 to M4

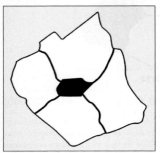

See map above for key to this map

(Restaurants listed in alphabetical order)

ASHOKA

105 Portland Street, M1   0161 228 7550

'The service can be a little slow, but the standard of food here is well worth the wait. Rashmi Kebab – god what taste, beautiful! £19. for one, but worth every penny.' mb. 'Lunch

time and there's only one other sad git needing a fix. Reasonably well decorated, but could do with a touch up. Asked by waiter if I was having lunch, I said yes, he walked off, came back with two Popadums and Chutneys. Raita - too salty and Onion Salad - devoid of anything but onion. Not impressed. Apparently, lunch £4.95 has no choices. Mystery Course Two - plate of salad arrived with good portion of Chicken Shashlik along with half a Nan. - excellent flavour, nicely spiced, very definite smoky flavour, tired salad, good Nan. Mystery Course Three - Chicken Jalfrezi - generous helping, good nicely spiced sauce, Vegetable Curry - good selection of vegetables but bland, Pullao Rice - generous portion, good flavour, light and fluffy.' DB.* Menu extracts: Chilli Chicken , green chillies, ginger, fresh coriander, capsicum and red chilli sauce. Rashmi Kebab, minced chicken, onion, green chillies, fresh mint, coriander, cooked over charcoal. Quail Makhani, butter, tomatoes, cream sauce. Hours: 12-2.30, not Sun / 6-11.30.

YOU SAY OK MANCHESTER CENTRAL
You might get a discount if you show them this Guide.

MI: MYSTIQUE 16 Princess Street, Manchester, M1 4NB

MI: TASTE MASTERS 119 Oldham St, M1. ~ 0161 831 9600. *'Great value for money.'* RW. Del: 3m, £10 min. Hours: 12-12; 4am Fri & Sat. www.tastemaster.co.uk

M2: LIGHTS OF INDIA 39 South King Street, Manchester, M2 6DE

M4: THIS & THAT CAFÉ RE ENTRANT 3 Soap Street, Manchester, M4 1EW. Est 1980. Taken over by Ismail Musa Mallu in 1992. 55 seats : 11-5 Mon-Fri / - 4 Sun. Avg. Cost pp: £5

RAJDOOT TANDOORI   RE-ENTRY

Carlton Hs, 18 Albert Sq, Manchester, M2 5HD
0161 834 2176

Re entered because it keeps on going. This was part of a small chain which brought 'upmarket-Indian' and the Tandoor to Manchester in the 1960s. Its menu and other details are in the Bristol entry. Avg. Cost Per Head Lunch: £19., Dinner: £17. Hours: 12-2.15 (not Sun) / 6.30 - 11.30. Branches: Birmingham, Bristol, Dublin and Fuengirola, Costa del Sol, Spain . www.rajdoot.co.uk

AKBARS   NEW ENTRANT

83, Liverpool Rd, Deansgate, M3. 0161 834 8444

Very sleek, branch of the Yorkshire chain. Modern decor, but in a very grand, 'Grecian temple' way, with fabulous bar area, lit with purple lighting, then with red lighting, the effect is amazing. The main restaurant, is minimally decorated with creamy walls, spot lighting, square tables are laid very simply with no tablecloths, clean cut black leather chairs, wooden floor (a little noisy when busy). A venue to be seen at! Branches: Bradford, Leeds, Rotherham, Sheffield and York. www.akbars.co.uk

SHIMLA PINKS

Dolefield, Crown Sq, M3 3HA　　0161 831 7099

Seats 170 diners. Taken over in 2002 by Jazz Pannum and his mother, Mrs GK Pannum. It is sophisticated, modern restaurant, light, bright, green plants, minimalist, autumn coloured sofas, spotlighting, stainless-steel bar with twinkling pin-spot lights. Chef Sudesh Singh produces food with a Punjabi flavour. Popadums are served with mint and yoghurt sauce, mango chutney and spiced onions, wow! Menu Snapshot: Spiced Potatoes and Garlic Mushrooms, £3.95, soft and fluffy spiced potato balls with sautéed mushrooms in garlic butter; Prawn and Mango Puri £3.95, light and crispy pancake style fried bread, embodied with, fresh Norwegian Prawns laced with a tangy mango mélange; Harrey Masaley Ka Gosht £8.95, cubes of tender lamb cooked in a medium spiced masala of spinach, coriander, mint, green chillies and bay leaves with green cardamom, pepper and cloves; Tikhey Jinghey £12.95, jumbo king prawns marinated in a tomato, onion and capsicum masala, cooked in a heady sauce with pickling spices in mustard oil; Dried Fruit and Nut Naan £2.95, soft bread stuffed with cherries, sultanas, raisins and coconut. T/a: 20% disc. Serv: 10%. Hours: 5.30-11, 11.30 Sat.shimlapinksmanchester.com

Manchester North

Consists of M7, M8, M9 M24 (Middleton), M25 & 45 (Whitefield) M25 (Prestwich), and M26 (Radcliffe)

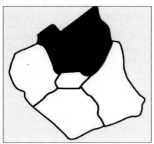

See map on page 221 for key to this map

KEBABISH　　　　　　　　　NEW ENTRANT

170 Cheetham Hill Rd, M8 8LQ　　0161 834 4544

'On the outskirts of the City Centre. Spacious, well lit modern restaurant with open kitchen. Christmas lunch party in so I wasn't on my own, for once. No alcohol at all. There isn't actually a starter menu so I went straight for the mains and ordered chilli chicken masala with plain rice. Nice green salad arrived as soon as I ordered with a raita and a chilli(ish) relish. Mains arrived quite quickly with a massive portion of lovely fluffy rice, Chilli chicken didn't look like the biggest portion but how wrong I was. Plenty tender, moist chicken in a rich spicy sauce with plenty of green chillies. Service very good up to getting the bill, it took 15 minutes and I had to ask the waiter 4 times. A very good curry nicely presented, and I love curried salad so more than happy to call in here again. Food & coke £8.50.' DB.

YOU SAY OK MANCHESTER NORTH
You might get a discount if you show them this Guide.

PRESTWICH M25: GARDEN OF INDIA 411 Bury Old Rd, Prestwich M25~ 0161 773 7784

RADCLIFFE M26: RADCLIFFE CHARCOAL TANDOORI 123 Blackburn Street, M26 ~ 0161 723 4870

WHITEFIELD M45: LA IMRANS Top of Elms Centre. ~ 0161 796 0557

Manchester East
Consists of M11 to M13, M18, M34, M35, M40, M43

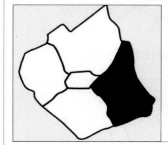

See map on page 221 for key to this map

BLUE CROWN

24 Ashton Road, Denton　　　　0161 320 0005

'Bright and clean T/a in the busy town centre. Comprehensive menu with plenty of house specials and also burgers, pizza, kebabs and fried chicken for those with a delicate constitution. Lovely starter, Meat samosas £1.50, obviously home-made, two tasty triangles of well spiced mince in filo case, served with chopped salad and a cool yoghurt sauce. Lamb Tikka South Indian garlic £5.50, nice, hot, spicy sauce surrounding well marinated chunks of tender white lamb (er, no, they sent chicken!), still enjoyable and the Pullao Rice was superb, really pungent and delicious.' RW. Menu Snapshot: Vegetable Mixed Starter £2.50, onion bhajia, vegetable samosa, mushroom dippers; Tandoori Lamb Chops £6.50 for

six; Chicken and Cheese Kufta £5.50, boneless spring
chicken marinated in yoghurt, herbs and spices cooked
with meatballs and cheese. T/a: 10% disc, £15 min. No
credit cards. Hours: 4.30-12; 1 Fri & Sat. CHEAP
POPADOM!

PEARL

119 Manchester Road, Audenshaw, M34 5PY
0161 301 5680

Naheem Akhtar is MD and Ashok Kumar (cv New
Delhi, Dubai and Mumbai) chefs. He says: *'For me, being
a chef is so much more than just cooking, it's a way of life'.*
Situated by the Ashton canal, this 200-seater offers free
car parking, disabled access, outside catering and an
impressive outdoor area. *'Friday lunch and just a few
customers. This restaurant is massive – so big I was knackered
by the time I got from the car to my table! Light, airy well
decorated this restaurant is obviously a pub with an Indian
restaurant as its eating area. Service is friendly and efficient.
Express lunch menu, guaranteed food served within 20
minutes, at £5.95 is very good value. Choice of 11 different
starters from which I chose the Chicken Pakora, 3 golf ball
sized pieces of chicken tikka in batter with a salad garnish and
two accompanying sauces. Batter could have been more crisp,
but the chicken tikka was nice and moist. For the mains there
is a choice of 12 standard curries, with Nepali being the
notion, with a choice of chicken, chicken tikka, lamb , lamb
tikka, prawns or vegetable (all the same price). For the main
I ordered Chicken Tikka Nepali billed as a hot spicy dish (4
chilli symbols on the menu) with pillau rice. Meal arrived
quite quickly, steaming rice and what seemed a rather small
portion of curry. The rice was nice and fluffy with a nutty
flavour and a big portion. Appearances were deceiving as
there was ample curry although not a great deal of tikka but
an abundance of little, dried, fiery, incendiary hot Naga
chillies. These gave the curry a distinctive flavour and one hell
of a kick. Very good meal, I will definitely be back to try the a
la carte menu.'* DB.   www.thepearlrestaurant.co.uk

VERMILLION & CINNABAR THAI
NEW ENTRANT

Sportcity, Lord North St, Platting, M40 8AD
0161 202 0055

Less than two miles from Manchester Centre is
Sportcity, the largest concentration of sporting venues in
Europe. It houses the 48,000-seat Man City football
stadium, the National Squash Centre, the 6,500-seat
Manchester Arena, the English Institute of Sport,
Manchester Velodrome, a Tennis Centre as well as a
state-of-the-art gymnasium. It is also home to Thomas
Heatherwick's iconic sculpture 'B of the Bang', the
UK's tallest sculpture, standing at 180ft, three times
taller than the Angel of the North. Equally spectacular
is Vermilion and Cinnabar a Thai restaurant and bar
which opened 2007 costing a staggering £4.5 million

and seating an impressive 200 diners and the bar 300. It
is owned by Iqbal Ahmed OBE, Chairman of Seamark
Plc (one of the Uk's largest prawn importers and his son
Manzur Ahmed. The interior is on three floors. Most
interesting are six 'cocoons' set around the space in
Cinnabar. These semi-private structures enable
customers to recline in the utmost comfort and
seclusion in the middle of a buzzing bar, complete with
dance floor and DJ. Thai and Thai-fusion food. Prices
fair. Hours: 6-2.   www.vermilioncinnabar.co

YOU SAY OK MANCHESTER EAST
You might get a discount if you show them this Guide.

DENTON M34: BARAKAT BALTI 699 Windmill Lane,
Danebank, Denton, M34 ~ 0161 320 3232

Manchester South
Consists of M14 (Wilmslow Road, Rusholme) M15,
M16, M19 to M23, M32, M33 and M90

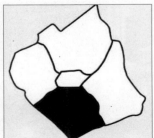

*See map on page
221 for key to
this map*

Manchester M14
Wilmslow Road, Rusholme ~ The CUrry Mile

Wilmslow Road, extends for nearly 6 m south from Manchester Centre. It passes through Rusholme, Manchester's main Asian area. To get there from the city centre it's best to walk – parking is normally a joke. Face south on the Oxford Road, with the BBC on your left, and go for about 800 metres, passing the Uni and then the Royal Infirmary. At the Moss Lane East junction, Rusholme and Little India starts. In the last few years the expansion has been amazing and is continuing unabated. From a drab and run-down look it now sports neon lighting to rival Las Vegas. Now, in the 600 metres from Moss Lane to Claremont Road, there are no less than 42 curry eateries – Indian snack and sweet shops, cafés and restaurants. As if that's not enough, there are numerous pubs, offices, chippies, Chinese, pizza joints, kebab houses and burger bars, Asian grocers and halal butchers. Some of the cheap and cheerful all-day cafés allow BYO (but always ask – it can offend some Muslims). Some are quite expensive licensed restaurants, the largest of which seats 400! A conservative estimate on curry consumption is 65,000 curries a week here. We believe this to be the curry record for a district. Any challenges? Go a further 900 metres along Wilmslow Road, and there are some 35 more curry eateries, making this a genuine Golden Mile. Almost any are worth trying. Most open all day and many until 1am. All are good value for money. Don't try reserving, you'll be lucky if they answer the phone. Just turn up, and if one is busy go to another. Our regular and prolific correspondent – DB – tells us that, *'my overall experiences of Rusholme have been a little disappointing both culinary and service wise, considering there are so many curry houses vying for your custom.'* Here are some of your favourites: See also www.rusholmecurry.co.uk

SHERE KHAN

52 Wilmslow Road, M14 5TQ   0161 256 2624

It was here in 1987 that Rafique Awan and his wife Nighat opened a restaurant with the concept to modernise the Indian restaurant trade. The concept was far from original, and at first sight Rusholme was a curious location to choose. But maybe that is why it worked. Up the road a bit, Manchester city had long had upmarket Rajdoot and others, but Rusholm was greasy-spoon land, Pakistani-style. Awan swept away dark, dated decor, replacing it with bright airy surroundings, serving good quality food at affordable prices for everyone. Diners loved it. And cutting a very long story which took place in a very brief decade or so, Shere Khan today is a £35m-plus empire with 350 staff producing curry sauces, poppadoms and other Indian foods for the retail market as well as operating Shere Khan branches in the Trafford Centre, Chester, Liverpool, Bluewater shopping complex Essex and Meadowhall, Sheffield. With these branches Shere Kahn joins the fast-growing casual dining sector which lies between fast-food and fine-dining formats. MD Steve Garrity explains 'Customers order at a counter and then relax in their seats as food is delivered to their table. We have two formats: Express and Casual Dining. Curry is on the menu as well as Halal pasties, grilled chicken, chilli and chips, paninis and muffins. There is a licensed bar and it serves lattés and cappuchinos too. The company is seeking franchisees for these two brands. The units require a space of between 650 - 2,500 sq ft. Hot red, orange and purple are the distinctive Shere Khan brand colours which to they say stand out within 'even the most crowded and competitive retail environment, i.e. any location which has a heavy footfall such as a retail food court in a shopping centre, busy railway stations, airports and high streets. Shere Khan is a high street brand in the making'. Garrity plans to launch three UK venues a year for the foreseeable future with Manchester, Warrington and Chester first in line. Chains in Dubai and Japan are also being planned. If all this expansion is to say the least rapid, it doesn't come without a price. With wealth comes the craving for power. Somewhere along the line Mrs Awan became a close friend of Cherie Blair. Mrs A was appointed to head a government group supporting ethnic businesses and given an OBE by buddy Jack Straw, while Mr A became a Government race adviser. In 2006, the very branch which launched the fortune was fined £40,000 after a live cockroach was discovered nestling in his popadums by a diner, and the whole venue was found to be infested and filthy. Later in 2006 the company was fined £30,000 for breaches of food safety laws at its

The Curry Mile by night
Photo: Pete Morris via Wikipedia

Trafford Centre branch. In 2007 MrAwan was arrested by Manchester police investigating his alleged employment of illegal immigrants. During the operation 70 staff were arrested involving many of the group's venues. The defence lawyer said: *'The restaurant is part of a big group and the senior management's eye was taken off the ball with the day-to-day handling of the business.'* We have always received mixed reports about the various Shere Khan branches. They should perhaps all be delisted, but it isn't all bad. If its owners take advice and focus back on their core business and if they can sell to those who do care, it may survive. If not??? Branches: Altrincham, Birmingham, B7 (2); Blackburn; Blue water shopping centre, Kent; Ellesmere-Port, Cheshire; Liverpool; Trafford Centre, Manch, M17. sherekhan.com

Elsewhere on Wilmslow Road

AL BILAL 87-91 Wilmslow Rd, M14 5SU ~ 0161 2570006. *'Quality variable, qty more than sufficient. Pops didn't arrive. Handi Chicken was on-the-bone – excellent. The Aloo Mattar far too greasy with undercooked peas and bland in taste. Bill £40 for three. 8/10.'* G&MP.

AL NAWAZ 74 Wilmslow Rd, M14 5AL ~ 0161 249 0044. Punjabi cooking. BYO.

DARBAR 67 Wilmslow Rd, M14 5TB ~ 0161 224 4392. BYO.

HANAAN 54, Wilmslow Rd, M14 5AL ~ 0161 256 4786. BYO.

LAL HAWELI 68 Wilmslow Rd, M14 5AL ~ 0161 248 9700. BYO.

PUNJAB TANDOORI 177 Wilmslow Rd, M14 5AP ~ 0161 225 2960. BYO.

ROYAL NAZ 18 Wilmslow Road, Ifco Centre, M14 5TQ ~ 0161 256 1060. BYO.

SANAM SWEET HOUSE 145 Wilmslow Rd, M14 5AW 0161 224 8824. Est c1968 by Haji Abdul Ghafoor, it was the second on the road. Now managed by AQ Akhtar and despite being huge (seating 160, plus a further 200-seat function room), it is so popular locally that it's often full, with queues waiting to be seated. 'The standard fare was very, very good . . . the Aloo Tikka was very tasty. A good first time visit.' TOC. 'Quite nicely decorated, staff not overly friendly. Excellent Popadums and chutney. Chicken Biriani, had flavour, fried onion garnish, tender chicken.' db. No alcolhol allowed. Hours: 12-12. Branches: Abdul's, 121 & 318 Wilmslow Rd, and 298 Oxford Rd.

SANGAM 9 Wilmslow Rd, M14 5TB ~ 0161 257 3922 Large spacious restaurant with warm welcome. www.sangams.co.uk Branches: Sangam 3, 202 Wilmslow Rd, Heald Green, Cheadle, Cheshire, 0161 436 8809. Sangam 2, 762 Wilmslow Rd, Didsbury, M20 ~ 0161 446 1155.

SHEZAN 119 Wilmslow Rd, M14 ~ 0161 224 3116

SPICY HUT 35 Wilmslow Rd ~ 0161 248 6200. MS Mughal's 60-seater. BYO. Del: 2m £10min. Hours: 5-2; 3-1 Sun.

TABAK 199 Wilmslow Rd, M14 5QU ~ 0161 257 3890. Mohammad Nawab's Tabak seats a MASSIVE 350 diners, on two floors. Hours: 12pm-1am.

TANDOORI KITCHEN 133 Wilmslow Rd, M14 5AW The Hussein family were the first to open on Wilmslow Rd (in 1967).

ZAIKA 2 Wilmslow Rd ~ 0161 224 3335. *'Asked for a bottle of Kingfisher, told they were out of stock, would Guinness do instead!'* DB. Good marketing Dave. Bet you said Yes!

Manchester M19
Burnage, Kingsway, Levenshulme

NAWAAB

1008 Stockport Road, M19   0161 224 6969

Mahboob Hussain bills this as the biggest curry house – 350-seats on the ground floor plus 600 on the first floor.

THIRD EYE

198 Mauldeth Rd, Burnage   0161 442 2900

Nepalese restaurant. Opened 1998. Seats 72. Cosy, traditional decor. Specials: Tangri, chicken drumstick stuffed with saffron minced lamb and nuts. Bhutan Chara, chicken with mushrooms and tomatoes. Kidney Masala, lamb kidney in spicy sauce. Disc possible if you show them this Guide. T/a: 10% disc. Del: £15 min, 3-m. Hours: 5-12.

TONDORI ROYALE

682 Burnage La, Burnage, M19   0161 432 0930

'Bob Hoque's 110-seater is very well-established (1980) and very well spoken of by the locals. 'It was packed! It is not difficult to work out why when you taste the cuisine. Atmosphere is electric and food well worth the 40-mile trip.' MB. It has a full house of familiar dishes. Fish dishes include Boal and Ayre. NW's favourite is Zhal Golda Chingri, king prawn cooked with chilli and ginger. *'Very good. Vegetable Pasanda had excellent flavour.'* RWI. *'A pleasant surprise tucked away in the Manchester suburbs. Try the Hopi for your starter – an interesting variation on the Chinese spring roll. Sizzling baltis with quality ingredients and accompanied by fluffy naans. Worth a go!'* PW. Discount possible if you show them this Guide. Del: £15 min, 3m. Hours: 6-1; 5-2.30 Sat & Sun.

Manchester M20

GREAT KATHMANDU

140 Burton Rd, West Didsbury 0161 434 6413

'Again a lunch time and again the only diner in a 40-seater, although 6 people did arrive and were asked if they had booked! Lunch menu choice shows little evidence of Nepalese dishes. It is very limited with the starters being, chicken tikka, tandoori chicken and Sheik kebab, with even less choice of a main, lamb rogan josh or chicken masala. However this dining experience starts with 2 pops & chuts. Sheik kebab, two large, nice and spicy, with a fresh salad and one of the biggest naans I've seen in a long time (not my favourite bread) delicious. After ploughing through this I started to wonder how I would manage a main course my reservations were heightened when the main arrived. I ordered the lamb rogan psh, and requested it a little hotter than usual. It arrived – a decent portion, with tender lamb and a lovely spicy sauce,

along with a vegetable masala and a portion of pillau rice big enough to feed 3 lovely and nutty. After a struggle I managed to finish most of the meal: I was totally stuffed. Service was excellent and friendly although he assumed there was something wrong with my meal as I hadn't finished it! The Price of this feast? £5.90. There will be next time.' DB. Branches: Third Eye, Mauldeth Road

NAMASTE NEPAL   NEW ENTRANT

164 Burton Rd, West Didsbury, M20 1LH
0161 445 9060

'Large, spacious, tidy restaurant. The only diner on a bleak, wet, windy Friday lunch time . It actually sells Nepalese dishes along with with some formula curries and a it took me ages to decide on my main course. Ordered 2 popadums with chutneys, while I decided. Three crisp black pepper popadums arrived with mango chutney, lime pickle onion chutney and raita, excellent. Decided on the chicken Namaste Bhotowan, a medium hot, dry, spicy dish, served sizzling. Having never eaten Nepalese I wasn't sure what I was going to get but isn't that half the fun? A good portion of both rice and curry arrived quite quickly, but not sizzling, and placed on the hot plate. Waiter offered to serve me but decided to serve myself. Curry was very dry, tasty with a lot of ginger coming through but spicy? Not really, but very enjoyable but a little too dry for my liking. This is a new experience for me and I will undoubtedly return as there is a lot on the menu that is very tempting. Menu prices reasonable for the mains but expensive for the starters, cheapest £2.50 for a half portion of Tandoori chicken (1 piece) full portion (2 pieces) £4.90 up to £9.60 for the mixed starter (more expensive than all the mains not seafood). Although pops and chuts only £1. The meal & drink £ 11.80.' DB.   www.namaste-nepal.co.uk*

Manchester M21
Chorlton-cum-Hardy

AZAD MANZIL   NEW ENTRANT

495, Barlow Moor Rd, M21 8AG   0161 881 1021

'Smart 60-seater on busy road. Tastefully decorated, split into two distinct areas. Interior is clean and neatly arranged, apparently get incredibly busy at weekends. Staff are knowledgeable, a skill that comes from being in business since 1964. Lamb Tikka Chat £2.95, very good, tasty, if slightly tough, bread topped with an exquisite rich and bitter sauce. Azad Manzil Premier Tasty Fish £8.50, an absolute picture of a plate, generous pieces of marinated and caramelised, cooked on a skewer, Bhag (tiger fish from Bangladesh), moist, succulent, delicate, distinctive taste. came with chilli dipping sauce, salad and chopped chilli. Lovely rice, small portion of thick Vegetable Curry Sauce. An absolute treat and very enjoyable, highly recommended. Tarka Dal was in fine fettle, generously infused with plenty of roasted garlic, onion and spices, very good. No fancy chocolates with the bill, but a handful of good old fashion Mint Imperials! .Real tablecloths

and napkins and piping hot towels for hand cleansing.' RW. Hours: 5.30 to late.   www.azadmanzil.co.uk

Manchester M28
Didsbury

THE ORIGINAL THIRD EYE

661 Wilmslow Rd, Didsbury   0161 446 2300

'Particularly recommended is the Aloo Chilli, Kidney kebab, Tarka Dal and they do a brilliant Garlic Nan with more garlic than Nan! . I love their Vindaloo with little pieces of chopped ginger garnish. Portions can appear small, but you will end your meal feeling nicely full rather than stuffed full.' DB. *'Staff polite and friendly.'* KN. Menu extracts: Fish Tikka, cod marinated in spiced yoghurt and barbecued. Kidney Kebabs. Bari Masala, mince balls seasoned with herbs and cooked in a curry gravy. Bhutan Chara, chicken with mushrooms and tomatoes. Pommi Nan, stuffed with potatoes, cheese, herbs and spices. Hours: 12-2.30 Weds-Sun /6-12.

SANGAM 2

762 Wilmslow Rd, Didsbury   0161 445 1168

An Indian and Thai restaurant. situated above the House Shop. *'Modern restaurant,seating 140. Pale wood, chrome and a projection clock. Very smartly laid out with attentive uniformed staff. Standard menu with a good selection of specials. Lovely Seek Kebab £1.75, hot, spicy, great aroma, tender mince, really succulent, accompanied by a great salad and a cool yoghurt sauce. Impressive Lamb Rezala £7, a well concocted blend of spices making up a tasty sauce, juicy, tender, gristle free lamb, very nice indeed. Garlic Naan £2, good, thin, moist, slightly crisp base, a little sparse on the garlic, which was spread on the top. Tarka Dhal £4 poor, very hot and tangy, slightly undercooked, no trace of garlic. Overall good, recommended.'* RW. Indian Menu Snapshot: Lamb Chop Tikka £4, four pieces' Shahi Masala £7, cream, yoghurt, garlic, tomato, chillies and onions, hot; Roasti Lamb £7, pieces of lamb, on the bone, medium spiced, cooked home-style. Thai Menu Snapshot: Thod Man Pla £4, spicy Thai fish cakes with lime leaf and fresh pickle; Goong Tom Kha £4.50, prawn coconut cream and galangal soup; Gai Pad Krapow £8, fried chicken breast with basil leaf and chilli. Licensed. Branches: Sangam, Rusholme and Cheshire.

YOU SAY OK – MANCHESTER SOUTH
You might get a discount if you show them this Guide.

SALE M33: AASHIANA NEW ENTRANT 123 Cross St, Sale, M33 7JN ~ 0161 976 120 Helal Ahmed recently took over. Car Park, A/c. 5-11.30 Mon-Thur; - 12 Fri-Sat; 4-11.30 Sun. www.aashiana.co.uk

SALE M33: SPICE CHEF 85 Washway, Sale, M33 0161 976 4577

Manchester West

Inc: M5, M6 (Salford) M17, M27 to M31, M41, M44.

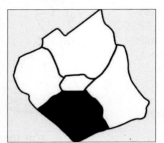

See map on page 221 for key to this map

Manchester M17

SHERE KHAN EXPRESS

Trafford Centre, M17 8AA   0161 747 8990

The pilot Shere Khan Express opened on a prime corner location in the upper rotunda of the Trafford Centre in 2001, and must be one of the trendiest in the area. Seating a considerable 430, it has proved a huge hit with customers looking for an alternative 'meal on the move' and its fame has spread. It's an informal, relaxed atmosphere with Bollywood movies on a giant plasma TV screen. *'Lunchtime Buffet c£9, Pops with mango chutney and onion, Onion Bhajia and Meat Samosas – very good, nicely spiced. Honey Chicken Wings - crispy, not much taste but I love them anyway. CTM – tasty but too sweet, Chilli Chicken Tikka Masala – seemed to be CTM with a few green chillies. Madras – nice chicken, sauce very tomatoey, Jalfrezi – quite bland. Acceptable Vegetable and Pullao Rice, Naan – not too thick, crisp around the edges. Un-named sweets on the buffet, had a fudge type things – OK, and two different types of custard thing that was delicious. Good value, if you don't, mind sacrificing quality for quantity.'* DB. From 10am Mon to Fri; Sat 9am, Sun 11am until 12pm. sherekhan.com

YOU SAY OK MANCHESTER WEST
You might get a discount if you show them this Guide.

M30: PASSAGE TO INDIA 168 Monton Road, Monton, Eccles, M30 ~ 0161 787 7546. M Hassan Choudhury and H Uddin's 90-seater. Hours: 12-11.30. Branch: Gate of India, Swinton.

Elsewhere in Gtr Manchester

Rochdale

LA TANDOOR   TOP 100

7, Bamford Precinct, Rochdale   01706 642037

Mrs S Habeeb's 68-seater is *'a superb restaurant, and be warned – book a table, as it gets very busy. We had Nargis Kebab and Vegetable Chaat for starters – a dream – and we*

followed with a main-course choice of Chicken Tikka Biriani and Chilli Chicken Balti, with a side dish of Malayee Kufta (vegetable balls in a coconut sauce with pineapple and peaches), Pullao Rice and Chuppatis. It was all excellent, followed by ice cream, face towels, a free drink and after-meal sweets. 5. We'd eat there every day if we were locals!' RK. *'Now enlarged. Food still fab. Had forgotten this place until we read the Guide.'* RN. You might get a disc if you show them this Guide, but probably not when they are very busy. T/a 20% off. Hours: 12.30-12.30; 1am Sat. Family banquets: Sun £9, 12.30-6.

Stalybridge

LAL THOOFAN   NEW ENTRANT

38 Grosvenor St, SK15 2JB   0161 338 6007

'Smart upstairs restaurant, with ground floor waiting area for T/a etc and bar. Very friendly and enthusiastic staff, comfortable accommodation for forty-eight diners. Bollywood DVD's projected onto wall, seem to be solely for the benefit of the staff! Real tablecloths, napkins, hot towel delivered with tongs. Paneer Tikka £3.20, outstanding, three large marinated pieces, with onion and green pepper, all gently roasted in tandoor, exquisite. Chat Massalam £6.95, excellent, perfectly cooked Chana with small, moist and spicy chunks of chicken tikka, really rich and thick heave sauce. Garlic Nan £1.70, really light and fluffy, slight crisp base and generously decked with chunks of garlic, brushed with ghee. Lassi, slightly salty, accompanied perfectly.' RW. Credit cards accepted. Hours: 12- 2.30 / 4.30 -12; to 2.30 Fri & Sat; 12-12 Sun. www.lalthoofan.com

Stockport (Hazel Grove)

BLUE NILE   NEW ENTRANT

403, London Rd, SK7 6AA   0161 487 4490

Formerly Balti Massala. Licensed. *'Very inviting from the outside, striking, modern, blue lighting. Friendly staff. Utterly exquisite Afghani Pasli £3.90, three, well marinated chops, dripped succulent spices, served sizzling, fabulously tasty meat, served with salad and yoghurt sauce. Chicken Balti Multani £7.50, excellent spicy sauce, enrobed moist, tasty pieces top notch Chicken Tikka, chick peas, onions, peppers, sliced chillies. Very good Naan £2, slightly crispy underneath and dripping with garlic. Proper hot towels served to freshen up. Great meal.'* RW. Hours: 5.30-12; 12.30 Fri & Sat /3-12 Sun.

Wigan

SPICE LOUNGE

19 Bretherton Rd, off Wallgate   01942 494909

All the regular curries are also on offer, but this restaurant has one of the best spins we've heard. It made

the national press when local woman, Louise Thomas, got curry withdrawal symptoms during the late stages of pregnancy. For her fix she chose the The Taste Of Bengal, asking the staff which curry would start her labour and they said they had just the recipe. Within minutes of leaving the restaurant that night she went into labour and ave birth to Lucy. *'Since then'*, says owner Giash Uddin, *'pregnant women have flocked to the Standish eatery to test the curry for themselves. It still works wonders and we get around three or four women a month coming in asking for the special dish.'* Is this why the venue has a childrens Menu? examples: Chicken Samosa; Chicken Korma; Rice (or chips!); Mini Naan; Vanilla Ice Cream, £6. *'Modern, friendly and comfortable restaurant. Friendly and effusive staff. Unlicensed, so BYO. Lovely Garlic Chicken Chat £3.75, really garlicky, spicy sauce, best quality marinated chicken, crisp salad, lemon slice, yoghurt sauce. Lamb Thawa £8.99, including a Naan Bread, really rich, juicy, well spiced lamb tikka, al dente chickpeas and onions, tangy, aromatic sauce. Naan had crisp base, no doughiness, lovely smear of ghee. Top notch, highly recommended.'* RW. BYO no corkage charge, and they provide you with free glasses. Del: 3 m, £15 min. Hours: 11.30-3, not Fri/ 5.30-10 daily. Branch: Taste of Bengal, 11, High Street, Standish, Wigan. www.thespicelounge.co.uk

YOU SAY OK

You might get a discount if you show them this Guide.

MOSSLEY: LAL QUILLA 5 Manchester Road, Mossley ~ 01457 839 777. Mr Mohammed Ali's 100-seater est 1998. Hours: 5-10.30; 11.30 Sat; 1 to 10.

OLDHAM: BLUE TIFFIN NEW ENTRANT Laurel Trading Est, Higginsham La, Royton, Oldham, OL2 ~ 0161 628 2005. 180-seater opened in 2006. bluetiffin.co.uk

OLDHAM: BRITISH RAJ 185 Lees Road. ~ 0161 624 8696

OLDHAM: TASTE MASTERS 119 Oldham St, M1 ~ 0161 831 9600. *'Great value for money.'* RW. Del: 3m, £10 min. Hours: 12-12; 4am Fri & Sat. www.tastemaster.co.uk

OLDHAM: MILLON Westwood Business Centre, Featherstall Rd, South Oldham ~ 0161 620 6445

STALYBRIDGE: BOWERFOLD SPICE Mottram Rd.~ 0161 303 9797. *'A great meal in a splendid 120-seater.'* RW. Hours: 5-11; 11.30 Fri & Sat; 3-10.30 Sun.

STOCKPORT: KUSHOOM KOLY 6 Shaw Rd, Heaton Moor, Stockport ~ 0161 432 9841

TODMORDEN: ZAIKA CUISINE 759 Burnley Rd, Carnholm ~ 01706 662801. Zulf Ahmed says his 50-seater is 'traditional and simple'. Del: 3m, £10 min. T/a: 10% disc. Hours: 5.30-11.30; Monday closed. www.zaikacuisine.co.uk

MERSEYSIDE

Area: North West
Population: 1,425,000
Adjacent Counties: Cheshire, Lancs, Greater Man

Liverpool

GULSHAN   TOP 100

544 Aigburth Road, L19   0151 427 2273

In 1986 Mustafa and Salina Rahman found the perfect spot in Grassendale, Liverpool, for their new Indian restaurant. Gulshan is a Persian girl's name meaning *'paradise or a mystic rose garden'.* The couple have recently invested a six-figure sum to create an additional fifty covers on the restaurant's newly-opened first floor and transform the interior. The original bar downstairs has been replaced, a spacious new reception area added and a substantial second drinks area built on the first floor. Says Mustafa: *'My father would be proud. He set up Liverpool's first Indian restaurant in the early 1960s.'* In that case your editor dined there, because it was the city's only Indian. Can't remember its name, but I do remember telling the taxi driver I was not looking for Curry's Electrical shop! Notable starters include puri dishes with a choice of toppings: aubergine, lentils, mushrooms or buttered prawns, etc. Main Courses include the usual cast-list of Tandoori, Masala, Balti, Biriani and vegetarian dishes. Specials include: Murghi Mossaka, chicken barbecued tandoori style then prepared with keema (minced meat), tomatoes, cream and wine, topped with cheese; Kalla Chicken, chicken kebab cooked with banana and yogurt; Almond Maas Korma, boneless white fish cooked with ground almonds, yogurt, cream, coconut and rose herbs. *'As a birthday treat, I was wined and dined by Jacs, she who now eats curry. Quite busy for a early Tuesday evening. Place a bit scruffy, but this was due to refurbishment work. Service was attentive, very good knowledge. Popadums, lovely, warm, crisp. Chutneys, uninspiring, only mango and onions, no lime. Keema Muttu with Puri, meat samosa filling on bread, tasty, very nice puri but large! '...Tilapia fish was covered in spicy sauce, overpowering it. Nantera, chicken tikka, green peppers, tomatoes, wine, fresh herbs, Jacs was happy. Chicken Tikka Rezalla, spicy, good portion of chicken. Garlic Naan, stuffed with slices of garlic and overpowering, as my work colleagues will testify.'* Are you trying to tell us, that you 'reeked' the next day? *'I expected a lot more form a Top 100 restaurant – didn't have the wow factor, though prices very reasonable'* DB. Hours: 5-11. www.gulshan-liverpool.com

MAHARAJA SOUTH INDIAN

34 London Rd, City Centre   0151 709 2006

Treasure this one please Merseyside. It specialises in south Indian Keralan cuisine. Hot is the norm in Kerala but they cool it for 'western tastes'! So if you want to up the chilli strength, tell them and the kitchen will be more than happy to oblige. Have the Rasam (hot and spicy soup, with floating slivers of garlic, curry leaves and a red chilli! – this is editor DBAC's benchmark, which if she doesn't get hiccups, it's not hot enough for her! Masala Dosa, Sambar and Coconut Chutney are south Indian favourites. Some diners have that choice for starters and go on to curries, which if you have room are worth trying. You can stay vegetarian if you like. All their vegetable curries are spot on. Contrary to popular belief, meat, chicken and fish dishes are the norm in south India. Try Lamb Cutlets: patties made of minced lamb and spices with bread crumbs and fried. Served with tomato sauce and salad. Malabar Chicken is cooked with coconut, curry leaves, garlic and mustard. Fish Mollee is a classic dish, so mild and gentle in its coconut base that even the Raj allowed it at table. And for pud Banana Leaf Cake: made of rice with a sweet filling of grated coconut, banana and jaggery wrapped in banana leaf and steam cooked. *'I was the only lunchtime diner. Opted for lunch Special Thali, non-veg. Spinach and Dhal Curry, quite bland, but a lot of garlic. Chicken Curry, very reminiscent of a Thai curry, with after taste of aniseed, beautifully spiced, very tasty. Fish Curry, again beautifully spiced with great flavour. Spicy Potato Curry, slightly undercooked. Basmati Rice, nice and fluffy. Chapatti, excellent. Followed by Rice Pudding, again excellent. Lightness of curries surprised me and portions a bit on the small side'* Dave, it is a lunch! *'but found myself completely stuffed when I'd finished very impressed a great dining experience.'* DB. Hours: 12-3 / 6-12.

MAYUR   NEW ENTRANT

130 Duke St, L'pool, L1 5AG   0151 709 9955

Co-owners Suhail Ahmed and Arif Mashood, who manages, are from a non-restaurant background but passionate about food, opened their 160-seater with 75-seat bar in 2007. Decor includes Italian furniture, Indian artefacts, red velvet, gold-gilded chairs and vibrant wallpaper. Chef Uday Seth worked for New Delhi's. Taj hotels and his brigade in Mauritius and Singapore. This is the promise: *'When diners experience Mayur, they will realise they no longer have to travel to Manchester's curry mile to taste delicious, authentic Indian cuisine, it will be here on their doorstep.'* This is reality from veteran reporter DB: *'Well Pat, I finally achieved my 100th different restaurant after 34 years of eating curry! It's a large, spacious, light, airy and nicely decorated (although the dreaded flock wall paper has appeared around columns). Thursday evening and it was reasonably packed. Shown to our table straight away and offered pops and drinks. Pops were actually papads (not my favourite) served with small dishes of chutneys (mango, ok lime, excellent and yoghurt, not great). 16 starters gave a reasonable choice, from which I chose the Bhatti Murg (posh chicken tikka) which was very nice. Jacs had the Kesari Jhinga, shell-on prawns in a yoghurt marinade, again very nice. Mains were quite limited 7 specials, 4 chicken, 3 seafood, 4 lamb and 5 vegetarian. Jacs went for the Saag Ghost I was going to order the Elaichi ka Bhuna Ghost, but before I could do so the waiter recommended it. He advised that both would be better with plain rice than pillau. I also ordered a Tandoori Roti. Jacs meal arrived in good time, they forgot mine, however it arrived very shortly after complaining (too quickly). Good portions of both mains and rice. Both meals had plenty of lamb, mine was pleasant without being great and was a touch hot for Jacs. The Elaichi again was pleasant with a tiny bit of a kick. Rice was very good and Roti was excellent. Service was for the most part pleasant until we paid the bill, they took the cash away and we had to ask twice for the change and in all waited about 15 minutes. We think that they accepted payment and the change as a tip as the manager had to open the till to sort it out. I expected more of this restaurant, there was a poor choice of mains, I only went for the lamb (not my favourite meat) because of the poor choice of both seafood and chicken dishes, Korma, Posh CTM, Saag or Jalfrezi which I can have anywhere. I wouldn't choose to go back but if would do in someone else's party, especially when there is a magnificent Japanese next door! The meal for 2: Food, £43, Drink £10.'* DB. Looks like Dave will be back on the mile! Reports please. Hours: 12-2:30 / 5–11; 12 Fri & Sat.

SHERE KHAN   NEW ENTRANT

19 Berry St, Liverpool Centre   0151 709 6099

Bright colours and an inviting staircase to the mezanine first floor. *'Nice decor, pleasant efficient service but again I was the only customer on a rainy Friday lunch time. Onion Bhajia, two good, well spiced, crispy, flat discs, no garnish, which I expected. Chicken Jalfrezi, arrived plated with Pullao Rice and half a Naan. Not the greatest portion, like Shere Khan Express. Rice & bread OK. Disappointing.'* DB. See Shere Khan Rusholme for more details.

YOU SAY OK

You might get a discount if you show them this Guide.

LIVERPOOL: ASHA 79 Bold Street, Liverpool ~ 0151 709 4734

SAFFRON: Was Shapla, 51 Whitechapel, Liverpool Uni 67 Renshaw St Liverpool ~ 0151 709 6587.T/a: 15% disc. Del: 3m, £15. Hours: 6-1; 3 Fri & Sat. www.unirestaurant.com

NEWTON-LE-WILLOWS: TASTE OF INDIA 56 Market Street, Newton ~ 01925 228458

THINGWALL: RED CHILLI 513 Pensby Rd, Thingwall ~ 0151 648 5949. 65-seater taken over in 2001 by chef G Miah. Hours: 5-11.30; 12 Sat.

Southport

THE KASTURI

40, Eastbank St, Southport　　　　01704 533102

'Fairly large restaurant, in nice 'seasidey' exterior.' RW. 'I visited a friend in Southport. He reckons this is the best in Southport. The food was good, marred only by the serving of cold chicken tikka as a starter (the restaurant were good about it), the service was good (otherwise). It should remain in the Guide.' JP. Hours: 5.30-12; 1 Fri & Sat.

Wirral
Bromborough, Moreton, Wallasey, West Kirby

The Wirral is neither a town nor a county and, until 1965, was part of Cheshire. Since then the northern part – a small, digit-like, curry-rich peninsula between the rivers Mersey and Dee – has been part of Merseyside. Ellesmere Port (q.v.) remains in south Wirral but is in Cheshire. Our choice of Merseyside Wirral curryhouse towns are in alphabetical order: See also Upton, Cheshire.

SURMA TANDOORI

271 Hoylake Rd, Moreton　　　　0151 677 1331

48-seater opened 1995 by Sharif Ali. T/a: 20% disc. *'Impressive upstairs restaurant. Well decorated and intimate. very smart staff, real tablecloths, plate warmers used throughout, good quality crockery. Chicken Chat £2.50, lovely light puri, delicate topping, tangy sauce with small pieces of tender tikka. Bhojelo Gosht £6.45, exquisite, wonderfully tender pieces of juicy and rich tasting lamb, plenty of onion and papaya. Garlic Naan £1.75, soft, plenty of garlic, slightly crispy crust. Matter Paneer £2.25, was glad I had this, rather sloppy side dish, adding contrast, cheese blended with lamb, excellent. Salad and pickle tray supplied with the meal. A great meal, recommended.'* RW. Hours: 5.30-11.30.

CHUTNEYS　　　　　　　　　NEW ENTRANT

26, Liscard Village, CH45 4JP　　0151 638 7151

'Nice, modern, well lit. Only managed T/a, have proved excellent. Always quite busy, heard good reports from fellow curry lovers. Chicken Tikka Biryani £5.95, not the greatest portion of chicken, but nicely spiced, good rice and very good Madras sauce, with a free Pops! Chicken Tikka Dhansak £6.75, nicely spiced to Madras strength, good portion of both pineapple and chicken. Boiled rice, not the biggest portion, but fluffy and well cooked, with free Popadums! Chicken Tikka Jalfrezi £6.25, chicken cut into large strips, not chunks, excellent flavours, could have been spicier with a few more chillies.' DB. Three cheers, for more chillies!

TANDOORI MAHAL

24, King Street, Wallasey　　　　0151 639 5948

This is one of Dave's favourites, and he updates us in each Guide. *'Has undergone a transformation that has destroyed the character of the place. It's now more open and quite bright and I feel it will be alien to the normal clientele...'* This is happening up and down the country and we agree, some refurbishment's are just to modern for their own good. *'...we received the normal warm welcome. Friendly atmosphere, good service, decent food. Chicken Tikka Pakora, five good sized pieces with salad and raitha, great flavour, excellent. Chicken Tikka Balti, excellent, eaten with chips! They will never win awards, but they will never be short of custom, hope this doesn't change.'* DB.

YOU SAY OK – THE WIRRAL
You might get a discount if you show them this Guide.

BROMBOROUGH: CURRY NIGHTS 5 Coronation Dr, 0151 343 9200. *'Ever-present and ever-reliable, can't beat it.'* JN. *'Food delicious, brilliant menu, staff v friendly.'* JO. Del: 5 m, £10 min. T/a: spend £10, 2 Pops free; spend £15, an Onion Bhajia free; spend £20, Veg Bhajee free.

MORETON: EASTERN STYLE TANDOORI 11 Upton Rd. 0151 677 4863

WALLASEY: BANGLA VUJON 225 Wallasey Village ~ 0151 637 1371

WALLASEY: BHAJI 135 Wallasey Village, Wallasey ~ 0151 638 9444. *'At last a biriani was some flavour.'* DB. Hours: Daily to 1030; 11 Fri & Sat; 10.30 Sun.

WEST KIRBY: ROYAL BENGAL 150 Banks Rd, Kirby ~ 0151 625 9718. Est 1971, taken over in 2000 www.royalbengalwirral.co.uk

MIDDLESEX

Area: All part of
Greater London
(west of London)
Population: 1,200,000
Adjacent Counties:
Berks, Bucks,
Herts GL, Essex GL,
London NW & W
and Surrey GL

The county of Middlesex is very ancient. It once contained most of London, though this distinction became diminished when central London became autonomous during Victorian times. What was left of the county (located west and north of London) was completely 'abolished' when Greater London was formed in 1965, a move unpopular with Middlesex residents. Confusion exists because the Post Office still

use Middlesex as a postal county. Postcodes add to the confusion. Enfield, for example, is EN1, EN2 & EN3 in postal Middlesex but is in (Hertfordshire) GL county. Potters Bar EN6 is the same. Barnet, in postal Herts with EN4 and EN5 codes used to be in geographical Middlesex but is now a GL borough!

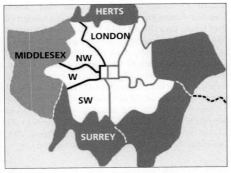

YOU SAY OK – ASHFORD, MIDDX
You might get a discount if you show them this Guide.

TAMANNA'S 15a Station Rd, Ashford ~ 01784 420720

PEPPERS 18 Woodthorpe Rd, Ashford ~ 01784 420131. *'One day I had lunch at Zarin's Ashford Kent, and then on the same day popped in here for dinner. Both excellent. Way to go!'* RL

Brentford

PAPPADUMS   TOP 100

Ferry Quays, Ferry La, Brentford   020 8847 1123

Smart, modern 150-seater on the bank of the River Thames and Grand Union Canal, alongside luxury apartments overlooking Kew Gardens. Personable Alston Wood from Sri Lankan manages. Park in the underground car park (or you'll get a wheel clamp). Owners Narinda and Satvir Sindhu pulled out all the stops creating its modernistic, double frontage, which looks out onto a large promenade area. Steps then lead you down to the   the river. When weather permits, diners are welcome to eat outside, on wooden benches with chairs. The restaurant's weighty wooden doors were shipped over from the subcontinent. Chef Gupta worked in Oberoi hotels . His light lunch menu includes Wraps, Kath Rolls and Indianised paneer Spring Rolls. and dishes from China and Thailand. Under the heading *'Exotic Oriental Delicacies'*, you will encounter Nasi Goreng £15, lamb and chicken satay served with spicy fried rice, topped with fried egg and peanut sauce; Honey Spiced Chicken £10; Thai Gaeng Pak 'stir-fried vegetables, tofu, scallions, mushrooms, hot and sour sauce. *'I decided to stick to Indian and chose Machhli Ke Pakode, fried cod strips coated with mild spiced gram flour. A generous portion was presented with a good salad and I enjoyed it very much. Pat had Kashmiri Lamb Seekh Kebab.*

Again a generous portion of tender, well pounded, spicy meat with salad. The chutney tray was left on the table for us to help ourselves. The menu highlights various dishes with a chilli logo, so we homed in on those choices. Chicken Chettinad, tempered with curry leaves, sun-baked red chillies and peppercorns,(three chillies). I ordered Aloo Udaigiri potatoes braised with coriander, cumin and Bikaneri spiced chillies. The Dal Makhani, slowly simmered black lentils came in a small, highly polished brass bucket, complete with handle, filled to the brim and decorated with a swirl of fresh cream came to the table - quite delicious. A portion of Steamed Rice escorted everything.' DBAC. Top 100. Hours: 12-2.30 / 5.30-11; 12-11 Weekends.   www.pappadums.co.uk

Eastcote

NAUROZ

219 Field End Road   020 8868 0900

This restaurant means 'new' in the context of new year etc. But owner Raza Ali is an old hand; he specialises in creating new venues, then selling them. (Five Hot Chillies, Mirch Masala, SW16 & 17 and Karahi King, Wembley). All have good pedigrees making them popular venues for the locals who tell us how much they enjoy it. *'Nauroz is a family concern attracting Asian families. All fresh food, including vegetables. This time they seem to have settled. Which is great for Eastcote. Authentic food, beautifully prepared, served in a spartan 'works canteen' kind of setting. Excellent quality and value.'* DT. *'Friends 21st birthday dinner. Open kitchen, which offers you the chance to see how the food is prepared. a little bit of theatre is always a good thing. Delicious food, value for money.'* LS. Another LS visited and agreed. *'I stumbled upon this restaurant during a business trip. I travel a lot and consider myself some what of an expert!. The food I ate was delicious and great value for money, all freshly cooked that day. It was extremely busy and had a great atmosphere.'* LS.

Edgware

HAANDI   NEW TO OUR TOP 100

301 Hale Lane, Edgware   020 8905 4433

Sister brach to Haandi SW3 (see entry) and the same tasty Punjabi cooking with an African twist at a much smaller price point. Everyone talks of the Kake di lamb on-the- bone, Asian style (and there are always plenty of local Asians in there.) is juicy aromatically flavour chunks of meat in a garam masala gravy. Also the sag Paneer was a fine rendition. Service charge: 12.5%. Hours: 12.30-3 Wed-Sun / 6-11 Sun-Thur; 11.30 Fri & Sat.

ZANZIBAR

113 High St, HA8 7DB   020 8952 2986

Opened 2001 by married couple, Sameer and Sheetal

Malik in a converted pub with decent beer in a large, bright dining room serving Punjabi/Kenyan-Asian food. Packed with Asians and filled with Bangra sounds. *The decor is basic, with plain wooden tables, mostly white walls and some rather odd, glittery wallpaper on one wall. Service was friendly and good. Pops were fresh and came with a simple mint chutney and a home made tomato chutney with a sour note and a vibrant chilli bite). I started with Achari Chicken, marinaded with chilli, mustard seeds and other spices then cooked. Served on a cast iron hotplate, the chicken was very tender and the marinade was really well judged, spicy with a little hint of sourness. Onion Bhaji is a cliché but can be good, and here was a very respectable version, the filling tasty, the outside cooked well. Tandoori King Prawns were cooked well but were spoilt by the use of very cheap farmed prawns, which had an unmistakable hint of chlorine about them. Methi Chicken had a pleasant, rich sauce which tasted of fenugreek, and chicken that was cooked properly but was not very high quality. The Bhindi, which most Indian restaurants overcook to a mush; was light and still had distinct texture. Garlic naan was well made, as was a paratha. A sweet Lassi was excellent, again a very simple thing but so rarely done to its best. Plain rice was impressive also, the grains distinct, cooked just right. I was impressed by the technique shown by the chef, who learnt his trade in the Taj Group. To be able to cook rice this well, and good bhindi, immediately marks him out as way above the norm. It is a shame about the very cheap ingredients. Portions are almost absurdly large. The waiter said at the end "oh, we could have done half size portions for you" which would have been great but was a bit late by then. Prices are not quite as cheap as you might expect given the area, though bear in mind the vast portions. Starters are mostly £6.95, main course curries generally £7.95 (prawns £12.95) with vegetables dishes also around the £7 mark. Naans were £1.95, paratha £2.45. Pullao rice is £4.25, a raita £1.95. The Zan Zi Bar, which is a couple of notches above the usual high street Indian. I paid £40pp'* AH: AndyHayler.com Review. Hours: 12-3 Mon-Sat / 5.30-11 Mon-Thur; 6-11pm Fri & Sat; 12-10 Sun.

Enfield

CHASE SIDE INDIAN

135 Chase Side, Enfield   020 8367 9979

Commenced trading in 2002. Proprietor, Aktar Hussain has many restaurants to his credit. This particular restaurant has a modern feel, being decorated in cream with pale wooden floors. Menu Snapshot: Duck Tikka £7; Shahi Chicken Biriani £8, Pullao rice, sultanas, coconut and almonds, served with mixed vegetable curry; Village Style Begoon £6.50, fresh slices of okra, ginger, garlic, onion, tomato, pepper and cashew nuts, topped with fried discs of aubergine, fresh coriander leaves , saffron and onion. Stocks: Cobra. T/a: 10% disc. Sun Buffet: £c8. Del: 4m £15 min. Hours: 6-12 daily / 12.30-5 Sun. Branch: Tikka Cottage, Hot House and Bengal Spice, all Hertford. www.chaserestaurant.co.uk

MEHEK

424 Hertford Rd, Enfield   020 8443 1844

Bright (royal purple and gold), a cheerfully modern and stylish restaurant. Ashik Miah runs a popular restaurant serving Bangladeshi curries and accompaniments, Lamb Xacutti £7 being the most popular dish. Menu Snapshot: Paneer Puri Sag £3.50, cheese and spinach on fried bread; Tava Gosht Lahori £7.50, lean lamb, tossed on iron skillet, spices, herbs, crushed garlic and julienne of ginger, light sauce, fresh tomatoes, capsicum and coriander leaf; Delight £7.95, marinated spring chicken, almonds, raisins, pineapple, lychee, panir (cheese) and cream, mild; all Balti dishes (from £6) served with Naan; Garlic and Chilli or Tikka Naan £2.50. Min ch £25. Service: 10%. Del: 3m £12 min. Price Check: Popadom 60p, CTM £7.25, Pullao Rice £1.75. Hours: 6-11.30; 12 Sat. Sun Buffet c£8. Branch: Bombay Spice, 201, Ordinance Road, Enfield. www.mehekcuisine.co.uk

YOU SAY OK
You might get a discount if you show them this Guide.

HAMPTON: MONAF'S 119 Station Road, Hampton ~ 020 8979 6021. Named after its owner, Mr A Monaf. 10% T/a disc. Hours: 12-2.30 / 5.30-12. Branch: Sheesh Mahal.

HARROW: HARROW TANDOORI 57 Station Rd, North Harrow ~ 020 8861 1571. Hours: 12-2.30/6.30-11.30.

HARROW SPICE 217 Station Road, Harrow, HA1 2TH. 1 course fixed price menu, including a glass of Cobra – £10.99

HAYES: ASHA 60 Station Road, Hayes ~ 020 8573 4717. Est 1977. Fully licensed and a/c. ' T/a: 10% disc, £10 min. Del: 5 m, £10 min. Hours: 12-2.30/6-12.

ICKENHAM: DARJEELING 89 High Road, Ickenham ~ 01895 679300. T/a 5% disc. Del min £30, 2m. Hours: 12-2.30/6-11.30.

BLUE GINGER

383 Kenton Rd, Harrow   020 8909 0100

The type of dive London Asians adore: It's brassy, charismatic, noisy (Bollywood movies on flat screens), comfortable (sofas), modern (black granite), spacious, bright and airy. All the family is welcome. Dads and lads tank up in the well-stocked bar while the mums and babes in their high chairs drool over the kiddie's menu. It's club-like and fun. The menu is Punjabi with a bit of Chinese, and the prices sensible. Some tables on an outdoor patio. Hours: 12-3 Tue-Sun; 6-11 daily

CONNOISSEUR CUISINE OF INDIA
TOP 100

37 High St, Harrow-on-the-Hill   020 8423 0523

It's near the School, right up on the hill. Once you've found a parking place, admire the views overlooking London. Proprietor Sonny Walia and his team ensure you get a warm and professional welcome. Chef Ramesh

Honatha trained at India's Sheraton Group. *'He's attractive and single – girls should try to book a table in the kitchen!'* DBAC. [Last time I go there with my wife, Ed.] *'Piaz Ke Pakode, gram flour coated crisp onion slices, sprinkled with chat masala, a large plate of crisply fried onion Bhajias as most know them arrived with a neat pot of coriander chutney – delicious. Pat loved his soft shelled crab, which came with a small salad of cubed tomato, onion and cucumber. Lachadar paratha was light and buttery. Aubergine, the smallest, plump baby aubergines, smothered in a spicy sauce. Chicken with pepper, lovely and spicy. Portions are generous.'* DBAC. Hours: 12-2.30 Tues-Fri / 6.30-10.30; 12 Fri, closed Monday.

RAM'S

203 Kenton Road, Harrow   020 8907 2022

You would imagine that every regional Indian cooking style now has a home in a restaurant somewhere in London. Yet here is another one – Surti a style of vegetarian cooking from Surat, Gujarat's main seaport city. Surat was where the English first landed in India in 1608, although this has no relevance here, not to say they must have eaten Kadhi (see below and p56) which passed into language as *'curry'*. Your editor's first chef-training was from Gujarati chef, Sat Gupta. He was from Baroda, but his wife was from Surat. The most memorable piece of advice she gave me was not to cook green vegetables in iron vessels or they will turn black. Let me set the scene: Gujarat has many vegetarians, and many superb restaurants in Wembley and Leicester. Gujarati cooking is mild and slightly sweet, using yoghurt and gramflour in many guises accompanied by fluffy rice, puffy puris, wonderously-cooked vegetables, sweet pickles and tempting puddings. Some Surti cooking differs in detail, especially with its use of green ingredients: green onion leaves (leela kanda) green garlic leaves, green moong lentils, fresh fenugreek and coriander leaves. The Surti Vaghar is a cooked mix of garam masala, red chilli, ginger and garlic. Favourite dishes include Lachko, a cake made from toovar dhal, turmeric, ghee and water served with sev and green chilli & onion chutney. Pattice, a potato rissole with a stuffing of coconut, chilli and sev. Patra a kind of Swiss Roll made from colcasia leaves on which is spread a spicy paste, rolled into cylinders, steamed sliced and fried. Ram's is a plain, white-walled café. The food is typically Gujarati sweet, though Surti chilli hot. Many typical vegetables were on the menu: such as beans, plantain, karela (bitter gourd), okra, purple yam (they turn out a good rissole version of this) and red and yellow, sweet potatoes (sakkarkan). Undhiyu is probably Surat's national dish. It contains all the above and typically has Muthias (deep-fried besan dough and fenugreek leaf). Dahi Kadhi (turmeric gold yoghurt and gram flour-based curry with ginger, curry leaves, mustard seeds and red chilli, appears with several vegetable options. A good rice dish is the ghee-laden Khichadi (rice and lentils).

Prices are more than reasonable, A la carte main courses from £3.50 The Thali meals offers a good choice of items, £4.99 lunch, £8.99 dinner. The ultimate choice is the £15 set meal of unlimited food and soft drinks. Service charge 10%. No smoking. T/a service. Hours: 12-3 / 6-11. Branches: Vijay NW6 and Satay, Uxbridge.

SAFARI

14A Broadwalk, Pinner Road   020 8861 6766

Another pit-stop London Asians adore: this one is a bit daunting from the outside (dark windows – like stretch-limos) but once inside it's all go (if a bit dark on the lighting side) with Asian families having a good time on food which is again above average Punjabi Kenyan (hence its name and decor). Hours: 6-12 Mon-Th; 1-12 Fri-Sun

SANGEETHA

196 Kenton Rd, Harrow   020 8907 9299

Harrow and surrounds is literally sprouting Indian venues, as its Asian population expands, and this venue is an example. It is part of a south Indian chain, and it is south Indian vegetarian. The dosa are light and yet satisfyingly chewy, their stuffing redolent of curry leaves, green chilli, coconut and mustard seeds. Their sambar and rasam had the right degree of tempering, piquancy and flavour. If my wife doesn't get hiccoughs when she sips her rasam, it ain't hot enough. On this occasion she did. The waiters told us to come back for their annual dosa and chutney festivals. Service: an inexplicably weeny 2.5%. Hours: 11-10.30 daily.

Hounslow

HORIZONS BAR

210 Hanworth Rd, Hounslow   020 8814 0044

Sleek, upmarket ambience, comfy black leather couches, plasma screens, polished porcelain flooring and top of the range computerised sound and lighting systems for live bands, It's the first culinary venture for owners, Bugsy Pankhania and Rakesh Patel, childhood friends, who bought an old Army Drill Hall which in 2005 they transformed it into a multipurpose venue, which now comprises a 400 cover banqueting suite, a bar and what is now one of the area's most popular restaurants. Much of the credit goes to head chef, Chandan Singh, who worked at five-stars like the Delhi's Taj Palace, Meridian and Hyatt Regency He specialises in kebabs – try the exemplary mixed grill. Hours: 12-2.30 / 6.30-11.30.

KARAHI MASTER LAHORE

795 London Road, Hounslow   020 8572 2205

Pakistani (Halal) 40-seater opposite Hounslow Bus Garage. Taken over by Mohammad Akmal. Specials

include: Roast Lamb Leg £17.50, or, if celebrating with friends, Stuffed Whole Lamb £100 sounds great. Lunchtime specials for £5.95, please ask. BYO is allowed, 1 bottle per person. A free drink to Curry Club members from Mr Akmal – cheers! Del: £15 min (6 free Popadums), 4m. Hours: 12-12.

MANTRA   NEW ENTRANT

253, Bath Road, TW3 3DA   08715 293 738

Very glitzy, eatery, perfect for the twenty and thirty somethings! Great for parties! White flooring, square glass tables, huge chandeliers and fabulous round red leather chairs, that encapsulate you, all very trendy! Head chef: Surinder Kumar. Good food reported.

NEW HEATHROW TANDOORI

482 Great West Road 020 8572 1772

'Another business trip to London and another visit here. The door was opened by a Nepalese waiter, big smile and warm "Good evening Sir". Showed me to a table, brought menu and lager immediately. Managing owner, Meojanur Rahman popped over for a chat. He commented that since the superb facelift, custom had increased. It was busy that Wednesday evening. Meat Samosa £1.95, delicious, plenty of spicy lamb inside an incredibly light pastry, Mr Rahman used to be a pastry chef! Ah! insider knowledge! *'served with crisp salad and lemon. Chicken Tikka Bhuna £5.45, beautifully served in a white ceramic pot and comprised large thick slices of smoky breast meat in rich, piquant sauce. Mr Rahman says he adds more chilli when the weather is cold! The breads, mango Kulfi and coffee were all delicious and served to consistently high standards. I appreciate that this restaurant continues to use hot plates on the tables. Too many restaurant are dispensing with them. Highly recommended.'* TE. Menu Snapshot: Chicken Mahisuri £7.50, barbecued chicken, onion, peppers, tomatoes in a creamy sauce; Egg Potato Vegetable Curry £3.20/£4.75, medium sauce; Dhal Lalmirch £2.95/£4.50 lentils with fried red chilli, Chicken Tikka Naan £2.50. Del: 4 m, £12 min. Sun Buffet: £6.95, children half price. T/a: 10% disc, £10 min. Hours: 12-2; 11-1 /5.30-1.30.

Northwood Hills

RASA SURABHI   NEW ENTRANT

3 Joel St, Northwood, HA6 1NU   01923 820070

The latest (ninth) of the Rasa empire, see London N16 and W1. Owner Das claims it to be the first contemporary, upscale Indian seafood restaurant in North London. The hotel, conceived along the same lines as Rasa Samudra in Charlotte Street, offers sumptuous Indian seafood delicacies with an exclusive a la carte menu covering a range of Kerala seafood selections. Kerala cuisines are heavily influenced by the age-old Ayurvedic principles which makes them healthy, wholesome and at the same time delectable. Hours: 6-11:00; Closed Mon www.rasarestaurants.com

Rayners Lane

CLUB 2000   NEW ENTRANT

427 Rayners Lane HA5 5ER 020 8868 2500

'Decor basic, no tablecloths, a few African masks and statues, lots of sparkly lights, two plasma screens and some worrying looking electrical wiring in places, but on this Sunday night the place was packed out with Asian families. The owners are Gujarati, but the menu has plenty of meat dishes and some East African influences such as several varieties of mogo (cassava). Prices are very fair indeed: pops 50p, starters £3.50 - £13 (but mostly c£4), main course curries were £6, naan bread rice both £1.50. A pint of Cobra beer was just £2.50, which would be hard to find in a pub, never mind a restaurant. Popadums were fried to order and were good and crisp, served with home-made chutneys: a thin but spicy tomato chutney, and a thick spicy mint chutney. Fish Tikka was excellent, chunks of tilapia marinated then cooked in the tandoor, served on an iron skillet with fried onions. Vegetable samosas were pleasant enough, with thin crispy coating but the filling was a little dull . However I was delighted to find Patra, a very rare dish on restaurant menus. This Gujarati dish involves Indian colcasia leaves filled with a spices and gramflour, set in layers, steamed then sliced and fried. The version here was the best I have eaten, avoiding the over-dryness that can afflict this dish; here the patra was tasty and moist with good texture. My main course Methi Chicken was rather ordinary, the meat seemingly very cheap, though correctly cooked, and the sauce tasting of fenugreek but used too much ghee for my liking. Bhindi Masala was better, the bhindi cooked a little longer than ideal but by no means mushy, the onion-based masala having plenty of spicy flavour. Chana Masala had reasonably tender chickpeas but a rather watery sauce while Mattur Paneer was rather dull . Naan bread was very good and rice was also nicely cooked, the grains clearly delineated. The bill for what turned out to be a mountain of food was just £24 for two, and there was enough left over for another complete meal. Service was friendly and efficient, and the closely packed tables lend to a relaxed, informal cafe atmosphere. This is authentic cooking which at times was very good indeed.' AH: AndyHayler.com Review. *'The secret here is to feast on the excellent starters, forget about the mediocre main courses and you'll have one of the best Indian meals in the country.'* RG via AH.

YOU SAY OK
You might get a discount if you show them this Guide.

NORTHOLT: EMPRESS OF INDIA 40 Church Road, Northolt~ 020 8845 4361. 52-seater est 1974 by Ali, Zaman & EH Khan.

NORTHOLT: AMIRTHAM NEW ENTRANT 200B Alexandra Avenue, Northolt, HA2 9BU

NORTHWOOD: SHANTI 48 High Street, Northwood ~ 01923 827856. Mofiz Miah's 60-seater est 1984.

RAYNERS LANE: PAPAYA 15, Village Way, Rayners La 020 8866 5582. Sri Lankan with Indian curries on the menu too. Serv: 10% Hours: 12-12 Mon-Sat; -11 Sun www.papayauk.com

RUISLIP: RICE N SPICE TAKEAWAY 73 Station Approach, S Ruislip 020 8841 5498

Ruislip

RUISLIP TANDOORI

115 High Street, Ruislip   01895 632859

This air-conditioned venue is an old friend of this Guide. It's a 52-seat Nepalese restaurant in black and white with flowering trees, Nepalese handicraft, pictures and a beautiful golden Buddha, which is, we're told, *'the main attraction apart from the Nepalese food'* by owner KB Raichhetri who might give you a disc if you show him this Guide. T/a: 10% off. Sun buffet c£9. Del: £15 min, 2-m. Hours: 12-2.30 / 6-12.

Ruislip
Tandoori Restaurant

FINEST NEPALESE CUISINE

Highly Recommended by
Les Routiers & Good Curry Guide

We have been established in Ruislip for over 20 years

115 High Street
Ruislip
01895 632859

Southall

From a single acorn (the now-gone Maharaja), there grew an astonishing number of sweet/snack centres, cafés and restaurants which are to be found on South Road and the Green, but mostly on the the Broadway, the main artery through Southall. Expansion westwards continues, where its unexpected bonus is a pleasing growth of Sri Lankan suppliers. These places cater primarily for their indigenous Asian population, a generally peaceful mix of Indian and Pakistani Sikh and Punjabi carnivores, enhanced by East African Asians and most recently, Somalis. If you are none of these, do not feel inhibited from entering. Everyone is treated equally and all are welcome. Some venues are licensed and modern, aiming at the younger Asians. Others are café-style and unlicensed. At all of them you'll find good, authentic cuisine in straightforward, functional eating-houses, at realistic prices. The food is served from early morning to late night, fast and fresh. One or two correspondents have bemoaned the use of the microwave to heat the food. We point out that a microwave is merely a heater, which has gained a poor reputation because it cannot heat pastry well (samosas for example). It is not to be despised, and does not demean the food it heats. Better that than unhygienic ally keeping the food warm in bainmaries for hours on end. Here we examine our (and our correspondents') favourite eating holes. Plans have long-been afoot to call this mile-long Broadway, Punjabi Bazaar, giving it an identity such as Chinatown W1. Arches and gateways will welcome you in English and Punjabi, and there will be colourful urban folk art, decorations on shop frontages and lamp posts with art designs from Amritsar and Lahore.

BALTI & TANDOORI WORLD

185 The Broadway, Southall   020 8867 9991

Not only does it do Balti dishes, aka Karahi by the Punjabis, and Tandoori items, it does a fascinating mix of dishes from Gujarat, Punjab, Kenyan Asia, and north and south India. *'Service is very quick and informative. Though it is unlicensed, waiters kindly fetched beer and soft drinks from the adjoining off-license. Customers can try their hand at cooking their own dishes. All dishes were of a high standard and were more authentic Indian-style cooking than some other restaurants we've visited.'* SF. Hours: 11.30-11.30.

BOMBAY

177 The Broadway, Southall   020 8560 4646

It is modern and trendy inside and out – all black and white paint and stained wood. There is a bar on which to prop yourself up on (if you can elbow the proprietor's friends out of the way who seem to treat the place like their local pub), a big TV for entertainment, many framed pictures of 'stars' and a party room which always seems to be full of beautifully sari-ed ladies having a roaring time with a booming disco and disappearing trays of steaming food being carried upstairs by some gormless youth. The menu is small but that's OK, with all you really need listed. The waiter noticed me gaping at the TV, turned over to Eastenders and put on English subtitles! Popadums are good with an excellent chutney tray – definitely handmade, lovely. Curries are well above average but with one criticism, they are a little salty for my taste. Good value wine list. Enjoyable.

BRILLIANT   AWARD   WINNER

72 Western Road, Southall   020 8574 1928

The Brilliant has long been one of the UK's most popular Indian restaurant and it has got even better with its 2007 redec. Launched in 1975 as a one-unit 36-

seater with a minimalist menu. Today, on the same site, but with two adjacent units added, the restaurant seats 250 and was the country's first restaurant to hold civil marriages. It has an upstairs banqueting suite, providing event catering and even karaoke nights. It is owned by Gulu Anand and Kewel Anand, who was awarded our Lifetime achievement Award in 2007. Many dishes have been made health-conscious. Long a pioneer in offering Vegetable Keema £8, soy mince with fresh peas, Brilliant's range of healthy options include: Tandoori Salmon, mildly spiced chunks of salmon with dill and no oil; Papri Chat £4.50, a crispy snack of chickpeas, tamarind chutney and low fat yoghurt; Methi Chicken £17.50 (for three), cooked with with olive oil and not an ounce of fat. Sides have also been given a makeover, Dhal Tarka £4.50, yellow lentils cooked with garlic and red chillies, though still retaining its flavour, eschews the traditional method of tempering which would usually leave a layer of fat on top of the dish. A greater choice of salads is on the menu while ghee (clarified butter) is now only utilised in moderation and even then merely to add flavour. Improvement has also been made in presentation. While Gulu and Kewel still oversee the running of the Brilliant, the mantle of carrying the restaurant's success into the future is passing to a new (third) generation of the Anand family. Gulu's daughter Dipna, (pictured below) is overseeing the menu. Shankar, her younger brother, is now GM. Both have inherited a passion and understanding of Indian food. If only more sons and daughters got into the lucrative trade of their fathers, instead of playing doctor and lawyer. In fact Dipna is taking her PhD in food studies, and already teaches it. Her dedication ensures the future of the Brilliant. More importantly, it proves that there is a career for young people, male or female (others take note) in the curry industry which will ensure its growth in the next generation. To recognise their achievements at such a young age, we have created a Special Industry Young Persons Award for Dipna and Shankar. Hours: 12-3 / 6-11.30; 12 Fri & Sat. Closed Mondays. www.brilliantrestaurant.com

CHHAPPAN BHOG

1 The Broadway, Southall   020 8574 7607

An Asian sweet shop, (Mithai), est 1992 in Lucknow by Ravinder Gupta and now here, which sells savoury items as well. 'Chhappan Bhog' was an ancient Hindu royal get-together at which the attendees would enjoy Indian sweets such as Burfi (fudge) and Halva. The shop sells 56 sweetmeats and snacks. Branch 145 Ballards Lane, Finchley, N3. 020 8371 8677. www.chhappanbhog.com

DELHI WALA

11 King Street, Southall   020 8574 0873

The state of Punjab is half in Pakistan half in north India. It is one of India's major culinary styles which began to evolve from early in the first millennium AD. It is perhaps the best known Indian food because the original curry restaurants in the developed world based their menus on Punjabi cuisine. Dairy farming is a major Punjabi industry and its prolific wheat crops, earn it the title 'the granary of India', and Parathas and Puris are staples. The food is very savoury and fenugreek leaf (methi) and mustard leaf (rai) are virtually staples. Our UK Punjabi restaurants and their diners are carniverous. so one might be forgiven for believing that all Punjabis eat meat. In fact about 40% of the Punjabi population are vegetarian, as is Deli Wala, serving robust curries like Methi Aloo, Aloo Ghobi Methi, Sag Paneer and Mattar Valor – Pea and Bean Curry. Hours: 10am-10pm.

GIFTO'S LAHORE KARAHI & TANDOORI

162 The Broadway, Southall   020 8813 8669

'Went by train after Southall parking problems. Good decision, because local road restrictions last until 8.30 pm. The Lahori leg of lamb pre-ordered was running late. The cunning ploy to get us to order starters worked, but the leg was so special when it did arrive, nothing was sent back. How they get the flavour so deep into the meat I know not, but the dressing and marinade were excellent and tasty right through. Pretty upmarket after its revamp, though still soft drinks only. So cost for 4, blow out meal was £52, of which the leg was £20 (plus the Cobra from from the "cousin's" shop next door). Must now go on a fruit diet for a few days I fear.' C & MC. BYO. Open all day. Branch Gifto Express, 147, The Broadway Southall. 020 8843 0101

GLASSY JUNCTION

97 South Road, Southall   020 8574 1626

Drive north over Southall railway station bridge, observing the tiny (and excellent) kebab house on its brow on the left and ahead you can't miss the amazing vista of Glassy Junction. It's a pub, whose exterior is clad

with gigantic Hindu figures. Being a pub, it serves booze just like any other pub. Its clientèle is largely young trendy Asians, the like of which abound in Southall. Bangra and Hindi movie music blares out. Add the chattering, and the noise is more deafening than a migrating flight of starlings. As to the food, there's a splendid selection of tandoori and curry items. *'If you intend to visit any of Southall's unlicensed venues, you can always have "a pre-visit" to the Glassy, though after that I find it as well to have water! Pakoras at the Glassy were as good as ever, though the place seems to have changed hands. It was getting a vigourous clean while we were there.'* C&MC.

KABUL AFGHAN NEW ENTRANT 1st Floor, Himalaya Shopping Centre, 65, The Broadway, Southall, UB1 1LB   020 8571 6878. Reports please, we need to keep these unusual little dining establishments alive. Hours: 12-12. Credit cards accepted.

KARAHI TANDOORI KABAB CENTRE

161 The Broadway, Southall   020 8574 3571

Owner AF Choudhury and Manager Dalawar delightedly tell that their venue, known locally as TKC, was an original of the genre, founded in 1965, early days in Southall's currinary development, and that there have been numerous copiers, not least the ones dead opposite. And what is the genre? Firstly, it is and was uncompromisingly Asian in food style and service, though, all are welcome, of course. In 1965, few whites visited it, now things have changed, and they are as taken for granted as the Asian clientèle. The venue is open-all-hours, and the price is right – inexpensive, and designed to attract regular local custom several times a week at breakfast, lunch, tea or dinner. Next, standard shop full-length windows ensure that when walking past, you are immediately attracted to the display cabinets containing all sorts of tempting snacks such as Pakora, Bhel Poori, Gol Goppas, Jeera Pani (cumin water), Tikki, Samosa, Indian sweets, etc. Alongside, and equally on show are the chefs, under head chef Farooq, and they soon learn to show off, much as do Tepinyaki chefs in the Japanese equivalent. Their freshly cooked Tandooris, Kebabs and breads, Punjabi Karahis and curries are cooked to order, and are quite delicious. Inside is a clean and tidy, no-frills café-style restaurant, seating 66, with formica tables, and waiter-service. Head chef Farooq's menu says *'please specify your taste of chillies when ordering'*. His Appetisers include: Reshmi Spring Lamb Boti, tender succulent pieces of lamb marinated in double cream roasted in the tandoor £3.50. Paneer Tikka, chunks of vegetarian cheese marinated with spices and baked in tandoor £3. Main courses: Nehari, shank of lamb served in a spicy sauce £4. Zeera Chicken, made with butter and cumin seeds £5. Sarson Ka Saag, mustard and spinach leaf £3.50. House Specialities: Chargha, fully roasted and tenderly spiced, free-range chicken, a recipe from the inner Punjab £6.50. Chappal Kebab, beaten mince steaks cooked and served on a sizzler, a speciality from the North-West Frontier

Province £4. Try the Kulfi Faluda, a Pakistani version of the Knickerbocker Glory £1.80. Pinad Da Buffet £6.99. All food is prepared with Halal meat. Alcohol is strictly prohibited. It gets very busy with all age groups, from the pensioners, mums and babes in the day to the young trendy ebullient fun-loving Asians at night and weekends. Hours: 9am-Md'nt. Branch: Tandoori Express on Jalebi Junction, 93 The Broadway, Southall.

MADHU'S   BEST IN UK AWARD 2004

39 South Road, Southall   020 8574 1897

Opened 1980. Punjabi cuisine with Kenyan twist. In those days it was a friendly, busy cafe-style restaurant It is as different now as it could be, though it remains busy and extremely friendly. In our 2004 Guide we made it the UK's number one restaurant. We know that when we make a restaurant number one, all the celebrity critics beat a path to the door. We are flattered, but this being Southall, we waited for them to pooh-pooh our decision, but to a man and woman, they all agreed. But more importantly you, our contributors, agree too. Loads of you have visited and written in. But before we quote a few of your views, I must describe one of our own visits. A friend of ours is a top international sales person in a blue-chip computer systems company. We promised to take him and his wife to the UK's number one Indian restaurant. He had not heard of Madhu's before, and as we got closer, you could sense a slight anx in him. We managed to park outside (very rare) and the anx was visible. But once inside, the décor, setting, table lay-up, and service, not to mention the food and drink, literally blew him away. *'Incredible . We get a lot of foreign visitors come to our offices. Often they ask to be taken for a curry. Up till now, no one had been able to guarantee a prestigious local. Now we can',* he confided later. Here are some more comments: *'Not much more that I need to say about this excellent establishment not that food quality, service and ambience were as excellent as would be expected for a restaurant aiming to keep it's place right there at the top. My notes aren't copious but suffice to say, my visitor from the USA and I were suitably impressed with the magical Buzi Bafu and the other dishes that we ordered. Overall opinion – outstanding, will continue to recommend to lovers of authentic Indian food and will continue to come back as often as I can!'* SO. *'We moved to the curry desert of Devon from Berkshire and regularly ate at Madhu's Brilliant, a great exponent of the skills of cooking great Indian food.'* AF. *'We were delighted to be told by Annan that the Iceland car park can now be used again for Madhu's for a visit to savour. Can you get him to disclose the Jeera chicken recipe please?'* ' C & MC. Menu Snapshot: Masala Fish £10, fillet of Tillapia (fresh water fish from Kenya's Lake Victoria) cooked with masala sauce, flavoured with roasted cumin seed; Makni Chicken £10, chicken pieces simmered in a mild gravy, enriched with butter and cream, aromatically spiced with cardamom and cinnamon; Methi Chicken £10, chicken pieces simmered with fresh and fry

fenugreek in a traditional savoury Punjabi sauce; Karela Aloo £7, combination of bitter gourd and potatoes, flavoured with pomegranate; Dall Makhni £6, black urid lentils, stirred over a slow fire for many hours, flavoured with green cardamom (one of DBAC's favourites); Hara Bhara Kebab £6 for six pieces, finger sized kebabs made from cottage cheese, green peas and fenugreek, flavoured with coriander (another one of my favourites); Aloo Papri Chat £5 for two, crunchy combination of fried wheat crisps (papri), boiled potato cubes, chickpeas, chopped onion in a fresh mint and tangy tamarind sauce, garnished with fresh coriander, served cold (delicious and again, one of my favourites); Mogo Jeera Fried £5 for two, fresh cassava pan-fried with roasted cumin and ground black pepper, or deep-fried and seasoned with spices (do try these fried, really good); Boondi Raitha £3.50, yoghurt flavoured with cumin, ground black pepper and tiny crisp gram flour puff balls. House Special, Boozi Bafu, on the bone £18/£36, spring lamb chops, gently simmered in onion and tomato sauce, with freshly ground spices. Hours: 12.30-2.45 / 6-11.30, Tuesday closed. www.madhusonline.com

MEHFIL   NEW ENTRANT

45 The Green, UB2 4AR   020 8606 8811

The Mehfil Hotel is near Southall station. It has 31 rooms and a bar and a 24 hour porter. The licensed restaurant serves above-average Punjabi food and Tandoori items, is friendly and has parking facilities, useful in Southall. Avg pp: Lunch: £15, Dinner: £25. Hours: 12-3 / 6-10:45; 11.45 Fri & Sat. www.MehfilHotel.com

MOJ MASTI

37 Featherstone Rd, Southall   020 8893 6502

Serving authentic Karachi Pakistani food and opened by Natasha Shaikh with husband Anees in 2005. Moj Masti seats 130 people in four modern-imaged rooms managed by Ali Ikram – the Kat-a-Kat food bar, Ju Ju`s jungle with water features, low lighting and greenery, an Oriental-style dining zone (upstairs) inspired by Pakistan`s northern border with China with has some influence on the country`s cooking culture (fried rice and chilli chicken on its menu). The fourth room is available for hire and has a dance floor. Moj Masti opens 8am for buffet breakfast (with such light dishes as lassi. halwa, chana, puri and aloo curries). As with all Southall restaurants, kids are welcomed. Children will enjoy Lollipop Chicken with chips and salad. Head chef Asif Ali's starters include Udaan Lajawab £3.50, chicken wings BBQd in special sauce. Specials include Goan Fish £7.20, coley or kingfish grilled or steamed with Goan spices; Nihari Lamb £5.90, Haleem, £5.90, lentils, wheat and lamb puree; Lahori Fried Fish and Chicken Peer Bhai. The most remarkable dish is Kat-a-Kat (Tak-a-tan) a Karachi speciality dish, rarely-found in the UK, named after the clattering noise the chef's special tools make as he simultaneously chops and cooks the ingredients on a tawa (flat pan). This is Pakistani's version of Tepinyaki in that it is performed in front of its customers. Before that at Moj Masti diners select their own meat, namely chicken (murgh), minced lamb (keema) brains (magaaz), liver (kalegi) , kidneys (gurda) or lamb testes (kapooray) and vegetables. Then they watch as it is cooked in front of them. All Kat-a-Kat dishes cost £6. This is one dish you must try. No alcohol served but BYO welcomed with no corkage charge. Del 3m, but no T/a. Hours: 8am to midday, main menu midday to midnight.   www.mojmasti.co.uk

NARGIS KAPURI PAN

25 The Green, Southall   020 8574 5041

In the subcontinent, Paan, pronounced 'parn', is a massive industry, involving an army of 'paan-wallahs', traders, who prepare 'paan masalas' or mixtures, dispensing their wares in smart restaurants, at home door-to-door, or at street kiosks. Paan is best defined as a collection of edible ingredients, ranging from very bitter to very sweet folded, samosa-fashion in the paan leaf. Paan (Betel) leaf eaten in one mouthful, as a digestive after a meal. The darkish green, heart-shaped leaf is bitter, the mouth-feel coarse and the taste acquired. The ingredients include certain aromatic spices, for example aniseed, green cardamom, cloves and fennel,cucumber, marrow, watermelon and pumpkin seeds. To counter the bitter tastes, sugar crystals or sugar balls are used. The exact choice of ingredients is left to the customer. For a small price you can experience a major taste aspect of real India in Southall. And the Indophile can buy tablas and sitars at Bina Musicals, a few doors down the street.

OMI'S   TOP 100

1 Beaconsfield Rd, Southall   020 8574 1831

Established way back in 1976 as a tiny caff, by Mukesh Kharbanda and partners. Mukesh himself cooks north Indian and Kenyan Asian curries. Now much refurbished Omi's seats 80, few of whom need spend more than a tenner for a fill-up. The front stands slightly back from the pavement, making room for parking for 6-8 vehicles. A short menu above the counter describes what is on offer, along with the Specials of the Day. The most popular dishes are Karahi Chicken, Ginger Chicken and Palak Chana. Since we were taken here years ago by Indian journalist KN Malik (*'I want to show you Indian food at its best'*), we can safely say this is the Indians' Indian restaurant. We love his food and adore Mukesh's idiosyncrasies. It has the usual plastic tables and chairs, making for a clean and tidy restaurant, but it's the freshly-cooked food you go for. Licensed. Del: small charge. Omis remains in our TOP 100.

Hours: 11am - 10.30pm; to 11 Saturdays; to 9.30 Sundays.
www.omisrestaurant.co.uk

PALM PALACE   TOP 100

80 South Road, Southall   020 8574 9209

Sri Lankan/south Indian, a scarce resource in the UK, and still unique in Southall, although several High Street shops sell Sri Lankan ingredients. The redec has now bedded itself in (expensive chairs, granite tables, smart wood floor etc, and black-shirted waiters, still as friendly as ever, their service, though a tad slow is always with a flourish). It is marginally busier than before, but I said it before and I'll say it again: Southall's Asians are a conservative lot – but the if-it-ain't-Punjabi-it-ain't-edible view is slowly changing. Even Sanjay from Madhu's is a convert to Palm Palace. And, as we say every time, so it should. My bench mark crab curry from an early ownership has never matched, but it's still an exciting dish, especially fired up to incendiary level for those of us who cannot do without chilli. There's nothing like picking and sucking out crab meat from legs and shell and dousing it in rich Sri Lankan gravy. Messy shirt-sprinkling stuff, yes, but a slow, pleasurable experience, which is a contender for my desert island luxury. Hours: 12-3 daily; 6-11 Mon-Thur; 6-11.30 Fri-Sun

PUNJABI KARAHI

175 The Broadway, Southall   020 8574 1112

Once you get towards the Hayes end of Southall's Broadway you are spoilt for choice of Karahi Kebab houses. Me, I think I'd better move house and live there, then I could rotate round them each day. The menu and concept, prices and hours is identical to the others on the block and is just as worthy of your visit.

NEW ASIAN TANDOORI CENTRE
TOP 100

114 The Green, Southall   020 8574 2597

There is nothing new about this venue. It began trading in 1959. Indeed it is still known as The Roxy, although its English transport caff namesake closed over four decades ago. In its place came an Asian version of the same – one of those long-standing restaurants which serve the local community morning, noon and night. Founders Mr Sagoo and Mr Thakhar strategically set up two such venues, located at either end of Southall. have finally retired and sold their 157 The Broadway venue to the next door halal butcher, who has renamed it The Kashmir. Well, I say nothing new, but they have had a smart redec. When you enter the Roxy, there may be a queue, even outside the door, but it won't take long before it's your turn. Long glass counters display tempting Indian sweets and savoury snacks (Bhajias, Kebabs, Samosas, Aloo Tikki, Dahi Vasa, etc.), curries (Murgh Masala, on the bone, Bombay Potato, Sag Paneer, Sag Gosht and more, all cold but will be reheated in the microwave on request), Chana Dal, Rice (Plain, Pullao and Biriyani) and breads. *'Pick up a tray and tell the chap behind the counter what you want and whether you are eating in or taking out. Portions are generous and I have to restrain myself from over-ordering. When you have paid (cash or cheques only), take your tray to the other room and seat yourself.'* DBAC. *'The absolute curry experience, should be compulsory for all members to visit! Sample the vast range of dishes on offer, all authentic and served up in a no-nonsense style. We ate vast quantities of food, including Pakoras, Dal (black bean), Chicken and Meat Curries, Rotis and rice. Service with a smile, staff friendly. Highly recommended, must be very high in the TOP 100.'* DB. They also serve a wonderful chutney, sticks of carrot, slices of onion, embalmed in a tamarind and yoghurt sauce, delicious. You can BYO (but please ask) though they do sell Cobra. Fresh fruit juice and Lassi are available. They don't take credit cards, hardly surprising as your meal will be under a tenner. New hours since last time. Now you can get an early Punjabi breakfast: try Mango Lhassi (as good as any smoothie) with a lentil dish eg (Kabli Chana) and bhatura, large deep-fried bread like a large puri, on which you sprinkle sugar, all washed down with Indian tea. Hours: 8am-11pm; to 12 Fri-Sun). It remains high in our TOP 100.

SHAHANSHAH VEGETARIAN

60 North Road, Southall   020 8574 1493

Gill Baljinder (manager) and Johl Sarbjit, have since 1984 specialised in cooking from north and south India at their vegetarian restaurant, which seats 30 diners. Samosas and other snacks are the most popular items ordered. Indian sweets are made on the premises, so you can be sure they are fresh. Set dinner £5. Sun lunch £4. Branch: Shahanshah Vegetarian, 17 South Rd, Southall.

TANDOORI EXPRESS ON JALEBI JUNCTION

93 The Broadway, Southall   020 8571 6782

Owner Abdul Chaudhury, manager Mr Shauket, and head chef Rassaq's bright and colourful venue appeals to the local young and trendy population. It is often full of chattering, bright young Asians babbling on in animated Southall cockney accents. A richly painted and decorated rickshaw can be seen outside on the wide pavement which enhances the environment. Also a cook makes Jalebis, those crispy, deep-fried squiggles, immersed in syrup, right there on the pavement. You can't get fresher than that, and if you've not seen it done, here's the only place in Britain we know of that does it on view. Great Pakistani curries and fresh breads are a big pull, along with snacks such as Samosas, Pakoras, etc. There is also a vast sweet counter to pile on the pounds (weight that is, not the bill). Starters include: Club Sandwich, finest chicken and lamb BBQ fillings £3. Shami Kebab, mince meat and lentil burger 50p. Dahi Bhalla, lentil flour doughnuts soaked in yoghurt £1.50. House specials: Masaladaar Raan, whole leg of lamb roasted in the tandoor with all the natural juices and flavours sealed within, a Moghul dish from Lakhshmi Chauk, Lahore, £15. Alcohol is strictly prohibited. Hours: 9am-11pm. Branch: 161 The Broadway, Southall.

Sudbury

FIVE HOT CHILLIS

875 Harrow Road, Sudbury   020 8908 5900

Cooking is Punjabi. The venue is a cheap and cheerful caff. The clientele is largely Asian, and the atmosphere is intensely friendly. Meat and Chicken on-the-bone, as it should be. Dishes which burst with flavour, and individualism. Price probably around a tenner, and they take credit cards. It is unlicensed. You can BYO with corkage no charge. Hours: 11-11, daily.

Sunbury-on-Thames

INDIAN ZEST
NEW ENTRANT & NEW TO OUR TOP 100

21 Thames St, Sunbury, TW16 5QF
01932 765000

When their Indian Zing (W6) took off into profitability during 2005, it was almost inevitable that chef Manoj Vasikar and his manager partner Bhanu Pratap would open a further venture. See their story and ethos in the London W6 entry. Set over two floors, it's divided into a number of dining rooms. The 70-seat main area is the Colonial room, which opens on to a private patio (with seating for 35 on warm days). Upstairs, the 35-seat Polo Suite is decorated with historical photos from archives of Indian libraries depicting the sport. The Regal Room is available for parties of up to 15 and also benefits from an open-fireplace and dedicated butler. The décor is designed to revive the Old World charm of the Raj clubs, with opulent fabrics, antique furniture and exposed wood. Manoj likes to blend Indian ingredients with modern techniques and flavours and all his tried and tested favourites are here. Starters include Vegetable Bhanavla – Manoj's version of an onion bhaji, a dish from his native Maharashtra, unusual in that it is first steamed and then griddled; Vegetable Bhanavla and Mussel Rasam. Main courses include dishes such as Monkfish Tikka; Tropical Vegetable Kofta and Lotus Leaf Curry; Nawabi Lamb Sali; Karawari Fish Curry,from India's west coast with an unusual flavour of the spice (trifala) only native to that area; Tandoori Artichoke and Paneer with a rich spicy gravy of cashew nut and roasted vegetable sauce; and Jumbo Prawns marinated in yoghurt, pomegranate seeds and dill griddled and served with onion, ginger & tomato relish. Amongst the desserts, which fuse British and Indian influences, are Tandoori Figs; organic Apple Muesli Crumble; and Mango, roasted coconut and saffron Kulfi. The food is complemented by an enticing wine list created by sommelier Vincent Gasnier designed to match Manoj's light and contemporary cuisine, including an Indian Sauvignon Blanc from the renowned Sula Vineyards in the Nashik Highlands, near Mumbai. Av price: 3 courses: £20 exc wine. Service: 10%. Parking: 30 cars. Hours: 11 – 3 / 5.30-12. Branch: Indian Zing, London W6. www.indianzest.co.uk

TEDDINGTON: BENGAL BRASSERIE 162 Stanley Rd, Teddington ~ 020 8977 7332

TWICKENHAM: THE NAZ 20 Church Street, Twickenham 020 8744 9181. Opened in 1990 and run by Neswar Ali and his son Mohammed Shayed.

TWICKENHAM: SHEESH MAHAL NEW ENTRANT 21, London Rd, TW1 3SX ~020 8892 3303 MA Monaf has recently refurbished to a very high standard. Chef: Umor Ali cooks Bangladeshi curries, like Lamb Nahari, lamb shank marinated in a spicy yoghurt sauce.

PALLAVI SOUTH INDIAN
NEW TO OUR TOP 100

3 Cross Deep Ct, Heath Rd, Twickenham
020 8892 2345

This Keralan first floor restaurant is a branch of the Radha Krishna Bhavan. The menu is the same (see SW17). It specialises in Keralan food, but also does a full listing of curry favourites (chicken, meat et al). *Pallavi is by no means your usual 'Indian restaurant'. In fact it is by no means your usual South Indian restaurant, if there is such a thing. It is situated on the first floor, on a none-too flattering parade of shops, above a small lobby or reception that acts as the Kerala Tourist Board! Upstairs is the restaurant, which is larger than you first realise though by no means grand. A further unusual touch, and one I am always pleased to see, is the kitchen by the side that is open and on show to diners. The service is always polite and attentive without ever being rushed. My daughter Lily, at a little over 12 months old, had her first experience of an Indian restaurant at Pallavi (part of a Masala Dosa) and the staff were all great with her; they even have a highchair in the restaurant. Service aside, what really steals the show at Pallavi is the consistency and quality of the South Indian food. As a vegetarian I am simply spoilt for choice at this place. The Dosas are up there with the Ravi Shankar of old and the India Club, i.e. the best, and the Utthapam is spot-on with the perfect level of chilli-heat. My omnivorous friend speaks equally highly of the meat dishes, in particular the Chilli Chicken. The range of high quality vegetable curries and side dishes is simply too long for me to list here. We are always drawn towards the 'Green Banana', 'Green Beans and Coconut' and 'Beetroot Thoran' as they are just too good to resist. The Green Chilli Paratha is the best example of its kind I've had anywhere, and all the food is not oily in the least. Basically, an absolute delight For my sins I am a Harlequins Rugby Club season ticket holder so regularly find I need cheering-up on my visits to Twickenham; Pallavi never fails to do the job – It is absolutely superb, top quality through and through. As you've gathered Pat, I cannot speak highly enough of this restaurant. For my part it is Top 100 material.'* AG. You are quite right Andy, and since it is owned by Mr Haridas, it should have been awarded that status long ago.

SAGAR

27 York St, Twickenham   020 8744 3868

This is another south Indian restaurant but with a difference. It specialises in Udipi vegetarian cuisine. This one is a branch of the Sagar, Hammersmith, W6. The background and menu details are the same. Hours: 12-2.45 Mon-Fri; 12-11.30 Sat; -10.45 Sun.

TANGAWIZI   NEW TO OUR TOP 100

406 Richmond Rd, Richmond Bridge,
E. Twickenham, TW1 2EB   020 8891 3737

Mr and Mrs Meghji opened Tangawizi in 2004, its name giving no clue as to its cuisine. In fact Tangwizi is Swahili for 'ginger', (the couple are Kenyan Asians). *The dining room is narrow and long, with quite upmarket furnishings: black wooden tables with inlaid fabric, clever lighting, walls in purple and orange with backlit panels, mood music in "Hakkasan" style i.e. very modern background music. On closer inspection the décor doesn't quite hang together. The front and bar area are very attractive, but the toilets are tucked away behind what seems to be a rather rickety partition, and a fabric-hung area towards the back also has an oddly unfinished feel to it. However if you don't look too closely you could pretend you were in a West end restaurant. Waiters are dressed in smart uniforms and the service is efficient and friendly. The key is the cooking team. This is where the chef from the ill-fated W1 Yatra went and he is joined by a tandoor chef from the famous Bhukara in Delhi. I have now had several meals here and this is one example: Complimentary popadums arrive and are above average, served with pleasant but home made chutneys e.g. chilli pickle, good lime pickle and ordinary mango and mint chutney that give little clue of what is to follow. My Chicken Tikka was six very tender, large pieces, which had taken on the marinade spices, served with a few smears of mint sauce. Tandoori Prawns were also very delicate, in this case the marinade being coconut-based. A little glass of Mango Lassi was extremely impressive, though it could have done without the mint leaf adornment which rather dominated the mango flavour. Prawn Biriani, though it did not have the traditional pastry-case top, nonetheless had superbly fragrant rice, cooked beautifully. There were not too many prawns, but other than that the dish was most impressive. Bhindi, a great test of a kitchen, was very good indeed, dry and retaining its texture with no hint of greasiness. Monkfish curry worked well, the fish cooked through properly with a mild but interesting sauce. Aloo Gobi retained the texture of the cauliflower and potatoes, with just the right amount of spiciness. The Makhni Dhal here is superb, made with kidney beans as well as lentils, and is just the same as at Bhukara in Delhi, with great texture and vibrant flavour. Both naan bread and paratha were very good indeed. For dessert they have rather wimped out, making just one: Halwa, and buying in others. This is a pity, since the Kulfi, bought in from Royal, is very ordinary indeed. Yet the Halwa was a delight, the carrot flavour coming through very well, the texture lovely. This is Indian cooking at a very high level indeed (not the bought in desserts). £45 pp for meal and house wine'.* AH: Andy Hayler.com Review. Many reports like this promote it to our TOP 100. Hours: 6.30-11, Sun closed.

Uxbridge

SPICE MERCHANT   NEW ENTRANT

61 Belmont Rd, UB8 1QT   01895 252925

Opened as Masala in 2001 and has recently been refitted and branded Spice Merchant. For the menu and details, see Beaconsfield. Avg Price: £43. Hours: 12-2.30/6-11. Branches: Beaconsfield , Cookham, Henley-on-Thames. www.spicemerchantgroup.com

SATYA

33 Rockingham Rd, Uxbridge   01895 274 250

Satya, meaning a feast, is located in two colourfully decorated, bright and airy rooms with shiny floorboards. The south Indian cast list is present and correct. Doas, Rasam, Sambar and the rest, and we like the fish repertoire, kingfish, pomfret and prawns, laced together with cardamom, curry leaf, turmeric, garlic ginger and coconut. And Udipi temple dish caught our eye.: Mathanga Erissery, gourd curry with lobia (black eye beans). Not as cheap as many in the genre. c£25 per head for food plus wine. The weekday lunch buffet at £6.50 is good value. Hours: 12-3 / 6-11. Branches: Ram's Harrow and Vijay, NW6.

Wembley

For Asian produce, cafés, restaurants and atmosphere Wembley is in our view as good as Southall. Unlike Southall, its large Gujarati/East African population gives Wembley food a different (predominantly vegetarian) taste from Southall. B ut we do observe that the Gujaratis are spreading further afield (to places like Harrow for example) and as with Southall, their places are being taken by south Indian, Sri Lankan and Somalis. There are still many good sweet/snack shops/cafés and restaurants crammed with Indian goodies, but now there is more choice. Here are your favourites:

ASIAN KARAHI

272 Ealing Road, Wembley   020 8903 7524

Small venue (25 seats) which exudes careful service and thoughtful cooking. The usual range of Karahi style cooking is available all week, but at the weekend, they offer some really authentic stuff, not for the faint-hearted: Nihari – marinated leg piece (shank) of lamb served with a spicy gravy, Paya – lamb trotters with thick gravy, Brain curry, Haleem – an almost gruel-like mash of crushed wheat and lamb and Haandi dishes all of very high quality. Spicing is done to taste.

CHETNA'S BHEL PURI   TOP 100

420 High Road, Wembley   020 8903 5989

A large, very popular vegetarian licensed restaurant with

vegan dishes. *'You often have to queue here. We waited on the pavement until they called out our number, but it is well worth it. They do deluxe Masala Dosas, and a great Vegetarian Thali main course. Their Bhel Puri is gorgeous, with its crispy, crunchy textures, and its tart, hot and savoury tastes, and there is a variant called Aloo Papdi Chaat'.* JM. Alongside dishes from Gujarat and south India, they serve pizzas , reflecting the craze, not only amongst Wembley Asians, but in Delhi and Bombay! Hours: 12-3 / 6-10.30.

CHOWPATTY

234 Ealing Road, Wembley   020 8795 0077

It's over a decade ago now since Chowpatty beach, at the northern end of Bombay's celebrated Marina Parade was famous for its wheeled stalls selling the world's most exquisite Bhel Puri and Chaat. Then the 'clean-up' authorities stepped in and banished the traders and renamed Bombay 'Mumbai'. All that is left is the memory, recalled at this vegetarian venue in the form of huge vivid murals. The Bhel and Chaat here also brings back those memories, and is as good as it gets. The owners themselves tell us they are not from Mumbai, but come from northern Gujarat, ie in the desert area which borders Rajasthan, where the cuisine is called Kutchi. So you can order Kadhi, Gujarat's national soup-like dish of turmeric, gram flour and yoghurt, or Bajra Roti, Rajasthan's millet bread, or Kutchi specialities the like of Baingan Oro (aka Baigan Burtha, the smoky grilled, mashed aubergine dish). Other Gujarati breads (not usually encountered in the UK) include Missi Roti maize flour bread with red chilli and Methi Thepla a wheatbread with fresh fenugreek leaf. Vegetable Kebabs are masterly, as are the Pakoras. On offer are Thalis £4-£9 are great as is the satisfying set buffet (11-4 Sun) at just £4.50. 'Chinese' items too, but there is enough original choice on the menu to leave that for another time. Service: 10%. Del 5m over £12. Hours: 11-3 /5.30-10, Mon-Fri; 11-11.30 Sat; 10 Sun.

DADIMA

228 Ealing Road, Wembley   020 8902 1072

Another exciting restaurant in that here is yet another speciality Gujarati restaurant. Here the owners tell us they're from Ahmedabad (Mahatma Gandhi's birth place. Dadima (granny in Gujarati) certainly is family run, and I wouldn't be surprised if Granny herself was there in charge of the kitchen. She would most certainly be the matriarch and what she says goes. I myself received my cooking lessons from my ex Raj Granny (and what she said went) and my first chef training from Gujarati, Sat Gupta. I found the sweetness and mildness of Gujarati food quite a shock, and a big change for my palate used as it was to chilli and savoury tastes. India is far more complex than that. Bearing in mind that a person's tolerance to chilli is a personal matter, for those who that do like it 'hot', will find the food of

Ahmedabad, and of Dadima, quite robust and spiky. *'We cook it with Lal Masala (mixture of red spices')* including chilli and coriander. Try Gran's Thali for a filling selection of Dadima-style cooking. Vegetable curries, rice, dhal, yoghurt, pickles and puris from £3. Hours: 12-3 / 5-10 Mon, Wed-Fri; 12-10 Sat & Sun.

GANA

24 Ealing Road, Wembley   020 8903 7004

Authentic Sri Lankan food including an array of rice-based dishes, and the celebrated Kotthu Roti (strips of chupatti interspersed usually with a spicy minced meat (keema) curry. Here it is more akin the Brum's Tropical Balti, in that the kitchen sink goes in: 'very special sir , said the waiter – lamb, beef, chicken fish and prawns. And it was too. Never met that combination before or since, but it was quite nice' heg. The don't take credit cards. Set lunch £4.50 House wine £7 Hours: 10-11.

KARAHI KING

213 East Lane, Wembley   020 8904 2760

Fabulous food, Kenyan Asian curries, kebabs and Tandoor items being showily prepared by the on-view chefs in their open kitchen. Try Mogo Bhajia a pakora of sweet potato complete with a super imli (tamarind) chutney, or the fabulous tandoori (including the breads) and note the love-it-or hate-it taste of Kala Namak (black salt). If you do get past the starters, try the curries for meat-eaters and vegetarians. Methi Murgh divine. No credit cards. No corkage, so BYO. Hours: 12-12 daily.

KARAHI RAJA

195 East Lane, Wembley   020 8904 5553

Established in 1993 by Mushtaq Ahmed. Restaurant seats 150 in two rooms. Pakistani curries are cooked by B Hussain. House specials include: Haandi Chicken – chicken on the bone cooked with herbs, tomatoes and spicy thick sauce. Paya – lamb trotters Lahori style. Vegetarian dishes: Karahi Egg, scrambled egg, tomatoes, coriander and green chillies. Unlicensed and BYO allowed, no corkage charge. Hours: 12-12 daily.

MARU'S BHAJIA HOUSE

230 Ealing Rd, Alperton   020 8903 6771

At Ealing end of this gourmet paradise road, is Maru's opened by yes, Maru in 1984, and it was one of the road's first, and as they say the first is often the best. It provides family unique style vegetarian curries from East Africa. Their Bhajias are the real thing, and they are even spelt correctly, rather than the formula Bhaji. Try their Potato Bhajias, besan-batter-coated, deep-fried and served with tamarind (imli) chutney as a real treat to die for. Strictly No alcohol allowed. Hours: 12-9.30pm.

MARUTI BHEL PURI

238a Ealing Rd, Wembley   020 8903 6743

A vegetarian restaurant serving inexpensive melt-in-the-mouth delights, such as Dosas with Sambar and, of course, the namesake Bhel Puri. Try their Karahi Corn-on-the-Cob. *'All fantastic stuff for the lucky residents of Wembley. I wish I lived nearer.'* DC. *'After eating our fill of Popadums, we started the proceedings with Jeera Chicken. Good value in terms of standard of cooking. When there is a concert or football match at the Stadium, a set dinner buffet is provided. Dishes were full of spices and excellent. Service was very friendly.'* AN. Hours: 12-10; closed Tues.

POOJA COTTAGE

305 Harrow Rd, Wembley   020 8902 4039

Est '85 by T Moniz, as Wembley Cottage, this 45-seater is Nepalese. Baban in the kitchen cooks up unusual delights which include Mariz (pepper) Chicken £5.95, Nepalese Chicken Bhutuwa, highly spiced £6.25. Chicken Chowla, tandoor-cooked with ginger/garlic £5.95. *'Not terribly impressed with the food.'* RM. *'Very impressed with the food.'* CT. Hours: 12-2.30/ 6-11.30.

SAKONI

119 Ealing Rd, Alperton   020 8903 9601

Alcohol is not allowed at vegetarian Sakoni, which to some (including Asians we know) is a shame, but which seems not to deter from its popularity as its longer hours (breakfast!) and expansion proves. This founder branch is now enormous, with its conservatory extension serving that Asian of Asian delights, Paan (see Nargis, Southall above and page 68) It's family-run by Gujaratis Kenyans who know about the food and tradition. But they offer variety to their regular Asian customers (of whom there are many) – dishes such as Chinese vegetarian noodles and Bombay Sandwich, white sliced bread with spicy spreading, a kind of relic of the Raj, the like of which you still, amazingly, find in Indian public schools and army messes. Such things make a change, but I for one prefer Sakoni's authentic Indian items (Dosai, Vadai, Utthapam et al), in a pleasant and informal atmosphere. *'Service good and quick. Generous portions. Chutneys are freshly prepared and not removed from the table every few minutes, which makes a change from most other Indian restaurants. Recommended.'* RM. Hours: 9am-11/12-10 daily. Branches: 116 Station Rd, Edgware; 6 Dominion Pde, Station Rd, Harrow; 180 Upper Tooting Rd, SW17.

SARAVANAA BHAVAN

531 High Rd, Wembley   020 8795 3777

Saravanaa Bhavan is a rival to the Woodlands chain of

south Indian vegetarian cafés that dominate south India and elsewhere. They are no-nonsense, no-alcohol, no-haute-décor caffs which serve substantially good vegetarian food at no-nonsense prices. Unlike its Tamil Nadu and Keralan sister branches, this one serves Punjabi and Chinese dishes. Hours 11-10, daily. Branch: Manor Park, E12.

WOODLANDS   TOP 100

402a High Street, Wembley   020 8902 9869

South Indian vegetarian food, expertly done. See reports in the branches Hours: 12-2.45/6-10.45. UK Branches: London SW1 and W1, W4.

YOU SAY OK

You might get a disc if you show them this Guide.

WEMBLEY TANDOORI 133a Wembley Rd, Wembley ~ 020 8902 2243. Nepalese menu at D Chhetry's venue. Eg: Momo, Simi Soup, Nepalese Chicken Bhutuwa, Nepalese Vegetable, Aloo Tama. Del: £16 min, 2m. Hours: 12-2.30/6-11.30; 12 Sat.

WEST DRAYTON: ACHARI NEW ENTRANT 363 Sipson Rd, Sipson, West Drayton UB7 0HU ~ 020 84761100

SIPSON TANDOORI 5 Harmondsworth Rd, W. Drayton UB7 9JJ ~ 01895 435515 160-seater owned by Sirajul & Rofiqul Islam. www.sipsontandoori.co.uk

NORFOLK

Area: East
Population: 818,000
Adjacent Counties:
Cambs,
Suffolk

Great Yarmouth

PLANET PAPADUM   NEW ENTRANT

5 Marine Parade, NR30 3AH   01493 330777

'With its seafront location, modern décor and colourful paintings of Bollywood dancers, Planet Papadum has quickly become by far the best around. It boasts an extensive menu of classic Indian dishes, but with a depth of flavour and quality of ingredients that is often lacking in other establishments. Manager Naz runs the front, while Head Chef Khan works his magic in the kitchen, producing food to suit all palates – a subtle, fragrant Lemon Grass Chicken for those who like things flavoursome but not too spicy; a zingy, tangy Balti Chicken Peshwari for those in the mid-range; and a fiery, explosive chilli chicken for those who prefer things sizzling hot. Vegetable sides are particularly good, making this a popular place for vegetarians, and if you're lucky enough to visit on a quiet night, then Khan might have time to cook you one of his many

'off menu' specials – just let him know how hot you like it and let him do the rest! The chef there, Khan, has amazing talent, and should stick far more of his own dishes on the menu, but I guess like lots of other Indian restaurant owners, he feels obliged to serve the chicken tikka massalas, kormas, etc, rather than presenting people with a menu where they might not recognise anything. All his 'off-menu' dishes are sensational, though - and got him quite a long way in last year's Tiffin Cup! SA. Hours: 12.30-3 / 5.30-11.30. www.planet-papadum.co.uk

Norwich

JEWEL OF INDIA

41 Magdalen St, Norwich   01603 666601

'Very fresh and clean interior if a little sparse. Small waiting area but seated immediately. Very attentive waiters and extensive menu, including fish and duck dishes. Chicken Dhansak the way it is meant to be, hot sweet and sour, deliciously different Hash Tikka, marinated duck, salads, popadums and pickles all very fresh. Portion sizes and meat content very good, food service a little slow (opening night) but arrived very hot with a delicious fluffy garlic naan. A very pleasant dining experience'. JB. 'Our third visit. Appetisers include more unusual duck and mushroom dishes. Main course of Bengal Naga c£12, the biggest prawns I have ever seen, delicately marinated in hot chilli and beautifully cooked – a complete meal in itself served with fresh salad and tandoori onions. Raj Hash, marinated duck c£9, again spiced beautifully to compliment the strong duck meat. Naan bread very soft and springy, popadums fresh as was salad and accompaniments, rice cooked to perfection. There is also a large selection of vegetarian dishes, including veg options of the main dishes and plenty of side dish choices. Usual selection of coffees, alcoholic drinks and desserts. Vegetable Dhansak £4.50, most beautiful version of this dish I have ever tasted - ingredients included chick peas, mixed beans and fresh potatoes and vegetables. This is a vast improvement to the many other restaurants that think they can get away with serving vegetarians second rate ingredients, namely cheap frozen mixed veg - for this alone this restaurant gets my vote!' JB.

SPICE LOUNGE   NEW ENTRANT

10 Wensum Street, NR3 1HR   01603 766602

'The ultra-modern decor is what hits you first of all, as you enter into the downstairs bar. Then you're whisked upstairs into the stylish dining room to feast on high-quality, authentic Indian dishes. Handi Murgh bursts with green chilli flavour and is cooked in the traditional Bengali style, while fish lovers will enjoy the Mahe Mahe Supreme, which sees boneless pieces of monkfish served with baby potatoes, or the Machlee Angara, a specially marinated sea bass grilled on a charcoal oven and then dressed with salad. Always seems to be full, it's always wise to book ahead. Mains from £5, to £10.0 region for king prawn and marinated fish dishes.' SA Hours: 12-2, not Fri /6-12.

YOU SAY OK

You might get a discount if you show them this Guide.

DISS TANDOORI 1 Shelfhanger Rd Diss ~ 01379 651685
Owned by Jahal Khan and M Ruhel in 1986.

DOWNHAM: DOWNHAM TANDOORI 56 High St, Downham 01366 386110. 40-seater opened 1996 by Abdul Ali. T/a: 10% disc. Hours: 12-2.30/6-11.30.

GREAT YARMOUTH: BOMBAY NITE 25a King St ~ 01493 331383. *Now twice the size and modernised, but with a few nice reminders of its traditional past. Keema Peas has just enough sauce; Rhongpuri chicken is a must for mint lovers, since it positively bursts with the stuff! Manager Naz ensures a friendly welcome. Excellent vegetarian set menu ensures no one in your party need go home hungry'.* SA

KING'S LYNN: INDIA GATE 41 St James Street ~ 01553 776489

NORWICH: SPICE PARADISE 41, Magdalagen St. Formerly Jewel in India, now specialises in Keralan South Indian. *'Especially interesting is the House Fish Soup and the South Indian Lamb Curry.'* DF. Reports please.

THETFORD: SAFFRON INDIAN CUISINE 17 St Giles Lane, Thetford ~ 01842 76200

NORTHAMPTONSHIRE

Area:
Central East Midlands
Population: 646,800
Adjacent Counties:
Beds, Cambs,
Leics, Oxon

YOU SAY OK NORTHANTS

You might get a discount if you show them this Guide.

BRACKLEY: PRINCE CALCUTTA 36 Market Place, Brackley ~ 01280 703265

IRTHLINGBOROUGH: EASTERN SPICE 56 High Street~ 01933 650044. 100-seater est 1972. Foyzur Rahman from 2004, mngr Majibur Ali. Hours: 6-11.30. www.easternspiceindiancuisine.co.uk

KETTERING: MONSOON BAR & INDIAN Ebenezer Place.01536 417421. 90-seater est 1998 by P Sadrani – colourfully painted Tudor style. T/a: 20% disc. Del: 4m. Hours: 5.30-12.

KETTERING: THE RAJ 46 Rockingham Road ~ 01536 513606. Goyas Miah's 110-seater. Del: 3m £10 min. Sun Buffet: £5.95. Hours: 12-2 / 5.30-2; Sun 12-12. www.therajrestaurant.net

Kettering

MAZZA   NEW ENTRANT

2, Kettering Bs Pk, Pegasus Ct, NN15 6XS
                                         01536 524888

'On arrival despite the venue being very busy with Christmas parties we were shown straight to our table and offered drinks, Pops etc which were delivered promptly and were excellent. Waiter took our orders using a PDA which beams the orders to the kitchen (only used for Starters & Main Courses). Starters - Tandoori mixed & Khadom Phool. TM very good. but the KP was a little bland and not as appetising as described on the menu. Main Courses - Chicken Chasnidargh & Crab Massala, Cheese Nan, Tarka Dall & Keema Rice. CC tasted excellent but was delivered to the table a little colder than I would have liked, The PDA ordering let them down as they incorrectly served Chicken Tikka Massalla which was returned and replaced by the Crab. Fi was very disappointed with the dish, the Crab looked as if it had been puréed and was a more like Crab Bisque, the Tarka Dall was fabulous as was the rice and Nan bread. Desserts - Were the usual "Ice Cream Variations only", but we selected a Mango Kulfi and Coconut Ice- cream to cleanse the palate. Overall a pleasant venue with excellent service and delightful ambience, offering something very different for Curry lovers in the Kettering area. We will visit again soon and try other offerings on the menu. Food, drink & serv £51.' DL.

Kingsthorpe

BOMBAY PALACE

9 Welford Rd, Kingsthorpe, NN2 8DE   01604 713899

'On the spur of the moment decision to visit this old friend, proved to be an excellent decision. Whilst staff and decor hadn't changed at all, the menu had undergone a massive revamp. New dishes include: Chicken Puri £4; Garlic Mushroom on Puri £3.50; Chicken Pakora £3; Vegetable Pakora £2.75; Venison dishes from £7. Spicy Popadums, very good with OK Chutneys; Vegetable Pakora, lovely, really nice; Reshmi Kebab £2.75, superb, cooked perfectly; Chicken Tikka Biriani £8, OK with very good Chapati; Meat Thali £9.95, very generous portions, beautifully cooked, I couldn't finish it all with lovely, fresh and light Naan Bread £1.10. First class service. Will not leave it so long to return!' DL. Del: 5m £10 min. Hours: 5.30- 1.30; 12 Fri & Sat

Northampton

COCHI

INDIAN PARADISE

39, Barrack Road   01604 622228

'Arrived, having not booked but they soon found a table and offered drinks and Popadums whilst selecting from the menu. Nice decor with excellent chairs upholstered in either blue or red with very high backs. Gosht Xacuti £9; Khumb Mutter £7 (with chicken tikka), Keema Naan , Chapati, Tarka Dall all beautifully presented and cooked to perfection. Service was a little too attentive at times, asked how our meals were at least half a dozen times.!' DL. Specials: Masala Roasty Duck, strips of tender duck breast marinated and cooked in a rich spicy tomato, onion and herb sauce; Hot Peri, chicken and meat cooked together with diced potato in a tangy sauce prepared with special fiery chilli sauce; Dhingri Palak , chopped spinach leaves and button

mushrooms lightly fried in a strong cumin and ginger sauce. BYO. T/a: 10% disc. £10 min. Del: 5m £8 min. Hours: 12-2 / 5.30-11. www.indian-paradise.co.uk

MEM-SAAB

357 Wellingborough Rd   01604 630214

'The Mem-saab opened in 2001 and was the first restaurant in Northampton to be owned and managed by Indians' [Munjit Kaur and her family, Ed] 'specialising in Punjabi food, rather than Bangladeshis. It's in the old Mansfield shoe factory and is spacious, light and airy with minimalist decor. It is divided into a very plush lounge area, boasting very comfy cream leather sofas where you can relax pre and post meal and the restaurant itself. All the staff are smartly unpretentiously presented in smart pressed shirts and neckties, which excludes the ladies who wear smart blouses. It is also very quirky to hear the Asian owners speak in a very broad Scottish accent sounding like a very educated Billy Connelly. I went on Sun afternoon for a three course buffet with the added bonus of Live Jazz. I have never been impressed with the e-a-m-a-y-l buffets as they tend be very unimaginative. However, the Mem Saab however surpassed itself on every course. The starters consisted of a salmon and red snapper dish, seekh and shaslik kebabs, onion bhajis, garlic tossed mushrooms, vegetable pakoras, chilled shrimps and popadums, these were also accompanied with fresh homemade pickles and chutneys such as tamarind, apple, piquant onions, mango chutney plus fresh green coriander and mint chutney. The main course offered a mildly spiced garlic chicken, a rich lamb dish in a clinging spicy gravy which boasted very large cubes of good quality lamb, a mixed aubergine and potato dish, ma-ki dhal which is very much a Punjabi speciality consisting of whole black urid dhal in a spicy buttery gravy and Kudi with gram flour dumplings which is a a Gujarati speciality with yoghurt and gram flour gravy lightly spiced with turmeric, a dish which I would never have dared to order as the description never has appealed to me but I'm really glad I did try it. Naan bread was also supplied and on my request chapattis were supplied at no extra charge (some of the best I have ever eaten). The sweet trolley had a vast array of fresh seasonal fruits plus Rasgullah. The afternoon was a very enjoyable experience and the unobtrusive background entertainment added to the pleasure. They have now opened a champagne & cocktail bar in the adjoining building which is called Corkers, reports are good but far from cheap but probably a small price to pay for a select environment and clientele.' PM. 'PS: Try the Lamb Nihari, served in thin gravy with aromatic spices in particular cardamom and ground cloves garnished with thin juliennes slices of fresh ginger.' Branches: Glasgow, Nottingham and Leicester.

RIVER SPICE TANDOORI

Garden Village, The Causeway, Gt Billing, N'ton
01604 411700

'In the grounds of a garden centre on the outskirts of Northampton in a former nightclub premises but the advantage of its location is that it doesn't attract the twenty pints and hottest curry brigade, but has strong appeal to those who enjoy a well-presented, superbly cooked, more authentic Indian meal in a very friendly and relaxed atmosphere where courtesy and service is second to none. After several visits, I went to try out the skills of the new Indian chef. The menu offers tried and tested favourites, unusual house specialities, plus some blackboard specials, which included a Kenyan-Asian dish of Piri Piri chicken, a special ginger chicken plus many authentic vegetable dishes. We made our choice and waited in anticipation in the bar. The meal arrived and we were not disappointed: the lamb dishes were cooked to perfection boasting a thick gravy, min oil and no over spicing; the chicken dish, a new introduction, was a dry dish cooked with fresh green chillies and honey, which I suspect is not authentic, but good all the same, whilst the two new vegetable dishes we tried consisted of very spicy paneer, which had been lightly fried and had taken on the flavours of the rich tomato gravy and an aubergine dish which was cooked in yoghurt-based gravy. All in all a very pleasurable dining experience pushing the culinary boundaries further towards the East than the West. I long to see one hundred percent authentic Indian dishes but this venue produces a compromise which attracts many ethnic diners on a regular basis.' PM.

TAMARIND   NEW ENTRANT

151 Wellingborough Road Northampton
NN1 4DX   01604 231194

Opened in 2005, and situated on Northampton's Curry mile, its owner Chef Tipu Rahman won the 2009 "International Indian Chef of the Year", organised by Edinburgh Raj's Tommy Miah. After taking this accolade Tipu was then invited to assist Mr Miah in cooking a meal for 50 influential European Union diplomats and officials at The Bangladesh Embassy in Brussels. Tamarind's ontemporary design features black and white décor, giving a feeling of spaciousness which is further enhanced by its glass frontage and mirrored rear wall. Since taking over the premises Tipu has also introduced a secondary entrance leading in from the spacious public car park, the layout of the restaurant is well thought out and is more than inviting. 'We were warmly welcomed by Chef Tipu himself, who was tonight taking the position of Matre'D, a role which he evidently had taken to like a duck to water. The menu not only showed the usual suspects but had the addition of Nepalese dishes and some interesting Chefs specials, the choice also extended to duck, swordfish, monkfish and I think venison as well as the usual chicken, lamb, prawns and king prawns. We had popadoms, were served with the usual array of chutneys plus the Tamarinds own Naga chilli pickle which had more than a bit of a kick and had a very pleasing unique flavour. For the main course we had chosen Tawa Monkfish, Chicken and Nepalese Lamb Bhutuwa and Chicken Jalfrezi. We also chose three vegetable side dishes, rice and a selection of breads. All the dishes were of generous proportion, boasting meat and chicken which were moist and tender presented in gravies

which were vastly different in appearance, texture and taste and were not over masked by too heavy spicing. We declined a sweet course which could have been a little more adventurous and decided to go for coffees and masala tea, the meal was concluded with brandies and baileys courtesy of Tipu. The price of a very enjoyable night for four was c£100; including drinks and a bottle of wine, which seemed more than reasonable taking into account the high quality of food and attentive service. We would not hesitate to return.' PM.

YOU SAY OK

You might get a discount if you show them this Guide.

NORTHAMPTON: FAR COTTON TANDOORI 111 St Leonards Rd, Far Cotton, N'ton ~ 01604 706282

MAHARAJAH 146 Wellingborough Rd ~ 01604 637 049. *'Superb cooking'.* DL.

RAJPUT BALTI 224a Wellingborough Rd ~ 01604 637336. Shahab Uddin's 50-seater,curries, cooked by chef Shofor Ali. Hours: 12-2.30/6-12.

STAR OF INDIA 5 Abingdon Av, Northampton ~ 01604 630664

Rushden

CHUTNEYS

86 High Street, Rushden	01933 411 994

'A round of Pops and chuts set us up nicely before the starters. Shamee Kebab - finely minced and ground steak fried with herbs and spices, and Chicken Tikka - lived up to the billing on the menu. Impressed with house special, Tandoori King Prawn Massalla - tasty, not too hot and cooked to perfection. Tawa Chicken - cooked with paprika, onion, tomato and herbs with a touch of garlic and shredded ginger. Shabzi Chaatwalla - crisp stir-fried vegetables in a sweet and sour sauce, mixed with chat masala, paprika and red chilli served with Pullao Rice - enjoyed. We shared a Cheese and Onion Naan, which made a refreshing change from my usual Peshwari. Each dish tasted as good as they sounded and portions were more than enough.' SW.

Wellingborough

INDIA NIGHT   NEW ENTRANT

16, High St, NN8 4JU	01933 441500

'*Though it is just 25 yards away from my work place, I had not given it much attention until an Indian colleague mentioned that the food was of a good standard also on Weds nights they do a starter, main course, side dish, rice or naan bread for just £6.95. Four of us went and had Rashmi Kebabs, two large very succulent lamb patties wrapped in a thin omelette, the spicing was fragrant and not overpowering, served with the usual green salad, and Tikkas also of a high standard. Mains: I had Achaari Lamb, cooked in pickling spices which was presented in rich spicy gravy enhanced with garam masala of which the tartness of kalonji and fennel was evident, plus they were quite happy to present the dish with a little more chilli*

and split green chillies on request which lifted the dish. My wife chose a dish described as chicken with cashews and honey which was called Jali, she was a little disappointed in its blandness. The two remaining ate Lamb Dopiaza and a rich chicken dish, the title of the latter cannot be recalled but both were more than satisfied with their choice. Whilst it may be a formula curryhouse, the chef had used his expertise and imagination to make the various dishes unique and prove that his menu was more than a one sauce does all. Included in the package was a side dish for each diner all of which were all a little different in their spicing and the dal tarka was rich thick and flavoursome. rice and breads were as expected. Overall the restaurant had paid attention to detail, the service was polite, attentive and unobtrusive and the young English waitress who's first night it was, seemed to be coping with her new roll with considerable ease. Whilst the fittings and décor was not expensive or state of the art it was thoughtfully and comfortably laid out making the most of what they could offer and they did offer considerable more than the average, even though the food promotion was to a fixed price the portions were not scaled down in fact they were very much on the generous side. I look forward to a return visit which will probably be in the very near future.' PM.

NORTHUMBERLAND

Area: North East
Population: 311,000
Adjacent Counties:
Borders, Cumbria,
Durham,
Tyne & Wear

Berwick-upon-Tweed

MAGNA   A-LIST

39 Bridge Street, Berwick	01289 302736

Jahangir Khan owns this 80-seater family business. It has been in our Guide since we started it in 1984. *'And no wonder'* says CC member Michael Fabricant, MP. Free car park 100 yards away. The building is impressive, made pretty by flower boxes. Inside is cosy, with inviting green sofas in the bar and the Magna's certificates, many of them ours, line the walls. *'A pretty restaurant with smartly dressed black-tie waiters.'* MF. It does very well cooked, unpretentious formula food. Specials include: Murghi Mossalla, Ash de Bash and Chandee Dishes, very mild with fresh cream and mango from £8.50. Shim Dishes, cooked with green beans from c£9. '*Once again I felt I had to put pen to paper. I feel my local, The Magna, still comes out on top for taste, quality, service,*

cleanliness, value and very polite friendly staff. I personally find this restaurant one of the most stress-free environments I can think of and my wife and I often have a drink or two after our meal and just relax. I'm glad to see it remains in the Guide's estimation.' BA. *'My husband and I have been coming to this restaurant for many years. We never book a table, we just turn up. Always greeted pleasantly and politely and given excellent service while we are there. Although we have very hearty appetites, we invariably take a 'doggy bag' home. We feel fortunate to have the Magna here.'* SS. *'Having spent the day visiting the many attractions, it is always important to have a good meal, in pleasant surroundings with good quality service and value for money – all is provided at the Magna. Staff always courteous, taking your coat and carrying drinks through to the table. Especially appreciated.'* KR. When we told Jehangir Khan that he was nominated this Guide's Best in the north Award, he was over the moon about it. We are over the moon with it too. T/a: 20% disc. Hours: 12-2 not Sun / 5.30-12.

THE VALLEY   A-LIST

The Old Station Hs, Corbridge   01434 633434

Corbridge station building in the beautiful Tyne valley, was built in 1835 for Stephenson's railway. It is no longer used as a station although it is on the important Newcastle-to-Carlisle railway line. Trains stop at Corbridge station throughout each day, but passengers do not use the old building any more. That is until Daraz (Syed Nadir Aziz) turned it into a stylish, upmarket Indian restaurant in 1991. Seats 80, car parking for 20 directly outside. A feature of which is a unique service, for parties of 10 to 80 from £28.50 a head, including return travel. Uniformed restaurant staff welcome you at Newcastle Central Station and escort you by train to The Valley. En route, choose four courses from the à la carte menu. The order is rung through on a mobile. Your starter is awaiting your arrival. *'It beats ordering a taxi.'* GM. Of course, individuals can make their own way here and back by scheduled train – but beware a fairly early last train. Or, there is parking for 12 cars. Why not book your T/a by phone en-route, collect, pay and eat it, without leaving the train As for the restaurant, there is a reception room and 80 seats in four connecting rooms (one of which opens onto the eastbound platform). Decor is lush and Indian. And the food Chef Pervez Ahmed's menu contains all the CC (currinarily correct) favourites plus some good specials. *'Arriving at this impressive building at about 7.30pm, we enquired if we could have a table for 8.15pm. We were assured there was no problem, so, gave us a chance to walk back along station road for a pint of decent, real ale at Dyvels. We arrived back on cue to study the menu in the bar, complete with a photograph of Daraz, the owner and Pat Chapman. Were shown to a window table, we watched a train pull into the station, just outside the restaurant. Entertainment as well! Very impressive menu, had quite a problem deciding on main dishes. Disappointed with Mixed Starter £8.95 for two - just*

one each sheek kebabs, lamb tikka and chicken wings with sizzling onions - are we spoilt in West Yorkshire Monica ate Luari Mangsho £8.25 and I, Special Bhuna Gosht £8.95 - I must say these were very good, but looked similar. Pullao Rice also very good and Naan tasty with portions just about right. A memorable meal for its situation.' T&MH. Menu Snapshot: Dahi Baigan £4.25 - grilled aubergine, stuffed with vegetables, topped with spice yoghurt; Chingri Varkee £4.50, grilled pepper stuffed with spicy prawns; Salmon Bhajia £11.50 - fried with fresh herbs, garlic, ginger and raw onion; Duck Masallam £10.95, breast marinated in herbs, cooked and served in a spicy, creamy sauce with coconut; Beef Adrok £9.95, topside cooked with fresh herbs and lot of fresh ginger. Chef's Choice: seven course surprise (the only surprise being that the chef chooses your meal) dinner - £59.95 for two and £110 for four - sounds wonderful! T/a: 20% disc. We are delighted that the Valley is nominated best in the north. Hours: 6-10; closed Sun. Branch: Valley Junction 397, The Old Station, Archibold Terrace, Jesmond, Newcastle. and Valley Connection 301, Hexham (see alongside). www.valleyrestaurants.co.uk

VALLEY CONNECTION 3   Market Place, Hexham 01434 601234. Prime location in the centre of the market place, next to Hexham Abbey. Very smart inside. For Menu details see The Valley above.

Hexham

DIWAN-E-AM

4- Country Mills, Priestpopple   01434 606575

Diwan-e-am was the Moghul palace meeting room. And Mr Choudury's 86 seat venue, est in 1983. is aptly named. 'Pleasant decor and environment, friendly and helpful staff. Menu extensive, but no curry house inventions such as vindaloo here. Starters include the excellent Diwan Khata Mita Soup (garlic and lentils) and Mathu Vortha (grapefruit with chilli and coriander). Main course selection includes a wide range of duck and fish dishes. More expensive than the 'usual' curry house, but good value given the high standard of the meals.' cf. House-style cuisine (staff curry) on demand for regular customers. You might get a discount if you show them this Guide. Takeaway: 20% discount. Hours: 5.30-11pm; Sun. 6.30-10.30pm.

YOU SAY OK
You might get a discount if you show them this Guide.

BEDLINGTON: FRONTIER KARAHI HOUSE 46 Front St, West Bedlington ~ 01670 820222. Hours: 5.30-1; closed Mon.

CORBRIDGE: CORBRIDGE TANDOORI 8 Market Square, Corbridge   01434 633676 SM Shahjahan's small restaurant est. 89 is above a bookshop. Hours: 12-2.30/6-11.30.

DIWAN-E-AM

4-5 Country Mills
Priestpopple
Hexham
01434 606575

Curry Club and Good Curry Guide recommended

Monday to Saturday: 5.30-11pm
Sunday: 6.30-10.30pm.

Morpeth

TANDOORI MAHAL

17 Bridge Street, Morpeth   01670 512420

Suroth Miah opened its doors in 1980. The interior is sleek, with white walls and a deep red carpet, which is also reflected in the very smart wooden chairs upholstery and the large lamb shades that hang from the ceiling. Crisp, white table linen and yellow roses decorate each table. Original art work hangs, sparingly, on the walls. It all makes for a very upmarket and calming dining experience. Food is served on large white oval platters, which shows off the vibrant colours of the food beautifully. Specials include: Murgh Tikka Paneer £4, marinated pieces of chicken tikka, fried with cheese, onions and green peppers; Tali Macchi £5, fish fillets marinated in spicy batter and pan fried, tempered with brown onions; Murgh Masala £8.50, spring chicken off the bone cooked with minced lamb, onions, spices, herbs, nuts and sultanas; Tawa Murgh £8, tangy moong dal and boneless chicken cooked with freshly prepared spices on a tawa griddle. Hours: 12-2.30/6-12; 11.30 Sun. www.tandoor-mahal.co.uk

NOTTINGHAMSHIRE

Area: East Midlands
Population: 1,045,000
Adjacent Counties:
Derbs, Leics,
Lincs, Yorks

Nottingham
(includes Basford, Beeston, Mapperley, Radford, Sherwood, and West Bridgford.)

4500 MILES FROM DELHI

41 Mount Street   0115 947 5111

The name says it all - it's literally 4550 m from Delhi. Danny Punia owns this 4000 sq m former public house, which has been transformed internally and externally to include a ten metre high glazed atrium in which the bar is located. A halved motorised-rickshaw (tuk-tuk) gives a new meaning to wall-hanging. Suspended cylindrical stainless steel lights over the bar, a bronze staircase and solid oak and recycled slate flooring on which sit 130 Italian made chairs with bronze inlay work in the dining

area overlooking an open kitchen. Chef Mahaneshwar Pal, previously with Delhi's Taj Palace Hotel has developed a North Indian menu that also includes a choice of set meals priced at c£18 per person. Popular dishes include Tikkas, and Seekhs, Aloo Tikkis and a selection of simmered curries cooked by the Dum Pukht pot method. (see p50). Punia hopes to open further branches, naming each after its distance from Delhi and has plans to open a 4320 m from Delhi in London, and 4480 m from Delhi in Sheffield. An open 'theatre' kitchen enables you to watch the chefs from Delhi as they work. 'Can you mention that restaurant is closed on a Sun, we made a trip there last weekend only to be disappointed.' JB. It is now open on Suns, but always ring first. Hours: 12-2.30 / 6-10.30. www.mfromdelhi.com Branch: Shimla Pinks, London Road, Leicester

THE INDIAN COTTAGE

7 Bentnick Rd (off Alfreton Rd), Radford,
Nottingham W   0115 942 4922

Pretty black beams, white frontage and inviting curtained windows at Naj Aziz's 40-seater in 2 areas (smoking and non-smoking). Very stylish restaurant, un-Indian, unfussy, light and bright, Wedgwood blue ceiling and magnolia walls. Walls are decorated with hanging carpets and backlit fretwork, tiled floor, large palms in white pots. We hear that the food is family-style. Hours: 6-10.30 Tues–Sat. Closed 16-30 Aug, a week at Christmas.

YOU SAY OK

You might get a discount if you show them this Guide.
BEESTON: BEESTON TANDOORI 150 High Rd, Beeston ~ 0115 922 3330
STAPLEFORD: MOUSHUMI 124 Derby Rd. ~ 0115 939 4929

SAAGAR   TOP 100

473 Mansfield Rd, Sherwood   0115 962 2014

Mohammed Khizer leads the kitchen brigade at his Victorian-style 98-seater on two floors est 1984. *'We found it to be good in all departments, and to me cleanliness comes before everything else. It was all spotless, and most inviting'.* RCF. *'Have visited this restaurant regularly since 1988. Wonderful Lamb Tandoori and Prawn Puri. My favourite 'Indian Restaurant.'* HW. *'A fantastic curry where I just moved from. I'm sure you know of this.'* JLR. Menu Snapshot: Kashmiri Chicken Tikka £4.90, topped with Kashmiri sauce; Chicken Anguri £9.95, mild and fruity, cooked with pineapple, banana, prunes, grape juice and fresh cream; Nizami Masala Chicken £9.95, cooked with nuts, coconut, yoghurt and sesame seeds; Butter Chuppati £1., Spinach and Yoghurt Bhajee £4.50. T/a: 10% disc. Front of house is managed by

Imtiaz Ahmed, leaving Mr Khizer to do his thing in the kitchen, assisted by Amjaid Parvaiz. Discount for Guide readers at lunch times. Hours: 12-2.15 / 5.30-12 daily.

Mapperley:

SPICE TAKEAWAY   NEW TO OUR TOP 100

459 Westdale Lane   0115 962 3555.

Farooq Younis is the proud owner of this takeaway, and is the nephew of the Saagar's Mr Khizer (see previous entry). He opened it in 2000 right in the heart of the town and has built up a loyal customer base. Most-ordered dishes are Chicken Korai, £5.95 and Spice Special BMG, £6.45, and Tandoori dishes. Delivery: Min order £10. Order and pay on line or via the website or phone in. Look out for discounts and if you mention this Guide, Mr Younis will giver you a generous 10% discount.Hours: 5-11.30; to 12 Saturday.; 4.30 to 11 Sunday. www.spicetakeaway.com

459 Westdale La, Mapperley
0115 962 3555

Southwell

SANAM BALTI HOUSE

117 King St, Southwell   01636 813618

Early Victorian listed building, est as the Taj Mahal in 1990, and taken over by Khalid Mahmood in 1994. The

50-seater boasts a splendid spiral staircase. Rooms are open-plan with ornate Moghul style arches to doorways. Beautiful jade colour, lighting subdued crystal reflecting the traditional Indian art. All tables are covered in fine contrasting linen, sparkling silverware and fresh flowers. Centre of attention has to be a 26-cubic-feet fish tank, which is set within an existing chimney and can be viewed from both rooms. Chef-owner, Khalid Mahmood or 'Chef Saab' originates from Pakistan's Kashmir. *'Tastefully decorated. All food was hot, excellent Pullao Rice and Peshwari Nan.'* LW. Specials include: Makhani Tandoori Chicken, Marinated Tandoori Chicken with Makhani sauce (green peppers, onions, tomatoes, methi, garlic sauce). you might get a disc if you show them this Guide. Hours: 5.30-11.30.

OXFORDSHIRE

Area: South Central
Population: 622,000
Adjacent Counties:
Bucks, Berks, Glos,
Middx, Northants,
Warks, Wilts

Abingdon

THE VINE　　　　　NEW ENTRANT

High St, Long Wittenham, Abingdon OX14 4QH
01865 407832

This pub was sold by Greene King to Angur Miah. Mr Miah plans to keep the Vine as a pub and provide Indian, Bangladeshi and Thai cuisine. Greene King put up the shutters last year raising fears the small pub would be sold and developed for residential use.Branches: Dil Raj, Ock Street, Abingdon, Memories of Bengal, Cholsey, near Wallingford.

Bicester

ARZOO　　　　　NEW ENTRANT

15 Market Square, Bicester　　　01869 242434

'Arzoo has replaced GCG entry Bicester Tandoori as one of the best restaurants my husband and I have visited. For starters we had Tandoori Duck and Sheek Kebab, both of which were beautifully cooked and well presented. We chose Boal Dopiaza and Roshini Lamb for our main course together with lime jeera rice and a garlic nan bread. Both main courses were excellent, the meat and fish were tender and tasty, the rice was a delight both flavoursome and very different from ordinary

boiled or pillau rice. The nan was fluffy and light. A very rare event for us was that we ate everything put before us. We finished off our meal with a portion of kulfi (to share as we were both very full) and coffee. All in all this was a very enjoyable experience, the restaurant is nicely decorated and the staff were all very pleasant and attentive. We shall certainly be making the long journey back to Oxford again to sample more of this restaurant's fare.' LH.

Cholsey

MEMORIES OF BENGAL　　NEW ENTRANT

12 Wallingford Rd, OX10 9LQ　　01491 652777

'Thank God this place is only 200 yards from my house! I visit weekly. It the former the Chequers pub and was restored at considerable expense by Angur Miah some 5 years ago and now provides an extremely consistent high quality service for both dining in and takeaway. Work colleagues who visit from New York and San Diego always ask to come here to eat. The food is excellent, notably the Hash Tikka, £5.95 or fishcakes for starter, the best lamb I ever had in a Rogan Josh, £6.95, great salmon, £9.50 if you prefer fish, and some different vegetables, for example a really nice pumpkin and cauliflower bhaji, £3.50. All the standards are available too of course, Dansak, £5.95, Dopiaza, CTM, Jalfreizi, £7.50, Madras, all to a very good and very consistent level. Meal inc drinks for 4: £108. Seats about 60 following the addition of a conservatory. The Aziz in Cowley Road, Oxford is very good, put this one on a par with that, but possibly nicer beacuse it's in a village location and slightly calmer! You may even see Tim Henman dining if you're lucky!' CI. Branches Dil Raj, Ock Street, Abingdon, The Vine Abingdon.

Henley-on-Thames

SPICE MERCHANT　　　NEW ENTRANT

25 Thameside, RG9 2LJ　　　01491 636118

Its USP is a small launch, moored at the restaurant, on which you can dine Indian and enjoy your drinks while cruising the Thames. Menu and details, see Beaconsfield. Branches: Beaconsfield, Cookham, Uxbridge. Avg Price: £43. Hours: 12-2.30 / 6-11. www.spicemerchantgroup.com

YOU SAY OK

You might get a discount if you show them this Guide.

BANBURY: SHEESH MAHAL 43 Oxford Rd, Banbury ~ 01295 266489. Mohammed Khalid is owner and manager.

CHINNOR: CHINNOR INDIAN 59 Lower Rd. ~ 01844 354843. Owner Saidur Rahman. Hours: 5.30-11.30; 12am Sat.

CHIPPING NORTON: ANARKALI 6 West St, Chipping Norton ~ 01608 642785. Owner A.Uddin. Hours 12-2.30/6-11.30.

DIDCOT: SUNKOSHI TANDOORI 226a Broadway, Didcot 01235 812796. Nepalese: eg: Shak Shuka, minced lamb, fresh cream, topped with egg, mild; Prawn Chatpat, green chillies, peppers, onions, ginger, hot. Hours: 12-2.30/6-11, 11.30 Fri & Sat.

FARINGDON: AZAD TANDOORI & BALTI 14 Coxwell Street, Faringdon ~ 01367 244977. Rabia Khanom Ali's venue. Hours: 5-11.30; 12-11.30 Sun.

HENLEY-ON-THAMES: GAZAL 53 Reading Rd, Henley ~ 01491 574659. Hours: 12-2 / 6-11.

RAJU'S 21 Reading Rd Henley ~ 01491 572218. *'Traditional food and decor.'* MS. Malcolm Smith new name Reading *'Best in Henley.'* RP. Oxford: Jamal Tandoori, 108 Walton Street, Oxford, OX2 6AJ ~ 01865 310102

OXFORD: KASHMIR HALAL 64 Cowley Road, Oxford OX4 1JB 01865 250165. Said Meah opened his 50-seater in 1970.

AZIZ   A-LIST

228 Cowley Road, Oxford   01865 794945

Azizur (Aziz) Rahman is an extremely personable man, and a successful restaurateur. From a start-up in 1990, he now has four Aziz restaurants in Oxon. This smart 90-seater has always stood out for sophistication in decor, service and accurately cooked real Bangladeshi food, and not in the manner of so many Bangladeshi-owned curryhouses. His ace in the hole is Master Chef Nurul Amin, a veteran chef with decades of top hotel experince in Dhaka. Because the menu is using Bengali words, dishes may seem unfamiliar, but it is an encyclopaedia of Bangladeshi food, and many of the old favourites are there too. Starters include familiar items such as Tandoori Murgh, Boti, Samosa Pyazee (Onion Bhaji) and Sheek Kebabs at from £4.15. Less usual are Maach Bora £4.75, a fish cake; Galda Chingri Aar Puri, £5.75 is sweet & sour king prawn with puri bread and Chott Pottie £4.15, chickpeas, egg and potatoes spiced with coriander. Mains include Hush Bhuna £9.50, duck with onion and tomatoes; Razalla £8.75 lamb or chicken with yoghurt, cream, butter and chilli,; Ada Gosht £7.95, tikka lamb, dryish with ginger, and onion;Murgh Kaliya £8.50, chicken with black pepper in a creamy sauce. Bangladesh being big fish on curries, there is a good selection: Bhuna Aiyr £8.75. with onion and tomatoes; Sak Buaal £8.75 with spinach; Galda Chineri Kodu £10.95 is large king prawns with pumpkin. Vegetable dishes (from £6.25) include the delightfully named Dimm Dall, egg and lentil curry; Sarso Baigun, aubergine fried with mustard seed; Sobzi Korma £6 mild and creamy; Sobzi Patia, sweet and sour vegetable and Sobzi Razalla, mixed vegetables with butter, cream &

Aziz Pandesia

Aziz Burford

Aziz Whitney

chillies. *'The ambience, service and food are all top quality. All the dishes that we tried were beautifully served, expertly cooked and well crafted, with a number of dishes (including a good range of vegetarian dishes) that I have not seen before. I remember a chickpea dish that I had as being particularly good (must take more notes next time!). Overall opinion: Excellent, will continue to happily recommended this restaurant and will definitely return.'* SO. *'Emphasis on subtlety. A splendid meal.'* WC. *'Impressive reports confirmed. Mid-week the place was packed. Decor is upmarket and smart, the food well prepared and served in generous quantities. This is where the middle class, the academics and well-off students of Oxford eat and entertain. Service was slow but the place was very busy. Parking can be a problem.'* PAW. T/a: 15% disc. Sun buffet 12-4.30, £9.50pp, children £4.75. Hours: 12-2.15 (not Fri); 12-4.30 Sun / 6-11.30 daily. Nominated Best Bangladeshi. Same details at Aziz Burford, 79 High Street, Burford, Oxon; 01993 823340 and Aziz Witney 79 High Street, Witney, Oxon, 01993 774100. Aziz Pandesia, Restaurant and Bar serves Indian, Bangladeshi and Thai cuisine at 1 Folly Bridge, Oxford, 01865 247775. www.azizuk.com

RUTLAND

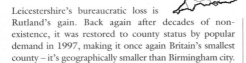

Britain's smallest county
Area: East Midlands
Population: 36,500
Adjacent Counties:
Cambs, Leics, Lincs

Leicestershire's bureaucratic loss is Rutland's gain. Back again after decades of non-existence, it was restored to county status by popular demand in 1997, making it once again Britain's smallest county – it's geographically smaller than Birmingham city.

Oakham

VOUJON BALTI HUT   NEW ENTRANT

4 Burley Corner, LE15 6DU   01572 723043

'Following a very trendy redesign. it's much more fashionable than most local Indians. Service is extremely impressive with friendly waiting staff quick to prepare orders and happy to accomodate larger parties at the last minute. If you need to wait for a table they seat you with a menu in the very comfortable bar area. The Voujon is equally as good with takeaways. The food itself is perfect – well presented, fresh and extremely tasty! I strongly recommend the Murgh Sagwalla and the house relishes to accompany the papadums are delicious! Orders are taken quickly even when it is busy and your dinner is ready in good time. Its prices are a little higher than some but it's overall exceptional.' RB

SHROPSHIRE

Area: North west
(Welsh Border)
Population: 450,000
Adjacent Counties:
Cheshire, Clwyd,
Hereford, Powys,
Staffs, Worcs

Bishops Castle

GANGES

12 Market Sq, Bishops Castle   01588 638543

'Small restaurant in a picture perfect rural market town – whose idyll is crowned with two working breweries. Real ale - fabulous. Interior is functional and inviting, good decor and stylish furnishings complete with crisp white linen. Lovely starter - Rashmi Kebab £3 - pair on tender, well spiced patties, topped with a moist, tasty omelette and fresh crispy salad. A pleasant yoghurt and mint sauce rounded the dish off. Roshuni Lamb £6 - enjoyable, hot, rich and dry sauce, thick with herbs and garlic. Good Garlic Naan £2 - if a little doughy, plenty of garlic. Tarka Dhal £2.50 - fairly well balanced, rather lumpy lentils.' RW. Menu Snapshot: Stuffed Green Pepper £3, chicken, prawn or vegetable; Tandoori Mixed Grill £7, Spring Chicken, Lamb, King Prawn, Minced Kebab with salad and Tandoori Naan; Banana Naan £2; Hours: 12-2.30 Sat & Sun only /6-12 daily.

Church Stretton

JAIPUR

6 Sandford Av, Church Stretton   01694 724667

'Parking really easy in this sleepy little town. Efficient rather than friendly service. Rectangular restaurant, nicely decorated, usual Indian prints hang on amber coloured walls. Shared Mixed Kebab - two pieces each of Lamb and Chicken Tikka, and a rubbery Sheek Kebab on the usual salad. On asking for the Raitha, go a blank look, then "Oh! you mean the mint sauce." This came in a gravy boat. Monica's Chicken Capsila contained large strips of chicken breast with chunks of capsicum, nicely spiced medium to hot. My Jaipur Special Jalfrezi - pretty good, although not sure if any king prawns were present, chicken and lamb well cooked, tender, adequate portion. Prices reasonable, mint chocolates arrived after the meal. Will eat there again.' T&MH. Menu Snapshot: Bengal Fish Masala £10, fillets of ayr; Shim Bhajee £3.50, french beans; Meetah Pullao Rice £1.95, fruit cocktail rice. T/a: 10% disc. Hours: 5.30-11.30; 6.30-12 Fri & Sat.

Shifnal

SHIFNAL BALTI

20 Broadway, TF11 8AZ   01952 460142

Owner mngr Faz Ali's 90-seater, est 1992. BYO. Faz says *'I change my menu every year so my clients don't get bored.'* Earlier examples: Bangladeshi Fish Fries £4; Bombay Duck (1 piece) £1; Machli Diya Bhojan £9 - fresh water Bangladeshi fish, garlic, coriander, lemon juice, green chilli - mild, medium or hot!; Chicken Tikka Coriander £9, served with salad; Apna Pachando £10, whole trout, fresh coriander, garlic, green chilli, lemon, turmeric, cumin, cinnamon and cardamom; Garlic and Mushroom or Peshwari and Coriander Naan c£3.50; Chutneys and Pickles are FREE. 'Celebration' meals include lobster from £45 and whole leg of lamb from £50 - wonderful for a special occasion, like a big birthday. Hours: 5.30-11.30; 12.30 Sat. www.faz.ali@blueyonder.co.uk

Shrewsbury

CLAY OVEN TAKEAWAY

131 Hereford Rd, Meole Brace   01743 343222

Martin Kabir opened his T/a in 2004. Clean and bright exterior, painted red and white. Cooking by chef Kamal. Menu Snapshot: Garlic Mushrooms £2; Special Clay Oven Biriani £6 - tender diced lamb, spring chicken, prawn, prepared with basmati rice, topped with egg omelette; Garlic Special Lamb c£5.25 - marinated lamb cooked with garlic, peppers and coriander, Tandoori King Prawn Mosala £7.50 - cooked in clay oven, then a delicate cream sauce; Coriander Fried Rice £1.80; Chilli Naan £1.40. Hours: 5-10.30. Branch: Shalimar, 23, Abbey Foregate, Shrewsbury.

SHERAZ

79 Wyle Cop, Shrewsbury   01743 242321

Taken over in 1990 by N Begum. Seats 75 on two floors. Menu Snapshot: Tandoori Salmon £3.60; Scallop Bunju c£6 - cooked with tomato, onion, garnished with fresh green pepper; Butter Chicken c£6 - very mild, cooked in tandoori with cream and butter; Keema Pullao Rice £2.00; Chilli Naan £1.70. Del: 3m £12 min. T/a: 15% disc. Hours: 5.30-12; 1am Sat.

SHUVECHA

82 Wyle Cop, SY1 1UT   01743 340560

'Opened in 2005. Decor is clean and modern. The service was good and very friendly. Starter: Stuffed pepper £2.95, good but could perhaps have a little drier due to the slightly runny meat filling possibly. Main course: King Prawn Agni 8.95,

Mushroom Bhaji 2.55 & Nan 1.85, both good although possibly a little bland. Overall good, I would go back. I suspect it may be one of the better Indians in Shrewsbury.' JP.

SOMERSET

Area: South West
Population: 878,000
Adjacent Counties:
Bristol, Devon,
Dorset, Glos, Wilts

YOU SAY OK
You might get a discount if you show them this Guide..

BATH: BENGAL BRASSERIE 32 Milson St, Bath ~ 01225 447906. 40-seater est 1987 by Mukhtar Ali with Chef Moqozull Ali. Mukhtar will give Guide readers a discount on Suns. Serv: 10%. T/a: 10% disc. Hours: 12-2.30/6-11.30; 12 Fri & Sat. www.bengalbrasseriebath.co.uk

BATH: JAFLONG RESTAURANT 78 Lower Bristol Rd, Bath ~ 01225 330144. Rashel Rahim is the owner: Hours: 12-2.30/6-11.30. www.jaflong-bath.co.uk

BATH: PRIA 4a Argyle St, Bath ~ 01225 462323. 40-seater owned by Ahmed Choudury's Rajpoot group, and managed by Pria T/a: 10% disc. Hours: 6-1.30, 2 Fri & Sat . www.priarestaurant.co.uk

BRIDGWATER: SPICE CLUB 10a Eastover, TA6 5AB ~ 01278 433334. Est 2005 by Mohammed A Miah.. Banquet Nt: Thurs, £9.95. T/a: 10% disc, £12min. Hours: 12-2/6-12. www.spiceclub.cjb.net>

CLEVEDON: MOGHULS TANDOORI 33 Old Church Rd, Clevedon ~ 01275 873695

Bath

EASTERN   EYE   A-LIST

8a Quiet Street, Bath   01225 422323

140-seater, owned by Suhan Choudhury, pink and blue with most impressive Georgian interior, in one large room with three domes. *'Average high-street curry house it is not! It's a spectacular, huge and most impressive first-floor restaurant. Soft lighting, pink and blue colours, restful atmosphere. Tablecloths and cutlery are of good quality, even the hot towels are so thick they could almost have been squares of carpet! Stuffed pepper, whole green stuffed with spicy diced chicken, barbecued, nicely blackened, delicately spiced, interesting but filling starter. Onion Bhajia, two round bhajias, the best we have tasted for a long while, light, crispy and spicy. Prawn Puree – excellent, large succulent prawns, tangy sauce. Good, fresh and varied salad garnishes. Chicken Tikka Masala – most ordinary, standard offering. Chicken Mon Pasanda, excellent, different, mild, yoghurt based sauce, very herby. Lamb Jalfrezi, large tender chunks of lamb, thick dark sauce, hotness hits you after first couple of mouthfuls.*

Vegetable Bhajee, good variety of diced vegetables, nicely spiced and enjoyable. Peshwari Nan and Pullao Rice were both good, nan not sickly and rice contained smattering of diced vegetables to make it interesting. Prices slightly above average, but for decor and type of restaurant, very reasonable. Service efficient and friendly. An excellent meal in an elegant restaurant.' MW. *'Incredibly wide menu Quality Excellent Quantity Copious Decor Out of this world Service Prompt and polite Comfort Excellent Comments We went for the non vegetarian set meal which came to £38 for the two of us. It included: Kebab; Chicken Jalfrezi; Sultan Puri Pullau; Mixed Vegetables; Naan; Popadums; Chutney; Sweet; Coffee. Also bottle of Bangla (£4) Mineral water £1.70. The kebabs were mightily impressive and highly spiced. Mark 9/10.'* G&MP. *'Unbooked visit. To their credit they accommodated us very well indeed, including bringing over a highchair for our 2 year old daughter, Lily, something I wish more Indian restaurants would do. The food was absolutely faultless. Lily has a liking for lentils so we tried her with a thin Dhal soup; she absolutely loved it! I had a Vegetable Dhansak and I asked them to make it a little hotter than usual; suffice to say it was absolutely beautiful, full of fresh vegetables (not just potato!) and just a little sweet as well as hot. Jackie's Vegetable Jalfrezi was equally impressive, including some chilli's with serious attitude! The accompanying Garlic Nan was light and was not overpowering in terms of garlic content. Our single side dish of Saag Ponir was soft and creamy yet still retained sizeable chunks of Ponir that sometimes disappear when the dish is cooked in this style. Overall, really excellent food and at about £40 in total, not bad value for money either. I must do start navigating by something other than your Guide as it continually points me to good restaurants and I end up writing positive reviews .'* AG. And the Guide be the pooorer without them Andy. Serv: 10%. Specials include: Mon Pasanda – slightly hot, enlivened with herbs and yoghurt, Shah Jahani – chicken breast, slightly spiced, shallow fried in ghee, blended with homemade cheese and cream, Sultan Puri Pilau – from Uttar Pradesh, spiced rice with lamb and cashew nuts, served with a gravy. Bangladeshi food nights, seafood buffet. Service 10%. min charge: £10. T/a: 10% disc. 10% discount if you show them this Guide. Hours: 12-2.30/6-11.30. Awarded best in the west. See page 31.

JAMUNA

9 High St. Bath	01225 464631

Ahmed Choudury's Jamuna seats 64. Menu Snapshot: Tandoori Platter £12.50, tandoori chicken, chicken tikka, sheek kebab, lamb tikka, Naan and Pullao Rice - what a feast!; Sultan Puri Pulao £12.95, spiced rice with lamb and cashew nuts, served with lamb curry; Vegetarian Platter £9.25, potato and cauliflower curry, mushroom bhajia, lentils, yoghurt, bread and rice; Garlic Naan £2.30. *'Entry to this restaurant is up some unprepossessing stairs to the first floor dining area. However, once there it is smart, with chandeliers and decorated in soft pinks and greens. The dining room commands a good view*

over the nearby gardens and River Avon. We arrived at 8.30, to find it remarkably empty (only one other table was taken). We were shown to a table for two, but asked if we could have a table for four to give a little more room. This request was refused, as according to the manager "it will be crowded tonight". So rather disgruntled at having to sit at a small table in a virtually empty restaurant, we studied the menu. The menu offers the usual dishes, with perhaps one or two less common items (for example Xacutti), but basically it is a standard list. The Onion Bhaji starters were very good indeed. Two large, crispy bhajias, which were loosely assembled making them crisp throughout and pleasantly light and crumbly. The Chicken Tikka starter was less remarkable, having a few pieces of only very lightly tandooried lumps of chicken, which were not particularly flavoursome. My main dish of Lamb Pathia was cooked in a rich, dark sauce it was certainly hot and pleasantly spiced, but the lamb was rather chewy The Chicken Tikka Bhuna was quite tasty. Mixed VegBhaji was a good mix of vegetables, nicely spiced and cooked, while the Peshwari Naan (plenty of coconut paste, but nothing else) and rice were average. The service was quick and efficient, and the prices (perhaps predictable in Bath) were above average, plus they add 10% for service (although to their credit they do not leave an empty space for a further tip). However, bearing in mind that the portions were just about adequate and the meal, while OK, was nothing more than a reasonable standard high street formula curry, meant that it did not live up to the image the interior presents, nor represents good value for money. It's nowhere near as good as the Eastern Eye that I used last time I was in Bath. Oh, and the table incident. Well, they did fill up as the evening progressed, although I noted that there were still several tables for four still empty when we left. We could have had one after all! MW. T/a: 10% disc. Hours: 12-2.30 / 6-11.30; 12.30 Sat. Branch: Rajdoot and group. www.jammunabath.co.uk

YAK YETI YAK

12 Argyle Street, Bath	01225 442299

Opened in early 2004 and is a family-run business offering Nepalese food. Access from Argyle Street is down numerous of flights of stairs. *'You are met with the pleasant smell of incense and a friendly waiter. The restaurant is agreeably simple, having plain tables covered in an easy-wipe tablecloth, painted rough stone walls and a nice, unaffected atmosphere. The only pointer to something different is a small area where you can sit on cushions rather than chairs, if you are supple enough. Apart from this area, it seats about 30. We had: Starters: Momo (eight small dumplings, steamed dumplings with spiced pork) , slightly heavy but quite tasty; Melekhu Macha (spiced deep-fried salmon chunks) (half a dozen sizeable salmon hunks), delicious crisply fried, delicately spiced and very moorish and served with homemade chutneys – a hemp seed chutney with the Momo and a different one with the salmon. Mains: Kukhurako Bhutuwa (pieces of spiced chicken stir-fried with tomato, onion, garlic and ginger), Khursani Kukura (marinated chicken stir-fried with green chilli, tomato and spring onions), spicy!; Aloo Tamar*

(fermented bamboo shoots stir-fried with potato and black-eyed beans), Bakula Banda (broad beans and white cabbage stir-fried with spices), Maaska Dhal (spiced split black lentils with herbs), a bit too smooth and 'buttery' in flavour for me; Chamsur Sag (spinach and watercress stir-fried with spices and herbs) and Hario Simi Ra Aloo (green beans and new potatoes cooked with spices). It proved a good selection, and all were delicious, different and very fresh-tasting. The service unhurried yet attentive and very friendly. Despite the slightly naff name it was a splendid little restaurant and we all thought it an excellent meal – pleasant, delicately spiced different food in homely unpretentious but comfortable surroundings. I'd go back any day, despite the limited menu.' MW.

INDIA COTTAGE

Shaftesbury Rd, Henstridge   01963 362963

'This fine curryhouse amid beautiful rural countryside, opened in 2003, has been beautifully adapted from for a dentists premises and comfortably accommodates 58. There's a good range of starters including novelties: Nargis Kebab,egg in mincemeat, barbecue and served with omelette; Fried Salmon or Cottage Kebab (minced kebab, rolled in dough and grilled; a very good range of Tandoori dishes and some delicious Masala dishes including King Prawn Masala, Butter Chicken and Chicken / Lamb Pasanda. Chef's Favourites offer some real delights and I very strongly recommend Chicken / Lamb Tikka Marchia, which is cooked in a brilliant red spicy sauce with green chillies. This has the "Wow!" factor. The usual standards are here, all beautifully delivered. Main courses are about £5 / 6, the servings are generous. Very welcome are Value Set Meals. Go for the Raja (for two and you get Tikka Wrap and Onion Bhaji for starters; followed by Chicken Balti, Chicken Tikka Masala, Sag Paneer, Bombay Aloo -- with Pullau Rice, Keema Naan and Popadums. All for £25! You will get a warm welcome. The service is immensely obliging and pretty quick. (Disabled access is OK over a shallow step.) Plenty of Parking. It's on the A357 on the Blandford to Wincanton road. Yours to the last spoonful, Devout in the Way of the Curry.' BG.

Minehead

ALCOMBE TANDOORI

67 Alcombe Rd, Alcombe   01643 706591

'Always enjoy visiting this excellent establishment including two visits during a week-long family break down in Dunster. Greeted by friendly, welcoming staff, despite our late arrival - 11.30pm having attended a bat-walk evening at the castle. The food was once again excellent and the staff lively, friendly and attentive. When you see the food list below it is because of the two visits, not because we were greedy (honest!). Fortunately, we didn't find Batwing Bhaji on the menu!' Starters Fish Potato Chola, which was delicious, lightly spiced fish with great textures; Chicken Momo - chicken cooked with an complimentary blend of spring onions, spices and green

pepper; Prawn / King Prawn Puri which were excellent versions of this perennial favourite; Mixed Kebab - a selection of chicken tikka, lamb tikka and sheek kebab, which were perfectly spiced and cooked – all very good indeed. Main Delhi-ite Sea Bass - perfectly cooked and spiced sea bass on a bed of spicy chick peas and potato- fantastic! Chicken Kata Masala - a most enjoyable blend of diced chicken, in a thick spicy sauce; Sunset Salmon - a salmon fillet fried with onions, peppers and tomatoes in a very complimentary sauce with yoghurt and coriander (the menu states 'defies description' and I can't argue with that and for all the right reasons). Devil's Tamarind was another stunning original with lamb that has been marinated in tamarind, cooked in the tandoori and then pan fried with spices – tangy and delicious, superb! Lamb Tikka (excellent) and Shabji Bhuna - medium spiced mixed vegetables; Chicken Korma also very good. Overall opinion – excellent, wouldn't hesitate to recommend and will definitely visit again when in the area. It's also a great treat to discover an Indian restaurant that offers not just one but two excellent fish dishes.' SO. Menu Snapshot: Mussels £5, Bengali style, garlic, salt, methi leaves, cream, butter and white wine; Chingrijhool £12, two whole king prawns in medium thick sauce, served with Pullao Rice; Gosht Ka Achar c£8, leg of lamb, braised golden brown, onion, ginger, garlic and unground garam masala, thick sauce. T/a: 10% disc, £10 min. Hours: 12-2/5.30-11.30.

YOU SAY OK
You might get a discount if you show them this Guide.

MIDSOMER NORTON: SHAPLA 43 High St, Midsomer Norton 01761 410479

NORTH PETHERTON: SPICE GALLERY NEW ENTRANT 44 Fore St, TA6 6PZ ~ 01278 662 982 www.spicegallery.co.uk

WELLINGTON: TASTE OF INDIA 2 North Street, Wellington ~ 01823 667051

WESTON-SUPER-MARE: AVON TANDOORI 16 Waterloo St, Weston ~ 01934 622622

WESTON: CURRY GARDEN 69 Orchard St ~ 01934 624660

YEOVIL: VICEROY 100 Middle Street ~ 01935 421758. 'Very clean, well presented, all staff friendly and helpful. All food, excellent quality'. DT. www.qualityfoodonline.co.uk

STAFFORDSHIRE

Area:
Northwest Midlands
Population: 1,070,000
Adjacent Counties:
Cheshire, Derbs,
Shrops,
W Mids, Worcs

Amington

JOBA'S INN   NEW ENTRANT

134, Amington Rd, B77 3PU   01827 59500

As the title suggests, Joba's is a public house, with an
80-seater Indian restaurant Nicely decorated inside, with
red and white leather chairs, white tables are simply laid
with cutlery and wine glasses. Please dress smartly and
has room for eighty. Silly rule on menu: *'We reserve the
right not to serve starters or side dishes without main dishes.*
We hate this stupidity, custom is custom after all. *'My
favourite, Chicken Tikka Pathia cooked at my favourite
restaurant, Joba's.'* AJS.Takeaway: 10% and 20% for
regular bar customer. Hours: 5.30 -11.30.

Chadsmoor, Cannock

SANAM BALTI HOUSE

193 Cannock Rd   01543 513565

A huge restaurant seating 160 in three rooms on two
floors. Waheed Nazir took over the Sanam in July 2000.
Unlicensed so BYO. Head chef, Mohammed Zabair's,
Mixed Grill at £10 is very popular and includes: Chicken
Tikka, Sheek Kebab, King Prawns, Tandoori Chicken,
Curry Sauce and Naan - WHAT A FEAST! Parking is
located just across the road, fifty places, so no problem
there. Menu Snapshot: Lamb Chops £2.95 - marinated
spring lamb chops, skewered and chargrilled; Fish
Masala c£3.50 - marinated haddock, deep-fried; Balti
Chilli Masala c£8 - finely chopped onions, capsicum,
tomatoes, hot green chilli sauce; Aloo, Mushroom,
Peshwari or Vegetable Paratha £1.75; Mushroom Fried,
Egg Fried, Garlic or Peas Pullao £2.65, Pickle Tray
£2.50. Del: 10m. Hours: 5.30-12.30; 2 Fri & Sat.
www.sanam-balti.8m.com

Eccleshall

LONDON HOUSE   NEW ENTRANT

28, High St,ST21 6BZ   01785 850055

*'Every time we go here, we wonder how it has escaped your
notice.'* [Because until you, no one has told us about it!]
*'Food is of a very high standard. My wife particularly enjoys
the Chicken Rezala, I go for the Chicken Lamb Vegetable
Mirchi. A particular feature we enjoy, and approve of, is an
arrangement whereby two curries are served side by side,
enabling two pleasures for the price of one, eg: Chicken Matar
Panir and Gosth Bhuna or Methi Gosth and Chicken Rogani.
Presentation is excellent and the whole restaurant is light and
attractive on a principal side street in this small town. Prices
c£6 - £7 per dish.'* DF.

Kingsley Holt

THORNBURY HALL RASOI   TOP 100

Lockwood Rd, Kingsley Holt   01538 750831

This unusual restaurant is approximately 10 miles east of
Hanley (off the A52) in a renovated Grade II listed
building, once a manor house. Since 1994 it has been
owned and managed by Mr and Mrs Siddique, who have
brought style and Pakistani food to this beautiful
location. It has three public areas, including a
conference room. Rasoi appropriately means 'kitchen'.
The main restaurant leads from the bar and is decorated
in gold and terracotta, ceramic floor, open fire for winter
evenings. The Shalimar room, named after gardens in
Pakistan, is decorated in green and gold, large windows
and doors leading to garden. Dance floor, sparkling
globe and sound system. Lahore dining room, large,
elegant, richly decorated Georgian plaster ceiling,
swagged curtains and a brass teapot, it nearly reached
the ceiling! Many of the old favourites are on the menu.
Starters include familiar items such as Tandoori Murgh,
Boti, Samosa Pyazee (Onion Bhaji) and Sheek Kebabs
from c£4.50. Less usual are Breaded brollies, deep fried
mushrooms £3 or Chaat-e-phal, seasonal fresh fruit,
potatoes, chickpeas mixed with spices, £2.50. Mains
include Karhai Dhasi Salan, chicken or lamb pieces
cooked with potatoes. £8; Thornbury khatta-mettha
chicken or lamb fried with pepper, sweet and sour, £8;
Karhai Lahori Chaska, chicken or lamb in a special sauce
masala, unique and hot, £6.90; Karhai Jhinga Rassadar,
Prawns cooked with special spices, coriander and
coconut, £11. Pulao Arasta Dehlvi, basmati rice cooked
in a very special 'stock' with golden onions, £3; Nan-e-
Babria wholewheat bread, filled with mincemeat ,£3.
*'The in-laws live close by. The main hall is very grand, but not
always open. Other areas are elegant and comfortable. Service
good, including some staff from the village in Pakistani dress.
Excellent flavours and quality. Sensible portions.'* DRHM.
*'Fantastic restaurant. Magnificent settings in a listed
building. Karahi Murgh Jalfrezi, the best my husband has
ever tasted.'* Mr&MrsC. Sun Lunch buffet is a real family
occasion, Booking is advisable. c£10, kids c£6, under 5s
free. Hours: 12-2.30/6-11; 11.30 Fri & Sat.
www.thornburyhall.co.uk

Leek

BOLAKA SPICE   TOP 100

41 Stockwell Street, Leek   01538 373734

Proprietor, Abdul Choudhury really appreciates his
TOP 100 status (unlike some others) awarded in 2004.
To celebrate, he invited civic dignitaries from across the
district, who all enjoyed a specially prepared four-course
menu. Mr Choudhury said, *'We are absolutely delighted,*

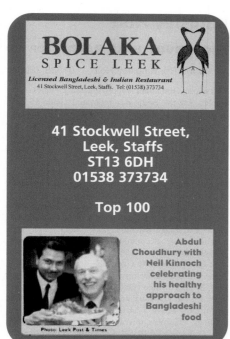

BOLAKA
SPICE LEEK
Licensed Bangladeshi & Indian Restaurant
41 Stockwell Street, Leek, Staffs. Tel: (01538) 373734

**41 Stockwell Street,
Leek, Staffs
ST13 6DH
01538 373734**

Top 100

Abdul Choudhury with Neil Kinnoch celebrating his healthy approach to Bangladeshi food

Photo: Leek Post & Times

we aimed to reach the TOP 100 and we have achieved it!' He also donated 20% of his takings to the Leek branch of the British Red Cross. We mention this becasue it is the level of care which typified this restaurant and which makes it worth of this award. And you agree: *'Primarily a formula curryhouse, but two features make it stand out – the Haandis menu and a small specials board. Keema Motor is an outstanding and rich mix of lamb, chick peas and spices. At Christmas, a divine Turkey Tikka Masala with vegetables. Aubergines in a Sweet Sauce is Wow! Service polite and efficient.'* PK. *'Friendly and cosy, good welcome. Tables clean and ready with candles and flowers. Quality unbelievably good every time.'* JA. *'Have dined here many times, food always very fresh and tasty.'* RM. *'A friend gave me a hint that this place had a good reputation. Pickles and Popadums offered as an appetiser were fresh and moorish. Starter, Chingri Begun and Mint Lamb Balti both impressed with flavours. Impeccable service.'* AEH. *'The best we have been too. Very friendly staff, clean tables, relaxing atmosphere and the best food – absolutely fabulous. Our favourite.'* SS. You might get a discount if you show Abdul this Guide. Abdul, please celebrate again being retained in our TOP 100.

PABNA

16 Ashbourne Rd, ST13 5AS   01538 381156

Mohammed Shuyab is the owner. *'Pleasant clean decor and highly attentive staff. Well spiced Chicken Tikka for starter. Excellent CTM and delicately flavoured Pullao Rice.*

I have visited on previous occasions with my father and look forward to the next visit!' NG. Menu Snapshot: Gilafi Sheek Kebab £3 - spicy; Melon with Cointreau £3, not curry at all, but sounds delicious, very pallet cleansing!; Tandoori Duck £8; Butter Chicken £6, tikka in creamy sauce; Amere Chicken £8.75, mango, wine, cream and almonds served with Pullao Rice; Naga Fall £7.50, yes, it's the famous Bangladeshi chilli – very hot!!!; Zeera Aloo £2.50; Banana in Ghee £2.50. Hours: 5-12.

Lichfield

EASTERN EYE   TOP 100

19b Bird Street   01543 254399

Abdul Salam's venue represents a Swat valley house, right up in Pakistan's northern mountain ranges (just a nan nudge from Baltistan). It is famous for its forests and ornate wooden carved furniture, showing Buddhist influences going back 2,000 years. The beams, pillars and window are from Swat. The bar front is from neighbouring Afghanistan, the chairs are Rajasthani and the table tops are from 150-year-old elm. *'Count the rings,'* enthuses Mr Salam. The toilets are a 'must-see' on your list. The theme is Agra's Red Fort – probably India's best example of a Moghul residence. The food is well spoken of. Specials include Murgh with Apricot, marinated chicken with apricot yoghurt sauce, cream and fresh coriander. Rajasthani Paro Breast – pigeon. Michael Fabricant, MP, MCC (member of the Curry Club) continues regularly to take his seat at the Eye as a loyal local, rating it highly, as do so many other reports we get, e.g. *'From entering you know it'll be good. Decor reminded me of Putney's fine Ma Goa's (London SW). In a mild mood, had Murgh Special with apricot which was delicious. My friend loved his Eastern Eye Mixed Massala (king prawn, lamb and chicken).'* RL. *'Still my favourite. Mr Salam still very much in charge, evolving the menu and new dishes. Cooking excellent – far superior to average curry fare. Chicken and Banana, Chilli Chicken, Special tandoori Masala (inc chicken, lamb, king prawns) are all excellent. Amazingly light Naans. Wine list still consists of an armful of bottles placed on your table to take your pick from – a tradition I hope will remain. Deserves to be in the TOP 100.'* PJ. *' The food was unusual and beautifully presented on huge oval china plates.'* K&ST. Discount promised on Sundays if you show them this Guide . Hours: 12-2.30 Sat only / 5-12.

Hartshill

BOMBAY CLUB

325 Hartshill Road, Hartshill   01782 719191

A thoroughly modern restaurant, minimalist chic, wooden floors, plain walls. Executive Chef: MZ Salim cheffed at the Oberoi, India. Menu: Tikke Murgh Malai £4, diced chicken breast marinated in cottage cheese

and cream, char grilled in the clay oven; Tangri Kabab £3.75, drumsticks char grilled with cream and cashew nuts paste - lovely; Lahsuni Jhinga c£8, char grilled king prawns in medium spiced brushed with garlic paste; Paneer Pakora £3.50, cottage cheese dipped in butter and deep fried - a starter not for the calorie conscious! Aud E Chengazi £9.95, roasted lamb slices cooked in a rich medium sauce with mint and coriander; Nilgiri Korma c£8, cubes of mutton sautéed with brown onion paste and green masala, served mild or hot! *'Most of the curry houses I have visited serve curries which are surrounded by a pool of oil but not this one. I have yet to find a place like it. The chef cooks the most delicious curries I have ever tasted. I have tried many times to get the recipes for two of my favourites but, not being adept at making curries I have ben unable to recreate it. Recommend Jhinga Mumtaz and Chicken Makhni together with rice made from nuts and honey whose name escapes me and if by any chance you are able to create them I would be grateful if you pass the recipe on to me.'* MM.

Newcastle-under-Lyme

KAVI

Clayton Lodge Hotel, Clayton Rd, Newcastle
01782 613093

The attractive 50 room Clayton Lodge Hotel (from £45.00 per night) has received a multi million pound refurbishment involving its ballroom and meeting area endowing it with beautiful marble floors and crystal chandeliers. Located about 2.0 miles from Stoke centre (2 minutes from J15 / M6) it has a major attraction for readers of this Guide – its Indian restaurant Kavi. White and black marble, blonde wood, a modern look and splashes of colour, and a plasma screen with Bollywood movies vies for attention with the open-plan kitchen. This is the preserve of chef Avinash Kumar, ex Baylis, Slough, Berks (see entry) and Claridges Delhi. Starters include: Mussels & Scallops c£8, flavoured with coconut; Shakar Kandi Chaat £5.25, sweet potato chaat topped with pomegranate seeds; Mix Vegetable Potli c£3.50, assorted vegetable spring rolls; Ajwaini Macchi £7.25, tandoori grilled haddock scented with carom seeds. Main dishes include: Venison Chop Masala £10.95, chops simmered in red wine and served with a masala sauce; Murg Kafrial £10, chicken breast charcoal grilled and stuffed with minced chicken served with a green Goan sauce; Quail Hara Masala £9.95, Whole fresh quail simmered in a mint and coriander chutney. Veg dishes include Palak ke Kofte c£8, spinach dumplings stuffed with prunes and served with a korma sauce. Desserts include: Gajar ka Halwa £4.25, carrot pudding wrapped in a French crepe; Rasmalai £3.75, milk pudding dumplings dipped in sweetened reduced milk. Open from 6pm, seven days a week. Branch Kavi's, Wolverhampton.   www.claytonlodge.co.uk

Stafford

CURRY KUTEER

31, Greengate St ST16 2HX   01785 2536279

Established: 1968. *'This traditional curry house has been refurbished, since we last visited in 2007. the service was prompt, attentive and although the visit was very early on a Friday evening, the restaurant was busy with diners and takeaway customers. The Chicken Tikka £3.30 - was pleasant, creamy, serving generous. Curry Kuteer, remains a value for money venue, run by a family who undeniably, love their customers.'* NG. Menu Snapshot: Adraki Kofte £3.50 - spicy tuna, ginger kebab, shallow fried, served with salad; lamb Biriani £7.95 - served with vegetable curry; Chana Masala £5.75 - chicken peas, coconut cream sauce' Kulcha Nan £1.95 - vegetable filled.

YOU SAY OK
You might get a discount if you show them this Guide.

CANNOCK: JASMINE 125 Hednesford Rd, Heath Hayes, Cannock ~ 01543 279620

HANLEY, STOKE: ASHA TAKEAWAY 42 Broad St, ~ 01782 213339

HANLEY, STOKE: MANGO TREE Ivy House, Bucknall New Rd, 01782 207470 *'Bringing remarkably good dishes to the area'.* DW. www.the-mango-tree.co.uk

HANLEY, STOKE: MONZIL 44 Broad St, ~ 01782 280150

HEDNESFORD: BENGAL BRASSERIE 44 Market St, Hednesford ~ 01543 424769

LICHFIELD: LAL BAGU 9 Bird St, Lichfield ~ 01543 262967

NEWCASTLE-UNDER-LYME: BILASH 22 Highland Keele Rd ~ 01782 614549

RUGELEY: BILASH 7 Horsefair, Rugeley ~ 01889 584234

UTTOXETER: KOHI NOOR 11 Queen St. ~ 01889 562153

SUFFOLK

Area: East
Population: 685,000
Adjacent Counties:
Cambs, Essex,
Norfolk

Bury-St-Edmonds

THE LAST DAY OF RAJ

Station Hill, Bury St Edmunds   01284 725727

'I am now an Undergradat Keele, and will continue to send a review after every dining occasion. If I could name on fault in The Last Day of Raj, it is its location, in one of the less fancy areas of my home town Bury, it being near the railway station.

The bright green lighting in the windows may also put some people off, if they were averse to such illumination. As I read in one report, I can confirm that the telephone is also quite loud!! However, the food is of a very good standard, and the menu is extensive. A group of us dined there, and the service was not slow, but not too quick. I had a Lamb Ceylon, and it was rich, with a definite hint of fresh coriander, and a generous coconut influence in the sauce. The Kulcha Naan was quite sweet and fresh, accompanied with some clean plain rice. My friends enjoyed a Chicken Vindaloo, a Chicken Madras, bhajis and a special rice dish, which had liberal helpings of fresh saffron on the side. The pricing for the meals was good; main courses between £4.50 and £8. However, Serv came to £10.80, which was rather high considering two of my friends were not eating main courses, but were enjoying some lighter dishes. I am very pleased with the level of service, the music, and the cleanliness. Recommended. Five cost £44.80'. DW.

VALLEY CONNECTION NEW ENTRANT

42 Churchgate St, Bury IP33 1RG   01284 753161

'White painted walls. blackand white throughout. comfortable leather chairs. service all waiters dressed in black, extremely attentive, prompt and polite. Some exciting dishes I've never seen before. Quality excellent. quantity copious. a couple of outstanding lamb dishes. very busy for amonday night. overall a most enjoyable experience. Bill £42.20 for one. A top notch restaurant with mark 8.7/10.' GP.

Felixstowe

BLUE NAAN   NEW ENTRANT

7, Hamilton Rd,   IP11 7AX   01394 671779

A stunning 130-seater owned by Anwar Hussain. His sons, Humayun and Tahir manage. It's beautifully decorated in a minimalist style, featuring rich blue and burgundy walls, with complimentary modern furnishings. Chef Motin offers Korai dishes, Balti Specials, Jalfrezi dishes, Biriani, plus English, Persian and many other dishes. Private dining lounge for 25 .

Ipswich

GULSHAN TAKEAWAY

9 Stoke Street, Ipswich   01473 692929

Originally opened in 1996, taken over in 2003 by Mohibur Rahman. Menu Snapshot: Vegetable Chat £2.40; Butter Lamb £6.75 - lightly spiced, butter, fresh cream and almond; Balti dishes from Jalfrezi to Tikka Masala, all c£8 regardless of whether you choose chicken, lamb or prawn, served with Pullao Rice or Naan ; Mushroom or Onion Fried Rice all £2.25; Stuffed, Peshwari, Keema, Garlic with Coriander or Onion Naan all £1.95. Del: 6m £12 min. Credit card accepted. Hours: 5-12 daily.   www.gulshan takeaway.co.uk

BRANDON: BRANDON TANDOORI 17 London Road, Brandon 01842 815874

BURY: MUMTAZ INDIAN 9 Risbygate Street, Bury ~ 01284 752988

FELIXSTOWE: BOMBAY NITE 285 High Street, Walton, Felixstowe ~ 01394 272131

IPSWICH: PASSAGE TO INDIA 27 Fore St ~ 01473 286220. 140-seater in 3 rooms est 1991 by R Uddin. Brother Nassir chefs. 44 starters! T/a: 10% disc. Del: 3m £30min. Hours: 12-2.30/5.30-12.   www.apassagetoindiaipswich.com

IPSWICH: TAJ MAHAL 40 Norwich Rd. ~ 01473 257712

LOWESTOFT: AHMED 150 Bridge Rd, Oulton Broad ~ 01502 501725 Boshor Ali's tiny 28 -seater is *'brilliant.'* PJ. Hours: 12-2.30/6-11.30. Branch: Jorna Takeaway, 33 Wherstead Rd, Ipswich.

LOWESTOFT: ROYAL BENGAL 69 High St. ~ 01502 567070

LOWESTOFT: SEETA 176 High St, Lowestoft ~ 01502 574132

NEWMARKET: ARIF INDIAN 30 Old Station Rd ~ 01638 665888. *'An excellent, well served meal.'* JP.

SURREY

Area: Home Counties
(south of London)
Population: 1,068,000
Adjacent Counties:
Berks, Hants, Kent,
London,
Sussex

'GL' denotes those former Surrey suburbs absorbed by Greater London in 1965.

Addlestone

SONALI TAKEAWAY

198, Station Rd, Addlestone   01932 830424

Mr and Mrs Shima Rob took over in June 2006. Regular customers are given a bottle of Cobra if they spend £18 or over. Menu Snapshot: Sonali Kebab Roll £3.50, Sheek Kebab in Naan, salad and mint sauce; Nipa's Garlic Kebab Golap £6.25, marinated minced chicken, fried leeks, extra garlic, cooked in the tandoor served with salad and mint sauce - fairly hot; Special Tikka Masala c£6, chicken, mild, sweet, fruity sauce with almonds, sultanas, cashew nuts, cream, coconut powder, lychees and butter; Chicken Chat £4 - chat masala, chicken, cucumber, a sweet and sour dish served on a puri; Moolie Bhajee £2.50, white radish, slightly hot; Quorn Rice £2.15; Peshwari, Garlic, Onion or Chilli Naan all £1.60. T/a: 10% disc. Del: £10 min, 5 miles. Credit cards accepted. Hours: 5-11 (lunchtime, please book in advance).

ASHTEAD: BALTI HOUSE Rectory La, KT21 2BA ~ 01372 277 245 *'Prices very modest. As usual, service, less than wonderful. Five of us, only two glasses were brought with the large bottle of mineral water and only Danny's glass was filled when the wine was brought, very strange. Young waiters were pleasant, but manager, unsmiling, unfriendly, very abrupt. Food was wonderful, all very pleased with every dish. Because the food is so good and surroundings pleasant, we will return, but it would be lovely to know if the manager has an evening off.'* HC.

ASHTEAD: MOGHUL DYNASTY
1 Craddock Parade. ~ 01372 274810

ASHTEAD: SHEHNAI INDIAN NEW ENTRANT 9 Craddocks Pde, KT21 1QL ~ 01372 273818. E K Khan wants you to know he serves fish, duck , lamb, mutton and chicken on his menu.

BYFLEET: RED ROSE OF BYFLEET
148 High Rd, ~ 01932 355559

CAMBERLEY: DIWAN EE KHAS
413 London Rd, Camberley ~ 01276 23500

CAMBERLEY: RAJPUR
57d Mytchett Road, Mytchett, Camberley ~ 01252 542063

CARSHALTON (GL), ROSE HILL TANDOORI
320 Wrythe Lane, Rose Hill ~ 020 8644 9793

CHIPSTEAD: CHIPSTEAD TANDOORI 32 Chipstead Station Parade ~ 01737 551219. Seats fifty diners in two rooms. Sun Buffet: c£8 adult, c£6 children. Banquet Night: every Tuesday, £9.95 each. T/a: 20% disc, £10 min - cash only. Del: £12 min. Hours: 12-2 / 5.30-11; 11.30 Fri & Sat. Monday closed.

COBHAM: SPICY CHIMNEY
40 Portsmouth Rd, Cobham ~ 01932 863666

CRANLEIGH: CURRY INN 214 High St. ~ 01483 273992. *'A high standard. Always delicious. Waiters always friendly and on Sunday nights, one does the bill, one fetches the food and a third holds the door! My wife and I have visited many excellent TOP 100s, but are always happy to come back to our 'local'.'* DB.

NOT OK: HAWELLI, BELMONT '*We had a meal here. It was awful. You are mentioned in the menu'.* MK. About 12 years ago I consulted to the Hawelli chain (of some 12 restaurants) and taught the chefs some new dishes. Since then it has undergone at least one ownership change and no doubt chef change too. But I guess the menu did not change. Not much I can do except mention it to anyone who cares to ask.

Camberley (Frimley Green)

SUNDARBAN

Lakeside Complex, Wharf Rd, Frimley Green
01252 838868

Curry on an 80-seater boat, with al fresco tables at a venue with an hotel, disco, cabaret club (where the World Darts Championships are televised from) and fitness centre with pool on the Lakeside Complex site! Sounds like the Editor is on something; but no, it's all true. So you can check in, swim, have a beauty treatment, fill up on the best Indian food outside London, watch a cabaret show, have a workout in the disco, go to bed onsite, have a work out in the gym before a hearty English breakfast and check out! Hours: 12-3/ 5.30-11.30; Sun 12-10.

Cranleigh

CARDAMOM

Freeland House, High St   01483 277145

'On a cold, snowy Tuesday evening the restaurant was almost full so it already has a good following. Very attractive appearance, nearly all white inside and out, fairly plain and modern. Glassware and cutlery particularly attractive and of really good quality. Different dishes are served on different shaped plates with a mound of rice already on the plate where appropriate. Generally efficient and pleasant service. All food was excellent, though Brinjal Bhaji £2.90 chunks too large and needed a bit more cooking with a more generous hand with the spice. Served nicely and in generous portions. I was really disappointed that the Indian desserts had been discontinued, it really is time English diners became a bit more adventurous and not just opt for an ice cream. Luckily, Gulab Jaman £2.50 was the only one left, very good.' HC. Menu Snapshot: Achari Gosth £9.95, lamb, citrus fruit, sour yoghurt, served with Pullao Rice; Badami Korma c£8, chicken tikka, yoghurt sauce, garnished with green pepper and fried onion; Duck Mosalla £10.95, yoghurt marinated sauce, mild spices, baby potatoes, served with Pullao Rice. T/a: 10% disc. Hours: 12-2.30; 3 Sun for buffet / 6-11. www.cardamonindian.co.uk

Croydon (GL)
(Includes Addington Hamsey Green, Selsdon and Shirley)

BANANA LEAF

27 Lower Addiscombe Rd   020 8688 0297

Opened in 1988 by Rajkumar Rengaraj, who will greet you on your visit, as he is also the manager. Nearest Tramlink / Rail Station East Croydon and Bus Route 289 and 410. Chicken Chettinadu £6.60 - tender chicken cooked in a rich, dark sauce of cinnamon, cardamom and onions, is chef T Sundaram's most ordered dish and is also one of my personal favourites, when I eat South Indian food. Seats seventy in two dining rooms. Menu Snapshot: of course the menu lists all the usual North Indian favourites, but lets forget those and go straight to the South Indian dishes: Masala Vadai £2.25, chana dhal, doughnut shaped savoury snack, spiced with black peppercorns, stuffed with ginger and fennel seeds, served with fresh coconut chutney; Curd Vadai - stuffed with coriander and tomato; Bonda £2.75, spicy potato balls dipped in gram flour batter and deep-fried; Masala Dosai £3.20, a crispy pancake, made from urad flour and rice flour with fenugreek, stuffed with spiced potato and onion served with sambar and fresh coconut chutney; Utthapam £4.30, pizza-style pancake topped with mixed vegetables; Rava Masala £4.90, made with semolina,

spiced potato, onion, curry leaves, ginger, cashew nuts and sultanas; Malabar Fish Curry £6.75, two pieces of Indian ocean Kingfisher in a sauce made from fresh coconut milk and a mixture of spices; Fried King Prawns £10 - marinated in ginger, garlic, fennel seeds and curry leaves, mixed with fresh coconut and potato, served with yoghurt mint dip, Tamarind Rice £2.60. Hours: 12-2.30 / 6-11.30; 11 Sun. www.azzz.co.uk / bananaleaf

CHILLI CHUTNEY   NEW ENTRANT

Allders Mall, Croydon, CR9 1SB   020 8726 0780

Owner Neelofar Khan is young and energetic and his mission is *'to make authentic and contemporary Lahori food accessible to the European and young Asian palate'*, deciding that what was needed was *'a thoroughly modern and vibrant ambience'*. Following, they say, frequent visits to India and Pakistan to develop the concept and source qualified Lahori chefs, the 130-seat restaurant opened in late 2003. It very soon became the official caterer for the UK Pakistan High Commission. Hours: 12-11 daily. Branch: Chilli Chutney, 20 The High Parade, Streatham High Road, SW16.   www.chillichutney.com

THE DEANS

241 London Rd, Croydon   020 8665 9192

The Deans opened in 1993 and is named after its chef-owner Salam Ud Din and manager Zaka Ud Din. It is a massive, fully-licensed restaurant seating over 150 diners in two dining rooms, decorated in white with the 'sparkly' mosaic mirror Indian arches to be found in the Moghul palaces. It has a small but typically authentic Pakistani Punjabi menu, serving tandoori items and well-spiced curries. RE tells us of four visits: 1: *'A large busy restaurant favoured by Asians. Also does a very brisk T/a. Apart from the popadums (they are grilled which I don't like), the food is excellent. Lamb Nihari was "special" – very tender, quite hot with a distinctive ginger flavour. Lovely dish.'* 2. *'Happy to go back as I was in the area. Seekh Kebabs freshly cooked and spicy, Chicken Tikka fresh and moist. Service is efficient and friendly.'* 3. *'Third time is supposed to be lucky – not this time. Seekh Kebabs and Chicken Tikka were fine, but the Dhal Gosht, so good last time, was awful – undercooked meat in a pale, tasteless sauce. A chap on the next table was complaining that his curry was far too salty. A shame. I will (eventually) go back, but not for some time.'* 4, *'After a*

culinary disaster last time, I decided to give it one more try – Glad I did. Seekh Kebabs were great, in a hot iron plate with fried onions. Haandi Dhal Gosht – very good, hot, spicy, full of flavour and very tender meat. Service good and friendly, busy with families.' RE. Specials: Handi dishes, chicken, Methi Gosht £5. Handi Aloo Chana, Dhal-stuffed Karela (bitter gourd). BYO no corkage. Del: £10 min, 3m. Hours: 12-2.30 / 6-11.30; 10.30 Sun.

KERALA BHAVAN

16 London Rd, CR0 2TA   020 8668 6216

South Indian Restaurant right next to West Croydon Railway Station. *'The usual Indian background music was playing as we entered this pleasant restaurant. There are about 50 seats, set in alcoves, which gave a more intimate feel and was very nice. The waiter was very friendly and attentive. It was about half full. Ray headed for the toilet as he always does – two reasons: Firstly to wash his hands as he eats with his fingers; and secondly to include in his reports to you. He thinks the toilets often reflect the standard of hygiene throughout the establishment. These were fine – everything worked and there was plenty of soap etc. Popadums came. They were nice and crispy and dry. Even I like popadums. For a starter Ray had Parippu Vada, which were two spicy fried lentil cakes. I tried a bit and said it tasted like a dry spicy bun. Ray said I was a Philistine, smothered his with onions, lime pickle and raitha and said I did not know what I was missing. For his main course, Ray had Kerala Meat Chilli. This consisted of quite hot cubes of very lean and tender lamb, which had been marinated in a sweet & sour marinade, then cooked with green chillies and capsicums. It was a dry dish, but very spicy. Ray enjoyed it and said he would recommend it. He also had a Kerela Veesu Paratha, a sort of bread in strands. This was most unusual but a good accompaniment to the chilli meat. He also had a dall, which was very runny & bland. The bill was £25 and there was an added 10% Serv.* R&RE.12-3 / 6-11.

PLANET SPICE   A-LIST

88 Selsdon Park, Addington, Croydon
                                020 8651 3300

Opened in 1999 by the very talented Emdad Rahman of Babur SE23 fame. This fantastic restaurant is well decorated in a modern and colourful style. Raj Pandey, ex Taj Madras is head chef and he delights his regulars with Masala Roast Lamb Shank, braised with spices and ground sesame seeds, then marinated in strained yoghurt and finally pot roasted to melt in the mouth - scrumptious! Menu Snapshot: Begun Dolma, baby aubergine stuffed with mildly spiced, creamy red pumpkin; Murgh Pattice, potato cakes stuffed with mince chicken, topped with dried peas curry; Gilawat Ke kebab, melt in the mouth mince lamb stuffed with lentils and raisins, flavoured with mace, cardamom and saffron; Betki Balchao, strips of battered Bekti fish stir fried with a hot and sour Goan sauce; Hariyali Murgh, boneless breast of chicken cooked in a smooth, hot green sauce

of mint, spinach, coriander and green chilli; Madras Snapper, tomato based hot fish curry tempered with curry leaves, mustard seeds and coconut; Crispy Fried Potatoes, thinly sliced potatoes, dusted with gram flour and fried mango powder, then deep-fried; Poriyal, green beans and aubergines combined with cashew nuts, onion seeds, coriander and garam masala; Subze Tandoori, red pumpkin, green peppers, onion, okra, tomatoes and carrots all marinated in traditional spices and yoghurt, Lime Rice with Cashews. Serv: 10%. Sun Buf: £9.95. Del: 3m £10 min. Hours: 12.30-2.30/ 6.30-11.30. Branch: Babur, 119, Brockley Rise, Forest Hill. SE23. www.planet-spice.com

Dorking

RED CHILLI

A24 Horsham Rd, Mid Holmwood, Dorking
01306 644816

Wasimul Choudhury opened his 100-seater in 2005 in a smart and bright building with parking outside and a big red chilli hanging beside the entrance door. *'It will have to rely on passing trade or build up a really good reputation. Fairly quiet on a Tuesday evening. Decor, really attractive and modern, sparkly lights in ceiling, not obviously Indian. Water feature in entrance. Lovely quality china and cutlery, waiters all in blue shirts and ties. Menu large but very conventional, shame, had hoped for a more adventurous choice. Service poor, friendly, just unprofessional. Wine opened incorrectly, plates handed across the table to the diner. But the food was excellent and attractively presented in plain white dishes. Everyone was really pleased with everything, King Prawn Butterfly - really special. Overall a very pleasant evening.'* HC. Menu Snapshot: Paneer Pakora c£3; Batak Raja Naga Shahi c£8 - duck with the famous naga chilli; Dhal Makhni c£5 - black urid dhal, ginger, garlic, cream, butte Hours: 12-2.30 / 5.30-11; 11.30 Fri & Sat. www.redchillidorking.com

Epsom

JIMMY SPICES   NEW ENTRANT

Derby Square, KT19 8AG   0121 643 2111

The group's fourth unit opened here in 2007 and serves Indian, Chinese, Thai & Italian cooking in a live theatre-style cooking display with large bar alongside. Hours: 12-2.30 / 5-11. Branches and more comment: Broad St, Birmingham, B1.   www.jimmyspices.co.uk

Esher

SHERPA KITCHEN   NEW TOP 100

132 High Street, Esher   01372 470777

A branch of our Award-Winning Gurkha Kitchen, Oxted. (See Oxted entry for details).

Ewell

SRI KRISHNA INN

332 Kingston Road, Ewell   020 8393 0445

Managing owner, M Krishna Das took over this restaurant in 2001. It seats seventy diners and serves Southern Indian cuisine and Masala Dosa is their most popular dish. Del: 3m £20 min. Set lunch and dinner £24 for two. min charge: £15. Hours: 12-3 / 6-11.

Farnham

DARJEELING

25 South Street, Farnham   01252 714322

MA Rahman and S Islam's 46-seater is stylishly decorated, with mahogany wood panelling everywhere, brass plates decorate the walls and there is a large brass peacock in the window. *'Very unexceptional in appearance and all the same as previous visits - consistent. Menu, prices, decor and general style are the same as hundreds of Indian restaurants all over the country, but the service is efficient and food well above average. Friendly and efficient with very modest prices. Extensive menu with a few Chef's Specials - the only restaurant, I know, to offer Broccoli Bhaji. Most enjoyable with a car park right opposite and they serve a very good Gulab Jamun - a plus.'* HC. Hours: 12-2 / 6-11.30.

Fetcham

FETCHAM TANDOORI

248 Cobham Rd, Fetcham   01372 374927

' We have consistently good reports from local friends. After a evening lecture a quick visit seemed a good idea. A lighter style decoration and attractive furniture made a much better impression, since our last visit, on entering. Made very welcome and drinks arrived promptly (the wine list is very poor). Extensive menu, nothing unusual. Popadums, unfortunately rather thick and stodgy.' The popadums that I like the best are made by a company called Liljat and are wrapped in cellophane with a picture of a small boys face and a hideous pink bunny rabbit! These popadums are really lovely, light and crisp. I think this is because they are incredibly thin. Anyway, the boxed ones you get in every supermarket, are quite horrid, far too thick and heavy. DBAC. *'Relished good, with exceptionally delicious mango chutney.'* Onion Bhajia - flat disc style, very good. Chicken Makhone - excellent, lovely thick, almondy sauce with very good Mushroom Rice. Excellent and generous Fish (boal) Masala, I was encouraged to have the fish as, 'it only has one bone in the middle'. According to one waiter, they find that diners are very wary of ordering fish because of the bones and even the chicken now has to be off the bone. Sag Bhajee - one of the best I have had. Brinjal Bhajee also excellent. We were really pleased, all the food was well above average. Service, friendly, attentive and efficient with a very pleasant atmosphere - we shall return very soon.' HC. Hours: 12-2; 3 Sun / 6-11; 12 Fri to Sun.

Guildford

BOMBAY SPICE

17 Park Street, GU1 4XB   01483 454272

'A very cold evening, we had the table moved away from the window, but it wasn't much better, the restaurant was inadequately heated. The wine ordered by Danny came unopened and was offered for inspection. At last, I thought, we have found a restaurant where they know how to serve wine - no such luck. The glasses filled too full, I was asked if I would like to taste it! The food was very good, all dishes were above average and the portions were generous. Mushroom Rice - particularly good. King Prawn Mahli - mild in a coconut sauce. Manager very professional, willing waiters just inept. Definitely will return.' D&HC. *'I had Khorai (sic) Chicken, Saag Paneer and Vegetable Paratha. I had Kulfi for dessert which was as creamy as Cornish ever is. The food was good - as expected - the service efficient. I didn't have to wait too long for the meal. Real linen on the tables - always a pleasure. I must ask them what their coffee is - one of those rare preparations which tastes as good as it smells. A very good dining experience.'* FM. Hours: 12-2.30 / 5.30-11.30. www.thebombayspice.com

CINNAMONS

4 Chapel Street, Guildford   01483 300626

'Decor very open, light and modern, could be any cuisine. Menu very appealing. Good, friendly service, all young men dressed in identical blue shirts and trendy ties. Food outstandingly good, attractively served in white china dishes and in sensible rather than generous portions. Only grumble, unacceptably slow. They did apologise and offered free liqueurs. Espresso coffee served with good quality chocolates. No Indian desserts. Definitely wish to return.' HC. T/a: 20% disc. Hours: 12-2.30 / 6-11.30.

YOU SAY OK

You might get a discount if you show them this Guide.

HAMPTON WICK: ORCHID 5 High St, Hampton Wick 020 8977 9111. Est 2006. *'Food is some of the best we've ever tasted, and the service superb.'* S&NB.

HERSHAM: RESHMI 90 Molesey Rd.~ 01932 219291. *'My mum, born and brought up in India, loves it!'* A&UK.

HORLEY: FORT RAJ BALTI 74 Victoria Road. 01293 822909

HORLEY: NEW CURRY BENGAL 25 Station Rd. ~ 01293 784255. Chef owner, Muhib Miah's modern 50-seater. Hours: 12-2/6-12. Branch: Lingfield Tandoori, 9, High St, Lingfield, Surrey. www.currybengal.co.uk

KEW: RARA'S NEPALESE DINING 279, Sandycombe Road, TW9 3LU ~ 020 8332 1020. Named after a Nepalese National Park and run by Baz and Prakash, from Bangladesh and Nepal respectively. A lovely stylish restaurant, decorated with silver wallpaper, beige high-backed suede chairs, mushroom-coloured banquet seating and classic white linen laid on square tables. Infact, the only colourful thing on the tables, are the crushed raspberry menu cards - very attractive. Pradip is the chef and Idira runs the front. Reports please. Hours: 6-11. www.rara-kew.co.uk

Horley (2miles north of Gatwick)

FORT RAJ

74 Victoria Road, Horley   01293 822909

'Needed a fix near Gatwick Airport. What a nice place!

Started with a Duck Tikka which was fairly unusual and caught my eye. The portion size was not great but it was just the job for a starter. The six pieces of spicy duck come with a generous side salad and a small tub of dipping sauce which had a subtle orange flavour (I would have personally preferred a hot chilli sauce but that was just me!). For a main course I chose the Chicken Xacuti which was similar to the recipe in your restaurant cook book. The portion was man sized and nicely presented. The food itself was great and with just a slightly bigger Tandoori Roti, the bowl and plate would have been clean. After finishing everything I asked for the bill and when it arrived it came along with a complimentary brandy! Total cost £18.45. £7.00 of this was my lager bill so the total food cost was £11.45. Well worth a visit! As by the way is its near neighbour The Curry Inn (less than 100 yards away) but that is another story. Cheers' DC.

Kingston-on-Thames (GL)

MONTYS TANDOORI

53 Fife Road, Kingston 020 8546 1724

70-seater Nepalese restaurant, owned by Kishor Shrestha. South Indian face-masks decorate the white walls and hang from cream drapes. Hand-painted silk pictures of Indian scenes cover the walls, the floor is tiled. Specials: See Ealing, W5 for details *'Service is excellent, unobtrusive, polite and no mistakes. Food is plentiful and piping hot.'* ST. T/a: 10% off. Hours: 12-2.30/6-12.

SRI KRISHNA INN

332 Kingston Rd, Kingston   020 8393 0445

South Indian (Keralan) food which you should plump for, rather than the curryhouse favourites. No one does better vegetarian food than Kerala. The bench mark is the dosa, sambar lentils and rasam soup. *'I tried these for the first time since returning from Cochin. Lovely'.* RC. *'Lentils, gourds and light spicing means inexpensive ingredients and the cost here is minimal. Two of us filled up for £28 inc Cobra'* RL. Set thali (Sun) £10. Hours: 12-3 / 6-11 Sun-Thur; 11.30 Fri, Sat Branch: Sree Krishna Inn 332 Kingston Road, Ewell, Surrey 020 8393 0445

Mitcham

CHAK 89

Bond Road, Mitcham   020 8646 2177

Opened in 2005 by Fukhera Khalid. Seats a huge 140 diners and serves Punjabi food: Tawa Chicken dishes, Garlic and Chilli Fish and Grilled Tilapia being house specials. Fukhera also has an adjoining banqueting room. Weddings and parties can be catered for in this elegant room, up to 600 people: Free pops. Hours: 6-12; 1am Fri & Sat. Monday closed.

BLUE JUNCTION

2 Crown Parade, Morden   020 8540 2583

Opened summer 2005, as primarily a contemporary bar. Its outdoor seating enhances its popularity as a stop for afterwork drinks and weekend parties. At lunchtimes there is a mixture of European and Indian dishes eg. Lamb Kofte Burger c£5, served with a yoghurt sauce, salads and sandwiches. Gourmet Wrap £4, Roti, or Naan with Spicy Lamb, Chicken or Paneer & Pea fillings served with lime pickle & yoghurt. Or there is the Balti Bowl c£5. In the evenings they serve a classical Indian menu. An old friend of this Guide and now restaurant critic on The Guardian, Humayun Hussain has even commented on the *'excellent vegetable dishes'* and he likes the chef: There's much to like about Chef Sebastian Fernandes menu'. HH. Here are some of the evening dishes: Lollipop Chicken £3.50, a starter of chicken drumsticks dipped in lightly spiced gramflour batter and fried. Lamb Dum Biriani £10, lamb sautéed in Indian herbs & spices, cooked with basmati rice and mint leaves. Raarha Chicken c£8, a Punjabi delicacy made with chicken, minced lamb, ginger, garlic & fresh chillies. Paneer Tikka Shashlik £8.50, cubes of paneer marinated in a yoghurt-based masala, with peppers, onions & tomatoes. Kerelan King Prawn Moilee £9.95, A Keralan-style dish from the west coast of India. Sautéed king prawns with curry leaves, cooked in traditionally spiced coconut milk. Hours: 11-11 Mon-Thur; 2am Fri; 2-2 Sat; 4-11 Sun.   www.bluejunction.co.uk

YOU SAY OK
You might get a discount if you show them this Guide.

MORDEN (GL): INDIAN VILLAGE
10 Morden Ct Pde, London Rd ~ 020 8640 8556

MOTSPUR PARK (GL): MOTSPUR TANDOORI
365 West Rd, Motspur Park ~ 020 8949 4595

NEW MALDEN (GL): CHARLIE'S INDIAN CUISINE
276 Burlington Rd, New Malden ~ 020 8949 7476

Newdigate (nr Dorking)

ALI RAJ

Parkgate Road, RH5 5DZ   01306 631057

Established 1994. Fully licensed. It's on a country road near Gatwick. We occasionally turn up on the way back from a week in Spain. We tell them of our curry-desert holiday. Typically, the waiters haven't been to Spain, so we tell them to go for a week on a cheap charter flight and consider opening a restaurant! On our last visit, it was very late, probably nearing midnight and as we approached the bar lights were still on. We stopped right outside the door (probably on yellow lines - but hey! only curb crawling curryholics are likely to be driving about at this time of night! Was the chef still there? We

were in luck! We had already decided on the plane over a G & T, that if they were still open and would accept a T/a order, we would not be fussy and just order simple dishes, like curry and rice, nothing too complicated. So, Chicken Dhansak £6.25 including Pullao Rice and King Prawn Jalfrezi £8.00 was ordered. While we stood at the bar, eagerly waiting for the brown paper bag containing our feast to emerge from the kitchen, the waiters cleared tables and polished glasses. We told them we had been to Majorca and dropped heavy hints that perhaps they should go to Majorca as the British holiday maker was in need of a good curry house (there are some bad ones, in Magaluf and Palma Nova, however, on our last trip we found a lovely Indian restaurant in Palma, called Basmati, it is near the Oliver fruit and vegetable market). After a short wait our T/a appeared and off we went. I must keep a plastic fork and spoon with napkins in the glove compartment of the car for our next visit! During the summer the owner grows tomatoes in the back garden. Large plants line the perimeter, heavy with ripening fruit. I don't think you can eat in the garden which is a shame as it has a very sunny aspect. Sun Buffet: 12-2.30, adults c£8, children c£5. min Charge: £10.00. Menu Snapshot: Chicken Chat £3, in a light tangy sauce; Ranghani £6.50, chicken with honey and ginger; Sundorbon £7, chicken, prawns, sweet and sour; Bengal Fish Korai £7.50; Sag Paneer £2.75; Mushroom Rice £2.75. Hours: 12-2.30 / 6-12.

Oxted

GURKHA KITCHEN   A-LIST

111 Station Rd, East Oxted   01883 722621

Oxted town is divided by the railway, like Woking, which is very irritating. We drove up and down Station Road West twice before we realised about the other Station Road, not so easily reached by car, on the other side of the tracks. We arrived at 8pm and our coats were taken immediately by the waiter, who sat us in the reception / waiting area. The floor is boarded, which makes it slightly noisy, but the whole look is very elegant. Beautiful hand-forged black steel chairs, the seat and back were wickered, the seat then covered in a small patterned carpet with a fringe on two sides. White linen tablecloths and napkins, large, fragile wine glasses, drinking receptacles for the connoisseur, their slender stems making a lovely bottle of Argentinean Norton red wine the more enjoyable. I asked our waiter if a lot get broken. 'Yes,' he said proudly, 'and I break the most.' At the back of the restaurant an area is decorated with a small roof as in a Nepalese village, fishing net and basket hanging from the wall. The food is accurate cooked Nepalese. But it isn't earthy village food. It's slightly evolved and modern, yet indisputably Nepalese. 'Yes, it's spot on. Extremely interesting menu with not one dish that appears on a standard high street curry house menu. We had

first class starters: Bhutuwa (excellent melt-in-the-mouth chicken livers stir fried in a delicately spiced light sauce served in a small wafer basket), Vegetable Khaja (filo pastry wrapped up like spring roll, but not so thick with vegetable filling and mint and mustard dressing. They were cut in half, diagonally, a small green salad with the dressing decorating the centre of the plate, the Khaja in four corners. Extremely mild, but tasty. Main dishes (Mooli Chicken, Piro Lamb and Hariyo Machha – monkfish wrapped in spinach prepared in a mild, dry fruit sauce) were all superb, with the flavouring of each being totally different and distinct from the others. Portions not large, but sufficient. Prices marginally higher than average.' MW. 'Nepalese cuisine served here in sophisticated modern surroundings. A mystery into the unknown as nothing whatsoever on the menu was familiar. However, fortified by large bottles of Kathmandu beer, we chose dishes that sounded good. All were, nicely spiced and tasty. Only the breads were disappointing but perhaps they were meant to be like that – who knows! Well worth a visit, helpful, friendly waiters. Only £60 for three – worth every penny!' CS. 'Friends 40th birthday celebration. Large party of over 20 adults, plus 10 children. Sun evening buffet. Food excellent as was ambience and service. Looked after our noisy group often and extremely well.' SO. Palungo Sag, steamed spinach sautéed with fenugreek seeds; the spinach was fresh. Gurkha Aloo, diced delicately, prepared in turmeric and cumin seeds, mild potato cubes fried a little brown on the sides. Rashilo Bhat, rice cooked with bay leaf, cardamom, garnished with brown onion £1.95, light,

The Gurkha Kitchen
111 Station Road
Oxted, Surrey
RH8 0AX
Tel: 01883 722621
Fax: 01883 382793

'Nepalese cuisine served here in sophisticated modern surroundings. Food excellent as was ambience and service.'

Steve Osborne

'Extremely interesting menu with not one dish that appears on a standard high street curry house menu. Well worth a visit' Malcolm Wilkins.

fluffy and flavoursome. Joano Patre, bread with carom seed £2, just like a Nan really, quartered, very good. Golbeda Ko Achar, fresh tomato pickle, spicy, a good accompaniment to all dishes. Everything was delivered in separate white china dishes, the plates hot. Hours: 12-2.30 / 6-11; 11.30 Fri & Sat / Sun buffet 1-10pm.

Richmond-on-Thames (GL)

ORIGIN ASIA   TOP 100

100 Kew Road, Richmond   0208 9480509

90-seater on 2 levels with open kitchen opened in 2002. '*What a gem this is. Situated on two levels inside, the lower level extends past the kitchen, which is semi open-plan to the restaurant, allowing you to see the chefs practising their art in front of your eyes as you pass. There is also a very pleasant alfresco dining area at the front on the restaurant. The quality of the food was superb with a number of innovative and authentic tasting dishes on offer. The Bater Khada Masala (marinated quails pot roasted in onion and tomato masala with crushed dried mango) was truly outstanding, as were the Lehsooni Whitebait (whitebait marinated in crushed garlic and caraway and then gram flour batter fried), Bhutta Kebab (kebab of fresh baby corn wrapped in a spiced mash of corn and potatoes) and the Gilafi Seekh Kebabs (char grilled minced lamb kebabs wrapped in fresh aromatic vegetables) for starters. For main courses, the Lamb Shank Xacuti (cooked in* a hot and spicy Xacuti masala) was sensational along with the Tawaki Bathak (duck breast pot roasted with coconut, cumin, mint and coriander) to name but a few. The service was excellent as well, with the staff coping admirably with our group of 12 raucous friends enjoying a stag night together. In fact we enjoyed it so much that two of us slipped in the day afterwards for a 'light' lunch! Obviously our behaviour couldn't have been too bad the night before, as we were not banished on sight! Overall opinion – truly excellent and innovative. I would not hesitate to recommend this establishment or to return here.*' SO. Hours: 12-2.30/ 5.30- 11; 10.30 Sun.   www.originasia.co.uk

YOU SAY OK
You might get a discount if you show them this Guide.

REDHILL: EXOTICA TANDOORI
18 Cromwell Rd ~ 01737 778624

REIGATE: VILLAGE BRASSERIE 10 West St ~ 01737 245695

RICHMOND: SWAGAT 86, Hill Rise, TW10 6UB ~ 020 8940 7557. Modern, light and airy, cafe-styled eatery, with a wooden floor, pale wooden open backed chairs, white-washed walls and white tablecloths.Looks out for specials, such as Kadai Gosht, Kurkuri Bhindi and Murgh Lamai Tikka.

STAINES: ANCIENT RAJ 157 High St ~ 01784 457099

SURBITON (GL): AGRA TANDOORI
142 Ewell Rd, ~ 020 8399 8854.

SURBITON: AJANTA 114 Ewell Road, ~ 020 8399 1262

SURBITON: JORAJ 163 Ewell Road, Surbiton ~ 020 8390 0251

VIRGINIA WATER: VICEROY OF INDIA 4 Station Apr ~ 01344 843157 '*A great exponent of the skills of cooking great Indian food*' AF.

Tolworth (GL)

JAIPUR

90 The Broadway, Tolworth   020 8399 3619

The external decor makes this venue unmissable. Its huge pink stone pillars make it stand out, a fact not unnoticed by the local council, who in the early days spent a considerable amount of time, and presumably money, trying to force owner SU. Ali to remove them. Fortunately bullying bureaucracy lost, and the pillars remain; indeed, they continue inside, giving a very Indian feel to the interior. India's Jaipur is the pink city,

OriginAsia

100 Kew Road,
Richmond, Surrey,
TW9 2PQ

www.originasia.co.uk

Delivery Hours
12 noon - 2:30pm   T 020 8948 0509
5:30pm - 10:30pm   F 020 8948 4071

Jaipur   INDIAN CUISINE

where every building is made from pink sandstone. Naturally the Jaipur's theme is pink too, with *'an amazing sugar-pink decor, with friezes of dancing ladies seemingly sculpted out of the wall.'* DD. *'Thoroughly enjoyable.'* DRC. *'One of my regular haunts.'* PD. You might get a disc if you show them this Guide.

Warlingham

INDIA DINING

6 The Green, Warlingham   01883 625905

Decorated in a modern style, white linen, cream walls, deep brown chairs, Asad Khan opened his restaurant in 2003. Manager is Golam Morshed and chef is Naresh Chand, from the Oberoi's first-ever hotel, the 5 star Cecil Hotel in Simla. Starters include Red Deer Tandoori Chops with crushed fennel and cumin seed, £12; Chilli-fried Squid tossed in hot, sweet and sour spices, c£8); South Indian stir-fry lamb on mini naan bread, £8. Mains include Rack of Lamb with sweetcorn sauce, £16.95 ; Pan Seared Duck breast with dill sauce £14 and Grilled King Prawns with seasonal vegetables £27. All mains come with masala mashed potato. Sun Lunch: two courses £9.95, 12.30-3. Early Dining: two courses and coffee £10.95, 5.30-7 Sun to Thurs. Del: 4m £15 min. Serv: 10% of parties of six or more. Hours: 12-2.30 / 5.30-11. Branches: 7 Station Appr, Hinchley Wood, KT10 OSP and 17 Upr High St, Epsom. KT17 4QY. Reports please.   www.indiadining.co.uk

Woking

JAIPUR   TOP 100

49 Chertsey Road, Woking   01483 772626

Jaipur is the pink city of India. This elegant 60-seater, established in 1993, is owned by Nizam Ali and his two delightful sisters, Reggi and Sophi, all of whom I met in their gorgeous Sylhet home, during a monsoon storm a few years ago. Menu Snapshot: King Prawn Butterfly £4, fried on breadcrumbs, Raj Badak Shaslik c£5, duck with capsicum, onion, ground cumin, Panir Shaslik £4 - curd cheese, capsicum and onions in tangy sauce; Lal Masley Tava £10, red salmon with tomato, onions and aromatic spices, served sizzling; Lamb Nepali c£6, hot, fiery dish of red chilli, potato and yoghurt; Chutney Tray £2.00 – includes mango chutney, coconut chutney, lime pickle, mint sauce, tamarind sauce and onion salad. T/a: 10% dis. Del: £12 min. Hours: 12-2.30 / 6-11.30. www.jaipurrestaurant.co.uk

YOU SAY OK

You might get a discount if you show them this Guide.

WALTON-ON-THAMES: ORIENTAL CURRY CENTRE
13 Church St, Walton ~ 01932 222317

WEYBRIDGE: GOLDEN CURRY
132 Oatlands Dr. ~ 01932 846931. Owner Enayeth Khan.

WEYBRIDGE: THE HUSSAIN
47 Church St. ~ 01932 844720. Owner M Suleman.

WHYTELEAFE: CURRY GARDEN 242 Godstone Rd ~ 01883 627805. Owners Akhlaqur Rahman & Moynoor Rashid.

WOKING: KHYBER PASS
18 The Broadway. ~ 01483 764710. Manager Jafar Abdul Wahab.

WOKING: LOTUS OF BENGAL
45 Goldsworth Rd. ~ 01483 766226. Owner Mostaque Rahman.

Worcester Park

MUNAL

76 Central Rd, Worcester Park   020 8330 3511

Amrit Thapa est his 74-seat Nepalese restaurant in 1998. Mahesh Rana cooks: Momo, meat dumplings lightly spiced Nepalese style, served with salad; Squid, marinated in herbs and deep-fried; Bhuteko Prawns, fried prawns, highly spiced all £3.50. Min Charge: £12. Del: 3m. T/a: 10% Disc, min £10. Hours: 12-2.30 / 6-11.30; 12 Fri & Sat.   www.munalrestaurant.co.uk

SUSSEX

Area: South
Population: 1,512,000
Adjacent Counties:
Hants, Kent, Surrey

This county has been divided into East and West Sussex since the 12th century, and obtained separate county councils in 1888. For the purposes of this Guide we combine the two.

Brighton

400 restaurants in this town and most including the Indians are overpriced for tourists. Here are the best of a mostly poor bunch (see also Hove)

BAYLEAF

104 Western Rd, Brighton   01273 773804

Established in 1998. Seats 87. *'Bingo, an oasis in the wilderness of mostly mediocre formula curry houses in Brighton. Bills itself as an Indian Brasserie and it's certainly different from yer average eatery. Light airy room with tiled floor, polished wood tables and a cool blend of jazz and blues background music. Not a Balti, Pakora or Vindaloo in sight*

– *about 12 starters and 12 mains, of mostly unusual dishes. The price for mains (about £6.90 per dish) was inclusive of side dishes of Dhal and Vegetable of the Day, so it was pretty good value. Food was uniformly excellent. Chicken Chaat gets a special recommendation – a really good interpretation of what is rapidly becoming in some places a very hackneyed (and oily- ugh!) dish.'* SM. *'An unusual and refreshing different menu, although for the unadventurous some standard curries are available. I had Chicken Chaat followed by a Bayleaf Khasi – fresh lamb pieces with onion and red chillies, which came with Dhal and a Vegetable Curry. Good quantities and the quality of food was excellent. Offered a drink on the house.'* MK. Specials include: Chicken Nilgiri (with spinach and mint). T/a: 15% disc. Del: £10 min, 3m. Hours: 12-3 / 5.30-11.30; 12-12 Sat .

DELI INDIA

81 Trafalgar St, Brighton   01273 699985

An Indian delicatessen and teashop providing Indian meals and snacks, teas and drinks. Owned by Jamie Keen and Farida Pathan, a cook since the age of 13, rustles up a regularly changing menu to eat in or take away which will always include at least two meat curries such as Chicken Kalya, and Minced lamb curry, both c£5 and two vegetarian curries, eg: Gujarati vegetables and Kidney bean and pepper, £4.40 and at least one dhal all served with either basmati rice or two chapattis in the price. Also available are savoury snacks, dips and soups and Indian sweets such as halwa, gulab Jamun and naan khataay (Indian shortbread). Deli items include a wide range of spices, chutneys and oils. Recipes and advice are available. *'I've eaten here several times and have thoroughly enjoyed the experience each time. Not only is there a wide and varied choice of delicious food but there is also an outstanding range of teas'* (99 varieties) *'the like of which I have never seen anywhere else. I have found the portions to be a good size and the prices very reasonable. Furthermore having the chance to purchase teas and ingredients for my own home makes each trip very enjoyable. I definitely recommend this to anybody with a fondness for good wholesome curry.'* PL. *'The vegetable thali lunch including 2 x veg curry, dhal, rice, veg samosa, two bhajis, two dips, chapatti: was excellent, really good value for money at £6.00 and a great way to taste different dishes. It all tasted fresh, healthy and home-cooked. It's great to have good quality Indian food in such nice, bright surroundings and also be able to buy ingredients in the shop or buy some food to T/a. I'm a big fan of Indian food and definitely recommend Deli India.'* JP. Hours: 11-7.30; 6.30 Sat;

BARNHAM: PASSAGE TO INDIA 15 The Square, Barnham ~ 01243 555064. Muhammed Yousuf Islam's 58-seater. Hours: 12-2.30/6-11.30; 12 Fri & Sat.

BEXHILL-ON-SEA: SHIPLU 109 London Rd, Bexhill ~ 01424 219159. Owner Abdul Kalam Azad.

BRIGHTON: BALTI HUT 2 Coombe Tce, Brighton ~ 01273 681280. 30-seater, est. '97 by Dost Mohammed. Curries from c£5. *'Excellently cooked & v delicious. Forget location prejudice.'* N&D. Service 10%. Hours: 6-11.30; 12 Sat.

BRIGHTON: NDIAN SUMMER 69 East Street, Brighton, BN1 1HQ. South Indian dishes..

BRIGHTON: NOORI'S 70 Ship St, Brighton. ~ 01273 329405

BRIGHTON: POLASH: 19 York Place, Brighton ~ 01273 626221. Nosir Ullah's 60-seater, is licensed but BYO, no corkage. T/a: 10% disc. Del: £10 min. Hours: 12-2/6-12.

MEMORIES OF INDIA

9 First Floor, Brighton Marina   01273 600088

'An unusual place to find an excellent Indian restaurant. A large well decorated emporium has plenty of good ambience. The staff and helpful friendly and attentive. We only had main courses, the Chana, Chicken Bhuna, and CTM were all good. The Chicken Dhansak was exceptional. Side dishes of Bombay potato and pakoras were also up to standard. If there is any slight criticism then it is that the prices were slightly high, but in view of the location, décor and quality it is a minor point.' AG. Hours; 12-12.

Chichester
MASALA GATE

8 St Pancras, PO19 7SJ   01243 776008

'Upon entering into conversation with owner Murad about his menu which is definitely different, it transpired that he has been trained under Marco Pierre White in London, and we could see this influence with the stunning presentation of the the starters. vive la difference! One member of staff, unusual for an Indian restaurant, a young lady, not English but Slovakian, with her charming accent, was the very model of a professional hostess, immediately seeing to customers with drinks and Popadums. To finish our meal, most unusual, a choice of Homemade Desserts, including Cardamom Creme Brulée and Cinnamon Panacotta with sweet chilli strawberries - has to be tried to be appreciated.' CVF. 12-2.30 /5.30-12. http://masalagate.co.uk

Crawley (2miles south of Gatwick)
BLUE INDIA   TOP 100

47 High Street Crawley   01293 446655

We ate here before a flight from Gatwick. The portions were so big, (and delicious) we had the overs packed up and took them on the flight with us to be enjoyed next day on the terrace accompanied by a bottle of Rioja – lovely!Extracts from Kirti Rewart's menu: Appetisers: Crab Malabar cooked with spices in white wine and mango, topped with cheese, c£6; Salmon Shah, flavoured with mustard, dill, coriander and fresh lime,

c£5. Magic Mushrooms coated in lightly spiced mince lamb and bread crumbs, fried until golden brown., £4; Shingara (Vegetable Samosa) c£3.50; Bollywood Shank: lamb cooked in a rich tomato and coriander sauce, cooked with spicy mince lamb, £14; Chicken Kama-Sutra. Lovers beware this is an aphrodisiac. *('didn't work the time we had it!'* RCF).Chettinad, a dish comprising 18 different spices. A choice of chicken or lamb - in a hot sauce of ginger, garlic and coconut, a delicacy of the Chettinad homes in Madras; Shatkari (a regional dish of Sylhet - Bangladesh), cooked in calamansi juice, lemon leaf and naga chilli .a crisp, hot and slightly tangy flavour Akhni biriani, cooked in a sealed pot, flavoured with cardamom, cinnamon, cloves and rose water served with a medium bhuna sauce. Wide choice of choice of vegetable dishes and breads. Desserts: Some Indian desserts on the menu but we liked the Menage a Trois: a mix of white and black chocolate mousse topped with dark chocolate. *'Restaurant is bright and spacious and is aimed more upmarket than average. Menu includes a good choice of Chef's Specialities as well as the standard range of curries. We started with a large tray of small triangular plain and spicy Pops £1 including mint sauce, chutney and tomato relish. Achari Jolpa Chicken - with peppers, tomatoes, coriander, Indian achar (pickle) and olives. My companions, Duck Xacutti - in masala with roasted aniseed, javantri (nutmeg), fenugreek, red Goan chillies, coconut and cinnamon; Macher Jhol Bengali - fish curry in a hot sauce, (a little too hot for my friend). We shared a Sag Aloo, Bhindi Bhaji, Pullao Rice and a tray of various small Naan breads. We still felt hungry, so finished with Carrot Cake and Indian Summer - mixed fruit, both served with ice cream. We all thought the food excellent and very tasty. Service was friendly and efficient.'* MPK. Hours: 12-2.30/6-11. Branch Haywards Heath.   www.blueindia.co.uk

TAJ MAHAL

2 High Street, Crawley	01293 529755

Crawley's oldest Indian eatery opened in 1969. Owner Belayat Hussain's 150-seater is divided over two levels, the lower of which has warm golden yellow walls, wine red high back chairs and sleek hardwood flooring that gives a polished, clean-cut finish. It also co-ordinates with the wood partition and banister that lead up to the upper level of the restaurant, which is more traditional with deep red carpeting and fitted cushioned seats. There is a miniature waterfall, which is enclosed in two fibreglass sheets and a couple of bubble tanks behind the slick granite bar. The large glass entrance windows let in a bright, fresh and natural ambience. Managed by Rajpal Singh with Chef, Gurudath Panapil, who trained at New Delhi's Taj Hotel. His speciality is Mangalorean cuisine, from the southern state of Karnataka, but at Taj Mahal he cooks up treats from across the country. Traditional Mangalorean dishes like Kori Gassi are served up alongside more popular options like Saag Gosht and Chicken Shaslik.   www.tajmahalcrawley.co.uk

ZARI

214, Ifield Dr, Ifield, Crawley	01293 553009

'The Zari is wonderfully different – up market, classy, clean, subtle light, dimmer switches, high back light wood chairs. Generous portions – two Rice and Sag Aloo £2.30 for three people. Although not advertised I often order a portion of masala sauce for my veggie daughter. T/a for four £39.95.' BW. Starters include : Machli Papeta na Pattice, flakes of fish, mashed potato, herbs and spices. Murgh Tikka Mariali, spicy green chicken tikka. Main course: Zari Jhalak Machli,crunchy pomfret on bed of crispy fried onions and aubergine salad, served with tangy sauce. Hours: 12-2.30 / 6-11.30.

Hailsham

RAJDUTT

46 High Street, Hailsham	01323 842847

Originally opened in 1978 then taken over in 1990. Abdul Ali heads the management team, serving seventy in two rooms. Head Chef, Abdul Malik's 'Specials' are very popular and include: Chicken Silsila - chunks of chicken breast in fresh herbs and spices. Menu Snapshot: Fish Tikka c£5, marinated salmon barbecued; Kurzi Lamb £69.95, whole roasted leg of lamb with accompaniments. T/a: 10% disc. Hours: 12-2 / 6-11; 11.30 Fri & Sat.

YOU SAY OK
You might get a discount if you show them this Guide.

BURGESS HILL: SHAPLA 226 London Rd, Burgess Hill ~ 01444 232493. No airs and graces at this restaurant, but boy did the curry hit the spot ' N&D.

CHICHESTER: MEMORIES OF INDIA Old Bridge Rd (A259), Bosham Roundabout, Chichester ~ 01243 572234. Owner Abdul Jalil. T/a: 15% off. Hours: 12-2.30/6-12.

CHICHESTER: SHAPLA TANDOORI Eastgate Sq, ~ 01243 775978. *'Service dump it all on the table and run. Still worth going.'* CC. *'Closest to the Theatre. I enjoyed their Chicken Dhansak (quite hot) and yes the Nan bread is excellent. Good value for money too.'* DC.

CRAWLEY: CUZINI NEW ENTRANT 22 The Boulevard, RH10 1XP ~ 01293 533350

EASTBOURNE: INDIAN PARADISE 166 Seaside ~ 01323 735408. Owner A Khalique.

EASTBOURNE: INDIAN NEW ENTRANT 14 The Waterfront, Sovereign Harbour, BN23 5UZ ~ 01332 479988. *'Newly opened. Very popular with harbour views. Branch in Rye'.* ND.

HASTINGS: FLAVOURS OF INDIA NEW ENTRANT, Castle Hill Rd, TN34 3QZ ~ 01424 8320989. *'Long-established, very large, warm and welcoming. Favourites: Lamb Silsila, & Achari Lamb.'* ND.

HASTINGS: SPICE OF INDIA 177a Queens Rd ~ 01424 439493

HAYWARDS HEATH: NIZAM 139 South Rd, RH16 4LY ~ 01444 457527. *'30 mile drive for us, but we go often ! Favourites: Goan Chicken Mosalla and Palak Chicken.'* ND.

HAYWARDS HEATH: CURRY INN 58 Commercial Square ~ 01444 415142. 58-seater est 1987 by Abru Miah. *'Very good average for the area.'* C & MC. Del: 5m £20 min. Hours: 12-2.30 / 6-11.30; 12 Fri & Sat.

HEATHFIELD: THE CURRY INN Station Appr, Heathfield ~ 01435 864930. *'Long-est, recently refurbished. Unusuals: Chicken Hunza, with fresh orange zest, and Sarson Batta Murgh, with mustard'.* ND. This is a branch of the above.

HEATHFIELD: MR INDIA 28 High Street, Heathfield ~ 01435 866 114. Manager Shah Athar.

HERSTMONCEUX: EASTERN PROMISE, NEW ENTRANT London Hs, Gardner St, BN27 4LB ~ 01323 832533. *'Consistently highly-rated in the county. Dishes include Murgh Khurchan, Mumtaz Methi Gosht and Shahjahani Chicken.'* ND.

HOVE: GANGES 93 Church Rd. ~ 01273 728292

HOVE: INDIAN SUMMER 5 Victoria Terrace, Kingsway, Hove. 01273 773090. South Indian.

HOVE: KARIM'S TANDOORI 15 Blatchington Rd. ~ 01273 739780. Is popular.

HOVE: KASHMIR 71 Old Shoreham Rd ~ 01273 739677 Est by Subab Miah in 1979. Lots of 'special offers'. Hours: 7-12.

HOVE TANDOORI 175 Church Road, Hove. 01273 737188

CURRY MAHAL

169 Portland Road, Hove   01273 779125

The Curry Mahal seats 100 in three a/c rooms. Est 1971 and taken over in 1999 by Shykul Malique. Menu Snapshot: Chatga Prawns £13.95, king prawns, marinated in a mixture of spices and cooked in a clay oven, curried in medium hot sauce with onions, green peppers, tomatoes and coriander; Komlapuriya Chicken or Lamb £11 flavoured with Grande Marnier and mandarins; Lamb Satkora £12 cooked with tender slices of lamb, satkora, tomatoes, onions, garlic and garnished with chillies and coriander, fairly hot. T/a: 10% disc. Del: £15 min. Hours: 12-2.30 Sat-Thurs / 5.30-11.30.

Lewes

SHANAZ

83 High Street, Lewes   01273 488038

'It has our local been for 10 years. It is a cut above the average. There are a number of things I like. First it is remarkably consistent. Jackie and myself, and friends who eat there, can never recall being "let down". For the most part the staff are friendly and polite and the place is well managed by Ali. The variety of dishes on offer is also a cut above – I am often at a loss as to what to choose. The dish I frequently plump for is Vegetable Naga. This seems to be cropping-up more and more but at the Shanaz they do it particularly well – it has that very distinctive Naga chilli taste and is just hot enough to make you sit up and notice. It also offers other less-seen dishes such as Lebu, cooked with fresh lemons, and Jeera. Jackie often has Prawn Dhansak, well spiced, reasonably chilli-hot and packed with good-sized prawns. I should also say that whilst it is not cheap, you do get a lot of food for your money whatever you order. The side dishes are also good, particularly the Tarka Dhal, which is not easy to get right all the time; it is just thick enough without being stodgy and well flavoured with mustard seed, onion and garlic. Sometimes you can question the Shanaz

not using fresh garlic in its Garlic & Chilli Naans and maybe on the odd occasion there has been too much potato in the veggie dishes at the expense of other vegetables, but overall it really is very good.' AG

SPICE MERCHANT   NEW ENTRANT

West St, Lewes, BN7 2NZ   01273 472356

'We awaited its opening in 2007 with great anticipation. Our first impressions were very positive: it's been expensively installed in the home of the old Lewes Music Library and has quite a smart, grandiose feel to it - chandeliers, high ceilings, and so on. The service was instantly very warm and attentive and the restaurant was packed, people even queuing to get in. An excellent wine list (lots of variety and a good price range) and an impressive looking menu – the usual suspects plus the occasional oddity (Gurkha's Revenge anyone? – it didn't even reach Madras-level heat – and he asked for it to be made extra hot!) and even a couple of Goan dishes. However, the menu was disappointingly short of options for vegetarians. In fact on both occasions I have asked if they could do something veggie for me and both times all they could offer was a Jalfrezi. The quality of the food was mixed. The vegetable samosas I had to start were a little soggy and bland, yet the onion bhajis and popadums were fresh and excellent. The mushroom rice with the main dish was a little greasy my palate and the vegetable Jalfrezi not well spiced or flavoured enough, not helped by an overload of potato. Matter Paneer was on the bland side and seemed undercooked. But Jackie's Prawn Dhansak was by all accounts very good indeed. The Garlic and Onion Naan has also been superb on both visits. And alongside all of this, whilst it is certainly not expensive, you do not get an awful lot for your money; the portions just need to be bigger. If it irons out these inconsistencies it will be a welcome addition to the Lewes Indian scene.' AG

Newhaven

LAST VICEROY

4 Bridge Street, Newhaven   01273 513308

AS Ahmed's fifty-seater opened way back in 1986. There are two menus, one with Korma to Vindaloo for the diehards, and the other with more useful dishes such as: Goat Cheese Samosa £5, pastry parcels stuffed with spinach and delicately spiced goat's cheese; Jalapeno Delight c£5, whole jalapenos stuffed with cream and cheese, fried with coated breadcrumbs; Chicken Lazeez c£8, fillets of chicken breast in a silky smooth almond and tamarind honey sauce; Mahi Monk Fish £10, chunks of monk, prepared in a rich lentil sauce; Lamb Shank £10, garnished with curry leaves, coconut milk, mustard and black cumin seeds; Shan e Pumpkin £4, cubes of pumpkin spiced with fresh curry leaves. Del: £15 min in town. Hours: 5.30-11.30. www.viceroynewhaven.co.uk

Nutbourne

TAMARIND & MOONLIGHT EXPRESS
TOP 100

Main Rd, Nutbourne, PO18 8RT 01243 573149

Set in this small village, in a freestanding building which could once have been a pub, whose distinction is a brown and cream Mk3 railway carriage standing forlornly at the back of the yard (now for sale). Ample parking puts one in the mood to enjoy the food. Inside ambience is welcoming as are the staff. There is a wide range of choices on the menu, and cooking is distinctive. *'Our T/a order was good, and we were very impressed with our subsequent dining-in. Extensive menu. My wife had Patrani Machli (salmon fillets with mild spices baked in foil), and she said it was among the best fish dishes she has ever had. I had the Goa Machli Curry also made with salmon and also excellent. Tarka Dhal and boiled rice were OK.'* RH

Peacehaven

INDIAN & NEPALESE SPICE & FLAVOUR

314 South Coast Road   01273 585808

Faizur and Ayesha Choudhury opened in 2002. Bright and airy restaurant decorated in citrus colours with a wooden floor and polished wood tables. Menu Snapshot: Chicken Bahar c£6, with sliced mango; Lamb Korai c£6, with peppers, tomatoes, and dry thick sauce; Dhal Samba £2.95, sour & hot lentils; Nepali Dishes: Prawn Duck Salad c£3.50; Napali Beef £6.50, with garlic, peppers and tomatoes; Roast Chow Chow £6.50, noodles stir-fried with roast tikka chicken and lamb, medium hot or spicy; King Prawn tawa £7.50, shallow fried (in shell) with spices served with salad. Min Che: £10. Hours: 5-11.

YOU SAY OK
You might get a discount if you show them this Guide.

RYE: SIMPLY SPICE 5 High Street Rye ~ 01797 224222. Owner Chef N Islam, holds regular 'Elvis' theme nts. Hours: 5.30-11.30.

ST LEONARDS-ON-SEA: GURKHA CHEF, NEW ENTRANT 20 Grand Pde, TN37 6DN ~ 01424 444440. *'Nepalese food. Lots of unfamiliar dishes, including MoMo and Aishwarya Kukhura.'* ND

JALI, NEW ENTRANT Carlisle Parade, St Leonards on Sea, TN34 1JG ~ 01424 457300. *'The only restaurant (of any type) in Hastings to have an AA Rosette. We save it for special occasions.'* ND

SEAFORD: BENGAL PALACE 30 Church St ~ 01323 899077. Est 1987 by chef Eleas Hussain. Hours: 12-2.30/5.30-11.30.

Sompting

ALISHAAN
NEW ENTRANT

West Street, BN150AP   01903 204466

Opened in 2008 by the Ahmed brothers in a 400 year old building known as the "The Smuggler's Restaurant". History says contraband was hidden there . Following a rebuild it now seats 106 in 4 rooms. You enter the lobby which has a long leather sofa, one room has the bar behind which is a party room holding 12. The main dining room seats 64 in a new extension. There is parking for 16 cars. Shahin Ahmed is head chef. Menu Snapshot: Chicken or Lamb Tikka Almashriqi, a mild dish topped with spinach; Chicken or Lamb Tikka Flaming, cooked with Sambuca , cream and cashews; Garlic Chicken Tuk-Tuk, marinated in garlic sauce, then grilled served with salad and mint Sauce, all £6.95. *'In our daily hectic schedules, it is a pleasure to be able to enter this oasis of calm and tranquillity, where the general ambience is of a high quality and attention to detail is of paramount importance.   As frequent diners, we have always been impressed by the courtesy and friendliness of the staff and the high quality of the food. For example, our two course meal last week included a starter of pops and chuts. My main course was a Vegetable Shahi Kurma topped by a boiled egg, while my husband chose a Chicken Tikka Noorjahan, accompanied by exotic coconut fried rice. We hope you take time to visit this local haven of tranquillity in your search for the 2009 Guide',* Revd EKH. *'The best Indian food we have ever had anywhere (UK, USA, Australia and Asia). The curries are complex, warm, delicious and chef is always willing to indulge me with extra chillies and spices. My advice is always order something you have not tried before.'* VW. Hours: 12-2 (not Fri) / 5.30-11.30.   www.alishaanweb.co.uk

Uckfield

RAJDUTT

Eastbourne Rd, TN22 5QL   01825 890234

Owner, Amol Sil's restaurant seats 70 in three rooms and there is acar park. Menu Snapshot: Amere Chicken c£8 - mild sauce with mango, fresh cream and almonds; Lamb Nashille c£8, fillets of lamb in green chilli, ginger, spicy hot sauce; Tandoori Chef Specials £10, chicken and lamb, skewered with tomatoes, capsicum and onion cooked in a brandy sauce; Murgh Noorani c£8, breast of chicken, stuffed with minced prawn in light herbs, finished in sweet, sour and hot sauce, served sizzling; Akbari Murgh c£8, tender chicken medallions smothered with pineapple, almonds, raisins, finished in a delicately ginger sauce. Interesting fish specialities: all £7.50, Kalamari Vojon - squid in delicately spiced, fairly hot sauce with thinly sliced capsicum, onions, crushed chillies and crushed mustard seeds; Roop Chanda Biran, pomphret fried with light spices onions and potatoes; Boal Dopiaza, fried chunks of boal in medium sauce. T/a: 10% disc. Hours: 12-2 / 6 - 11; 5.30-11.30 Sat. Branches: Maloncho, Staplehurst, Kent; Maloncho, Peacehaven, East Sussex and Raj, Calpe & Jeava, Spain.

Worthing

INDIAN OCEAN TAKEAWAY   TOP 100
66 Teville Road, Worthing   01903 528888

Located near Worthing main railway station. Established in 1998 by Yusuf Khan, who has clearly built up a loyal following, by *'giving them just what they want!'* These are just some of their comments: *'Indian Ocean was recommended by a friend. Food is very tasty and always cooked to perfection. Service is extremely polite and friendly.'* D. *'Not only is it across the road from where I live, the proprietor, his family and staff are always very polite and friendly. Very nice food, very tasty and plenty of it.'* SB. *'Tasty, well priced food and good polite service.'* JN. *'Del service is very quick.'* BF. *'The best Prawn Bhuna - c£5.'* HE. Menu Snapshot: Mixed Starters £3.45 for two - Onion Bhajia, Lamb Tikka and Chicken Tikka, served with salad and mint yoghurt sauce; Chicken and Mushroom Curry £5.45; Keema and Peas Bhuna £5.45; Prawn and Mushroom Korma £5.45; Keema, Peshwari, Garlic, Panir, Spicy (chilli, garlic, coriander) and Kulcha (vegetable) Naan all £1.75. Desserts also available, from Chocolate Mousse to Raspberry Parfait - all £2.95 - just the way to finish off a spicy meal! Credit card accepted and over the phone, so no fiddling change with the Del driver at the door. Del: 5m £8 min. Hours: 12-2 / 5 to late! See page 30. www.indianoceantakeaway.co.uk

MAHARAJ NEPALESE   NEW ENTRANT
67 Rowlands Rd, BN11 3JN   01903 233300

Roj K Lama is the owner and Head Chef. Decor is simple & soothing with several original hand-carved traditional peacock windows, thangkas (buddhist paintings) and water colours of Nepal. Typical dishes include: Momo, Nepalese minced chicken or lamb dumpling, steam cooked then served with a tomato pickle; Khasi Taang, lamb shank cooked on a low heat and prepared with marrow in a medium sauce; Khasi ko Choila, grilled lamb mixed with spices, tomato, onion with a touch of chilli. Sun Buf: £8.95 adult, £5.50 under 12. Mon: e-a-m-a-y-l, £9.95. Hours: 12-2.30/6 -10.30. www.themaharajofworthing.co.uk

TAJDAR
Horsham Rd, Findon Village   01903 872225

Worthing knows the proprietor of this 80-seater, but not here. Abdul Monnan, owned Worthing's former TOP 100 restaurant - Mahaan. He sold up in July 2005 and decided on a new restaurant - Tajdar. Chef's Specialities: Chicken Chilli Masala - spicy hot dish, fried in a mixture of chillies, capsicum, coriander and tomatoes, served with Pullao Rice; Salmon Chutney - small flakes of red wild salmon, cooked in ghee with garlic, red chilli, coriander and served with boiled rice; Lamb Rezala - slightly hot and sweet, cooked in a tangy sauce, served with Pullao Rice - all £10.45. Chauffeur Service: a pick-up and drop-off service, for customers within 5 miles of the restaurant and are in a party of four or six, the cost for this is £5 each way - sounds like a good deal! And if you don't feel like the traditional stuffed and roasted turkey with all the trimmings, but do feel like a curry, then you are in luck, 'cos Abdul opens for lunch on Christmas Day. Del: 5m £10 min. T/a: 10% disc. Hours: 12-2 / 5-11.30. Branch: Millan, 274, Upper Shoreham Road, Shoreham , West Sussex www.tajdar.com

YOU SAY OK
You might get a discount if you show them this Guide.

WORTHING: AKASH TANDOORI 62 South Street, Tarring, Worthing, BN14 7LS ~ 01903 210597. 'Their Phal is the hottest in Worthing.'. ND

SHAFIQUE'S 42 Goring Road, Worthing ~ 01903 504035. At Shafique Uddin's 48-seater, est 1986, the Thali's are good value: Del: 5 miles. Sun Lunch: buffet c£8. Hours: 12-2.30/5.30-11; 12 Fri & Sat. www.shafiques.com

TASTE OF BENGAL TAKEAWAY 203 Heene Road, Worthing ~01903 238400. Est 1984; Managing owner AM Kalam; Chef, Faruk Kalam. Hours: 5.30-11.

TYNE & WEAR
The county of egg Naans!

Area: North East
Population: 1,100,000
Adjacent Counties:
Durham,
Northumberland

Gateshead
(includes Bensham, Bill Quay, Low Fell and Shipcote)

THE LAST DAYS OF THE RAJ   A-LIST
168 Kells Lane, Low Fell   0191 482 6494

Athair Khan's upmarket 100-seater has stylish decor – pure 30's Art Deco, complete with grand piano. Live music Thursdays. Crisp linen tablecloths laid on beautifully presented tables, brass light-fittings, ceiling-fans, trellis-climbing plants, and fresh flowers. Luxurious surroundings, with friendly and efficient waiters. The bar is spacious and well stocked. This restaurant must have one of the biggest and most comprehensive menus in the country; it is quite a delight. You will find all the

regular formula curries with some regional and authentic dishes including recipes from the British Raj, Country Captain, a dry dish cooked with chicken breast, onion, ghee, chillies, ginger, garlic, turmeric and salt. Raj Lamb and Cabbage is cooked with yoghurt, poppy seeds, lemon juice, green coriander, garlic, onion, fresh coconut, green chillies, ground coriander, ginger, cinnamon and cumin with ghee. You will also find on the menu a few dishes with an oriental flavour, such as Dim Sum, Oriental King Prawn Rolls and Butterfly Breaded Prawn, and there is a Pizza or two – quite fabulous, definitely a TOP 100 restaurant. Hours: 12-2 (closed Sun) / 6-11. Branch: Last Days of the Raj, Durham Road, Low Fell, Gateshead. www.thelastdaysoftheraj.co.uk

YOU SAY OK GATESHEAD
You might get a discount if you show them this Guide.
BILL QUAY TAKEAWAY 78 Station Rd, Bill Quay ~ 0191 495 0270. Owner Syed Amir Ali.
CURRY GARDEN TAKEAWAY 53 Coatsworth Rd, Bensham ~ 0191 478 3614. Owner Abdul Malik Choudhury.
LAST DAYS OF THE RAJ TAKEAWAY 218 Durham Rd, Shipcote ~ 0191 477 2888
LAST DAYS OF THE MOGUL RAJ 565 Durham Rd, Low Fell, Gateshead ~ 0191 487 6282. Run by Ali and Ali. Special: Raj Lamb and Cabbage. Hours: 12-2 Mon-Sat/6-12.

Gosforth

THE DAYS OF THE RAJ

Harewood House, 49 Great North Road,
0191 284 9555

'Situated above a golf shop. We were greeted and shown to the waiting area just beside the piano "very posh". Very smart and very clean. We started with pops and chuts, which we soon finished. As we waited with anticipation for our main courses, the pianist entertained us with a mixture of old and new classics. Fifty-five minutes later, our main courses arrived. King Prawn Sri Lanka £8, good, with just the right amount of coconut. Duck Bhuna £6, Ok, but would have benefited from some better pieces of meat. Butter Chicken £5.50, got the thumbs up. Naans and Rice, all good, as were the mixed sweets and betel nuts that were served with the bill. Service was a little chaotic. Overall, did enjoy the meal, which was reasonably priced.' DMcK. Hours: 12-2 Mon-Sat/6-11.   www.thedaysoftheraj.co.uk

Newcastle-upon-Tyne
(Includes Denton Burn, Forth Banks and West Jesmond)

BINDI CAFE

261 Whickham View, Denton Burn
0191 274 5505

'It is, as it says, a cafe-style curry house with ceramic tiled floor and wrought iron chairs and tables. Knowing the area, I wondered about leaving the car but when we found a parking right out side and what our co-diners were driving - it put my mind at ease. Greeted at the door by a well dressed waiter. Starter with Fried Paneer - looked a little lonesome on the plate by itself, but tasted great. Chutney Mary.' is that your wife? 'had King Prawn Bhajia £3.50 - got the thumbs up. My main course was delicious - Chilli Chingri Masala c£8, while Chutney Mary opted for King Prawn Uree, which she enjoyed, especially the fresh green beans. We shared Pullao Rice and Egg Naan - of a good standard. Staff very pleasant and attentive and facilities very clean - lilac toilet seats - cool! All very reasonably priced.' DMcK. Del: £8 min. Hours: 5.30-12.

LATIF

1 Clayton St West, Newcastle   0191 230 3780

'Latif is the third name for this elegant restaurant in the last 10 years. Mr Syed Latif offers an extensive menu with all the usual dishes. A great restaurant for every occasion with friendly and helpful staff.' DMcK. Menu Snapshot: Nawabi Baro Chingri £4.75 - king prawn with herbs and spices, rolled in breadcrumbs, deep-fried in ghee, served with salad and mint sauce; Chicken and Egg Pullao Rice £2.95; Beef Rasoon £7.50 - medium sauce, extra garlic and fresh coriander. T/a: 30% disc. Hours: 12-2.30 not Fri / 6-12 daily.

RASA NEW ENTRANT & TOP 100

27, Queen Street, Newcastle Quay, NE1 3UG
0191 232 7799

This Rasa branch is the only one that is outside London and is situated on the glamourous quayside overlooking the Tyne. Menu Snapshot: Seafood Karu Muru £5 - crunchy stir-fried king fish, telopia fish and prawns tempered with shallots, curry leaves, green chillies and zest of lemon juice; Rasa Utthapam £5.50 - the Indian pizza made of rice and lentil batter, topped with tomatoes, curry leaves, chillies and onions, served with Sambar and Coconut Chutney; Tharavu Roast £8.75 - duck in a thick sauce of ginger, garlic, onion and coriander; Crab Varatiathu £10.95 - fresh crabs cooked in turmeric and chilli water, stir-fried with shallots, black pepper and curry leaves (try this dish was a bread, eg: Paratha £2.50. Service: 12.5%. Hours: 12-3 / 6-11. Branches London N16, W1, WC1 *(see these for more menu details)*. www.rasanewcastle.co.uk

SACHINS A-LIST

Old Hawthorn Inn, Forth Banks,
Central Newcastle 0191 261 9035

Originally opened in 1984, taken over in 2000 by Kulmeet Arora. This is an Indian restaurant, serving Punjabi curries. 'We have been open for over two decades, and I think we are known as Newcastle's best kept secret.' says Kulmeet, though Sachins have been in our TOP 100 for several editions, and now you are in our A-LIST. He continues: 'we are the only Punjabi restaurants in the city, run by Punjabis with a passion for Indian food.' And superb Punjabi it food it is too. (See page 58). Chef, V Joseph's Chooza Lucknowi £20.95 (for two) - a full baby chicken cooked in spices, stuffed with minced chicken and served with a mild mince chicken sauce - is his House Special, however, Jalfrezi and Makhani does fly out of the door! Menu Snapshot: Machhi Tandoori £7.50 - pieces of monk fish marinated and barbecued in the tandoor; Aloo Tikka £4.50 - potatoes mixed with peas, spices and deep-fried in small pieces served with tamarind sauce; Paneer Pakora £4.50 - pieces of curd cheese deep-fried in gram flour batter; Lal Goshat £7.50 - Punjabi hot dish, diced lamb marinated in yoghurt, red chillies and spices, cooked on a very slow heat; Bhein Aloo £4.25 - lotus roots and sauté potatoes, steam cooked in an oil based masala and served with sauce; Malai Kofta £4.25 - fresh grated vegetable marrow cooked with gram flour batter and deep-fried, served in a cream, tomato and onion sauce; Daal Makhani £4.25 - mixed split black shiny and yellow beans cooked in butter and fresh cream. Hours: 11.30 - 1.30, Sun closed and 6-11.15. www.sachins.co.uk.

SPICE BOLLYWOOD

Yellow Quadrant, Metro Centre 0191 460 9449

Ravi Dhuggas' Punjabi restaurant in the centre. provides a welcome menu change to the many curry house formulae venues. We hear of great savoury tastes at affordable prices. More reports please.

SPICE CUBE

Gate Complex, Newgate St. 0191 222 1181

Located on the top floor of The Gate leisure complex, is Jalf Ali's Indian bar, cafe & restaurant. This Punjabi is no curryhouse! It has a glassy, stainless-steel modern look with hard floors, and Punjabi Zee Music pounding out on on a large wall-mounted plasma screen in the lounge area. The service is professional and discreet, and the cuisine is by Oberoi Hotel-trained Dinesh Rawat. Fast food includes wraps, masala burgers, naanwiches and kebabs. *'A la carte includes starters such as Tandoori Citrus Prawns, Lamb Tikka and Shish Kebabs. Mains includes the usual selection of goshts and murghs, tikkas, tandooris, subs and accs and we were drawn to Kashmiri Kofta Curry and Spice Cube's piece de res Vindaloo Beef. All cooked to a high standard at reasonable prices'.* LC. Hours: 12-2.30 / 5.30-11.30; 12-11.30 Sat & Sun. www.thespicecube.co.uk

THE SPICERY

Denton Bank, Denton Rd. 0191 274 9464

Bangladeshi restaurateur Martin Rohman, whose chain of restaurants the largest in the North East, entirely revamped Denton Bank's previously neglected Sporting Arms pub in 2006, pulling it away from its former notorious reputation. It holds 100 covers in the main dining area and 20 in the bar. The contemporary minimalist and elegant decor is defined by its dark wooden floors, aubergine walls and discreet lighting establishing an intimate and stylish ambience. Trained and brought over from Bangladesh, Spicery's head chef Moklis Rahman creates the regular menu with tandoori and fish specialities including Machli Tomato and Murgh Handi Lazeez. Branch: Cinnamon, North Rd, Durham.

THALI

44 Dean St, Newcastle 0191 230 2244

Syed Ahmed's Thali seats 52 and he says he is in charge of 'supervision'. Tikka Masala and Jalfrezi is very popular with customers. Menu Snapshot: Dahi Baigon £3.50, grilled aubergine stuffed with mixed vegetable and fresh yoghurt; Baja Mach £4.50 - lightly spiced fish, pan-fried and served with spicy onion sauce; Murgh Badami £8, breast of spring chicken cooked in a creamy sauce with ground cashew nuts and almonds; Raitha

£1.50, cultured yoghurt in herbs with cucumber or bananas; Egg Pullao £3.25 - fresh egg, herbs and spices cooked with basmati rice. Note: starters are only available when ordered with a main course - Silly rule – sometimes we just want a huge plate of mixed starters with salad and chutneys - makes a good and filling early or late dinner. You might get a disc if you show owner Syed Ahmed this Guide. Hours: 12-2.30 / 6-12.

VALLEY JUNCTION 397   A-LIST

397 The Old Station, Jesmond,
Newcastle North   0191 281 6397

Daraz and his brother Locku are correct when they claim to have *'the most original Indian Restaurant in Great Britain where you can dine in style in an old signal box and railway carriage'*. The sure do have a penchant for purchasing old railway things and making money from them. Style is the word, First they spend a great deal to achieve it. This venture was formerly the 'Carriage Pub'. The carriage in question was built for the Great Northern Railway at Doncaster in 1912. Numbered 397, it was a saloon for *'wealthy families to hire for their journeys'*. Says Daraz: *'we bought it in the third month of 97. It was numbered 397, and the coincidence couldn't be ignored, hence the name 'The Valley Junction 397'.* Now incorporated into the restaurant, it is decked out in greens and golds, and still earns its keep for the well-heeled. Like its sister restaurant, it has quickly earned a reputation for good food, indeed the menus are identical. Says RL: *'A delightful dining experience. (For those not familiar with the area, it is next to Jesmond Metro station, down a subway. Our table was in the old railway carriage – a tight squeeze, so a lot of 'scuse me's.) Chringri Moslai delicious, Chicken Kebab great too. One minor quibble would be the phone ringing, and the waiters calling through to the bar.'* RL. Chingri Varkee, grilled green pepper stuffed with spicy prawns. Tandoori Dhakna, chicken wings marinated in fresh herbs and spices, served with minty yoghurt sauce. Murgh e Khazana, breast of chicken cooked mainly with mild spices and honey, in a creamy sauce. Mangsho Pesta Ke Shadi, top side of beef cooked with a blend of mild spices and pistachio nuts. Branch: The Valley, The Old Station House, Station Road, Corbridge, Northumberland. and Valley Connection, 301, Market Place, Hexham,

VUJON   A-LIST

29 Queen St, Newcastle   0191 221 0601

Stylish restaurant, seating 90 on two floors, with a party room for 40., established in 1990 on Newcastle's quayside, by the elegant Mr Matab Miah. Like its owner, Vujon exudes class, care and style. From the uniform to the decor, it's all just perfect. *'The waiters seem to smile all the time.'* RL. *'Comfortable, well-lit and very clean. No standard curries, but starter and main courses proved interesting and a good choice.'* KDF. *'Most luxurious*

surroundings in Newcastle. Excellent tandoori starter.' T&KM The food is somewhat stylised and can disappoint those expecting the regular curryhouse experience. But stick with it and be open-minded. For those with an inexhaustible appetite, try the Vhandaris Surprise, a ten course banquet. *'We had it and enjoyed it, but we dieted for a day per course – 10 days!'* HEG. *'For main I had the Zaal Jhool Murgh (£9.90) , described as a traditional Bengal curry – chicken breast cooked in a spicy sauce. Unfortunately it was not particularly interesting.'* MC. It received our best in the north East 2004 Award. Remains in our A-list. Hours: 11.30-2.30 (except Sun) / 6.30-11.30.

Sunderland

CAF BLUE COBRA

15 Green Tce, Sunderland   0191 567 2022

'Bright and inviting Indian restaurant in the centre of Sunderland. The food was very good with a number of interesting vegetarian and seafood dishes on the menu, but I relied on my benchmarking dishes of King Prawn Puri and Lamb Korai, both of which were very good. I visited with a large group of people from a course that I was on and everybody was impressed. The service was very good and the staff friendly and efficient. Overall opinion – very good. Would recommend and visit again.' so Hours: 12–2, not Sat; 6-11.30.

NAZ

4 St Thomas St, Sunderland   0191 510 2060

Seats 150 in two dining rooms. Ahmed Bashir is the owner and head chef, and he has some interesting dishes on the menu. Menu Snapshot: Aloo Pakora £2.45 - chunks of potato and onion, marinated in gram flour, spices and fresh coriander, then fried; Bhuna Channay on Puri £2.45 - spiced chickpeas served with puri (fried crispy bread); Murgh Monchorie c£8, spring chicken, tomato ketchup and purée, ginger, garlic and green chillies; Nargis E Kofta c£6, lamb minced meat balls, herbs, spices, cooked in gravy, garnished with coriander; Jhinga E Kabir Biriyani £9.95, basmati rice, herbs, spices, prawns, flavoured with saffron, garnished with egg and tomato, king prawns, with vegetable curry; Gulab Jamun £1.90 served hot or cold. Del: 7m £8 min. Sun lunch buffet: c£8 a person. Hours: 12-11.45.

YOU SAY OK

You might get a discount if you show them this Guide.

NEWCASTLE: RAJ 31 Pudding Chare. ~ 0191 232 1450. *'A cosy little restaurant with a friendly atmosphere and pleasant decor'* DMcK.

SOUTH SHIELDS: PASSAGE TO INDIA 4 Burrow St. ~ 0191 427 5202. *'The food is nice, the staff very obliging. Food reasonably priced.'* DRK. Hours: 12-2/6-12, 1am Fri & Sat.

SOUTH SHIELDS: SAFFRON BALTI HOUSE 86 Ocean Rd. ~ 0191 456 6098. Owner Abdul Kadir.

SOUTH SHIELDS: STAR OF INDIA 194 Ocean Rd ~ 0191 456 2210. First in South Shields, it opened in 1960, owned by M Faruque since 1972. Seats 60.

SUNDERLAND: CHESTER TAKEAWAY 69 Chester Rd High Barnes ~ 0191 510 8835. Owner- Chef, Syed Moynul. Credit cards accepted. Hours: 5-12, 1am Sat.

WHICKHAM: JAMDANI 3 The Square, Front St. ~ 0191 496 0820. Owner A Miah. Hours: 12-2/6-11.30.

WHICKHAM: MOTI JHEEL TAKEAWAY 9 Front St. ~ 0191 488 0851. Owner Mr MM Rahman. Hours: 12-2/6-11.30

WHITLEY BAY: HIMALAYA 33 Esplanade ~ 0191 251 3629. Owner Abdul Goffar. Hours: 12-2.30 / 5.30-12.

KISMET 177 Whitley Rd, Whitley Bay ~ 0191 297 2028. Owner Shohid Ahmed. *'The best Indian we've been to.'* KW. T/a: 10% disc. Hours: 12-2 (Fri closed) /6-12.

WHITLEY BAY: SHAHENSHAH 187 Whitley Rd ~ 0191 297 0503. Owner Abu Taher. *'Food first-class.'* MB. *'My local for a year.'* SN. *'Busy in a quiet and efficient way.'* PP. Hours: 12-2.30/6-12.

WHITLEY BAY: TAKDIR 11 East Pde ~ 0191 253 0236. Owner Majibur Rahman. Hours: 5.30-12. Branches: Akash, 3 Tangier Street, Whitehaven, Cumbria; Al Mamun T/a, 5 John Street, Cullercoats T&W.

WINLATON: BALTI HOUSE 18a The Garth, Front St. ~ 0191 414 2223. Est 1996. Seats 42. Specials include: King Prawn Peli Peli, King A 34-seater. Owner F.I. Khan continues to promises a T/a disc of 20% if you show them this Guide. You can't get fairer than that! Hours: 6-12. Branch: Balti House, Newcastle.

WARWICKSHIRE

Area: Midlands
Population: 526,000
Adjacent Counties:
Derbys, Shrops,
Staffs, W Mids,Worcs

In Warwickshire - Tandoori Mixed Grill is referred to as 'De-Lux'.

YOU SAY OK
You might get a discount if you show them this Guide.

COLESHILL B46: POLASH BALTI CUISINE 107 High St, 01675 462868. 32-seater run since 98 by Adbul Mannan. Parking for 30 at rear. Chef Taj Ullah's Specials: Bengal Fish Masala, on-the-bone, cooked with coriander, served with rice. *'What an experience! Such attention, such choice and such cooking! Our congratulations and thanks to the Polash'.* HFC. T/a: 10% disc. Del: £15 min, 3m. Hours: 5.30-12.

COLESHILL B46: RAJRANI, NEW ENTRANT 102, High St, B46 3BL ~ 01675 463777. *'In our local top 5. They do a very good Tawa'.* PA. www.rajranirestaurant.co.uk

KENILWORTH: INDIAN EDGE 50 Warwick Rd, Kenilworth ~ 01926 850100. 64-seater est 2005 by Mutashir (Matt) Miah, Shelim Adbul, mngr and Kobir Ali, chef. Note: no min charge, but one main dish must be ordered by every diner. (silly rule!) Hours: 5.30-12; 12.30 Sat.

BALTI COTTAGE

107 High St, Coleshill, B46 01675 464122

A chapatti throw from the NEC and the airport (c5

mins) is this 42-seater serves all your favourites and chef specials. Try the Shashlick Murghi Rongila, barbecued chicken, nicely spiced with a touch of masala sauce, garnished with fried tomatoes, onions and peppers. £9.95. *'We love it! Excellent greeting, clean upmarket, lovely smiles, wonderful food.'* SS   Hours: 5.30-12. www.balti-cottage.com

Henley in Arden B95

PICKLES

Liveridge Hill, Henley, B95 01564 784411

Azizur Rahman opened his large establishment, (90 diners on special nights, 120) in 2004. It's stylish and upmarket with wooden floors and simply-laid tables with crisp white linen, square white china, and unfussy dark leather chairs. Prices very reasonable. Menu Snapshot. Shredded tandoori chicken parcels with carrot and red chard salad c£4.50; Trio of samosas served with cucumber salad and dip £4.45; Tandoori duck and noodle stir-fry served with spring salad c£5; Chittagong Crab Salad with garlic croutes and mango dressing c£6; Grilled courgettes filled with dall naga c£9, served with

tomato petal salad; Lamb cutlets marinated with cumin c£11, served with roasted root vegetables and roshuni tarkari sauce; Pan fried black bream c£12, served with spiced aubergines and malabar sauce; Shredded confit of duck flavoured with tandoori spices c£13, served with spinach rice and orange Jalfrezi sauce; Spiced spring vegetable parcels c£9, served with coriander couscous and peach dressing; Carrot, Pullao or Mushroom Naan £2.75. Del: 3m, £15 min. Hours: 12-11. www.picklesfusion.com

Kenilworth

THE COCONUT LAGOON   A-LIST

149 Warwick Rd, Kenilworth   01926 851156

Opened in 1999 within the Peacock Hotel, Kenilworth. It is an astonishingly good restaurant, as good as any in London and big surprise for the provinces, where genuinely "Indian" establishments are so few. Since our last Guide, more Coconut Lagoons have been opened, see branches. Decorated in the vibrant spicy colours of southern India. Seats 60. *'Bright, clean, very pleasant surroundings. Very knowledgeable staff gave clear explanation of food, origin, preparation etc. So good we went back the next night!'* AD. *'Our first visit, recommended by friends. Warm, courteous welcome. Excellent guidance to menu, food beautifully presented.'* JK. Reminded us of holidays in India. Menu Snapshot. Masalai Paniyaram, spongy and savoury crumpets served with tomato chutney. Karaikudi Cutlet, minced lamb cutlets with almonds and sultanas on a spicy sauce. Paneer Roti, pan fried crispy soft cheese with onions and tomatoes in a light and fluffy roti. Shakoothi, Goan style chicken roasted with mild chilli, tamarind, mustard seeds and fenugreek in a thick sauce, served with mango rice and Avial. Goanese Vindaloo, cooked with garlic, red wine and flavoured with cider vinegar and dried chillies, served with tamarind rice and lentils with snakegourd. Konkani Porial, crisp mangetout parcels of minced pork cooked in sherry and lightly steamed - mild and flavoursome. Accompanied with mango rice and stir-fried vegetables. Andra Shank, an absolute favourite of Pat and myself shank of lamb slow cooked in a delicate kuruma bringing out its full range of flavours, served with lemon rice and Avial. Malabar Omelette, strips of Malabar coast omelette in a thick curry with lemon rice - a complete meal! Avial, poached aubergines, french beans, carrots, potatoes and green banana in a thick coconut sauce. *'Starters innovative, main courses small but well presented, excellent quality.'* GS. *'Different from any other we have visited, from internal decor to the ambience one experiences and most importantly the cuisine. Choice and quality of food that really is a world of difference. Well done!'* JEC. We can verify the above as we have visited several times and have stayed the night, which is a must - lovely colonial suite with everything you could possible want -

recommended. *'Booked a table in the Malabar Room but were offered both menus and ordered from the Coconut Lagoon menu - better choice. Good ambience. Don't like the credit card slip being left open, when a service charge as been added to the bill. Tasty chutneys served with Popadums.'* G&MP. Feast dinner c£26, four courses. BYO allowed - corkage c£8. T/a: 10% disc. Branches: London EC1 and Stratford-on-Avon. www.coconutlagoon.com

RAFFLES   A-LIST

57 Warwick Rd, Kenilworth   01926 864300

Under the same ownership as Coconut Lagoon. *The menu is made up of Malaysian Malay, Malaysian Indian and Malaysian Chinese. Very different range of dishes from each culture, from starters to main courses. Style of restaurant redolent of old Empire and evokes a real feeling of being in Raffles Hotel in Singapore. Lighting and atmosphere good. Make the best Gin Slings I have ever tasted - including Singapore.'* [That, Clynt, wouldn't be difficult; the Singapore Slings at Raffles, Singapore are very poor indeed, however, I am pleased to say that the cocktails served here are fantastic. DBAC] *'Caution: take great care if you go beyond three. Food is truly out of this world. Menu changes with new dishes being introduced every few months or so, but favourites have been retained. Claypot and Pandri Perratal are simply a must. Absolutely delighted.'* CRS. *'Our favourite restaurant. Unusual and imaginative menu, food superb, beautifully cooked and presented. Service impeccable. Toilet immaculate.'* IS. *'Group of 60, prearranged banquet Malaysian menu. Greeted with a Singapore Sling , good start to evening, food served on platters, more than ample. Everyone has an enjoyable evening. Highly recommended.'* RD. *'Superb Colonial decor, fine crystal glasses and crisp well laundered linen. Ikan Goreng - delicious, Udang Bakar Kerinc - sensational, Hianese Chicken - unforgettable - I could go on!! Exceptionally consistent - can't wait to return!'* BW. Murtuabale - savoury Indian bread layered with minced beef, lightly toasted in a griddle, a light and crisp texture; Mysore Anda, slow cooked lamb served with Roti and Malaysian Coleslaw.; Pandri Perratal, pan fried spicy pork in a uniquely blended rich sauce served with yoghurt rice, beetroot, a bundle of long green beans, coleslaw and Appatam, an exquisite dish given the contrasting spicy pork together with cool yoghurt rice. A superb experience, but at a price! Three course dinner c£25, Four course dinner c£26. Hours: 12-2.30 /6.30-12.30. Georgetown branches: London SE1, Stratford-on-Avon, Leeds & Not'm.   www.rafflesmalaysian.com

YOU SAY OK
You might get a discount if you show them this Guide.

LEAMINGTON SPA: BALTI VHUJON TAKEAWAY 50a Queen Street, Cubbington, Leamington Spa ~ 01926 423828. MJ Hussain, owner. Hours: 5.30-11; 11.30 Fri & Sat. Sun closed.

LEAMINGTON SPA: BOMBAY TANDOORI 38 Regent St, Leamington, CV32 5EG ~ 01926 420521. 58-seater est 1980 by

MK Ahmed. Del: 3m, £9.95 min. Min Ch: £9.95. T/a: 20% disc; 10% Sat. Hours: 6-1; 2 Fri & Sat.

NUNEATON, ATTLEBOROUGH: MILLENNIUM BALTI 8c The Square, CV11 4JY ~ 024 7635 4480 *'The millennium special curry was highly rated.'* G&MP.

NUNEATON: RAJDHANI 1 Cambourne Dr, Horeston Grange, Nuneaton ~ 01203 352254

RUGBY: TITASH INTERNATIONAL BALTI 65 Church St ~ 01788 574433. *'Impressive. Food does not disappoint. Not the cheapest but good value for money.'* N&JG. T/a: 20% disc. Hours: 5.30-12.

STRATFORD: LALBACH BALTI 3 Greenhill St ~ 01789 293563 45-seater sit in 1985 by Joynal Abedin. Hours: 5.30-12; 2 Sat. Branch: Bengal Brasserie, 5, Worcester Road, Great Malvern. .

STRATFORD: USHA 28 Meer St ~ 01789 297348. Opened 1966, then called the Kashmir. Nazrul Islam took over in 1995. T/a: 15% disc. Hours: 5.30-12; 12.30 Sat.

WARWICK SPICE 24 Smith St. ~ 01926 491736. 60-seater. Proprietor, Hussain. Del: 3m, £15 min. T/a: 10% disc. Hours: 5.30-11.30; 12 Sat. www.warwickspice.co.uk

Stratford-upon-Avon

COCONUT LAGOON   A-LIST

21 Sheep Street, Stratford   01789 293546

'The restaurant is on two floors, with an interesting balcony overlooking the ground floor. Delightful decor. Wonderful Ghee Thosai c£4.50, conical rice flour pancake, home-made chutneys. Unusual vegetables egsnake gourd. A pearl in the Stratford oyster.' PO. See Kenilworth for details.

GEORGETOWN   A-LIST

23 Sheep Street, Stratford   01789 204445

Malaysian restaurant and a branch of Raffles, Kenilworth Warks, where you'll find menu details.

THESPIAN'S

26 Sheep St, Stratford   01789 267187

Fully licensed and air-conditioned. Menu Snapshot: Aam Chicken £3.50, cooked in spicy hot mango sauce; Grilled Quail c£5, marinated in honey, tamarind and chilli, then roasted; Shami Kebab £3.50, minced lamb spiced with fresh garlic, coriander, chick peas and fried; Chicken Naga c£8, hot and spicy. *'Provided me with a very enjoyable curry at sensible prices. Portions very generous and very pleasant management!'* CC. Good fish choice: Roshni Delight c£7.50, mildly spiced Tiger Prawns, cooked with egg yolk, cinnamon, cardamom and garnished with cheese; Saffron Fish c£11, salmon soaked in egg yolk, pepper and garlic, fried in olive oil, served with salad and Saffron Rice; Meen Kakri c£9, Silver hake in a spicy sauce, turmeric, chillies, coriander, onions and garlic; Lobster Beruda c£12, medium spiced with aubergine, served with Pullao Rice; Boal Bhuna c£9, from the rivers of Bengal cooked with green chillies. Del: 3m, £15 min. T/a: 10% disc. Hours: 5.30-12. www.thespiansindianrestaurant.co.uk

WEST MIDLANDS

Area: Midlands
Population: 2,600,000
Adjacent Counties:
Staffs,
Warks, Worcs

West Midlands was introduced as a metropoliatain county in 1974 and contains the conurbations from the Black Country at its west, through to Coventry in the east. At its hub is Birmingham city.

Birmingham City

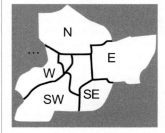

Birmingham postcodes, B1 to B48
Population : 1,018,000

Unquestionably Britain's number two city, Brum has come vibrantly alive with investment in its infrastructure. For the purposes of this Directory, we divide the city into geographical areas, in which are grouped postcode zones B1 to B48 although, as ever, there is no sequential logic to postcode numbering. They are frankly a jumble. But it is the system which exists. B1 to 48 are mostly contained within the M6. M42, M5 ring. To help ngeographically, we have divided the city into cardinal zones, using major roads as our arbitrary boundaries. We start with Birmingham Central, then go to the adjacent Balti Zone, next North of the city, then East, South East, South West, and West. Further B postcodes, B62, Halesowen to B93, Solihull follow, listed alphabetically by suburb name.

Birmingham Central
Postcodes B1 to B5

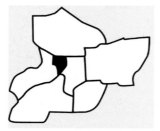

See previous page for key to this map.

(Restaurants listed in alphabetical order)

ASHA'S RESTAURANT   NEW ENTRANT

12 Newhall Street B3 3LX   0121 200 2767

Asha's is owned by Bollywood superstar singing diva Asha Bhosle. She already has branches in Kuwait and Dubai. This one opened in 2007, under the guidance of Russell Scott, former COE at Harry Ramsdens and he decor is top-notch. The bar overlooks the dining area some of which is contained within attractive circular railings. Staff wear smart uniforms, the women, black or cerise-pink saris. Background music is modern, mixed by a DJ with some of Asha's tracks. The venue serves quite specialised Indian cuisine. *'As a little girl,'* says Asha, *'I used to wander around in the huge kitchens of my father's traveling theatre company of more than 500 actors, singers, musicians and helpers who worked long hours. Their food was cooked by his chefs in huge cauldrons and watching them I was fascinated. After a performance we all used to dine together. This is where my interest in cooking began.'* For the restaurant Asha developed a number of home-style recipes which she says she would be happy to cook for her family. Delhi's Chef Modh Saleem Quereshi (son of the legendary Lucknow dum pukt chef) scaled them up to restaurant proportions and trained the kitchen brigade. Starters include a kebab menu, with Murg Malai Kebab, boneless chicken, marinated in cashew nut paste, yoghurt, cheese and cream; Barrah Kebab, baby lamb chops marinated in ginger-garlic, yoghurt and spices and Kebab Sultan Puri, minced lamb cutlet stuffed with chopped onions and mint leaves-cooked on a griddle. Mains include the rarely-found but delightful Murg Keema, minced chicken cooked with coriander and chopped onions; Muscat Gosht, boneless lamb cooked in clarified butter in a spicy, rich tomato gravy; Mai's Prawn Curry, Prawns cooked in a coconut and whole turmeric gravy and Varsha's (Asha's daughter) Fish Biriani. Vegetarians will enjoy the likes of Mushroom Kurkure, stuffed with cheese and bell pepper, battered and deep-fried; Khatti Meethi Dal,

yellow lentils cooked with jaggery (sweet) and cocum (sour) in a Madhya Pradesh recipe and Hare Matar Subzi, dry green peas cooked with grated coconut. For dessert, if you have room, try another restaurant rarity, Agra Ka Shahi Tukra. It's a kind of bread and butter pudding, where fried bread is soaked in a sweetened saffron milk reduction, garnished with nuts. It's much nicer than it sounds! The dishes are far-removed from curryhouse fare, and may get criticised for their unfamiliarity. But the cooking and the reports we get are good. With three venues thriving, the group wish to open a min of 10 franchised Asha's restaurants in the major UK. We are pleased to place Asha's in our TOP 100 Hours: Lunch: 12.30-2.30 Mon-Thur; from 12 Th & Fri / Bar only: 2.30-5.30 / Dinner 5.30-10.30; to 11 Th & Fri/4-11 Sat & Sun. www.ashasrestaurants.co.uk

ALOKA

6 Bristol Street, Digbeth, B5   0121 622 2011

The Darjeeling, Steelhouse Lane, was Brum's first curry house. It opened c 1946, and has long-gone. The Shah Bag was next on Bristol Street, and had opened by 1957. I know because I always came here by Midland Red bus once a week on my day off, from as 'far afield 'as Coventry, where I lived and worked. Hard to believe now but Coventry had none then I don't know when the Shah Bag became the Aloka, but it is now. During the 1960s, the spread of the curry house was as prolific as the city's building. Now it's Birmingham 320, Coventry 50. So here's to the Aloka, a pioneer indeed!

BARAJEE

265, Broad St, 1st Floor, B1   0121 643 6700

Owned by successful restaurateur Moula Miah, of Rajnagar International Restaurant Group, (see Solihul, West Midlands) Barajee overlooks Brum's exciting canal system. Dishes on the menu include monkfish cooked in olive oil, garlic and bay leaves and simmered in spiced tomato sauce. Chefs: Abdul Rouf and Abdul Khalique have also developed set menus where prices start at c£16 per head for a veg meal and c£20 or a meaty version. Lunch & dinner daily. www.restaurantbarajee.com

BLUE MANGO

5, Regency Wharf, Broad St, Gas St Basin, B1
0121 633 4422

The 120 seater Blue Mango Brasserie & Bar has chefs, under Nitin Bhatnager, from different regions of India. *'Very modern decor with lots of crazy huge flower arrangements on the tables. Only visit if you are very hungry - the enormous Onion Bhajia starter is a meal in itself. They should make a separate dish out of the delectable chickpea curry with accompanies the Samosas - excellent food.'* JG. Upstairs is the 170 seater Jimmy Spice's Buffetworks where

you can mix & match Indian, Thai, Chinese & Italian food. Closed Suns. www.bluemangorestaurants.co.uk Branch: Jimmy Spice, B'ham, B1.

ITIHAAS   BEST IN UK AWARD, 2007/8

18 Fleet Street B'ham B3   0121 212 3383

Raj Rana is the driving force behind Itihaas. His previous background was jewellery and property management. At 28 in 2005, and with no catering experience he opened a restaurant. But he didn't want just another Birmingham curry house, of which there are hundreds. He wanted to bring to Birmingham the type of upmarket Indian establishment till then only seen in London. Birmingham until then had nothing like it before. Raj says 'Itihaas is a pure labour of love for me and is simply one man's interpretation of royal cuisine and royal service, yet still having a relaxed and informal atmosphere.' His property background led him to a 5,500 sq ft site on the corner of Fleet Street and Newhall Street, rather aptly in the Jewellery Quarter and the edge of Brum's Business Sector, and he bought its 125 year lease. 'What I got was, a concrete shell.' It was below seven storeys of luxury apartments, requiring a massive odour filtration system which pumps smells to the roof, where they are cleansed. Next Raj set about furnishing and decorating it with literally no expense spared. It cost Raj some £2m to achieved this goal, but you need more than money. Very early on he recruited Satpal Gill (Saif) to take charge of the culinary side. Until then Saif had been a senior chef at Madhu's Southall Middlesex, the Top UK restaurant in our last Guide. Itihaas is a unique name in the trade; it means history, and apart from its own recent history, the menu, which is one of the best we've seen, carries a fascinating history of India, and more of that later. Next Raj employed a manger: Ajay Bhatia, who glides around supervising front of house. On arrival, pretty hostesses wearing traditional silk saris will receive you and will seat you in one of their three dining rooms. The 'Colonial Dining Room,' seats seventy diners, has plate glass windows which are shuttered in traditional colonial style, with dark polished wood. The windows overlook the canal, and a terrace, which can be accessed through double doors. At the time of our visit the canal was in possession of the odd supermarket trolley, a bicycle etc, you know the stuff. Brum council have made some vague promise re spending tax payers money to restore the canal by cleaning out the rubbish. And I bet the tax Itihaas is paying will more than pay for it, so once cleaned and kept clean, it will be a great spot to enjoy a cocktail and canapé party or for a more formal seated occasion and enjoy a clean waterway. Inside, the luxurious look is completed with white table linen, sparkling crystal, and chandeliers. Perhaps you could say it is decorated a little like a Gentleman's club, it's definitely very smooth. Downstairs the 'Maharajah

Dining Room' which seats sixty, is decorated with Indian artefacts, paintings and carved stone elephants. The third dining room, the 'Tiffin Room' is accessed from the Maharajah Room, through two large, 300 year old Indian wooden doors, or so the publicity material says. Knowing India's propensity for manufacturing antiques, take the hundred off and I'll believe it! The 'Tiffin Room' seats an exclusive twelve, and to add to the experience, the room possesses it's own bar and you will be assigned your very own butler, wow! Under Saif is head chef, Sheraton Delhi Hotel trained, Amardeep Saka, heads the, twenty-strong, kitchen brigade. The food is Punjabi with a Kenyan Asian twist, with a little fusion and a soupcon of Chinese. Menu Snapshot: Mirchi Murgh c£8, tender baby chicken, tossed in fresh ginger and garlic, pan fried with fresh chilli, dressed with coriander and tomato juliennes; Chingari Jingah £9.95, king prawns, with chillies, roasted garlic and lemon; Chotte Kofta c£9, lamb balls spiced with cardamom and clove, with tangy sauce; Nana-sa -Dosa c£7, crispy pancake, filled with spiced potato and vegetables, served with coconut chutney and lentil soup, yum yum!!; Maari Aloo c£7, dry roasted potato wedges, ground black pepper, drizzled with tangy soy sauce; Pilli Pilli Bhogah c£6, assorted fresh vegetables lightly fried in spiced crispy batter; Masala Champay c£10, juicy lamb chops barbecued in the clay oven drizzled in a chutney made from paprika and lemon, I've eaten these, VERY good! ; Padhina Keema c£10, minced lamb, tossed with ginger, garlic, cumin, coriander and mint leaves, Pat really likes Punjabi-style Keema; Paneer ka Tukrah c£9, homemade cheese, marinated in garam masala, yoghurt, ginger, chilli and coriander leaf; Koila Murgh c£13, whole chicken marinated in yoghurt and herb paste, seared over hot charcoal; Bhangan Aur Tamatar ka Bhartah c£7, smoked aubergine with sun dried tomatoes, peas, red onions and thick masala sauce; Hara Bara Kofta c£7.50, pan fried mixed vegetable dumplings, think dry tangy sauce, garnished with ginger and chilli; Pyaz aur Lassan ka Kulcha £2.50, garlic and onion stuffed bread, one of Pat's favourites; Gosht Basmati c£11, spring lamb, cooked on the bone, basmati rice, saffron and herbs, we both fight over this one!; Bhundi Raita £2.50, deep-fried gram flour pearls , homemade yoghurt, roasted cumin and coriander. Now to the puddings!!, Garam Gazarh Hallwa Naraam Kulfi £3.25, hot carrot cake with almonds and pistachio, served with kulfi, I know this is good, 'cos I've tried it. Coconut Kheer £3.75, Punjabi rice pudding, grated coconut, cardamom; Mithai Chawal aur Hallwa £3.75, sweet basmati rice, raisins, cashew, almond, a semolina cake, lovely! We are absolutely delighted to award this restaurant the Best in the Midlands and the best UK restaurant. Our reasoning is that this is a courageous venture. But more importantly, for the first time it has brought London-style Indian culinary sophistication to Birmingham, and about time too. And we have to say that it has caused some grumpiness from two rival

Brummie restaurants, who feel they are better than Itihaas. Are they You tell us. Our unique TOP restaurant award has only been given to five restaurants since we started giving this Award in 1991. Itihaas is the sixth. (see page 29). Hours: 12-3, Mon-Fri only and 6-11.30 daily, 10.30 Sun. www.itihass.co.uk

JIMMY SPICE'S

5a, Regency Wharf, Broad St, B1   0121 643 2111

Over the past 15 years, Amrik Singh Uppal and Kuldip Singh have been involved with such Guide entrants as Killermont Polo Club, Poppadum Express, Shimla Pinks, Blue Mango, 4550m from Delhi and Pickle Johns, not to mention the pan-Asian Yellow River Cafe chain. Now under the trading name East & West Restaurants Group, their new ambition is to establish a UK chain of venues. Jimmy Spice's Buffetworks opened in 2004 in an old glassworks in the prestigious Regency Wharf development and seats 180. The concept is novel; offer authentic cuisine from India, Thailand, China and Italy all served as a eat as much as you like! buffet. Simply choose from the dishes on display and the chefs will immediately cook in a theatre style display in front of you. Uppal and Singh have a strong management team who arguably believe the food served at most UK establishments has *"lost its authenticity and has been Anglo-sized"* (sic their website). They cite the lack of skilled ethnic chefs in the UK as one of the causes of the problem. To run the culinary activities, they hired Gopal Singh, who had been with India's Hyatt, Oberoi and Taj hotels. Prices: Sun to Weds: c£13 pp / Thurs to Sat: £14.95 pp,Child: c£7 / Lunch: c£6, pp. Child: £2.99. Hours: 12-2.30 / 5-11; 10 Sun. Branches: 64 Station Rd, Solihull, B91; 101 The Parade, Sutton Coldfield ; 1 Derby Square, Epsom, Surrey . www.jimmyspices.co.uk

MAHARAJAH   A-LIST

23 Hurst St, Birmingham, B5   0121 622 2641

N Bhatt's Maharajah is a small place (62 seats on two floors) and booking is recommended. The food is Indian, cooked by Gurmaj Kumar and Jaskarn Dhillon. The menu looks a little ordinary, but the food is still always spot on. Ask about the Special Dish of the Day. I recall this restaurant serving Biriani topped with edible silver leaf (vark) when it first opened in 1971. It was the first time I'd seen it used in Britain, though traditionalists in India would not contemplate the dish without it. It was a Moghul fetish, of course, the emperor permitting a gold leaf garnish only on the food for himself and the chosen member of the harem (the dish of the day!), while his wives had to make do with silver leaf. They believed it to be an aphrodisiac. It is not for me to comment on the validity of this claim and neither can the Maharajah's diners – they no longer serve it, sadly. Service is mature and careful, and the place is often full to bursting. Waiting bookers are deftly dispatched to the downstairs bar. Such competence is rare and welcome. We continue to receive plentiful reports on the Maharajah. *'Having spent many years enjoying some of the better Indian restaurants in London I do not share your enthusiasm for all types of curry.'* [really? Ed!!!] *'but very much favour Nepalese and North Indian cooking. I can think of few worthwhile restaurants to visit other than the Maharajah. The menu is short and I nearly always have Chicken Dhansak. My father calls it the 'Prince of Curries'. If you get a good hot sweet sour one with pineapple or lemon then I can see why. The Maharajah's is good but not the best, no pineapple or lemon juice!'* [It's not a curryhouse!!! ED.] *'However the service is good, friendly and efficient and the food is consistent if not inspiring.'* RAC. Hours: 12-2 / 6-1; closed Sun & bank hols.

MILAN INDIAN CUISINE

93 Newhall St, B'ham B3   0121 236 0671

Dhirendra Patel's 120-seater, established in 1989, is decorated in pastel shades, giving it a light and airy feel. The bar area is typically Indian with beaten copper drinks tables and large coffee pots. Chef Balbir Malhi's menu features all the usual curry house favourites from Korma to Jalfrezi but there is also an extensive vegetarian section. Paneer Tikka £2.50, spicy paneer cooked in the tandoor. Stuffed peppers filled with coconut, potatoes and coriander. You might get a discount if you show Mr Patel this Guide. Hours: 12-2 (not Sat) / 6-12; Sun closed. Branches: 129 Stoney Lane, B11, 238 Soho Rd, Handsworth B21, and 296 Abel St, Milpitas, nr San José, Ca, US.

MOKHAM'S OF DIGBETH

140 Digbeth High St, B5   0121 643 7375

Of Naz Khan's venue AM says *'Mokham's pride themselves on their cooking so you may have to wait as all the food is freshly prepared. Tandoori Sheeksh Kebab is certainly one of the best I have ever tasted. Balti Exotica is meat, chicken, prawns, mushroom and pasta, without doubt unique in my experience. A very substantial dish, served up in the traditional black bowl, it was beautifully spiced and the pasta blended superbly but when combined with my Nan bread it left me feeling huge.'* And RW says: *'Small but smart genuine Balti house in the city centre. Very friendly, family run. Extensive menu. Fresh popadums, light and well cooked chat, tender Lamb Tikka cuts in a mild to medium sauce. Light and fluffy naans buttered and pleasantly sweet.'* RW. Unlicensed, BYO welcome and you might get a disc if you show Mr Patel this Guide. Hours: 12-2.30 /6 - late

SHIMLA PINKS

214 Broad St, B'ham B5   0121 633 0366

Owner Kamile Ahmed. '*Desperately cold and tempted to go to the nearer Chinese from the concert hall, but we remembered how much we enjoyed Shimla Pinks several years ago. No reservation was needed for a Friday evening. A large restaurant with acres of empty tables, which remained empty while we were there. It is still excellent, very stylish restaurant with an attractive modern decor, quality china and cutlery with shaped handles so the knives are placed upright on the table. The menu is large and attractive and really needs a long period to read thoroughly. The wine list is good, much better than most Indian restaurants. Serving staff are in all black and were very helpful and efficient. Popadums, very thin and crisp with superb relishes. Chicken Besaali, a more tangy butter chicken; Malabari Sole Curry - really excellent; Onion Bhajia, very different, large strips of floured onion in a sort of untidy heap presented on a garnished long platter.' Saag - very good, in a creamed style. The menu has seabass and monkfish, not the usual Indian fishes. Food beautifully presented on large white plates sprinkled with parsley. Everything, the food and service, was excellent. Food was not expensive, especially considering the quality and presentation, but the drinks are quite highly marked – the young couple at the next table were horrified at the price of the beer.' HC. 'Pricey (meals for 2 with a bottle of wine was £102) but the food was of good quality. Murgh Sagwala (chicken cooked with fenugreek and spinach) was tasty as was the Lamb Rogan josh and the Connoisseurs Mixed Thali for starter was excellent (especially the salmon). Side dishes of Bhindi bhaji and Methi Aloo were competent. Mind you, I do hate having a service charge of 10% automatically added. Overall, nice ambience but I'm not sure the cost was justified.*' RN. Branches: Shimla Pinks Manchester M3. Oxford, Johnstone Strathclyde, and London EC. Hours: 12-2.30 weekdays / 6-11.

Birmingham Balti Zone
Consists of B10 to B13

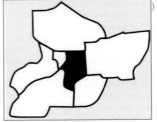

See page 280 for key to this map.

The Balti Zone starts about 2m south east of the city (follow the A34), and is thickly spread around the suburbs of Small Heath, Sparkhill, Sparkbrook and Moseley (B10 to B13). The population is largely north Pakistani, mostly from Kashmir's Mirpur, adjacent to which is the district of Baltistan, high up in the Pakistani mountains. You'll find recipes and more about this subject in my 'Balti Bible'. Those who doubt the existence of Baltistan should visit K2 Baltihouse, upon whose walls is the biggest map of the region that I've seen, and it is from there that Balti originated. Andy Munro, contributor to this section, says '*arguing this is like claiming that jam comes from Jamaica*'. Indians deny Balti's existence saying Balti means a (slop) bucket. But they are at war with Pakistan, so they would demean it. Damian Whitworth in the Times says '*Whatever the truth, the balti industry is booming, with more than 50 balti houses in Birmingham alone. Balti tours bring in parties for cooking demonstrations and dining. The 2007 Britain Rough Guide listed "getting lost in the balti triangle" as one of Britain and Ireland's 25 top experiences.*' Lost or not lost, if you follow the opinions of those lucky scribes who visit here, and inform us of their views, you won't starve since you are certain to find the nation's best Baltis.

Birmingham B11
Sparkbrook, Sparkhill

ADIL I   A-LIST

148 Stoney Lane, Sparkbrook   0121 449 0335

Established 1977. The menu reads: '*We have a bring-you-own alcoholic drinks policy at Adils. There is an off-license right next door.*' I wonder if they own it Menu Snapshot: Green Chilli Bhajia £1.00; Chicken and Mushroom Balti £5.10, I know that this is a very popular choice; Balti Lamb Aloo £5.10, another popular choice; Tandoori Naan 90p; Tandoori Table Naan £4.00 - many can share this elephants ear of a bread! other wise you can choose one of the following from £1.50, Peshwari (nuts and fruit), Garlic, Keema, Kulcha (vegetable stuffed), Dhaniya (coriander), Mushroom, Paneer (cheese) and Ginger; Kulfi £1.50, Mango, Malai (cream) or Pistachio

flavour; Gulab Jaman 90p; Barfi 70p, chocolate, pistachio, almond or cherry flavour. *'Menu Incredibly wide Quality Variable Quantity Fine Decor Conventional Balti House Service Good Comfort Uncomfortably cramped Comments Starters: 22 x popadums; Green chillies bhaji £1; Tandoori chicken £2.30; Mixed grill £5.50; Sheek kebab £2.20 x 6; Onion bhaji £1.50; Pakora £1.20 x 2 Katlama £1.50; Chicken pakora £2.50 x 2; Tandoori Fish £2.20; Chicken tikka £2.90; Lamb tikka £2.90; Prawn puri £2.90. Main course: Tropical Balti – not enough meat; Balti Lamb Desi with peas and aloo – magnificent; Balti Chicken Jalfrezi x 2; Muchi Special; Balti Chicken Spinach and Mushroom; Balti Chicken Tikka Mince with Prawn; Balti Chicken Tikka Spinach; Balti Chicken Mushroom Jalfrezi; Tandoori Mixed Grill; Balti Chicken Tikka Mushroom. Accompaniments: Table Naan £4 x 2 Mark 7/10. Wildly differing standards here: the Tandoori Mixed Grill was awful, the Tropical Balti little better but the Balti Lamb Desi and the Balti Chicken Tikka Mince with Prawn were both superb. Bill £142.15 for 11.'* G&MP. Fully air-conditioned. Del: 2m (£1 per extra mile), £15 min. BYO. Price Check: Popadum 50p, Balti CTM £5.35, Pullao Rice £1.50. Hours: 11.30-2.30 / 4.30-12;12-12 Sat & Sun . www.adilbalti.co.uk

MILAN SWEET CENTRE

191 Stoney La, Sparkbrook   0121 449 1617

A branch of the Milan restaurant in 93 Newhall Street, Birmingham b3 (see entry above). This is a T/a venue for Indian sweets, and savoury snacks. The selection is huge and satisfying, at prices too cheap to ignore. Sister t/a branch at 238 Soho Road, Handsworth, b21

ROYAL NAIM   TOP 100

417 Stratford Rd, Sparkhill   0121 766 7849

The Nazir brothers' restaurant is huge – 180 seats on two floors, yet it doesn't feel oversized. It's open all hours, of course it's BYO, no corkage charge and the food prices are very reasonable. You can fill yourself for £6, and blow up for £16. You are made welcome and are served with prompt efficiency throughout. The portions are still huge, and more importantly, the food is as tasty as you can get in any style of 'Indo-Pak' restaurant. Order from the menu located under the glass table top. The selection is huge, with every Balti combination you can think of and some more. Then leave it to Chef Shaffique and his crew to get cooking, while your taste buds tingle. But before your choice arrives, get nibbling on a popadum, if for nothing else, to taste the lurid red delicious chutney that accompanies it. Unless your stomach is horse-sized, don't order more than one Balti, and don't eat too much before it arrives – it's a huge portion. Order rice if you must, but doing it the Pakistani way, with no cutlery, and huge naan breads to tear and scoop with is hugely satisfying. And then it arrives, served the Balti way, in 10" steel karahis (Balti pans) the food cooked in the pan, made black with

thousands of hours of cooking. It's more than filling and great fun. The Naim also produce deep frozen Baltis for retail outlets and local schools. *'No wonder Birmingham's education standards are starting to rise!'* am. *'The atmosphere was building before we found the actual restaurant because of the community in which it is situated and the numerous other Balti restaurants surrounding it. The basic nature emphasised the excellent food. Owner very attentive and helpful. Returned a month later. Once you get the Balti in front of you and taste it you don't want it to end.'* SR. *'Visited on a busy Sat night. Standard of service, choice, quality of food and value for money is very high. Party of eight, four adults, four children, plenty of choice for all. Our large Naan £3 covered the table. Washed down with a jug of Lassi. Ras Malai for pudding is hard to beat. My children insisted I make a detour two days later on our return from Kendal to Suffolk to revisit the Royal Naim.'* DB. You might get a disc if you show Mr Nazir this Guide. Del: £10 min, 3m. Hours: 12-1am; 12-3am Sat.

TY'S JAZZ & SPICE

132 Stratford Rd, Sparkhill   0121 773 1632

Authentic Kashmiri cuisine here 'and excellent too' AN. The clue's in the name. This place hums, literally with its emphasis on live jazz on certain days. Established in 1999. Seats 80 in chic, modern decor. *'Very impressive decor, high ceilings, drape curtains, chandelier. Mixed Grill, Lamb Tikka, Chicken Tikka, Tandoori Fish, Sheesh Kebab, wonderful mixture of flavours. Very large quantities, top-quality ingredients. Service slow with starters but these were obviously freshly cooked, so understandable.'* GG&MP. Private park for up to 30 cars with CCTV.

Birmingham B12
Balsall Heath, Sparkbrook, Sparkhill

AL-FRASH

186 Ladypool Rd, Sparkbrook   0121 753 3120

'After Al Frash's very extensive facelift it looks very professional and attractive. We hadn't been too impressed by the buffet style of recent times and this does seem to have vanished.' R&NT. *'Menu Extensive with some unusual choices. Quality Outstanding Quantity Copious Decor Pale painted walls Service Polite, prompt and interested Comfort Comfortable chairs. Tables quite well separated Comments Starters: Popadums x 7; Tandoori Chicken £3.50 superb marinade, very tasty, huge portion; Bhuna on Puri Meat £3.50 very good, big portion; Nargis Kebab £3.50 beautiful; Bhuna on Puri Chicken £3.50 very flavoursome. Main Course: Lamb Marricha c£8 spicy and delicious; Jeera Chicken c£8; Chicken Tikka Pepsila c£8; Tandoori Mixed Grill c£9 the best! Side Dishes: Cauliflower Bhaji £3.25. Accompaniments: Pullau rice £2.10 x 2; Chilli Naan £2.20. Drinks: Cobra 6 x £2.90; Bitter Lemon 1 x £1.20. Bill: £77 plus £5 tip. Mark: 8/10.'* G&MP. BYO

ALI BABA

250 Ladypool Rd, Sparkbrook   0121 449 4929

We like Mr Aslam's logo: a chap holding a sizzling Balti, sitting on a flying carpet (beats cars for home Del) *'Clean comfortable. BYO (no charge). Very good Sheek Kebab 70p, freshly cooked and spicy. Nice Roti. Lamb Bhuna, prepared with extra chilli, very accommodating.'* RE. You might get a disc if you show Mr Aslam this Guide.

IMRAN'S BALTI HUT

264 Ladypool Rd, Sparkbrook   0121 449 1370

'Baltis, superb. Family Nan, unbelievable – 3 feet by 2 feet. BYO from "offy" next door. Excellent value for money.' RS. *'Claims to have been around at the time of the first-ever splitting of Balti bread in Brum. Spacious and includes in-view cooking for those who like to see a Sheekh Kebab being cooked live. My main course Balti Chicken and Mushroom had an impressively spicy kick. Unusually you can also get a family Chapatti also Quail Balti (which has now achieved almost protected status).'* AM. BYO. Hours: 12pm-12am.

KING'S PARADISE

321 Stratford Road, Sparkhill   0121 753 2212

Owned by Mahboob Hussain. *'Balti Tandoori Butter Chicken, very smooth-tasting, in bright red sauce with some onion in there. Peshwari Naan, large, tasty with just a hint of syrup.'* G&MP. Mushroom Naan sounds great! BYO. Private car parking. You might get a disc if you show Mr Hussain this Guide. Hours: 12-2.30 / 5.30-12.

KUSHI

58 Moseley Road, B12   0121 449 7678

Messrs Mohammed and Haydur's 62-seat *'Kushi appears to have picked up just about every cup apart from the Jules Rimet. However, never mind the awards, try the food. Kushi's Kebab is one of the best of its kind as are the sizzling Shashliks. Wide choice of main courses including Kushi's new and highly valued range of "saffron" dishes. Good selection of Naans from Keema to Kulcha.'* AM. *'All nine of us agreed that this was a magnificent Balti house.'* G&MP. You might get a disc if you show them this Guide. Del: £10 min. BYO. Hours: 5.30-1; 2 Sat; 6-12 Sun.

LAHORE KARAHI

357 Ladypool Rd, B12   0121 449 9007

This one is probably the best of the buffet bunch. RE is a frequent customer, and here is an amalgam of his views. *'A large self-service, always bustling busy restaurant, with space for 300 diners. Small car park at the rear, but otherwise can be difficult. Many Moslem and Sikh customers. E-a-m-a-y-l – amazing variety of food for c£7. Sheesh kebabs*

good and tasty, roti not too thick, lamb dall superb, mixed dall nice consistency, spinach lamb, on the bone really tender meat and delicious. Keema Peas – delightful. Great food and great value. The trouble with buffet style restaurants as good as Lahore is knowing when to stop eating. Having said that I then went for seconds! Highly recommended.' RE. *'Everything qualifying for the top melt-in-the-mouth award. Highly recommended.'* MJB. BYO

LAHORE KEBAB & PAN HOUSE

187 Ladypool Road, B12   0121 440 3264

'You can't go much more down market than this. Predominantly a T/a offering just seekh kebabs, fish massala, samosas, pakoras, tikkas etc. In other words no main courses. However, what they do serve is freshly cooked and very good. Worth going for a cheap snack.' RE.

ROYAL AL FAISAL

136 Stoney La, Balsall Hth, B12 8AQ   0121 449 5695

Spelt Faisal, or Faisel, the other venerable Balti, contemporary with Adil's (1982) from whom it is a few doors away, is Mohammed Ajaib's smartly decorated restaurant in shades of green. Seats 150 diners, tables of four. *'Parking is quite easy with on-street parking right outside and their own car park across the road. No alcohol is served so BYO. Large open kitchen allows the dinner to watch as the meal is prepared. Service friendly and efficient. Pops arrived as I took my seat, nice and fresh with a good chutney tray and more importantly free! I ordered Chicken Jalfrezi with plain rice. Asked if I would like it medium or hot, I plumped for Madras strength, medium according to the waiter. Large jug of water bought to the table aroused my curiosity, the meal arrived nicely presented in white square bowls. The rice was lovely and fluffy, the Jalfrezi had plenty of chicken, a minimal amount of peppers, great flavour and a nice spice kick which developed as the meal went on and in fact kicked me all the way back to Wallasey. I'm glad I didn't ask for it hot! An excellent meal. Menu stated that a 10% service charge would be added at their discretion which didn't materialise. Food cost £9.15. '* DB. *'Pulled off M42 to visit. 6.30pm – very busy. Starters: Tandoori Chicken, Onion Bhajia, Mushroom Bhajia, Sheek Kebabs with Popadums and Chutneys plentiful. Main courses: wide range of Baltis, vegetarian and meat, Tarka Dal Balti – first class. Excellent value for money. Convenient shops nearby to purchase your own drinks.'* DL. *'Food is good but the Lahore Karahi Buffet has the edge. Twice in one week is OK in the name of serious research! Must return soon.'* RE. BYO. Hrs: 11.30am-12am.   www.alfaisal.co.uk

SEVEN SPICE

53 Moseley Road, B12   0121 440 4408

Cooking is from the Punjab, so expect spicy but not necessarily hot curries. Menu Extracts: Pops a mere 25p

– is this the cheapest Samosas also a bargain at 55p, either meat or veg. Min charge: £7. Credit cards accepted. BYO. Secure car park at rear. T/a: 10% disc.

SHANDOR

353 Ladypool Rd, B12   0121 449 5139

'Very similar to Lahore Karahi Buffet next door, but on a smaller scale. Not so much choice, but what there was was excellent.' RE. *'Visited as result of write-up in Guide. Ethos has changed – to a buffet style – pay one price and e-a-m-a-y-l . Many other local restaurants have also changed to this style. A pleasant experience, none-the-less. My wife enjoyed it because she could try a bit of everything.'* Mr&MrsT. *'Incidentally it is licensed and £4.50 for a bottle of Sparkbrook's finest Liebfraumilch must make every hour a happy one.'* AM. Private car parking. Hours: 12 to late.

SHEREEN KADAH

543 Moseley Rd, B12   0121 440 4641

'Busy and cheerful. Large open barbecue by the window where the kebabs etc are freshly cooked to order. Sheesh Kebabs were excellent, balti meat superb. Unfortunately, my wife's Chicken Kurma was awful – too spicy and the sauce had curdled. To be fair they took it off the bill. Very good value.' RE. On subsequent visits RE reports: *'Food was excellent, service was brisk and friendly, the clientele was largely Asian. Back to a good standard after my disappointing visit.'* RE. *'In the display cabinet is a selection of Kebabs on an array of sharp skewers which look like a Zulu armoury after an attack on Rourke's Drift.'* AM. BYO. Children welcome before 11.30pm, [that's way past their bed time!] Menu Extracts: Popadum 30p; Family Nan £2.60. Chana Fried Rice £1.40, Tropical Biriani £8, Ras Malai £1, Barfi 45p, Jalebi 45p. Hours: 11am-12am.

Birmingham B13
Moseley

DEOLALI BAR RESTAURANT

23a St Mary's Row, B13   0121 442 2222

Better known for its Pakistani Balti houses, Moseley, is now unexpectedly home to a new Indian fine-dining experience, Deolali. Even its name is unexpected. Deolali is a town 100m north-east of Bombay. In the 19th century the British Raj army had a transit camp there. Soldiers who had finished their tours of duty were posted there to await their return home on troop ships. But these only left India between November and March, and at worst a soldier might have to wait for eight months in the raging Indian summer, with literally nothing to do. Sheer boredom caused some to behave eccentrically, and the word 'doolally' entered the dictionary meaning "mad" or "eccentric". Co-owner Tariq Zaman smiles if you know this (so tell him!), but

he is serious about his restaurant and has dug deep into his bank of ideas and his pocket to ensure the restaurant stands out from the crowd. Taking his extensive restaurateur knowledge, Tariq knew he wanted a design concept completely unconventional that wouldn't necessarily depict a standard Indian restaurant. The building was an old coach-house for the next door pub that dates back to the 18th century, where he fashioned a minimalist interior, which he describes as a barn conversion because of its high ceilings and solid oak beams. Split across three levels, the first floor leads into the entrance and stepping up to the second level is the 50-cover bar and a private dining area that seats around 15, with views of the 130-seat restaurant. The dark brown leather seats and oak flooring and tables are each placed to complement the beams, which are the highlight of the interiors. Head Chef Salim Sukha picked up his trade at Goa's fabulous seven-star Leela Beech Hotel and Delhi's luxury Hyatt, before joining Tariq at Spice Avenue and The Spice Exchange (Guide entrants) which Tariq owned. Sukha takes a modern approach to traditional cooking. The menu, which is brimming with fresh dishes includes such specials as Goan Green Masala Salmon and Deolali Monkfish as well as sweet desserts like Lemon Mousse served with Mango Sorbet and Gulab Jamun with Honey and Ginger Ice Cream.

K2

107 Alcester Road, B13   0121 449 3883

N Pasha and M Niam's 58-seater is named after the highest mountain in Pakistan, shown on the biggest map of Baltistan (to prove it exists to the doubters) on one wall. Peppered Chicken £3.10, is Chino-Tibetan (a Baltistan influence) with its sweet and sour chicken prepared with a mixture of black and green pepper, ginger, soya sauce, sugar and lime.

SPICE AVENUE

562-4 Moseley Road, B13   0121 442 4936

In a corner-site on the fringe of the Zone, it's a smart licensed restaurant with rear car park *'which is handy. Attentive and friendly staff. Food OK. A bit overpriced [compared with the rest of the Zone].'* RE. *'The Balti Ginger Chicken is a straightforward but excellent combination. However, the lamb Shahan is an excellent exotic alternative with tender lamb cutlets stuffed with garlic mushrooms. Accompanying onion kulcha will make your eyes and mouth water.'* AM. 'Menu Conventional Quality Outstanding Quantity Adequate Decor Pale walls Service Superb Comfort Acceptable Comments Starters Popadums x 12 Prawn Puree £3.95 Tandoori Mixed Grill c£5 x 5 Main Course Balti Mix c£8 x 3 Balti Chicken Tikka £6.25 x 2 Hara Gosht c£7 Naans Keema Naan £2.25 x 2 Peshwari Naan £1.95 x 2 Garlic Naan £1.75 Plain Naan £1.25 Mark 9/10 Extremely impressive meal all round.' G&MP.

SWEET CHILLIES CUISINE   A-LIST

836 Yardleywood Rd, B13   0121 443 2737

Iqbal Hussain's impressive building, houses this stylish restaurant. A very grand porch welcomes you, complete with colonial palms and a red carpet! Inside, a modern, contemporary feel, including wooden floors, deep brown leather high back chairs or booths (they look really comfortable!), white linen and spot ceiling lights - lovely. Menu Snapshot: Bombay Duck 80p, dry roasted fish; Sweet Chillies Spice Wings £2.90, marinated in sweet, hot and tangy paste, stuffed with ground herbs, barbecued in the clay oven, served with fried onions, peppers, tomatoes and coriander leaves; Baigan Maza Dhai £3.50, aubergine deep-fried and filled with spiced minced chicken and vegetables, garnished with home-made, low fat Raitha; Shobzi Celery £2.80, chopped and fried celery in butter sauce, cook with citrus flavour vegetable and topped with poppy seeds; Pigeon Musaka c£7, layers of pigeon breast, stuffed with spicy mushrooms, served with a spicy game sauce and Paratha; Lamb Shank Tara c£8, lamb shank braised, medium hot, served with spicy mint and curry sauce, served with herb noodles; Deewana Naga Gosht / Murgh c£7, marinated lamb or chicken, cooked with Sylheti chilli and onions, in a very hot and spicy sauce; Shahi Chocolate Korma c£7, chicken, lamb or vegetable braised in a chocolate gravy, enriched with cream, almonds and coconut, Neramisha £2.75 - red kidney beans, Bengali runner beans, medium gravy with onion, capsicum and coriander; Chillie (sic) Chips £1.95, steak cut chips cooked in chillies; Bengal Spice Naan £2.40 - garlic and coriander filled unleavened bread with cheese topping, chillies can be added. Del: 2m, £12 min. T/a: 15% disc. min Charge: £10. Hours: Lunch – pre-booking only / 5.30-11.30; 12 Sat; 11 Sun. Branch: Sylhet Spice, Kings Heath, Birmingham; Shahi Palace, Foleshill, Coventry; Bengal Delight, Holbrooks, Coventry. www.sweetchillies.com

Birmingham North

Consists of B6, B7, B19 to B24, B35, B42 to B44

See page 280 for key to this map.

B7: SHERE KHAN   NEW ENTRANT Star City, 100 Watson Rd, B7 5SAB~ 0121 326 0691. Shere Khan's casual diner and first drive-thru. Franchisees Shoaib Patel and partner John Saddique. See Shere Khan, Rusholme, Manchester for history etc.

B21,HANDSWORTH; MILAN SWEET CENTRE TAKEAWAY 238 Soho Rd. ~ 0121 551 5239. Branch of Milan, Newhall St B3 (see entry). This is a T/a venue for Indian sweets, and savoury snacks. The selection is huge and satisfying, at prices too cheap to ignore.

Sister t/a branch at 191 Stoney Lane, Sparkbrook, B11.

B23: NOORAANI BALTI HOUSE 248 Slade Rd,B23 ~ 0121 373 5227. 40-seater est by M Jahangir in 1994 Del: 3m, £7 min. You might get a disc if you show Mr Ahmed this Guide. Students disc: 10% on all T/a. Hours: 5-2.

B23: SAMRAT TANDOORI 710 Chester Road, B23 ~ 0121 384 5900. 48-seater est 1983 by Iqbal Raza Chowdhury. Del: 6m, £10 min. Hours: 5-1; 2 Sat.

B23: STOCKLAND BALTI TAKEAWAY 332 Marsh La, Erdington, B23 0121 377 8789. Owned and mnaged by Mrs Amina Begum since '93. Del: £10. Hours: 5-12; 1 Fri & Sat.

Birmingham East

Consists of B8, B9, B25, B26, B33, B34, B36, B37, and B40 (NEC)

See page 280 for key to this map.

Birmingham B25
Yardley

YEW TREE COTTAGE

43 Stoney La, Yardley, B25   0121 786 1814

Established 1979 by Jamal Chowdhury. The unassuming exterior hides a huge restaurant, seating 180 diners on two floors. Inside it is nicely decorated with wooden flooring, large green plants, white linen and comfortable upholstered chairs - all very bright and tidy. Restaurant Theme Nights: Sun: Buffet, c£7 children/c£5 children – booking advisable; Monday: Gourmet Dinner £9.95 adult/c£7 children – four courses from the a la carte menu; Tuesday: Balti Night - £6.50, choice of any Balti with a Naan; Wednesday: Chef's Choice c£8, tasty treats the from the head chef, starter and main course; Thursday: Ladies Night c£9: Bhajia, choice from a la carte menu and a glass of wine - sounds great! Menu Snapshot: Could be the biggest menu I have ever seen, there are an incredible 223 dishes to choose from - Tikka Sandwich £3.50, Tikka in a Naan with salad dressing; Mix Grill Sandwich £4.50, Chicken and Lamb Tikka, Sheek Kebab in Naan; South Indian Garlic Chilli Murgh c£7.50, barbecued chicken, fresh garlic, chilli sauce, fresh coriander, crispy green chillies - hot; North Bengali Fruity Murch c£7.50, creamy, mild, fruity dish with barbecued chicken pieces; Masala Kulcha £1.50, leavened bread stuffed with capsicum, onions, spices then cooked in the char coal oven. Del: 3m, £15 min. T/a: 10% disc, £10 min. You might get a disc if you show Mr Chowdhury this Guide. Hours: 5-12.30; 1.30 Sat; 6-12.30 Sun.

B9 SMALL HEATH, IIB NE GHANI 264 Green La, B9 ~ 0121 772 8138. Est 1981, taken over by Nazrul Hussain in 1998 with

Bilal Miah manager. Chef Abdul Ahad' in open kitchen. BYO. T/a: 10% disc. Del: £8 min 3m. Hours: 4.30-12; 1 Sat. .

B26: SHELDON, SHABAR TANDOORI 4 Arden Oak Rd, B26 ~ 0121 742 0636

B26: TITASH INTERNATIONAL 2278 Coventry Rd, B26 ~ 0121 722 2080. Decent alternative to the ghastly offerings at the NEC and hotels of varying pretensions.

B26: VARSHA 2250 Coventry Rd, B26 ~ 0121 743 6572. *'Achari and Handi dishes have not been bettered elsewhere.'* JP.

Birmingham South

Consists of B14, B27 to B31, B45, B47, B48, B60

See page 280 for key to this map.

YOU SAY OK BIRMINGHAM SOUTH
You might get a discount if you show them this Guide.

B14, KING'S HEATH: KINGS BALTI 13 York Rd, B14 ~ 0121 443 1114. 62-seater est 1994 by Salim Miah. Licensed to sell beer, not spirits or wine, so BYO (no corkage charge). T/a: 10% disc, £5.50 min. Hours: 5-11.

B14, KING'S HEATH: MILLENNIUM BALTI 796 Alcester Rd S, B14 ~ 0121 430 6155. Seats 44. Unlicensed, BYO OK. T/a: 10% disc. Del: 3m £8 min. Hours: 5.30-12.30.

B27: DEVDOOT
1st Floor, 37 Westley Rd, B27 ~ 0121 706 4842

B27 ACOCKS GREEN: MOGHUL
1184 Warwick Road, B27 ~ 0121 707 6777

B28, HALL GREEN: MIZAN 1347 Stratford Road, B28 ~ 0121 777 3185. KA Rahman's 66-seater. T/a: 10% disc. Min charge: £5. Special: Saag Kamal Kakri, spinach and lotus roots. Hours: 12-2 / 5.30-12; 12.30 Fri & Sat.

B29, SELLY OAK: DILSHAD INTERNATIONAL 618 Bristol Rd, B29 ~ 0121 472 5016. Est 1978. Seats 80. Specials: Achar Gosht, Champa Koli Bahar, Fish Bengal. T/a: 10% disc. Hours: 5.30-late.

B30, COTTERIDGE: RAJPOOT 1831 Pershore Rd, B30 ~ 0121 458 5604. Watir Ali's 94-seater is *'A glitzy, friendly little place. All the family use it regularly.'* JAD. Hours: 6-2.

B30, STIRCHLEY: YASSER TANDOORI 1268 Pershore Rd, B30 ~ 0121 433 3023. 80-seater est 1987 by A Hussain and Sarwar Khan. Unlicensed BYO OK. Balti Chef's Special Tropical £7, prawn, chicken, lamb and mushroom. T/a: free Popadum, mint sauce, £10 min. Del: 3m £10 min. Parking for 12 cars. Hours: 4.30-12; 1 Sat.

Birmingham West

Consists of B15 to B18 & B32

See page 280 for key to this map.

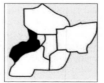

(Beyond this is Halesowen, Smethwick, Warley and West Bromwich – see entries)

YOU SAY OK – BIRMINGHAM WEST
You might get a discount if you show them this Guide.

B16, EDGBASTON: J JAYS 2 Edgbaston Shopping Centre, Five Ways, B16 ~ 0121 455 6871

B32, QUINTON: SOHO INDIA 417 Hagley Rd West, B32 ~ 0121 421 3242

Remainder of West Midlands

Coventry

MONSOON   TOP 100

20 Far Gosford St, Coventry   024 7622 9651

'Menu conventional; Quality top class; Quantity copious; Beige-yellow pale wallpaper with prints of Asian women; Service: ultra quick; Comfort: Acceptable – reasonable space between tables Comments My concerns over the Monsoon having lost its elevated status as a result of the previous owner leaving were well and truly allayed following this visit. It maintained its outstanding standards in every respect with this meal. You simply can't beat it in terms of Balti House Cuisine. Starter - Tandoori Chicken £2.25, superb. Marinated wonderfully, huge portion, delicious taste. Main – Balti Keema Tikka c£5. Nasi Goreng £2.25. Popadums 50p x 2. Pint Cobra £2.60. Total Bill £13.05. Mark 9/10.' G&MP. 'Menu Limited Quality Good Quantity Very Good Decor Pale painted walls Service Excellent Comfort Fairly small restaurant, tables quite close together. Approx 28 covers Comments Starters Popadums x4 Chicken Pakora c£3 Superb Tandoori Chicken c£3. Well marinated, but small quantity. Main Course Lamb Pathia £4.75 Lamb Ceylon £4.75 Accompaniments Garlic Naan £1.75 Keema Rice £2.30 Bombay Aloo £2.50. Total Bill £32. Mark 9/10.' G&MP. And on another occasion: 'Starters Masala Fish x2 c£3 wonderful Chicken Pakora £2.25 very very good very spicy Sag Purée c£3 excellent very light. Main Course Chicken Tikka Dhansak £5.25 outstanding Chicken Balti with Mushroom and Spinach £5.45 absolutely stunning 10/10. Balti Mince with mixed vegetables very good; Vegetable Biriyani too hot for me but made with fresh vegetables. Accompaniments: Nasi Goreng £2.25 Pilau Rice £1.65 Peshwari Nan £2.25 Popadums x 4 free!+ drinks Bill: £46.85 + £3.15 tip Total £50 Overall mark 92%. G&MP.

THE OCEAN   NEW TO OUR TOP 100

46 Jubilee Crescent Radford   024 7659 9455

'Old style Indian, kitsch flock wallpaper, service outrageously over the top. We were greeted with "you're late!" as we arrived. Nothing is too much trouble and we exchanged witty badinage throughout the meal. Quantity copious. Four outstanding starters. Main courses almost as good with the chicken dansak which was thickened with lentils to give a sweet/ sour contrast. Lamb Bhazaa, Chicken BegumBahr well marinated, tingly and spicy without being overspiced and Chicken Jaipuri all superb. £60 for 4.' Marks visit 1: 88.3%. Visit 2: 89.4%. Rated no 2 in Coventry.' G&MP.

ROJONI   NEW TO OUR TOP 100

477 Beake Avenue Coventry

Menu Fairly wide with some unusual special dishes. Quality Very Good. Quantity: Copious. Décor: Strikingly colourful. Vibrant. Service: Exemplary. Comfort: Excellent. Starters: Popadums x6 Dhal Soup £2.50 Very comforting with slices of garlic and lemon. Tandoori Chicken £2.85 Absolutely gorgeous- marinade spot on. Chicken Chat c£3 Very spicy. King Prawn Puri Not very special. Main Course Tandoori Mixed Grill £8.50 Very good. Lamb Mirch Masala c£6 Sauce excellent but lamb chewy c£6. Chicken Jhallosi c£7 x2 Very well done ' chicken very spicy. Accompaniments Peshwari Nan £1.85 Pilau Rice £1.85 x 2. Side Dishes: Cauliflower Bhajee c£3 Mattar Paneer c£3 Total cost £80.20 + £8 tip. Mark 87%. We were very impressed!' G&MP. So are we and the media are always asking us for the wherabouts of a red-flock venue. It should be Grade 1 listed! And just for you and Melinda, Graham, we are making it a TOP 100.

TURMERIC GOLD

166 Medieval Spon St.   024 7622 6603

Opposite Bonds at Skydome. Jay Alam's restaurant seats ninety diners in six rooms, on two floors (the waiters must be fit!). The exterior of the building has been painted royal blue, and is alive with a gorgeous forest of flowers. For real twosome pampering you can dine in one of the luscious booths (illustrated above). Menu Snapshot: Crab Spring Rolls £5.25, beansprouts, carrot, celery, crab meat, wrapped in a roll, served with spicy sauce; Goa Tiger Prawns £5.75, grilled tiger prawns, spinach, with coconut and cream sauce; Rawlpindi Curry Puff £5.25, highly spiced lamb, dried red chillies, sweet vinegar sauce, puffed bread, served with chat masala dressed, crispy salad; Emperors Chicken Chilli £11.25, stir-fried with fresh green chillies, carrots, mushroom, capsicum, pineapple, and coriander leaf, served sizzling. *'Menu :Extremely extensive Quality: Good Quantity: Adequate Decor: Garish with pictures of bare breasted ladies on the wall Service: Faultless Comfort: Fine Comments Starters:: 4 x spicy popadums; 2 x plain popadums; Chicken Pathia c£4.50; Rawalpindi Curry Puff £5.25; Sheek Kebab £5.25; Paneer Shashlick £3.75; Main Course: Lamb Mustard Chilli Bhuna c£9; Chicken Ginger c£9; Achari Chicken c£9; Tandoori Platter c£13!! Accompaniments: Peshwari Naan £2.65; Lemon rice £3.25; Pullau rice c£3; Side Dish: Cauliflower Bhaji £3.45 – flavour beautiful but texture mushy; Drinks: glass of red wine £3.70 x 2 Stella Artois £3.30 x3 Bill; £100 (including £6.70 tip) – the most we have ever spent as a group of 4. Mark 8/10 Excellent meal'* G&MP. Cobra £3.30 a bottle, house wine £10.25 a bottle. T/a: 15% disc. Price Check: Popadum 70p, CTM £7.75, Pullao Rice c£3. Hours: 12-2 / 5.30-11.15; 12.15 Sat.   www.turmericgold.co.uk

G&MP'S SAY OK: COVENTRY

Grahame and Melinda Payne annually visit dozens of different restaurants all over the uk, especially in their home-city. They advise that there are certain Coventry restaurants which should be in the Guide. They are in descending order of excellence:1 Monsoon, 2 The Ocean, 3 Akbar's, 4 Thai Dusit, 5 Bengal Delight. The first two are in our TOP 100 list. Here is G&MP's alphabetical Currinary Coventry:

AKBAR'S 7 The Butts, Earlsdon, Coventry~ 024 7622 8899. *'Seats very difficult to get into – the sunken areas didn't help. Pale painted walls with lights everywhere. menu fairly wide if rather unimaginative. Quality good. quantity generous. Service outstanding. We were all extremely impressed with every aspect of the meal. £74.60 for 4.'* Mark: 87.1%. Rated no3 in Coventry.' G&MP.

ALLY'S BALTI HOUSE 48 Earlsdon Street Earlsdon Coventry CV5 6EL ~ 024 7671 5709. *'Quality very good. Quantity moderate. Décor rustic and old-fashioned. Service reasonable and prompt. Comfort draughty. Reasonably priced, unprepossessing and unfashionable but nonetheless good value. Starters were uniformly excellent with the stuffed chicken pepper and chicken pakora best. Of the main courses ally's special balti was the highlight. some of the food was too spicy but generally this was a good effort. £50 for 4.'* Mark: 81%. G&MP.

BENGAL DELIGHT 168 Holbrook Lane, Holbrooks, CV6 4BY ~ 024 7668 6789 Rated no 5in Coventry. G&MP.

BLUE FUSION 135 Walsgrave Road, Bell Hill. *'A newly opened restaurant disappointingly ordinary'.* G&MP.

BLUE MANGO 76 Albany Road Earlsdon, CV5 3JU. 44-seater. *'The roop chanda and aloo chat both outstanding'.* G&MP.

DESI DISH Far Gosford Street. *' Menu Extensive and unusual Quality, quantity, decor ,service and comfort OK. Pops 80p x 3, Peshwari Naan £2.50, Metha Maaz £9.95, Chicken Korma £8.50, Aloo Murgh Masala £8.50, Side Dish Aloo Chole £4.50, Pullau Rice £1.95, Peshwari Naan £2.50, Onion Kulcha Naan £2.50. Lager x2, Coke x 2, Jug of Lassi £5.'* Mark. 80%. G&MP.

KAILASHA 149 Far Gosford Street, CV1 5DU ~ 024 7622 2233. *'Rather disappointing.'* 71%. G&MP.

THE MINT 13, The Butts, Earlsdon ~ 024 7622 6111. *'Menu: very extensive with many unusual choices Quality: Excellent Quantity: Copious and how! Decor: pale pastel painted walls in one long room in ultra modern style Service: Faultless Comfort: Deep leather chairs, beautiful wooden tables widely spaced with no infringement on others Starters: Paneer Tikka, beautifully marinated; Reshmi Kebab , good; Tetul Mix, extremely generous portions, beautifully presented; Chicken Tikka Chat v g and generous. Main course: Chicken Pasala, wonderful marinade in beautifully creamy sauce c£7; Lamb Afghan Chana, lamb slightly chewy but otherwise excellent c£7; Chicken Gurkha Masala very nicely spiced with a kick to it c£8. We have visited several times since it*

opened in 2006. byo and a very welcoming ambience to boot. All in all a most welcome addition to the ranks'. G&MP.

MONSOON 20-21 Far Gosford Street ~ 024 7622 9651. *'Quality superb, quantity copious, décor mustard and claret walls. Service excellent. Starters were sublime, mixed grill and the salmon kebab. Main course vegetable biryani was equally faultless. £36.40 for 4.'* Mark 91.7%. Rated best in Coventry.

NASHAA 154 Longford Road CV6 6DR ~ 024 7636 6344. *'Quality no problem, quantity generou, décor pale yellow walls, service exemplary, comfort pleasant welcoming atmosphere. Starters were better than main courses. tandoori chicken was beautifully tasty and well marinaded. Of the main courses the chicken dansak was much too spicy, the tandoori mix grill was fairly average apart from the chicken tikka which was excellent. the chicken korai and chicken rezalla were both exceptionally fine. £76.20 for 4.'* Mark 83.2%.

ROJONI 477 Beake Ave CV6 2HT~ 024 7633 2211

SHAPLA TANDOORI 171 Daventry Rd Cheylesmore, ~ 024 7650 6306. *'40-seater with creamy regency with chandeliers and fans décor. Extremely conventional menu, quality excellent, quantity copious, service very good. Generally vg quality meal with few weaknesses. £71.20 for 4'* Mark 80.6%. G&MP.

SONARGAON 153 Daventry Rd, CV3 5HD ~ 024 7650 1120. 'Good'. G&MP.

THAI DUSIT 39 London Road CV1 2JP 024 7622 7788. The name means a Tthai buddhist paradise and this beautifully appointed restaurant certainly lives up to the promise. The decor, artefacts, atmosphere and most importantly the staff transport customers into Thai culture and the atmosphere is extremely friendly and unhurried. Thai chefs weave their magic bringing a taste of Thailand to the city. Easy parking. Lunch & Dinner. Rated no 4 in Coventry. G&MP.

VARSITY SPICE 118 Gosford Street, CV1 5DL 024 7652 0799. *'Very dark décor with extensive use of mirrors, service fairly slow but everything was freshly cooked. Menu quite extensive, quality very good,quantity copious. comfort partitioned tables with alcoves which makes it much more comfortable. a couple of minor weaknesses but overall an excellent effort for this comparative newcomer. good use of marination but one meal was a trifle overspiced, the mutton in the lamb rezella was gorgeous.'* Bill £73.05 for 4. Mark 82.5%. G&MP.

Meriden

TURMERIC GOLD AT MERIDEN
NEW ENTRANT

155 Main Road, CV7 7NH   01676 521055

Located in a Georgian building in the affluent village of Meriden, said to be the centre of England, Jal Alam's new venture combines traditional cooking with a

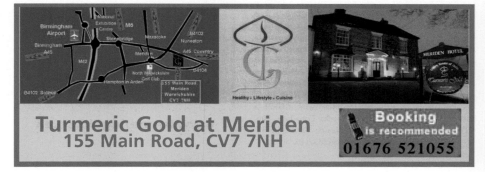

modern, healthy twist, using, he says *'minimum oil at the same time as making sure food colouring and salt are minute'*. [let's loose the former, Jay – we don't need it. Ed] Facilities include rooms for private parties and gatherings. Hours: 12-2 / 5:30-11; 10:30pm Sun.. Reports please. www.turmericgold.co.uk

YOU SAY OK
You might get a discount if you show them this Guide.

DUDLEY: BALTI 4 U TAKEAWAY 63 Halesowen Rd, Netherton, Dudley ~ 01384 240230. Afruz Ali opened in 2000, Azom Ali is head chef. Del: 4m. Hours: 5-12.30; 1.20 Sat.

HALESOWEN, HASBURY, B63: AMEENA 192 Hagley Rd, B63 ~ 0121 550 4317. Hiron Miah's 78-seater (est. 1974) *'Waiters cheerful and attentive.'* MS. Del: 3m £10 min. Hours: 5.30-12; 1 Fri & Sat.

HALESOWEN, B63: RED PEPPERS 8 Hagley St, B63 ~ 0121 550 8588. Owner chef, Mr Islam iopened in 1989. Del: 3.5, £10 min. T/a: 10% disc. Hours: 5.30-12; 1 Fri & Sat.

KNOWLE, B93: BILASH 1608 High St, B93 ~ 01564 773030. Mashud Uddin and Nowab Ali's venue seats 64 . 'Very good quality.' J&MCL. T/a: 10% off. Hours: 5.30-12am. Branches: Bilash, 82-90 Priory Road, Kenilworth. Bejoy T/a, 763 Old Lode Lane, Solihull.

KNOWLE, B93: KNOWLE INDIAN BRASSERIE 1690 High St, B93 ~ 01564 776453. 45-seater est 1995 by Hossain Miah. *'Cheap, quality excellent, quantity huge.'* G&MP. T/a: 10% disc. Del: £12 min 3m. Hours: 5.30-11.30; 10.30 Sun.

LYE: HARRYS OF LYE 179 High Street, Lye, Stourbridge DY9 8LH *'The food is superb, but very slow service.'* AHJ: Andy Herrin: yellowfingers.co.uk

LYE: PEPPER AND SPICE 204 High St, ~ 01384 893933. Sabber Iqbal's 40-seater is BYO. Del: £7 min. Hours: 6-12.

SMETHWICK, BEARWOOD, B66: Haweli 509 Hagley Rd. ~ 0121 434 4869. Opened in 1993 by Mohammed Ashraf. Del: 1m. Hours: 6-12, 1 Sat.

Oldbury

KAVI   NEW ENTRANT

6 Wolverhampton Rd, B68 0LH   0121 429 3757

Rishi Sharma has opened a branch of his Kavi Indian Fusion Restaurant at Jonathan's Hotel. The restaurant is modern, with a large screen showing Bollywood musicals. See branch: Newcastle, Staffs for details

SAFFRON

909 Wolverhampton Rd. B69   0121 552 1752

'Saffron is situated just off the M6, on the way back north from the NEC, and as everyone who has visited the NEC, knows, that the food is awful and expensive, so, no excuse, off to the Saffron for a lovely meal! 'As a lunch diner I was surprised that there were other diners as this restaurant is a fair way outside a town centre. A modern, well lit and nicely decorated establishment. The service was prompt and unfussy, although I gave up trying to get a plain Madras sauce with Biriani. Ordered Popadums, crisp and light, Chutneys, onion, mango and yoghurt, very acceptable. Murgh Biriani, seemed like a small portion when it arrived with the rice plated and

moulded, but when attacked it was surprisingly a lot of food.' I've been there, thought, "what a mean little portion," and then when I have finished my meal, it looked like I hadn't even started! 'Garnished with fried onions and coriander (no omelette), the rice had a good flavour, in fact was very spicy, chicken well cooked and tender. Vegetable curry sauce containing peas, green beans, tinned carrots and a hint of cauliflower was quite mild but very tasty. Overall, I would love to try this restaurant in the evening as I feel it has great potential.' I object to a 10% service charge and then having the credit card bill left open.' DB. Naughty naughty in fact, Very Naughty, naughty!T/a 10% disc. Hours: 12-2.30 Mon to Fri / 5.30-11.30.

Solihull   B90 to B93

JIMMY SPICE'S

64 Station Rd, Solihull, B91   0121 709 2111

Serves Indian, Chinese, Thai & Italian cooking in a live theatre-style cooking display with large bar alongside. The group's second unit opened here in 2006 in the former Wates Wine Lodge as a 300-seater with a 100-seat bar called NYC. Hours: 12-2.30 / 5-11. Branches and more comment: Broad St, Birmingham, B1. www.jimmyspices.co.uk

THE LLOYDS

7 Station Rd, Knowle   01546 477577

Air-conditioned. Seats 140 diners. Proprietor Nanu Miah opened his restaurant in February 2003. It is quite amazing that Naga Chicken is his most popular dish, and with its extremely hot chilli, I can only think that his regular customers are what the American call 'Chile Heads.' Menu Snapshot: Boal Biran (cat fish) £3.95, fried with a touch of butter, herbs and garlic; Tandoori Mixed Grill from 5.95, served with mint sauce and fresh salad; Shobji Bihari Tawa c£5, bindi, cauliflower, green beans, courgette, peas, sweetcorn, sprouts, medium spiced, dry curry; Cheese and Garlic Naan £2.25. Licensed but BYO allowed. House Wine £9.75. Credit cards not accepted. T/a: 10% disc. Del: £2 min. min Ch: £10. You might get a discount if you show them this Guide. Hours: 5.30-11.   www.thelloydsindian.com

RAJNAGAR INTERNATIONAL TOP 100

256 Lyndon Rd, Olton, B92   0121 742 8140

Dr Moula Miah is the owner, and a nicer man you will not find. He has taken the Bangladeshi curryhouse formula to its heights at his three venues (see branches). It is a useful 10 minutes from the NEC and airport. Modern décor, clean lines, great unfussy food and care from the Doc himself and his staff. *'It really is exceptionally good.'* MM. *'Interior decor, pale pink and cream walls, cream carpet – optimistic re spillages!, stylish tables and chairs with monogrammed linen exudes quality*

and class. Attentive service, swiftly delivered Popadums, chunky pickles and cold lager. I chose Meat Samosas (spring roll style), Chicken Tikka Dupiaza, Pullao Rice and Nan – ALL SUPERB!' TE. Hours: 5 till late. Branches: Shades of Raj, 52, Station Road, Solihull, Barajee, Broad Street, B'hm. www.rajnagar.com

Stonnall

MANGO TREE   TOP 100

Chester Road, WS9   01922 457344

Opened in 2003 and run by Rajinder Ram, aka Raj, (whom your editor met when working on Carlton Food Network TV) with his wife Sangeeta and in-laws Anita and George Kattapuram. former Veeraswamy Head Chef is South Indian Marriappan Sethurajapillai aka Murray, whose speciality is seafood. (note the lobster dishes). Curry chef is ex Taj Gateway, Bangalore chef Tikhan Khan is the curry expert, with Gnana Prakasam on Tandoors and South Indian cuisine also from Taj. You'll find the range of north Indian favourites plus Biryanis, Idli Sambhar and Masala Dosa, but perversely on from Suns to Thursdays! *This is Southern Indian food unlike most Indian restaurants which as you know are Bangladeshi. Fish is a speciality, so too the Sun Lunch. This a lovely restaurant not the normal curry house'* BP. www.mangotree.biz

Sutton Coldfield

JIMMY SPICES   NEW ENTRANT

101, The Parade B72 1PL   0121 355 1912

Details:: Broad St, B'ham, B1. www.jimmyspices.co.uk

YOU SAY OK
You might get a discount if you show them this Guide.

STOURBRIDGE: CELLARS NEW ENTRANT 187, Lower High St, DY8 1TT. *'Opened 2002 and remains as good as when it opened.'* JP.

KARMA 2F High Street, Wollaston, Stourbridge ~ 01384 375919. Former Neel Akash, Chef Mujibur Rahman's 60-seater. *'Good food but we felt didn't somehow feel welcomed.'* AH: Andy Herrin: www.yellowfingers.co.uk T/a: 10% off. Del: £8 min, 3m. Hours: 5-12.

SUTTON COLDFIELD B73: ASIAN GRILL 91 Park Rd, Sutton C'fld, B73 ~ 0121 354 7491. Opened way back in 1968. Hours: 5.30-12; 1 Fri & Sat.

SUTTON COLDFIELD, B74: RICKSHAW TAKEAWAY 1 Stockland Ct, 121, Chester Rd, Streetly, ~ 0121 580 9400. Est by Mr Rahman in 1996. Del: 5m £10 min. Hours: 5-11; 10.30 Sun.

WALSALL: EAST END 9 Hawes Close, Walsall ~ 01922 614800. Muhibur Rahman is proud of his veteran 1967 curry house. Hours: 5.30-12.

WALSALL: GOLDEN MOMENTS 3 Ablewell St, Walsall ~ 01992 640363. 100- seater est 1993. *'Having eaten Indian food for 25 years this establishment must rate as the one of the best. Staff, service, surroundings and food are excellent.'* BD. T/a: 15% disc. Hours: 6-12.

WALSALL: KING BALTI 89 Ablewell Street, Walsall ~ 01922 620376. Good BYO curryhouse owned by Dudu Miah. Hours: 6-1.

WARLEY B66: AL MOUGHAL 622 Bearwood Rd, Warley, B66 ~ 0121 420 3987. Pakistani-style 100-seater BYO managed by Mumtaz. *'Clean, downmarket, cheap and cheerful.'* PAW. Hours: 6-12.

Walsall

SAFFRON

42 Bradford St, Walsall   01922 627899

Fully licensed 105-seater, smart restaurant in two rooms, opened in 1963. *'Superb genuine Balti house within easy (post meal) wobbling distance of the railway station. Excellent starter, Nargis Kebab, spicy Scotch egg style, crisp salad, yoghurt sauce. Mixed Balti, lovely medium thick sauce with a well balanced and mouth watering blend of spices, sizeable chunks of lamb and chicken, plus some small but juicy prawns, medium hot. Lovely light Chuppatis. Good service, real tablecloths.'* RW. E-a-m-a-y-l buffet: c£8 Weds. & Thurs eves & Sun lunch. Menu Extracts: Chicken Tikka £5.50, with orange or lemon sauce; Spice and Garlic Fish Fry £2.50; Salmon Samosas £2.25; Cheese Layered Crispy Paratha £1.90; Liver Puri £2.65 Prawn and Coconut Puri £2.75. 'All delicious!' rl. You might get a disc if you show Mr Ahmed this Guide. Del: £8 min. Hours: 5.30-12.30; 1.30 Fri & Sat; 12.30-12.30 Sun.

Wolverhampton

KAVI

Park Hall Hotel, Park Drive, Goldthorn Park, Wolverhampton   01902 331121

Park Hall Hotel is a privately member of the Best Western Group. It is set in five acres of grounds and is an 18th century listed building, once the ancestral home of the Dudley family, then a school. In 1947 Grigg and Brettell Brewery bought the building and Park Hall has continued to run as a hotel since that date. It has plenty of rooms and a huge car park, but its real gem is its restaurant. Enter the foyer and the bar and as you come to Kavi Indian note the waterfall and glass floored pool complete with large goldfish. The restaurant itself is on two levels., the upper running along the whole area,

looks down onto the main room. A plasma screen playing Bollywood movies is set amongst Indian decor. Menu snapshot: Starters, include Tikkas and Tandoori items with such ingredients as Tiger Prawns, Rabbit, Salmon and Paneer. Prices average £6.50. Main courses include also offers a good mix, 17 dishes, which include Guinea Fowl, Lamb Shank and Duck; Amritsari Talli Machi, pan seared fillets of fresh seabass on a bed of sautéed red cabbage with mild pasanda sauce; Jhinga Kali Mirch both c£10, jumbo prawns in masala sauce. www.parkhallhotel.co.uk

NEEL AKASH

31 School St, Wolverhampton   01902 716 975

Simply decorated in soft yellow and pale blue, with wooden chairs and white plastic tables, giving an informal cafe style at Mr Ahmed's pit-stop. Menu Snapshot: (with T/a prices) Tandoori Fish £3.95; Lamb Tikka £5.50, served with salad; Methi Gusta £5.50, beef, onion, coriander leaves; Karahi Chinghri and Murgh c£7, king prawns cooked with chicken, fresh coriander, green pepper, garam masala, cinnamon, served in sizzling iron karahi; Cucumber Raitha 90p; Kulcha Naan £1.50, stuffed with vegetables. Del: 3m, £10 min. T/a 10% disc. Price Check: Popadum 50p, CTM £6.25, Pullao Rice £1.95. www.nellakash.co.uk Branch: Basmati, 230, Birmingham Road, B43.

WILTSHIRE

Area:
South West England
Population: 627,000
Adjacent Counties:
Berks, Dorset,
Hants. Oxon

Calne

SPICE OF BENGAL

Wood Street, Calne   01249 811833

'Slightly out of the town centre and doesn't look very impressive from the outside. Two or three tables were occupied, when we arrived. A fairly big restaurant, steady stream of diners and T/as while we ate. Impressive decor, not sumptuous or posh, just very smart and cosy. Prompt service, efficient, slightly friendly, which is the way I prefer it. Sheek Kebab c£3, came on a bed of shredded cabbage, a bit of tomato, cucumber and sweet Raitha, excellent, slightly hot, very moist. A slight delay before our mains were served (four couples came in), Chicken Tikka Patiala (served with mint chutney) and Chicken

Korai c£7, perfection. Broad strips of tender chicken tikka, not the usual chunks, with creamy sauce and garnished with strips of boiled egg. Monica's Korai, cooked very well with chunks of onion and capsicum. We shared Mushroom Rice, chopped mushroom a bit chewy, but enjoyed and a Naan. Also, Aloo Gobi as a side dish, his was awful. A very satisfactory £25.30 with linen napkins and microwaved hand towels. All in all, very impressive.' T&MH. T/a 10% disc. £10 min. Hours: 12-2 / 5.30-11.30; 12 Fri & Sat.

Chippenham

AKASH TANDOORI & BALTI

19 The Bridge, Chippenham   01249 653358

Established in 1979 by Nurul Huda Islam, an old friend of this Guide, having been in since our first edition and who might give you a disc if you show him this Guide. His cheerfully decorated restaurant, in lemon with royal blue, seats forty-six diners in three rooms. Lamb Shang c£13, lamb on the bone in a medium sauce is Chef Nazrul's most popular dish. Menu Snapshot: Duck Tikka £5 and Tandoori Chops £4.50, both served with salad; Shahjani Chicken £7.50, with garlic and minced lamb; Chicken Choti Poti £6.80, with eggs and chick peas; Tandoori Fish Masala £2, with Bangladeshi fresh water fish. Hours: 12-2 / 6-12; 12.30 Fri & Sat.

Everleigh

GOA BALTI HOUSE

Devizes Road, Everleigh   01264 850850

Founded by *'the brilliant and charming Hasan'* says RG on the site of a garage and filing station. So let's get filled! *'A long time family favourite of ours and great for a family get-together. Hasan (the boss) had decorated the restaurant with a big 'happy birthday' sign. Delightful ambience, spacious, obviously well appointed, but somehow homely too, in this very quiet little Wiltshire village. The premises used to be a garage, so has inherited splendid, copious parking. Enterprising menu with old high street favourites are well represented which would satisfy the most hardened old 'blimp.' Recommended starters Chicken Liver on Puri; Stuffed Mushroom; Prawn Patia; Chicken Stick Masala and the Mixed Kebab is a prize winner. Main courses we have sampled and found delightful are Chicken Shashlick; Karahi Gosht; Kashmiri Chicken; Cucupaka, Tandoori baked chicken with minced meat in metal pot; Goa Special, tandoori baked chicken laced with almonds, sultanas, cashew nut etc in a spicy yoghurt sauce and their fabulous Chilli Chicken Masala. There is also a fine list of vegetable Balti dishes and they have a very good hand in Parsee dishes, sweet, sour and pretty hot, very much my thing at the moment.' Chicken Dhansak is one of my favourites!'* RG. T/a 15% disc.

YOU SAY OK
You might get a discount if you show them this Guide.

CHIPPENHAM: ASHOKA 62 Market Place, Chippenham ~ 01249 461234. Swapan Roy's nice special: Kakra Bhuna c£8, crab meat cooked with fresh herbs, onions, garlic and tomato.

CHIPPENHAM: TAJ MAHAL 51 Causeway, Chippenham ~ 01249 653243

LUDGERSHALL: MUGHAL 33 Andover Road ~ 01264 790463. Mrs Bushra Rahman 's 44-seater. Hours: 12-2.30/6-12.

Marlborough

THE PALM   TOP 100

Knowle Farm, Froxfield   01672-871818

'Wiltshire can now boast a grand, new Indian restaurant; and I mean grand, too. The Palm at Froxfield, on the A4 between Hungerford and Marlborough, opened in 2006. It is a very welcome addition to the curry landscape. 't's the place place to take the kids when you visit them at Marlborough College. The Palm, to put no finer point on it, is really classy. It was initiated by Hasan, the founding force behind the brilliant Goa restaurant, Everleigh. With help and encouragement from friends and colleagues at the equally renowned Gandhi, Winchester, Hasan has opened really spacious and well appointed premises at a former run down steak house. The Palm looks splendid as you pull in and you'll notice the very large parking area at the rear. The entrance is wide and has splendid access and is easily negotiated by wheelchair. Seating accommodation is designed comfortably to accommodate groups of diners and there's room for about 140 guests. The menu is is not curryhouse, rather it is real home-style Indian cooking. Menu Snapshot: Palms Machli (sea bass marinated in lemon and garlic, with tamarind and pineapple sauce). There's an enticing range of Kebabs that includes a particularly fine mince lamb Seekh Kanjara and all the usual Tandoori and Tandoori Masala dishes. Mains: listed under 'Authentic Indian Dishes' you will find several utter gems, including Karahj Gosht/Murgh (a Punjabi country dish of braised lamb/chicken with a sauce that includes ginger, onion, tomatoes, red chillies and fresh coriander) and Fish Ameritoshori (salmon fried in chunks with cashew nuts and tomato). The Dhansak is highly recommended and among Chef's Specials you will find a beautifully warm and creamy Kashmiri Chicken; magnificent Green Fish (Halibut) Curry; Garlic Chicken; Lamb/Chicken Jalfrezi and a superb stir fried Chicken Peshwari beautifully seasoned with cumin seeds. The Vegetable side dishes are delicate and well varied and you must try Aloo Baigan – potato and aubergine curry. Have no fears – for the traditionalists there is a fine selection chicken/lamb old friends – Dupiaza, Rogon Josh, Madras (and be warned, this is fiery) and Bhuna. But my advice is go up country and explore new territory. As for prices, well, considering the comforts of the place, the cheerful service and the exciting bill of fare a main dish for more or less £10 plus the odds and ends is very well worth it indeed. There is a very good take away service, too. An

added point in their favour is the disabled toilet. Now these should be obligatory and are required under the recent legislation. They should be taken for granted but we all know, they ain't. Al in all, The Palm has the lot.' RG. Hours: 12-2.30 / 5.30-11.30.   www.thepalmindian.com

Salisbury

ANOKAA   TOP 100

60 Fisherton St, SP2 7RB   01722 424142

Set in the heart of Salisbury, Anokaa is smart and popular. The decor is captures all the colours of India and the chic table settings enhance the venue's understated elegance. The waiters in traditional outfits will warmly welcome you in a true Indian styles; their service is efficient and subtle. Owner Solman Farsi works closely with head chef Vijay (ex Taj, Lucknow) to deliver dishes which, although traditional have been 'lightened up to suit modern palates'. 'Lightening' may include inexplicable adjectives. For example appetisers include 'hand-picked' Crab Cake '(hand-picked – what else; feet?)', 'fused' with ginger, basil and fennel seeds, £6 Orrisa Style Chilli Fried baby squid, with cumin, yoghurt and cucumber, or Multani Jhinga - wild (wild not tame) King prawns 'cured' in a special marinade of yoghurt, £6.50. Main course dishes are equally interesting including vegetarian dishes. There is an a la carte menu and the food is presented beautifully. 'I had Bhaarotiya (chicken breast stuffed with spinach and served on korma sauce with saffron rice). My husband had Old Delhi-style chicken curry,in aromatic spices with fresh cream and tomato with saffron rice. We also had Tarka Dall. Both were so delicious that we had to swap plates halfway through. The decor is modern and tasteful. Background music is modern and pleasant. The service is friendly. We were the last customers of the night and we didn't feel under pressure to rush our meal so they could close. We paid just under £30 including a glass of wine and a beer, which was very good value. Shame I live in Surrey, otherwise I would be a frequent customer.' SK 'This exciting new restaurant has been beautifully decorated and furnished in a modern design that serves dishes that are out of the ordinary an are extremely tasty. The dishes are a little more expensive than others in the city, which is only to be expected in a restaurant of this calibre of service, decor and cuisine. On weekdays they also serve an excellent help yourself lunch at a very reasonable charge with a variety of starters, main dishes and a sweet. I have also had several of their T/as in the evening and have found the food to be of an excellent quality and ben made to feel equally welcome as when I have eaten in the restaurant. Commended.' RC & DY. 'I have to break into print about the Anokaa. First impressions, The staff were in traditional dress, and gave a good warm welcome. The restaurant was very clean, with good décor and the background music was modern Indian. The table was nicely positioned and nicely prepared. The menu was interesting because they had all the specialist dishes at the top and the regular well known restaurant dishes further down in small

print. Quality of service was very good we were not rushed, there were good gaps between courses. The food was as good as I have had. Toilets were very clean. I would go back and I agree with the top 100 rating, bearing in mind I have visited other Curry Club top 100 restaurants like the Malabar Junction (Central London) and Tamasha in Bromley, this restaurant is up there with them. Choices we had on the night: Shami Kebab, £5.70; Mata Adrak Ki Aloo Tikki £3.95; Curry Lababdar £13.25, like a Lamb Pasanda but hotter and richer with a more acquired taste; Narangee £11.90, a form of Korma with southern influences. 2 Naan Bread, Basmati Rice. Total £43 minus the drinks and Pops.' CG. Pre and post theatre menu has a two course meal with wine for £15pp available from 5.30- 7 and 9-10.30. Lunch buffet or Thursday: enjoy the table magician. Hours: 12-2 / 5.30-10.30.   www.anokaa.com

Swindon

PICKLE JOHNS

25, Wood Street, Swindon   01793 509921

Atul Sarpal's Pickle Johns Pub & Restaurant (named after Indian gentlemen from the early part of the twentieth century, who was sent to this fair land to be educated in some of England's finest public schools (Eton, Harrow, Winchester). On their return to India they had adopted English manners. and the English in turn perceived them as jovial and eccentric characters. In India, they were named "PickleJohns". Most of the dishes are Indian cuisine but some are English and fusion. Hours: 12-2 / 6-11:30. Branch: Popadum Express, Southampton Hants.

RAFU'S TANDOORI   TOP 100

30 High St, Highworth, Swindon   01793 765320

Opened in 1982 by Mr Rafu as the Biplob; renamed to prevent confusion. It remains popular. *'Very good'* G&MP. *'Menu large and varied choice. Complete satisfaction. Best Jalfrezi in the West. Good service, pleasant atmosphere, superb location. Everything nice except the prantha (too greasy).'* ZI. *'Menu had wide variety and choice. Quantity more than adequate. Service very courteous and polite. Atmosphere very convivial. Very good quality meal and good value.'* KS *'We visit weekly. Extensive and varied menu. Generous quantities. High quality. Outstanding service. Excellent Bangra. Hasina Chicken – best in Europe!'* IG&JN. *'The wine list is very good for an Indian restaurant. Whenever we go to Rafu's we know we are going to have a top-class meal, with friendly people, in pleasant surroundings.'* JS. Hours: 12-3 / 6pm-12am / 5 to late.

YOU SAY OK
You might get a discount if you show them this Guide.

MELKSHAM: MELKSHAM TANDOORI 26 Church St, ~ 01225 705242. Mr Mahammed Mayna's 50-seater is in an attractive Cotswold stone building adjacent to a car park.

SALISBURY: ASIA 90 Fisherton St, Salisbury   01722 327628. 'It was packed on both visits, a good sign. Mainly formula but always flavoursome and enjoyable. Pleased we went.' so.

SALISBURY: SHAH JAHAN
111 South Western Rd, Salisbury, SP2 7RR

SWINDON: BHAJI'S Takeaway 76 Thames Av, Swindon ~ 01793 533799. Opened 1997 by Iqbal Ahmed with Chef Uddin. Del: 4m £12min. Hours: 5-11.30; 12 Fri & Sat.

BIPLOB 12 Wood Street, Swindon ~ 01793 490265. Rokib Alo and Fozlur Rahman's 60-seater has a separate lounge/bar area seating 20. House specials inc Tandoori Duck Bonani (cooked with cream, cashews & brandy) and Fish Buzon – Bangladeshi river fish. Min ch £10. Hours: 12-2.30 / 6-12. Branches: Raja Takeaway Cheltenham, Rajdoot 35 Castle St Cirencester, Glos.

CURRY GARDEN 90 Victoria Road, Swindon 01793 521114. R Khan's 80-seater dates from 1969. T/a: 15% less. Hours: 12-2 / 5.30-12; 12-12 Sun & bank hols.

GULSHAN 122 Victoria Rd, Old Town 01793 522558. Abdul Kahha's 80-seater is on two floors connected by a spiral staircase. *'Nice idea – revolving sweet tray with the bill.'* DS. Sun all-day buffet c£8. T/a: 15% disc. Hours: 12-2.30 / 6-12; 1 Sat.

LALBAGH 171 Rodbourne Rd, Swindon 01793 535511. Abdul Kahhar opened his 54-seater in 1997. Sun Lunch: buffet £9. Hours: 12-2 / 6-11.30. www.lalbagh.net

SPICY AROMA 144 Cricklade Rd, Gorse Hill ~ 01793 488700. 64-seater est 1996 by Abdul Rouf Ali. Min ch c£7. Sun lunch buf: c£8. T/a: 10% disc. Del: 5m £12 min. Hours: 5-12.30; 1.30 Sat.

WARMINSTER: AGRA 32 East St. ~ 01985 212713. Chef Kamal Uddin's and mngr Shofique Miah's 52-seater in two rooms. Tapeli (fish) Roshni & Pistachio Korma dishes favourites. Min Charge: £5pp. Hours: 12-2/6-11; 12.30-10.30 Sun. Branch: K2, Heathrow

WOOTTON BASSETT: MEMORIES OF INDIA 21 High St. ~ 01793 852365. Opposite the aptly-named Currier's Arms! *'Freshly made dishes. Massive portions'* TE. *'This little gem deserves a mention. Extraordinary food, quality and service at a low price.'* AE. Hours: 12-2.30 / 6-12; 1 Fri & Sat.

WORCESTERSHIRE

Area: Midlands
Population: 552,000
Adjacent Counties:
Glos, Hereford,
Shrops, Warks,
W Mid

Evesham

MAHEEN'S

68 Bridge Street, Evesham   01386 49704

'Excellent outlook, over-viewing the River Avon. in bottom storey of a large building. On first impressions, the entrance was not favourable, however once inside we were greeted by a Sanjeev Bhaskar lookalike, Mukit Miah. The restaurant is modern and minimal, in fact it looks more like a wine bar. The tables had black tablecloths with white trim, artificial black lillies were also black, I liked it. Service was prompt, only draught Carlsberg and Tetley bitter. Starters were predictable, but prices were as cheap as we've seen for a long time. My spiced

Popadum arrived with burnt edges and Monika's plain looked like it came from a packet. Any misgivings were quashed when our mains arrived, delicious Lamb Zeera c£6, in a rich tomato sauce. Chicken Chilli Bahaar c£6, tender slices of chicken in a bright red sauce with a couple of sliced chillies which despite these was not too hot. A large plate of Mushroom Pullao £2.25 and a Naan £1.50 was more than enough. I really meant it when I said to the waiter that we really enjoyed it.' T&MH. Hours: 6-11.30; 12.30 Fri & Sa.

YOU SAY OK WORCS
You might get a discount if you show them this Guide.

BEWDLEY: THE RAJAH OF BEWDLEY 8 Load St. ~ 01299 400368. Anwar Uddin's 34-seater in a grade 2 listed cottage. 'Food excellent, extremely friendly service.' SH. 'Good' G&MP. Special: Tandoori Lobster. T/a: 10% off. Min ch: £5. Hours: 5-11.30.

RILYS OF EVESHAM 2 Waterside. ~ 01384 45289. Chef Hoque's Buffet Nights Mon-Tues nights, 7-10, adult £9, children £6. Hours: 5.30-12, 11 Sun. www.rilys.co.uk Branch: Hotel Montville, Reddich..

GREAT MALVERN: BENGAL BRASSERIE 5 Worcester Rd ~ 01684 575744. Masum Choudhury took over in 2000 . Hours: 5-12.

KIDDERMINSTER: EURASIA TAKEAWAY Unit 1, 19, Stourbridge Rd ~ 01562 825861. Owner Syed Hussain. Del: 4m £10 min. Hours: 5-12.

KIDDERMINSTER: NEW SHER E PUNJAB 48 George St ~ 01562 740061. Puran Singh cooks Punjabi food (est 1971). Eves only .

REDDITCH: BALTI SPICE TAKEAWAY 65 Popular Rd, Batchley, Redditch ~ 01527 596802. Hours: 5-12; 1 Sat.

TENBURY WELLS: SHAMRAJ BALTI HOUSE 28 Cross St, Tenbury Wells ~ 01584 819612. Mr Rahman' s 60-seater + party room 14, T/a: 15% disc. Hours: 12-2.30 Sat. & Sun / 5-12.

WORCESTER: BOMBAY PALACE 38 The Tything, Worcester ~ 01905 613969. Abdul Rob's 40-seater has 7 parking spaces at rear. T/a: 10% off. Del: £10 min. Hours: 6-12; 1 Sat.

WORCESTER: SPICES TAKEAWAY 9 Barbourne Rd. ~ 01905 729101. Del: 3m, £1 Del. Hours: 5.30-12, Sat to 1, Tuesday closed. Branch: Shunarga, 44, High Street, Pershore.

WORCESTER: SPICEY BITE TANDOORI 79 Wyld's Lane. 01905 353235. Owner: Mamun Rashid. Free Del over £8. Hours: 5.30-12. www.spiceybite.co.uk

Redditch

HOTEL MONTVILLE & INDIAN FUSION

101 Mount Pleasant, Southcrest   01527 544411

This small hotel with restaurant opened in 2005 by Mukid Rahman. All rooms are nicely appointed and have their own ensuite facilities. The fusion restaurant seats 86 diners in two rooms and is decorated stylishly in natural tones and polished wood., spot lights and the odd green plant make for a very relaxed upmarket atmosphere. Seafood is their speciality, have a look at these lovely dishes: Roopashi £3.95, Bengal Chandu dish marinated with a touch of butter, garlic, onions, cooked in the clay oven; Machli Chaat £3.95, mackerel cooked in garlic, tomatoes and capsicum; Spice Lemon Prawn c£7, a whole lobster grilled in a sweet and sour

sauce; Lime and Ginger Seabass c£9, pan fried served on a bed of sautéed spinach and red pepper, accompanied by cumin new potatoes, drizzled with vine cherry tomato and fish broth, very fusion! For those are are not keen on anything from the sea (that's me!) Chicken Dakhna c£3, marinated chicken nibblets cooked hot and spicy in the clay oven; Afghan Chi Chat £3.95, chick peas and chicken cooked with spice then wrapped in a soft flat and thin bread, perfect lunch time food! Other treats include: Duck Naga c£8, the famous Bangladeshi chilli; Amli Liaon c£8, Tandoori lamb pieces spiced with bay leaves, garam masala and baby tomatoes; Cheese Naan £1.95. Min Charge: £10. Hours: 6-11. Branch: Rilys of Evesham and Waterside, Evesham, both in Worcs.

Upton-on-Severn

PUNDITS

9 Old Street, Upton   01684 591119

'We booked the previous night, a good job, the place was very popular, despite being the most expensive in the area. A memorable place because the maitre greeted my wife with a kiss on the cheek and shook my hand even though it was our first visit. Enjoyed my Morche Roshun (garlic and chilli) Chicken Tikka, billed as hot, however, I may have been suffering from mouth numbness caused by my Chicken Vindaloo in Ilfracombe a few days previously. Good service.' T&MH. Menu Extracts: Chomothkar Talk Murgh Roti medium spiced, lemon chicken tikka on thin chapati bread; Podina Roshun (mint and garlic), mint sauce, whole roasted garlic cloves, roasted tomatoes and coriander with vegetables, chicken, lamb or prawns.

Worcester

MONSOON   TOP 100

35 Foregate Rd Worcester   01905 726333

White painted angled pillars and wooden stained concertina doors make this 120 seater restaurant stand out on Foregate Road. Established in 1999 by Rahman (manager), Choudhury and Choudhury. Reception has been painted in a creamy colour with comfortable sofa's upholstered in paprika. The restaurant has a light and airy feel, with bleached wooden flooring, paprika and cinnamon painted walls, original art hangs sparingly on the walls with matching chairs in paprika, cinnamon, turmeric and indigo. Natural wooden tables are economically laid with crisp white linen napkins and generous wine glasses. Specials: Tangri Kebab, drumstick marinated in cashew nuts, spices and served with tamarind chutney. Achar Wali Machi, salmon steak pickled in spices, served cold with salad. Parsi Jhinga, tiger prawns in mint, turmeric, garlic and tamarind juice.

Lamb Shikampuri, mince lamb balls stuffed with coriander, ginger, onion, raisins in curry gravy. Daal Panchmela, a mix of five varieties of lentils. Stays on our Top 100. T/a: 10% disc. Hours: 6-12; 1 Fri & Sat. Branch: Cheltenham Tandoori, 2 Great Norwood Street Cheltenham, Gloucs. Tel: 01242 227772.

PASHA

56 St Johns, Worcester   01905 426327

Manager, N Haque's restaurant, seats 68 diners. Opened in 1987 as Pasha Indian Cuisine and has remained under the same management. Menu Snapshot: Nargi's Kofta £2.50, spicy minced lamb deep-fried in butter, served with a light omelette and fresh salad; Mushroom Delight £2.50, stuffed with spicy vegetables and deep-fried; Methi Gosht c£6, with fenugreek, medium hot; Chicken Hasina £5.50, mildly spiced, dried fruit and nuts with fresh cream; Garlic Potato £2.75, rich sauce; Mushroom Pullao Rice £2.75, selection of Chutneys 45p. Sun Buffet: c£7 adult, £4.50 under 12's, 12.30 - 2. Cobra £3.10 a pint. House wine is a good value c£8 a bottle. You might get a disc if you show them this Guide. Del: £1 charge. Hours: 12-2 / 5.30-12. www.pasha-online.co.uk

RAJKOT   NEW ENTRANT

The Tything, Worcester   01905 27402

'A good experiences to share. Excellent restaurant, stylish and very unlike a traditional curry house. They do have the normal standard curries buried in the menu but it's mainly an extensive menu of regional specialities and unusual dishes so lots of new experiences. Particularly strong on fish, seafood and also offer venison, duck and others – we're completely vegetarian so didn't sample them!. The vegetarian Thali is excellent and presentation is superb on all dishes. The service is first class with friendly staff who laugh and joke with the customers. A great experience, not cheap, but worth every penny for a smart night out and one of my all-time favourite restaurants – shame we live 250m away! I believe it's owned by the same people who have the Cafe Mela also in Worcester.' GC.

SPICE CUISINE   TOP 100

39 Bromyard Rd, Worcester   01905 429786

Hidden away behind Birmingham Midshires Building Society, just over the river bridge from Worcester Town, it has been owned by the same family for years, Muslims from Pakistan. *'Plain, simple and clean decor. Friendly and efficient service. Staff Curry - lamb on the bone in a thick, tasty, spicy sauce, cooked for hours with a thin rolled and crispy Nan. Manager - Iffty Shah (cousin of Masteen who manages the Kashmir in Birmingham).Toilets always clean with hot water, soap and dryer. Chicken on the bone and Aloo for me - excellent as usual. Lamb Chops, on the bone, which was the staff curry for the night. About six chops which had been*

cooking for hours so that the meat was falling off, served with a rich, quite hot sauce - superb. Roti to go with it, what else would you want for a Sun dinner. Washer-upper has been promoted to Tandoori Chef and made a very good start with Seekh Kebabs. Unlicensed: BYO - they will chill and open it for you.' RE. T/a: 10% disc. Del: 3m, £10 min. Small car park at rear. Hours: 5.30 -11.30.

NORTH YORKSHIRE

Area: North
Population: 1,042,000
Adjacent Counties:
Cumbria, Durham,
Lancs, E & W Yorks

1997 county changes returned 'Cleveland' south of the Tees, to North Yorks. At the same time, the changes created a 'new' Yorkshire county by transferring territory and towns from 'North Humbs' into East Yorkshire. This restored Yorkshire as Britain's biggest county. Because the area is so large, we deal with these four counties in their current administrative formats and in compass order, N, E, S, W.

Beadlam, (Hemsley)

HELMSLEY SPICE CLUB

Main Road, Beadlam   01439 772400

The Spice Club in Beadlam was once the White Horse Inn, now completely refurbished it is the latest in the Jinnah group. It is situated on the busy A170, midway between Helmsley and Kirbymoorside, off road parking is available in their private car park. It's a modern and contemporary restaurant with 65 covers plus a separate bar where customers are welcome to have a drink whilst waiting for a takeaway or just to enjoy the ambience. Menu details: see Harrogate and York below. Hours: 5.30-11. jinnah-restaurants.com

Bedale

TASTE OF INDIA

32 Market Place Bedale   01677 423373

Bedale is an old Yorkshire market town with a large cobbled square, plenty of free parking surrounded by interesting shops. Est 1989, this smallish restaurant has undergone extensive refurbishment. *'A group of us decided to try it last Wednesday evening and had a mixed, but enjoyable overall, experience. Popadums with pickles, Mixed*

Kebab, Meat Samosas £2.10, Onion Bhajia £2.00, Chicken Tikka Curries, Rice, Saag Aloo £2.45 and Naan £1.50 were all fresh, superb quality, nicely spiced an thoroughly delicious. The portions were generous and with drinks and coffee, the bill came to £15 per head, which proved excellent value for money. The service (from a sullen lad with a silly haircut) was second rate and only repeated prompting ensured that our needs were met.' TE. Tony, I can hear myself saying 'the youth of today' just like my parents! T/a 10% disc. Hours: 6-11.30; 12 Fri & Sat.

Harrogate

JINNAH

34 Cheltenham Parade   01423 563333

Est 2003 and seats 110 in a converted stone chapel, which was part of a Wesleyan school and is now a listed building. 'The interior is pleasantly different, being cavernous with its high ceilings and two large hanging lights. Seating is either in the main well or along the slightly raised area around the edge. Decorated in terracotta and green colours with brown and beige chairs, and green imitation marble easy-wipe table tops, wall lights, plates and cutlery (yes, even the knives and forks) with the name of the restaurant. Smartly dressed waiters impart the look of quality. It was Sat night and packed. The menu was almost too clever by half with too many dishes described as 'amazing.' Onion Bhajias £2.25, were two large flat patties like hamburgers in shape (they could have been put in a bun and called bhajia burger) and were OK, pleasantly spiced, edges nicely crisp but the middle was stodgy. The service was friendly and efficient.' MW. Hours: 5.30-11; 12 Sat; 12- 11 Sun . Branches Beadlam and York. www.jinnah-restaurants.com

MUJIB   NEW ENTRANT

32 Devonshire Pl, HG1 4AD   01423 875522

Chef Nazrul Ali specialises in 'Indian fusion' drawing on his experience of Indian, French Provençal, Italian, Oriental and Thai cuisine to create the menu. The dish Joi Yorkshire, for example, mixes traditional English roast lamb and light spices with Yorkshire pudding and Bhuna sauce. Reports please. Branch: Mujib Whitby Rd, Ellesmere Port, CH65 8DN ~ 0151 357 1676.

Ripon

MOTI RAJ

18 High Skellgate, Ripon   01765 690348

'A busy road with many buses passing, the owner was washing the windows when we arrived (using an old ghee bucket for the water!). We sat at the bar and were given ice-cold Cobras and the menus, containing a 'priced matrix' format of meat/fish against the variety of curry sauces, so simple and logical, other restaurants take note. Recently refurbished in soft pastel shades with double layer of linen on the tables. Toilets were immaculate. Warm Pops, fresh pickles, seven delicious curries, four blends of rices, three different breads and a lovely Sag Aloo £2, were delivered, set on proper hot plates and demolished by us all, wash down with even more Cobra, nothing was left! Following coffee, the bill worked out at £22 each which is very reasonable for a good city centre restaurant. A mature favourite of locals and visitors to Ripon. It offers excellent service, high quality cuisine and good value for money, highly recommended.' TE. You might get a disc if you show them this Guide. Del: 3m, £8 min. Hours: 5.30-12.

Skipton

AAGRAH   A-LIST

Devonshire Pl, Keighley Rd   01756 790807

'Compact 50-seater that oozes quality, from the sturdy menu to the stylish decoration, inc lavishly decorated wooden chairs at tables with thick cotton tablecloths. Nicely appointed interior with a pleasing colour scheme and well finished decorative ceilings mouldings and sparkling chandeliers. Very efficient and knowledgeable staff. Pakistani / Kashmiri cuisine from a comprehensive menu with several specials. Comp Pops & Chuts. Exquisite starter, Bihair Kebab £3, several thin strips of top notch lamb, marinated in garlic, onion and spices then briskly fried to give a pungent aroma and an absolutely mouth watering taste, flavoursome and succulent meal perfectly balanced with a complex and challenging spicy accompaniment. A fresh salad with the emphasis on onion, complimented perfectly with a squeeze of lemon and cool mint sauce dripped over the top. The main course was even better, Jinghra Achar £9.95, top quality king prawns with a pronounced yet delicate flavour with a fleshy, not rubbery, mouth-feel. These were served in an incredibly complex sauce with a stunning aroma, a really rich taste that had a bite. Served with a brilliant Peshwari Naan £2.50, a leavened bread spread with a sticky coconut jam, light and tasty, generously topped on the outside with coconut, almonds, onion, sultanas and more pistachio nuts, delicious. A top class meal that I will remember for a long time.' RW. Has anyone tried the Whole Stuffed Lamb £199.95, whole lamb marinated in vinegar, yoghurt, garam masala, bay leaves, ginger and garlic, stuffed with rice, boiled eggs, new potatoes, mushrooms, and then oven baked, served with side dishes, rice and salad, sounds absolutely wonderful! If you have, report please. The menu says it feeds fifteen people, what a banquet! Hours: 6-12; 11 Sun. Menu details and list of branches see Shipley. W. Yorks.

Tadcaster

AAGRAH   A-LIST

York Road, Steeton, Tadcaster   01937 530888

The 6th Aagrah. 120-seater, opened 1996 on the A64 near York, with easy parking. Details in Skipton above.

Thirsk

RAJ OF INDIA

42 Long Street, Thirsk   01845 526917

'A lovely market square and the famous horse racing course and the Raj, a mature restaurant with its sister, 'Tandoori Night' in York. I was working at the North Yorks Police HQ and they recommended it. Balti dishes with deliciously spiced sauces, served on proper hot plates, swiftly by smart, cheerful waiters who are focused on attentive customer service. Very busy with locals, business people, tourists and race-goers.' [and cops?] *'I especially liked the smart, elderly (70's) gent with a military bearing who marched in and said to the waiter, "I'll have a large Beef Madras and a litre of house red!"* TE. Free Pickle Tray with every T/a. Menu Snapshot: Aloo Chat £2.10; Raj Special Biriani £6, Tandoori meat, chicken and prawn with saffron rice cooked together in almond and sultanas, served with Vegetable Curry; Sirloin Steak Masala £6.50, best English steak marinated and served with mushrooms and Pullao Rice; Kulcha Nan £1.70, stuffed with onion and cheese. Hours: 12-2.30 Sun only / 6-11.30; 12 Fri & Sat.

Yarm

RAJ BARI

49 High Street, Yarm   01642 888004

'After some brilliant walking on the North Yorkshire Moors, we were ready for a curry! We found two Indian restaurants on the high street, one quite posh, the Raj Bari, which opened in 30 minutes, which meant a swift pint in the pub. It's a modern and comfortable restaurant with traditional Indian nicknacks. Swift and efficient service, not particularly friendly. Usual starters of House Special Mixed Starter £3.95 for me and Sheek Kebab £3 for Monika. Both good but had to ask for Raitha.' That really annoys me, traditionally, Tandoori starters are always served with salad and Raitha! 'I ate Chicken Jalfrezi £6 and Monica Chicken Tikka Rogan £7, we shared Nan bread and Mushroom Pullao. I was a little disappointed, but M thought the dishes rather good; I must have been having an off day. Prices reasonable.' T&MH. Min ch: £9. Sun night buffet. T/a 10% disc. Hours: 12-2, not Fri / 5-11; 11.30 Fri & Sat.

York (Nether Poppleton)

BENGAL BRASSIERE

York Busn Park, Ings Lane   01904 788808

Owner, Dobir Malik opened his lovely restaurant in 1999. It's a new, brick-built, building with clean lines, and inside, decorated brightly with cream walls, fuschia upholstery, wrought iron light fittings and seats 100 diners. The menu is not your ordinary curry house, with Bengal Special Chicken Patil c£9 being the most ordered dish! Menu Snapshot: Morich Bahar £3.95, fried whole green pepper filled with aloo, chana, begun herbs and spices; Murgh E Dilruba £3.95, fillet of chicken breast wrapped in cheese; Liver Tikka £3.95, chicken livers marinated and served with green salad; Paneer Pakora c£3, cubes of cottage cheese, battered and deep-fried; Duck Tikka Masala c£9; Korma Murgh Tikka c£7, mild and creamy chicken tikka with coconut and almonds; Chicken Tikka Chom Chom c£8, barbecued chicken, potato, chickpeas in medium sauce, garnished with coriander and spring onion; Chilli Begun c£6, aubergine, spicy sauce, green chilli and capsicum, Chilli and Coriander Naan £2. Hours: 5.30-11.30. www.bengal-brasserie.com

JINNAH AT FLAXTON

Malton Road, Flaxton, York   01904 468202

Large and imposing purpose built restaurant on the A64 mid way between York and Malton. Seats 150 people in two lounges, two bars and an extensive dining area. *'Cleverly constructed so that the interior is split into cosy areas around a central pavilion. Manned by uniformed staff who glide around in a manner probably not seen since Lyons dispensed with the Nippies.'* Blimey Ralph, that's showing your age. – we're talking the 1940's (and for those who haven't a clue what us wrinklies are on about, educate yourselves on the web!) *'Pleasant starter, Chaat Patta Chicken £3.25, a dish I last tasted in Brick Lane. Plenty of thin slices of breast meat, marinated in an incredibly rich and sticky sauce with a delicious bite. Slices of onion and red pepper added bite, superb. Main course kept up the high standard, Hasina Lamb £9.95, top quality meat without a trace of fat or gristle, mouthwatering sauce, piquant blend of herbs and spices fused in sweated down spinach. Fantastic pungent aroma, with star anise and cardamom and chillies added zing. Good Chuppatis £1.50 for two. Real tablecloths and hand folded napkins. Beaming manager, knew most customers by name. Very enjoyable.'* RW. *'Our Guide has proved invaluable; we have particularly enjoyed our visits here.'* N&G. Buffet: Mon & Weds, 5.30-10, adults £10, kids c£6. Hours: 5.30-11; 12-11 Sat & Sun. Sun Buffet, 12-10. Branches: Beadlham, Harrogate and elsewhere in York. www.jinnah-restaurants.com

VICEROY OF INDIA   TOP 100

26 Monkgate, York   01904 622370

Part of the Jinnah group (see above). *'A most enjoyable and varied buffet served all day Sun at a reasonable price of £9 (less for children, including - slightly surprisingly our 14 year old son). The rest of the menu calls for a return trip when we are in the area'.* SH. 5.30-11, Mon to Fri; - 12 Sat; 12-11 Sun Branches: York Spice Club, 1 Monkgate; Jinnah T/a, 18 The Village, Haxby, York. 01904 750082.

YOU SAY OK - N. YORKS
You might get a discount if you show them this Guide.

HARROGATE: RAJ RANI TAKEAWAY 235 Skipton Rd, ~ 01423 529295. Owner Ahad Miah is offering Guide readers 15% disc on T/as over £15 on Mons and Tues.

MALTON NORTON: RAJ TANDOORI 21 Church St,　01653 697337. Est 1992 by S Islam. T/a 10% disc. Hours: 5.30-12.

NORTHALLERTON: AROMA 1 Zetland St. 01609 774239. Owner Chef Nitamul Hoque. T/a: 10% disc. Hrs: 6-11.30; 12 Fri & Sat.

NORTHALLERTON: LION OF ASIA 88a High St,~ 01609 772767. *'Down a narrow dark alley, up some iron stairs, through a metal door and a greasy-spoon type interior, not the most attractive location, but the curries are good.'* TE. Hours: 6-12; 1 Fri & Sat. Monday closed.

NORTHALLERTON: SPICE OF INDIA 1a Friarage St, ~ 01609 777600. *'Good cuisine, cheerful service and value for money.'* TE.

RIPON: BALTI HOUSE 16 Kirkgate.~ 01765 602597. Near the Cathedral, so tourists a-plenty who pay 15% more than Moti Raj! *(see below)* Del: 3m £10 min. T/a 10% disc. Credit cards not accepted. Starter & side dishes can't be ordered without a main course. Ludicrous rules especially as they have a min ch £7 pp and you can tell 'em that from me! ED. Hours: 5.30-10.20; 11.30 Fri & Sat.

SETTLE: SETTLE TANDOORI
9 Commercial Courtyard, Duke St. ~ 01729 823393. 50-seater est 1998 by Abdul Rob. Hours: 5.30-11.30.

YORK: TAJ MAHAL RE-ENTRANT 7 Kings Staith, YO1 1SN ~ 01904 653944. Stand on the bridge over the river Ouse and it's

easy to see with a great river frontage though only two tables in the window give a view. T/a 10% disc. Hours: 12-2:30/5:30-12.

YORK: AKBAR'S 8, George Hudson St, YO1 6LP, 01904 679 888. See Akbar's Leeds, W.Yorks for details.

YORK: AKASH 10 North Street ~ 01904 633550 38-seater owned by JU Ahmed. Hours: 5-12.

YORK: SAFFRON DESI NEW ENTRANT 107 Micklegate. *'Very good with early evening specials'*. JP. Branches 1362 Leeds Rd, Bradford BD3 8ND.www.saffrondesi.com

EAST YORKSHIRE

Area: North
Population: 580,000
Adjacent Counties:
Lincs, N S & W Yorks

1997 county changes created this 'new' Yorkshire county by transferring territory and towns here from 'North Humbs'.

Beverley

AKASH

63a Toll Gavel, Beverley　　　01482 882090

'Fifty seater, very popular restaurant, situated upstairs in a pedestrianised centre of this busy market town. Very experienced and efficient staff. Large open room, simply decorated and nicely furnished. Reshmi Kebab £2.60, two, very juice and succulent, with a perfectly cooked omelette on top, small, crisp salad and thick yoghurt sauce. Meat Thali £15, half portions of prawn, lamb, chicken and vegetable curries, all distinctly different and tasty, all complimented each other. Also provided a Nan bread, very light, fluffy, enjoyable and Tandoori Chicken, very well marinated, nicely charred at the edges and salad. Overall an excellent meal.' RW. Menu Snapshot. Aubergine Bhaji and Puri £2.20; Tandoori Mixed Korahi c£7, chicken and lamb tikka, sheek kebab, tandoori chicken and king prawn, medium hot sauce; Special Nan £1.75, stuffed with cheese, garlic and coriander leaves. Hours: 5.30-11.30; 12　Fri & Sat.

Brough

ASHAM BALTI

108a Main Road, Newport　　01430 449289

Mr Shamsul Islam has owned the Asham since 2005, he is also chef. *'I still fondly remember my first experience of Bangladeshi cuisine, Sher E Bangla, Hammersmith. I was a young telecom engineer at the BBC in west London around the time of the Bangladesh war. Bangladeshi restaurants were opening up all over London and I had never tasted anything like the delicious meals that were on offer at prices even I could afford. Now back in my home we lacked a really good curry restaurant. The opening of Asham Balti has put that right. All the usual curry favourite are on offer, but for the polite and helpful staff, nothing is too much trouble. Specialities include Bangladeshi fish garnished with Aloo Methi and Naga chilli, which I have never experience before.'* RS. Specials: Roshoon Eh Mirchi Murgh c£6, chicken in hot thick sauce, garlic, green chillies, peppers, onion and

tomatoes and coriander leaves; Maachli Biriani c£9, two whole trout, shallow fried with onions, served with fried long grain Patna rice, garnished with tomato, cucumber, onion, lemon, coriander leaves and green chillies. You might get a disc if you show them this Guide. Del: 7m, £2 min. T/a: 10% disc. Hours: 5-11.30.

YOU SAY OK - EAST YORKS
You might get a discount if you show them this Guide.

BEVERLEY: NASEEB 9 Wednesday Market ~ 01482 861110. Very pretty 44-seater est 1988 by Abdul Muzir. Hours: 6-11.30.

HESSLE: LIGHT OF INDIA TAKEAWAY 27 The Weir. ~ 01482 649521. Saiful Islam Tarafdar's Light is under the shadow of the fabulous bridge. Hours: 5-12; 12.30 Sat.

HULL: TANDOORI MAHAL 589 Anlaby Rd. ~ 01482 505653. 'At Abu Maksud & Mizanur Tarafder's 64-seater we've always received first class service and excellent food.' PT. Hours: 6-12.

SOUTH YORKSHIRE

Area: North
Population: 1,280,000
Adjacent Counties:
Derbys, Lincs, Notts,
E & W Yorks

Doncaster (Woodlands)

AAGRAH   A-LIST

Great North Road, Doncaster   01302 728888

Opened in 1995, the fifth the very popular Aagrah (so booking advisable). This 90-seater is a franchise run by cousin Liaquat Ali. 'I would put it at no. 1 in Doncaster, and there's a lot of competition.' JF. Specials include: Achar, Hyderabady and Masala dishes. T/a: 10% disc. Hours: 6-11.30; 12 Fri & Sat; 11 Sun. Menu details and list of branches see Shipley. W. Yorks.

YOU SAY OK - SOUTH YORKSHIRE
You might get a discount if you show them this Guide.

BARNSLEY, DODWORTH: CURRY MAHAL 28 Barnsley Rd, ~ 01226 201188. 64-seater opened in 1999 by MG Uddin. Hours: 6-late. www.currymahal.com

BARNSLEY: JALSA 7 Pitt St. ~ 01226 779114. Comfortable, smart 50-seater with a delightful reception area and bar est by Emdadur Rahman in 1992. Hours: 6-12.

BARNSLEY: K2 TAKEAWAY 5 Royal St. ~ 01226 299230. Owner/manager/chef Ditta's Kashmiri Balti. 'Excellent.' TH. Hours: 6-3am; 4 Sat; 12.30am Sun.

DONCASTER: INDUS 24 Silver St. 01302 810800. Karim Din's (mngr M Ilyas) long-established (1968) 175-seater, old friend of this Guide. 'Sophisticated.' DC. 'Always our favourite in Yorkshire.' WHH. T/a: 10% disc. Del: £20. Sun buffet £12. Hours: 12-2 / 6.30-11.30.

DONCASTER: TICKHILL: Taj Cottage 9 North Gate. ~ 01302 745745. Est 2002, MK Zaman's 90-seater is in three rooms. Typical English bldg, white washed & black beams. Hours: 6-11.30.

DONCASTER: TAJ MAHAL 32 Hallgate. ~ 01302 341218. Raja Munir Akhtar, opened his restaurant in 1989. Hours: 5.30-12; 1 Sat. Branch: Peterborough, Cambs

PONTEFRACT: SPICE RAJ NEW ENTRANT
18 Market Place, Pontefract, WF8 1AT 01977 799560.
'A warm welcome when we went downstairs to this exceptionally clean, brightly lit, warm, recently refurbished basement restaurant. We were shown to the seats of our choice. Background music, not too loud; fresh flowers on each table; homely, warm, friendly yet professional. Staff chatty and friendly without being overwhelming. We did not have to wait too long and what we ate was very well cooked and completely delicious. The nan breads were the best I have ever had. I would recommend it to anyone and will be a regular customer in the future. Overall it is an excellent experience'. S&AJ.

PONTEFRACT: VICEROY Front St. 01977 700076. 84-seater owned since 1991 by chef,Akram Lohn. Chilli Chicken, most popular dish. Del: 3m £7 min. Hours: 5-1.

ROTHERHAM: AKBAR'S Meadowbank Rd. S61 2NF, 01709 555 500. See Leeds, W.Yorks for details.

ROTHERHAM: MUGHAL CURRY CENTRE
1 Bellows Rd, Rawmarsh 01709 527084

ROTHERHAM: HIMALIA TAKEAWAY 129 Ferham Rd. 01709 512321 'Most non-locals will drive past without knowing it's there. Est 1995 and family-run with open-kitchen, the food always has been very good.' AM. Del free over £6, 4m. Hours: 6-12; 1 Fri & Sat.

Sheffield

ASHOKA   A-LIST

307 Ecclesall Rd, Sheffield   0114 268 3029

Established in 1967. Now owned by Mr Rahul Amin. 'The best Indian restaurant we have been to, including many in the London area and Birmingham. We went back to it every night of the week [while attending a scientific meeting in Sheffield]. We cannot praise its delicate and distinct flavours too highly, and the friendly, efficient service. ' J&AF. Yours is one of many contented reports, so we are happy that this well-established and well run venue stays in the elite A-LIST. Most ordered dish Bhel Puri, (see page 64), Liver Puri – chicken livers, stir-fried in masala, served 0n bread. 'One of the finest Indian restaurant in South Yorkshire. Diners are assured of excellent service, an amenable atmosphere and outstanding service. Comprehensive and high quality wine list. Book early to avoid disappointment.' D&CS. 'Just wanted to send you a glowing report. Not only was the vegetarian curry superb, but the waiters were friendly' KH. T/a: 10% off. Hours: 6 (Sun 7)-11.30.   See page 36
www.theashokarestaurant.com

YOU SAY OK - SOUTH YORKSHIRE
You might get a discount if you show them this Guide.

SHEFFIELD, DORE: Almas Indian Brasserie 34 High St ~ 0114 262 0883. Opened 1996 by Bodrul Islam. Locals love the Methi Murgh and Methi Gosht Masala, both c£7. Hours: 6-11.

SHEFFIELD: BENGAL SPICE 457 Manchester Rd. 0114 288 8666.

SHEFFIELD: BILASH TAKEAWAY 347 Sharrow Vale Rd.~ 0114 266 1746. Est 1986 by Abdul Jahir (mngr Ibrahim). 'Had their takeaways for over 10 years and every time, we ring the chef to compliment him, never been disappointed.' ANON. Hours: 5.30-12; 1 Sat. www.bilashtandoori.co.uk

SHEFFIELD: DILSHAD
96 The Dale. ~ 0114 255 5008. Hours: 6-12; 12.30 Sat.

SHEFFIELD: ELINAS
282 Sharrow Rd.~ 0114 267 9846. Hours: 5.30-11.30; 12 Sat.

SHEFFIELD: EVEREST TANDOORI
59 Chesterfield Rd, S8 0RL ~ 0114 258 2975. Owner N M Raja.
Hours: 6-1am; 2 Thurs; 3am Fri & Sat.

SHEFFIELD, CROOKES: JAFLONG
182 Northfield Rd. ~ 0114 266 1802. Hours: 6-12; 1 Fri & Sat.

SAFFRON CLUB   TOP 100

The Old Baths, Glossop Rd, Sheffield
0114 2766150

Naz Islam's Saffron occupies part of Sheffield's historic
Glossop Road Baths, a building dating back to 1871. In
keeping with the building's historic pedigree, Naz has
kept his interior classic, but with a contemporary edge.
The 68-seat restaurant is divided into four distinct
quarters with a mixture of carpet and hardwood flooring
and wallpaper and paintwork that lends an element of
sophistication to each section. The cuisine is also split
into classic and contemporary style dishes. While the
classic menu retains a strong degree of traditionalism,
the contemporary dishes give diners the chance to try
something a little different. With over 15 years
experience, Executive Chef, Faruk Khan specialises in
Mughal cooking. Menu Snapshot: Halka Squid Masala
£4.20, squid flame fried in light spices; Aloo Palak Tikki
£3, pan-fried potato cakes with a spinach and cheese
filling; Parsee Murgh £3.50, minced chicken with garlic
and ginger, deep-fried; Aanari Jhinga £10, king prawns
cooked with ground pomegranate in a slightly tangy
sauce; Maachi Biran £10, medium spiced fish, pan-fried
and served on a bed of garlic spinach accompanied with
curry sauce; Hariyali Murgh c£8, chicken cooked with
mint, coriander, fresh and pickled chillies in a spicy
sauce; Lamb Hyderabadi Biriani £8.50, saffron rice
served with cucumber and tomato raita and curry sauce.
The wine list, it is a cut above the average with many
interesting choices. T/a 15% disc. Hours: 12-2/6-11.

THE SPICE VALLEY

570 Manchester Road, Stocksbridge, Sheffield
0114 283 1292

*'Had dishes I'd not heard of before including Chicken Geera
(sic) (cooked with ginger). Chana Purée for starters was very
nice, whilst the Geera was plentiful and very tasty; Peshwara
Naan was huge. The highlight had to be Mango Lassi, (£3.95)
for a large jug, actually handmade in the place and not out
of a bottle. My friends had a Jalfrezi and a CTM between
them with no complaints. The staff were very friendly. All in
all, a good effort, though could have played Indian music on
the tape rather than the canned stuff they had on.'* AM. .
Hours: 6-12 / 1 Fri & Sat.

WEST YORKSHIRE

Area: North
Population: 2,125,000
Adjacent Counties:
Derbyshire, G Man,
Lancs, N & S Yorks

Batley

BOMBAY PALACE

3 St James Street, Batley   01924 444440

Location: off the A652 Bradford Road from Dewsbury,
easily accessed from M1 junction 40. Balti 74-seater in
an old converted bakery, with many features still
apparent, such as the dough mixers. Opened in 1992 by
G. Maniyar and Shahid Akudi. Brick walls display
Moghal paintings, open fire. *'Upstairs with a light
industrial theme, very pleasant surroundings which includes a
separate family room. Popadums are complimentary after
giving your order. Food excellent, every dish has its own flavour.
As the level of hotness tends to be gauged higher than most
restaurants, this will suit the fire eaters. Portions are generous,
one rice is enough for two. Staff extremely friendly and
efficient.'* PVI. *'My wife and I have been regulars since it
opened. Our current favourites are Seekh Kebabs – beautifully
spicy, not too hot, fresh and tasty. Nargis Kebabs – full of
flavour with a velvety texture. For special occasions there are
banquet menus, which again represent excellent value for
money.'* TN. Specials include: Shikari dish, Achari dish,
and Palace Raan, whole leg of lamb, marinated for 24
hours in herbs, yoghurt, almonds and cashews, cut into
slices, plenty for 4, £65. BYO. You might get a discount
if you show them this Guide. Del: 3m £10 min, 2m £6
min. Hours: 6-12.

SAFFRON   NEW ENTRANT

367 Bradford Rd, Batley   01924 441222

120-seater, opened 2006. *'Celebrated my birthday here. It
is very tastefully decorated and has friendly staff in black
shirts. For starters we had mixed kebabs (one sheek kebab, one
chicken kebab and one shami kebab) and also chicken
kebabs. Our main courses were Lamb and Lentil Handi (a
House Special) and Aloo Chana served with Pilau Rice. They
were well cooked and nicely presented, tasty and very enjoyable.
It seems to get quite busy, not surprising as the quality of the
food is very high.'* LH. Del: 5m, £10 min. Branches Ilkeley
and Guiseley   www.saffronrestaurants.co.uk

Bradford
(inc: Baildon, Chapel Green, Great Horton, Idle, Manningham and Thornbury)

Bradford has a high pedigree curry background, with its very well-established, largely-Pakistani population. This means Halal meat and few veg at the many unlicensed cheap n' cheerful spit n' sawdust caffs. Since many are strict Moslems, not all welcome alcohol. In such establishments, please check with the staff that you may BYO, and even if 'yes', always drink discretely and in moderation. The restaurants, sweet shops and cafés are much more widely spread around than, say, Southall. Curryholics must locate them, for their excellent, uncompromising ethnic food at real value-for-money prices.

AKBAR'S   NEW ENTRANT

1276 Leeds Road, Thornbury, BD3 8LF
01274 773311

'*Looks a bit scruffy from the outside but was amazing on the inside. A huge and extremely busy restaurant (absolutely packed on a Tuesday night) and obviously a firm local favourite. Went with a party and everyone was in agreement that though the food was good, it was generally spiced a lot hotter than they were used to. My bill was £16.00*' MC.Full details, see Leeds.

KARACHI

15 Neal Street, Bradford   01274 732015

Claims to be the UK's first curryhouse. It wasn't (*see p16*). It's not even the first in Bradford. The Kashmir (*see next entry*) opened in 1958. The Sweet Centre, Lumb Lane in 1964, and the Kashmir, third in 1965. Still, it's a long time in curry circles. '*Limited menu but others dishes can be asked for, provided no long preparation is required. Proudly home-run with friendly and unflappable staff. Cheap, cheerful and excellent food. To round off a cracking meal I had a homemade Pistachio Kulfi, frozen solidly, but melting into a sweet and spicy mush.*' RW. '*Food is good quality, service is friendly. Decor reminded us of a school canteen, and the Guide is correct – the toilets are dreadful. Goes without saying that in Bradford it came with three chapatis. However, this was its undoing, as they were too thick meaning that you left feeling bloated.*' HR. Hours: 11am-1am; 2am Fri & Sat.

KASHMIR

27 Morley St, Bradford   01274 726513

Holds about 200 on two floors, downstairs – formica tables, upstairs – carpeted, tablecloths. '*A very popular restaurant with its local clientele.*' AT. '*Seekh Kebabs 60p very good flavour, Meat Roghan Josh £ 3.90 – not as spicy as other dishes but still good. Good service, pleasant staff.*' L&CH. Hours: 11am to 3am. Branch: Kashmir, 858 Leeds Rd, Bradford Centre. 01274 664357 (near the hospital).

KEBABEESH

165 Newline, Greengates   01274 617188

Proprietor, Tayub Amjad's play-on-word restaurant (kebab-ish – get it?) serves Pakistani-style curries with interesting wines (check out the list, Red Bell Black Shiraz from Australia and Cutler Creek Zinfindel from California are both reasonably priced.) A modern, open plan and strikingly stylish restaurant seats seventy-five diners. Creamy walls, earthy coloured, large slate tiles cover the floor and absolutely lovely, handmade wrought iron chairs surround marble topped tables. Cubed glass walls, green plants and ceiling spot lighting add to the calming look. 'We all had a fabulous night on Sat, but it was the food that made it!' ls. Menu Snapshot: Jalapenos c£3, green peppers, filled with creamy sauce and coated in crispy breadcrumbs; Fish and Spinach c£7, chunks of Haddock, spinach leaves, fenugreek, rich sauce; Chicken Manchurian c£7, chicken off the bone, deep-fried in spicy batter, served with sweet and sour Punjabi sauce; Lamb Peshwari c£7, tender lamb, cooked in a delicious rich sauce, using whole and nectar of almond, garnished with fresh green coriander and medium spices; Spicy and Potato Nan £1.95. Del: 5m £5 min. Hours: 5-12; 1 Sat.

KO-HI-NOOR

1 Simes St, off Westgate   01274 737564

Est 1983 as the Bombay Brasserie . Taken over in 1998 and renamed by Ali Shan. The building was once a Presbyterian church and makes a fantastic venue, seating 150. '*Great atmosphere, and food, indeed a memorable occasion, and something quite out of the Bradford norm.*' AN. Hours: 5.30-11.30; 12.30 Fri & Sat; Sun 12.30-11. '*Scores 81%*' DB.

MUMTAZ PAAN HOUSE

386 Great Horton Road, Great Horton,
Bradford SW   01274 571861

'*Still as good as before, fifteen previous visits. Karahi dishes superb, various strengths offered! Breads top rate as are the pickles.*' HW. '*They serve only the real thing! Hard to check your bill due to payment method (the waiter leaves a copy of your order at the table inside a folder which you take to the cash desk, where codes are entered into the till, and you are uncertain whether service charge has been added). Despite that, food was superb, and I shall return.*' PS. '*One of the finest curry houses in the country.*' AF.

PAZEEKAH

1362 Leeds Rd, Thornbury, Bradford
01274 664943

Ex bus driver Mazhar-ul-Haq's tells us he likes to change the decor and the menu regularly, '*because that's what*

customers want to see.' Successful BYO 130-seater Pakistani venue. Chef/manager is son Mohammed Jamil. Hours: 4-12.30; 1.30 Sat. They also own an 18,000 sq ft Asian Superstore, selling Asian food, and utensils at 91 Edderthorpe St, off Leeds Road, Bradford.

RAWAL

3 Wilton St, off Morley St, B'fd   01274 720030

Owner-Chef Abdul P Butt cooks Pakistani curries in his open kitchen, Mobin Iqbal manages the 50-seater and promises a 10% disc to Guide readers. Special: Grand Slam, mixture of meat, chicken, keema and fresh vegetables, with Pullao Rice £5.70. Zam-Zam Special, meat, chicken, king prawns, and chick peas, served with Pullao Rice £5.70. Rawal claims *'Once tried never forgotten'.* DC agrees: *'Great price, great food'.* T/a: student 10% disc. BYO. Hours: 5-2; 3 Fri & Sat; closed Mon.

SHABAB

1099 Thornton Rd, Bradford   01274 815760

'A modern detached building, with lots of Indian artefacts. Glass covered tables, low Indian-style chairs, nice carpet. Table for 2 no problem and were asked to sit in the T/a area. After 5 minutes no one asked if we wanted a drink, so I asked a passing waiter, profuse apologies were offered. Prices had been slashed, my Vegetable Platter cost £1.75, (from £2.50), Seekh Kebab £1.45 (not £2.20). Fantastic, really, really tasty, Murgh Mushroom Balti for me and Gosht Jalfrezi for Mon, Zeera Aloo, Mushroom Pullao and a huge Naan. Complimentary Popadums at the start, but no sweetened fennel or aniseed. c £25 for 2 inc tip. Thoroughly recommended.' T&MH. Branch: Shabab, 2 Eastgate, Leeds, 0113 246 8988 www.shabab.co.uk

SHAH JEHAN

30 Little Horton La, B'fd   01274 390777

Aka Omar's, after their owner/chef Omar Gulzar Khan. His three branches have identical menus. This one seats 150 over 3 rooms. It is stylish and luxuriously decorated, with lovely leather sofas to relax on, while waiting for a T/a, and pretty red chairs for your table. Good comments on all three branches, usually: *'An extremely smart restaurant with friendly service throughout. We had the whole leg of lamb ordered 24 hours in advance. Superb. Highly recommended.'* CT. *'Very, very, very good.'* LH. Hours: 12-2.30/5.30-12. Branches: 6 North Gate, Baildon, Bfd N; 726 Manchester Rd, Chapel Green, Bradford S.

YOU SAY OK   W Yorks 1 of

You might get a discount if you show them this Guide..

BATLEY, BIRSTALL: **SPICE GARDEN** 2 Market Pl. ~ 01924 471690. Specials at Abrar Hussain's Pakistani 74-seater include the Grand-Slam – it's four different meats, vegetables, prawns, massive portion – so now you know! T/a: 10% off. Del: £7, 3m. BYO. Hours: 5-12.

BRADFORD: **ASHA** 31 Cheapside. ~ 01274 729358

BRADFORD: **INTERNATIONAL TANDOORI** 40 Manville Tce, off Morley St, Bradford ~ 01274 721449. *'The food, while not being particularly sophisticated, is excellent.'* MB.

BRADFORD, MANNINGHAM: **SHIRAZ** 133 Oak La, Bradford N ~ 01274 490176. BYO. Owners: Gulbahar & Aslam. Afzal cooks Kashmiri curries & Baltis. Hours: 4pm-2am.

BRADFORD: **SHISH MAHAL** 6 St Thomas Road   01274 723999. Mohammed Taj's 54-seater *'is next door to one of the best pubs in Britain, The New Beehive – tremendous real ale with genuine character. The food at this BYO restaurant is nothing short of marvellous. Flavour literally explodes in the mouth. Friendly and informal service.'* SL. Hours: 4pm-3am.

BRADFORD, IDLE: **TASTE OF BENGAL** 79 Bradford Rd, 01274 618308. 30-seater owned by Mrs Abdus Subhan (mngr Abdul Qayum). Del: 3m £10 min. T/a 10% disc. Min ch: c£6. No Credit cards. Hours: 6-12; 12.30 Sat. www.taste-of-bengal.co.uk

SWEET CENTRE   TOP 100

106 Lumb Lane, Bradford   01274 731735

Opened in 1964, and was Bradford's second curry venue. At the counter you order savouries and sweets by the pound. I know because way in 1982, I purchased 120 samosas here for a Curry Club function, and we all found the measuring process a wee bit complex. Eventually they settled for 15p each and the sams. In 1983 they acquired next door and expansion began. This sufficed until 1999 when a refurb took place. The 100-seater sit-down restaurant is top-notch too: ' *'Excellent. Srvice good and the food very tasty.'* SL. Asian Breakfasts available. The massive 280-seater banquet room alongside at 110/4 Lumb Lane shares the phone, the kitchens and the same wonderful food and service. Hours: 7.30am- 10pm.   www.sweetcentrerestaurant.com

Below: Resembling the Back-to-the-Future diner, and sadly long-gone, this was the 1983 incarnation.

Garforth

AAGRAH   A-LIST

Aberford Road, Garforth   0113 287 6606

Nephew Wasim Aslam manages this 175-seater, opened 1993. Fourth of the very popular Aagrahs, refurbished 2006. Car parking for 90. Hours: 6-11.30; 5.30 Fri & Sat. Menu details and branches see Shipley. W. Yorks.

Guiseley

SAFFRON

Guiseley Retail Pk, Otley Rd.   01943 877222

'On the way back from the Test Match at Headingley we called in and they were just laying the buffet out. Pops & chuts OK. No choice of starters but we were served with Seekh Kebab and Tandoori Chicken Tikka. Both were beautifully spiced. There was a selection of five chicken and lamb dishes together with Palak Paneer and Bombay Aloo were brought to the table and we were invited to help ourselves, all well seasoned and spiced. We could have had any one of them as a main meal and been more than happy. A large naan and pullau rice came too. High quality ingredients, and the care and attention was carried forward to the desserts. They were not the ubiquitous jelly, fruit salad etc. but Jalebis, Rasmali, Gulab Jamun and more – all freshly made. All this is served in a well appointed dining room by attentive and knowledgeable staff. At under £10 a head you get a top class Indian meal for the price of an average, bog standard takeaway. The a la carte menu looks outstanding with novel slants on traditional dishes at a very reasonable price. We would recommend this to anyone who enjoys the food of the subcontinent. For those who don't know if they will enjoy it; the staff will ensure they do. Just ask.' RW.

Huddersfield

AAGRAH   A-LIST

250 Wakefield Rd, Denby Dale   01484 866266

'Occupies a former pub on the main road through Denby Dale, a town more famous for its pies! The layout makes for a surprisingly intimate restaurant, yet being spread across two floors gives a lot of covers. Well executed decoration, in keeping with the former role of the building, think smart pub with a subcontinental theme. Brilliant starter, Makrani Jingra £4.50, really piquant batter that allows the taste of the large and top quality king prawns to shine through and was perfectly complimented by the dipping sauce. The salad was up to scratch as well. Lamb Hyderabadi £7.70, absolutely top notch gristle and fat free lamb in a really rich and thick sauce that was bursting with a whole host of tastes that almost overwhelmed the palate. Garlic Nan £1.95, nice, just a hint to doughiness. Tarka Dal £2.60, a tad light on the garlic. Highly enjoyable and equally recommended.' RW. Hours: 6-11.30; 10.30 Sun. Details: see Shipley. W. Yorks.

DEWSBURY, RAVENSTHORP: ZAM ZAM TAKEAWAY 5 North Rd, ~ 01924 469677. Taken over by Perwaiz Khan in 1994. Main dishes are served with either three Chapatis, Rice or Chips. Hours: 6-12.30; 2.30 Sat; 1 Sun.

HALIFAX: CROWN TANDOOR 31 Crown St. ~ 01422 349270. Hours: 6-1; 3 Sat.

HUDDERSFIELD: SERENA 12 St Peters St, ~ 01484 451991. Ihsan Elahi est his 62-seater modern, chic (+ party room 40) Pakistani venue in 1993 Chef Hussain's specials are *'good quality, value for money, service excellent.'* JT. Service 10%. T/a: 15% disc. Hours: 6-11.30.

ILKLEY: EXOTIC TANDOORI 10 Church St. 01943 607241. Shah Marshal Alom's 50-seater has golden arches and hanging plants. Special: Boul Mas, Bangladeshi fish. Hours: 5.30-12.

ILKLEY: SABERA 9 Wells Rd. 01943 607104 This old friend of the Guide first opened in 1974. Taken over by Abdus Sattar in 1998. *'Clean with pine panelling and 48 seats. I enjoyed my Kalajee Gurda Dil and will return.'* DM. Del: 2m £10min. Hours: 5.30-12.

KEIGHLEY: SHIMLA SPICE 14 South Street, Keighley 01535 602040. Mohammed Ayub and bros built their 75-seater on a corner site in 1998. Decorated beautifully, ornate plasterwork on ceiling and walls, colonial fans, large chandelier, 'Tiffany' lamps and cane furniture. Unlicensed, BYO. Del: 5m £8 min. T/a 10% disc. Hours: 6-12; 1 Sat. Branch: 69, Otley Rd, Shipley.

KNOTTINGLEY: JEWEL IN THE CROWN 110 Weeland Rd, 01977 607233. Pakistani curries at Adnan Miraf's 40-seater. *'Excellent food at reasonable prices. Service friendly .'* IB. Hours: 6-12.

Leeds
(includes Headingley, Horsforth, Kirkstall, Oakwood, Morley and Stanningley)

AKBARS   TOP 100

15 Eastage, Leeds   0113 245 6566

n 1988, Shabir Hussain, 18, decided he wanted to open his own restaurant. In 1995 the dream was realised with the opening of a small restaurant, seating 28, on Leeds Road, Bradford. Since then Akbar's has expanded into a considerable group. See branches below. Akbar's specialises in sizzling pan-cooked baltis from Baltistan, an extreme mountainous region of north Pakistan. Menu offerings: Allam Khan's Lahori Style Dishes, Original baltis, Special baltis, Handi of the day, traditional Desi-Apna Style, accompaniments and Desserts. *'After a business meeting our leader invited five of us to Akbars for dinner. Centrally situated on Eastgate (near the famous Playhouse) we were swiftly met at the door by a smiling waiter and seated with a Cobra beer. Akbars is a large Victorian building, converted to be an 'theme' restaurant with lots of black marble and the upstairs bar fronted by an Egyptian Tutenkhamun display. The ceiling was filled with a myriad of star lights (or was that the effect of the drink) The overall effect was an exotic ambience that set the scene for a relaxing meal. We noted that for a wet Tuesday night, Akbars was very busy with locals and business clients. Warm, crisp Popadums and a tangy selection of pickles were washed down with more Cobra and some nice Rioja followed by starters of Sheek Kebab £1.95, Chicken Tikka £2.65, Chicken Samosa*

£1.95 and Prawn and Chicken Puri £2.45, all were tasty, well cooked and presented with a crisp side salad. Around us it was amusing to observe the waiters carrying tall stands with hooks carrying various Nan breads the size of bath mats! Of course, we had to have two of these 'Family Nan,' £3.50. Despite their size, had a lovely, light texture (Akbars must have a giant tandoor to cook these). Pullao Rice, Sag Aloo and Dhal (not Sophie) were also ordered. Main course comprised of Chicken Tikka Bhuna £5.45, Chicken Tikka and Keema Balti £5.65, Chicken and Chilli Balti £5.45 and a Lamb and Spinach Balti £5.45, these were all beautifully spiced and served in large pots, with a min of oil. All portions were over generous, so were could not manage a sweet, despite the excellent choices.' I see on the menu, Gajar Halwa (carrot cake), which I love! An upmarket restaurant with excellent cuisine, efficient service, providing a highly enjoyable experience.' TE. Branches; 1276 Leeds Road, Bradford, 01274 773311; 6-8 George Hudson Street, York 01904 679888; 73-83 Liverpool Road, Deansgate, Manchester, 0161 834 8444; Meadowbank Road, Rotherham, S61 2NF, 01709 555500 www.akbars.co.uk

AKBAR'S THE GRAND   TOP 100

Minerva Hse, 16, Greek St. Leeds   0113 242 5426

Branch of Akbar's *(see above)*. Akbar the Grand was the epithet given to the greatest Moghul emperor. A wonderful restaurant, leather chairs, glass tables, pin spot lighting. *'Certainly lives up to its name with highly modern decor across a spacious split-level restaurant with ceiling, wall and floor lighting creating a luxurious ambience. On entering we were swiftly greeted and shown to our table by a smartly dressed waiter who placed fresh linen napkins on our laps and took our drinks order. Ice-cold Cobra, crisp Popadums and delicious sauces were followed by curries, King Prawn, Chicken and Tikka Dupiaza and a fragrant Pullao Rice, served in large ceramic bowls. The massive 'Family Garlic Nan' arrived hanging on a tall pedestal, we tore into it and found it had a beautifully light texture. Definitely recommended.'* TE. www.akbars.co.uk

AZRAM'S SHEESH MAHAL

348 Kirkstall Rd, Leeds NW   0113 230 4161

Opened in 1987, and taken over by head chef Azram Chaudhry in 1999. It seats 76 with a further room for 38. Azram's as the locals know it is easy to find on its prominent corner site. And of those regulars, Azram says *'many eat there every week. I know them on a personal level, and they treat it as a second home. They come from all over, and include personalities from Yorkshire TV just up the road. Even The Australian cricket team have enjoyed the food at the Sheesh Mahal.'* Howzat! Pakistani Specials include: Kofta Special, Balti Murgh, Murgh Punchabi Masala; Chicken Laziz £5.90, with garlic, lemon, tomatoes and black pepper; Gosht Palak Paneer £6.50, Indian cheese, lamb and spinach; Keema Chana £6.20, minced lamb with chickpeas. *'Highly recommend the food, service and*

ambience. All dishes reasonably priced. Azram is a first rate host, well liked by clients. Welcomes children and family groups.' EP. You might get a disc if you show them this Guide. Hours: 5-12. Branch: Sheesh Mahal, 48, Harrowgate Road, Chapel Allerton, Leeds. www.sheeshmahal.co.uk

DARBAR   TOP 100

16 Kirkgate, Leeds Centre   0113 246 0381

A turbaned doorman welcomes you at *'a very ordinary street-level door, but upstairs the decor is a revelation.'* hjc. It's exotic, with traditional Moghul paintings and an antique Haweli (palace) door, specially brought from India. 'Has a very impressive interior. Room is large and the decor promotes the Indian Palace feeling – spacious yet warm and elegant'. AG *'Excellent restaurant, especially at lunchtime, self service buffet. Probably deserves TOP 100, although I am always slightly suspicious of Indians with grandiose decor.'* RC. [You'd be suspicious of India then, Robert! -Ed]. *'Very good service and cooking. And, the decor is marvellous.'* SL. 'Overall this restaurant is superb. HJC. Special: Murgh Lahori, bone-off spring chicken, tangy spices, green coriander, cream, yoghurt, tomatoes and ginger. Daal Mash, white lentils cooked in butter with ginger, garlic and fried onion. Strawberry Lassi (large jug). min charge: £18 evenings. Lunch e-a-m-a-y-l c£6. Hours: 11.30-2.30 / 6-11.30; Sun closed. www.darbar.co.uk

GEORGETOWN   A-LIST

Dysons Clock Building, 24, Briggate, Leeds
0870 755 7753

Opened in Leeds in the historic Dyson's Clock Building attached to the Leeds Marriott Hotel, Colonial Malaysian Restaurant, It is a very elegant restaurant indeed,with all the original shop fittings, perfectly restored. You can eat curries from Malaysia, Indian and China. I have eaten here and it is all fabulous. Singapore Slings are the BEST! Full details see Kenilworth Warks.

HANSA'S GUJARATI VEGETARIAN
A-LIST

72 North Street, Leeds   0113 244 4408

This is a rarity, even in the London area: a Gujarati vegetarian restaurant, but here in Leeds it is a northern treasure owned by Mr Kishor, front of house and Mrs Hansa Dabhi, chef, whose pure Indian vegetarian food proves once again that a good curry need not always contain meat. Hansa has been serving her brand of home-cooking with influences from her East African and Gujarati background since 1987, making it 'Leeds' best kept secret!' But it is not this Guide's best kept secret. We awarded Hansa's UK best Vegetarian in 1992 which keeps them in our A-LIST. Hansa does all things perfectly – Starter delights such as Bhel Puri and Dosa. Dhokhra, A typical Gujarati savoury steamed cake made with lightly spiced gram flour and semolina, mixed with yoghurt, steamed and then stir-fried with mustard seeds. Served with coconut chutney, £ 3.50; Patra, colocasia leaves pasted with a curried batter, rolled, steamed and then stir-fried with mustard and sesame seeds. And who can resist this challenge? Spice Bomb, Hansa's wickedly spicy masala mixture sandwiched between two potato pieces then deep fried in a batter, waiting to explode in your mouth. Try it if you dare! £3.95. Mains include Ravaiya, baby aubergines, stuffed with spicy masala with coarsely ground peanut £6.50 and Doongri Batetas, saucy curry made with potato and onions (Doongri). For those new to Gujarati food, try the Thalis: 2 shaks (curries) rotli or puri, plain or pilau rice, daal or kadhi, farsan, Shrikand or mango pulp, papad and a glass of lassi- sweet or salty. £ 9.75. For more info on Guarati food see p53. *'I particularly enjoyed the crunchy, spicy flavour of the Shrikand.'* DM. *'As a non-veg I went with an open mind. Food was fine but portions small.'* DB. *'Exquisite Lassi, portions small.'* DO'R. Sun Buffet Lunch, 12-2pm, c£7.50 Adults, £3.50 Kids. Early-Bird: Buy-one-get-one-free:5-6 weekdays. Hours: 5-10; -11 Fri 6-11 Sat; 12-2 Sun. www.hansasrestaurant.com

NAWAAB KHAN

496 Roundhay Road, Oakwood, Leeds
0113 240 9911

Seats 110 diners, in three rooms. Owners JEE Humphrey & M Sajid. A clean and tidy restaurant decorated in cream and red. *'Menu is exhaustive with hundreds of varied speciality dishes such as Nosheri Lamb, Achari Chicken and Nihari lamb which I find myself ordering time and time again. Dishes are all simply superb in terms of their taste, variety of flavour and quality ingredients.'* T&C. *'Our family party meal was at the Nawab Khan restaurant and it was excellent, we intend to become regulars at this venue.'* R. Menu Snapshot: Prawn Pakora £3.25, with onions, herbs, spices, coated with gram flour and deep-fried; Sindi Machli £3.50, haddock marinated in spices, dipped in egg yolk and breadcrumbs, deep-fried; Nosheri Chicken c£8, boneless chicken marinated, garlic and ginger sauce, pot roasted, fresh tomatoes, cumin seeds, bayleaf, cardamom, garnished with coriander leaves and grated ginger. Dall Bhuna £6, lentils cooked in mild sauce; Herbal Nan £2.50, filled with coriander leaf, onion, cumin seed, mint leaves. Hours: 6-11.30; 12-11 Sun.

NAWAAB

1 Wellesley Hotel, Wellington Street, Leeds
0113 244 2979

'After a business meeting on a cold winter evening in Leeds, our team visited Nawab, centrally situated on Wellington Street (near the Railway Station), we were swiftly met at the door by a smiling waiter and seated with a Cobra beer. Part of the ground floor of a large Victorian hotel, converted into a modern 'brasserie' theme. Nawab was very busy with local office workers. Warm, crisp Popadums and a tangy selection of pickles were washed down with more Cobra's followed by Chicken Tikka Dupiaza c£6, King Prawn Madras and Chicken Madras c£6 with fragrant Pullao Rice and Nan Bread £1.50. Nawab is an upmarket restaurant with excellent cuisine, efficient service and provides a highly enjoyed experience with good value for money.' TE. Branches: Nawaab, 32, Manor Row, Bradford and Nawaab, 35, Westgate, Huddersfield. www.nawaab.net

POLASH   TOP 100

103 Town St, Stanningley   0113 256 0989

M Arif's huge 150-seater spacious restaurant est in 1985 in former Conservative Club is popular. *'I had a family party and asked the Polash to cater for me. The resultant banquet was beyond praise.'* EF. *'Our daughter, then 14, says that the Polash Chicken Korma was her favourite, even though she has tried others in many other Indian restaurants.'* BT. *'We were impressed. Food tasty. Service a little stretched at busy times.'* LEF. *'Always welcoming and courteous, high standard, always consistent, always start with Chicken Tikka followed by King Prawn Khass.'* JS. *'Combination of service and freshly cooked food, makes the Polash our favourite.'* MHR. *'Very smart inside. Good mix of standard and unusual dishes – Chana Aloo Puri was superb. Friendly attentive service.'* M&SR. *'Standard of food and service is superb. Choice is tremendous, carefully prepared, garnished*

and served with a smile. Reasonably priced – half the cost of the Aagrah!' MR&MRS DH. ' Tandoori Mixed Grill, an enormous plate full of Tandoori Chicken, Chicken and Lamb Tikka, Lamb Chops, Seekh Kebab, Liver and fresh salad with a Vegetable Curry [does anyone actually finish that lot?] Very popular facility.' RW. 'Speciality curries are our firm favourites: Nargisi Kofti (inc Mushroom Rice), Murgh Keema Aloo (inc Lemon Rice) and Garlic Chicken Balti (inc Pullao Rice) – truly excellent.' DF. 'Proprietors are always on hand to oversee, spotless kitchen.' PJS. 'Well presented, tasty, freshly prepared and served food. Meat is lean – important to us.' DA. 'Good car park. Deceptively large restaurant, we had pre-booked. Seething on a Sat night, much activity from waiters, slowish service. Vegetarian Platter, excellent value, very nicely presented and very tasty. Chilli Chicken Mushroom was not what I expected – chicken, grilled, Pullao Rice, Mushroom Curry, salad and mild Korma sauce – no room for anything else.' T&MH. Hours: 5.30-11.30 Tues-Sat & Bank Hols. www.polashrestaurant.co.uk

YOU SAY OK
You might get a discount if you show them this Guide..

LEEDS, MORLEY CHIRAAG BALTI 30 Chapel Hill. 0113 253 5720. 40-seater, owned since 1997 by T. Hussain. 'Excellent Seekh Kebabs;, Very tasty Balti Lamb Rogan Josh. Service good, staff very pleasant.' L&CH. Hours: 6-12. 1 Fri & Sat; closed Tues.

LEEDS: KASHMIR 162a Woodhouse La. 0113 245 3058. Unlicensed, BYO 72-seater , mngr T Mahmood. Hours: 12pm-3am.

LEEDS, HEADINGLEY: TARIQ'S 12 St Michaels Rd. 0113 275 1881. 64-seat Balti Hs owned by Bobby Sharma. Special offer meal deal, Thur & Sun before 10pm. Dining in – free pops & chuts – nice touch. 'Windies were playing England and it was stopped by rain. After waiting till early evening in hope, there was a stampede down to Tarriq's just round from the cricket ground. Got there first, luckily – they were queuing within minutes. Superb meal made up for a wet day.' IB. Hours: 5.30-2.30; 3 Sat; 12.30am Sun.

PONTEFRACT: ROTI North Baileygate. ~ 01977 703915 Pakistani food at Arshad Mahmood's bright& airy 110-seater with a tented ceiling (party room 40). Abdul Aziz's kitchen on view behind glass. 'Excellent quality, bordering on the expensive.' KH. Hours: 5-12.

PONTEFRACT: VICEROY 6 Front St. ~ 01977 700007. Pakistani food at this 60-seater est 1990, taken over in 1994 by Chef Akram Hussain Lohn managed by Susan Ruckledge .T/a: 30% disc. Del: £6 min. Hours: 5-1am.

Shipley

AAGRAH　　　　　　　　　　　　A-LIST

27 Westgate, Shipley　　　　　　01274 594660

At the time of writing, there are nine Aagrahs, all in Yorkshire, and all TOP 100s in this guide. It was here in 1977, refurbished in 1999, that this 50-seater was opened by Mohammed Sabir. The notion to expand came from son Mohammed Aslam (then a London bus driver) assisted later by brother Zafar Iqbal, who now runs this one. It is notable for its Kashmiri-style decor with attractive block-print table linen and those fabulous handmade, hand-painted colourful lacquered chairs with the cute tinkly bells, especially commissioned in Pakistan

(£60 each). Gradually Aslam encouraged his extended family to join the enterprise as managers, staff and cooks. With increasing impetus the other branches have been brought on-stream, as stylish and upmarket restaurants. We hear contentedly from many regulars who visit twice or more a week, and visitors from afar. Their average age is over 25 (no after-pub teenage louts here). Their average spend of £20 gives the chain a turnover of c.£4 m. The food is Pakistani, which self-taught cook Aslam has insisted that all family members also learn, training in both the kitchens and out front to NVQ level. This way the service and food in all the Aagrah restaurants is of equal standard. There is ample choice in the identical menus and here is a Snapshot: Starters include Yahknee, spicy chicken soup, and Panir Pakora, Indian curd cheese fritter; Chicken Liver Tikka £2.60, marinated and cooked over charcoal, served with salad; Makrani Jhinga £3.90, tail prawns marinated with lime juice and green chillies, dipped in paste and deep-fried, served with sauce and salad; Paneer Kebab £2.60, crushed cheese, mixed with spices, coriander leaves, green chillies, mint leaves and deep-fried, served with salad; Vegetable Ginger c.£6, cauliflower, courgette, aubergine, carrot, peas, turnip, and capsicum with a substantial amount of ginger, garlic, tomatoes, coriander leaves, aniseed, green chillies and black cardamom. Main courses include many meat, chicken and fish dishes. Aslam's current pièces de résistance are Murgh Hyderabady, spring chicken, tangy spices, coriander, cream, yoghurt, tomatoes, ginger; Balti Liver, with garlic, ginger, chillies, tomatoes and coriander. Balti Bhindi Aloo Paneer, curd cheese, bhindi and potato, onions, ginger, garlic, coriander. Family Nan, Cheese and Onion Nan. T/a: rice and 3 chapattis free. T/a 10% disc. Hours: 6-12; 1 Fri/Sat. See page 19

AAGRAH BRANCHES: N. YORKS: York Rd, Steenton, Tadcaster, Nr Yorks, 01937 530888; Devonshire Pl, Keighley Rd, N. Yorks, 01756 790807. **S. YORKS:** Great North Rd, Woodlands, Doncaster, S.Yorks, 01302 728888. **W. YORKS:** 4, Aberford Rd, Garforth, W. Yorks, 0113 287 6606; 250, Wakefield Rd, Denby Dale, Huddersfield, W. Yorks, 01484 866 266; St Peters Square, Quarry Hill, Leeds, W. Yorks, 01132 455667; 83, Bradford Rd, Pudsey, W. Yorks, 01274 668818; 27, Westgate, Shipley, W. Yorks, 01274 583338; Barnsley Rd, Sandal, Wakefield,W. Yorks, 01924 242222. .

AAHRAH PLANS:

CAFÉ AAGRAH. Opens later in 2008 in Clarence Docks, Leeds. will be serve café-style Asian fusion food in a fast casual environment from a central theatre kitchen. It will containa bar and separate cocktail menu, and al-fresco dining.

NEW HQ: Plans are also advanced for a newly-built 20,000 sq foot building in late autumn 2008. Situated within 1.6 acres, it will house a 275-seat ground floor restaurant, which will be largest in the Aagrah Group. Exterior landscaping will featuring a Mughal garden with specially imported paving stones from India, car parking for 100 cars and the permanent home of the Aagrah Mascot, Lulu the Elephant. An al-fresco area with outside grill will be available in good weather. On the first floor, a 420-seat banqueting suite will have its own dedicated lounge and bar area, a private VIP room with balcony and a separate banqueting kitchen, a music system, LED lighting and a dance floor or stage.

ISLES AND ISLANDS

When he failed to capture the British Isles, Napoleon dismissed us as a nation of shopkeepers. Were he around today, he might observe that we are now a nation of curry house keepers. Some isles, including Lundy, the Isles of Scilly, Uist, Mull, etc., have no curry houses but, for neatness, we group those that do together. For those who delight in collecting useless information, Lerwick, capital of the Shetland Isles, contains the nation's most northerly curry house (and still probably that of the whole globe). It is 600m from London and 800m from our most southerly curry house in St Helier, capital of Jersey.

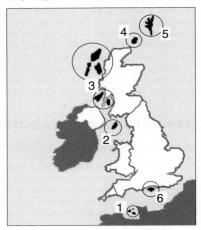

CHANNEL ISLANDS

1 on the map
Area: off the French Normandy coast.

ALDERNEY

NELLIE GRAYS INDIAN CUISINE

Victoria Street, Alderney 01481 823333

Established 1996, owned by Matin Miah (formerly the head chef of Jersey's Bombay Brasserie), and managed by Ashraf Makadur. Seats 50 in two dining rooms. Two parking spaces at rear of building. Jalfrezi most popular, chef's special Tarkari. Ser: 10%. Hours: 6-11; 12-2 Sun.

GUERNSEY

Population: 66,000

L'Eree

TASTE OF INDIA

Sunset Cottage, L'Eree 01481 264516

Owned and managed by Tony Fernandes, who is from Goa, since 1989. Pink stone wall design with maroon seating for 60 diners. Chef Paltu Bhattachajee holds court in the kitchen serving specialities such as Sardines on Puri, Tandoori Lobster and Bhuna – market price and subject to availability. T/a: 10% disc. Set lunch: c£12 and £26 (for two). Hours: 6-11; closed Mon. Branch: Taste of India, St Peter Port.

St Peter Port

SPICE INDIAN CUISINE

North Plantation, St Peter Port 01481 722422

Owned buy Matin Miah since 2004. Hours: 12-2/5-12.

TAJ MAHAL

N. Esplanade, St Peter Port 01481 724008

Mujibul Hussain's 60-seater is located in the heart of St Peter Port opposite the main public car park. *'Charming and attentive staff. Interesting menu – imaginative main courses and unusual vegetable side-dishes (Uri Besi, mangetout and butter beans; Balar Aloo, mashed potatoes with garlic; Baygoon (aubergine, spinach and chickpeas) which was sampled by non-veggies with some envy! Delicious Chicken Sholay arrived fled in brandy. All food was fragrantly spicy with subtle differences between each dish.'* CC. Hours: 12-2 / 6-11.30; 12 Sat.

TASTE OF INDIA

2, Mill Street, St Peter Port 01481 723730

Established in 1990. Seats 50. Owned and managed by Tony Fernandes. Decorated in maroon. Specials: Bamboo Shoot Masala – a dry curry. T/a: 10%. Hours: 6-11; closed Mon. Branch: Taste of India, L'Eree.

JERSEY

Population: 75,000

St Aubin

SHAPLA

Victoria Road, St Aubin 01534 746495

'Hasina Kebabs, lamb marinated in yoghurt, tandooried with onions, peppers and tomatoes, really tasty. Chicken

Jalfrezi, aroma terrific. Simply perfect lamb Rogan Gosht. Polite and helpful waiter.' MB. Hours: 12-2 / 6-12.

St Brelade

BENGAL BRASSERIE

11 La Pulente, St Brelade 01534 490279

'Favourite dish is the Chef's Balti – like no other – chicken, lamb, prawns, egg, kidney beans, mange tout, you ne it. Portions more than adequate. Service best on the island, staff very friendly. Al fresco in the summer. Only 30 yards from St Ouens beach. Best place to see the sunset.' GL. Hours: 12-2 / 6-11.30.

St Helier

CAFE SPICE

53 Kensington Pl, St Helier 01534 22960

A small 40-seater, *'has changed name from Shezan. Interior has a pleasing contemporary, clean style. Service – greeting and at table good. Dhansak was especially good. Also included are Noodle dishes with Chicken Tikka and other dishes featuring pasta!' Still very well worth an entry in the Guide.'* RW.

INDIAN OCEAN

7 La Motte Street, St Helier   01534 20147

'Has changed it's name from Taj Mahal. Definitely the smartest and best Indian restaurant in St Helier and maybe the Island. Very well appointed and spacious with contemporary furnishing and paintings plus objects d'art. Meet and greet welcoming – and service good. Usual Indian favourites – all well cooked and presented. Sauces well prepared with good depth of flavour.' RW.

NEW RAJ

8 Burlington Pde, St Saviours Rd, St Helier
01534 874131

Owned and managed by Kass Malik since 1984. Seats 60 in two dining rooms. *'Visited three times in the last year – the first time was good, but the last two visits have been disappointing. The meet and greet is variable. Service is generally good. On my last visit the food – Chilli Chicken garlic/ Bombay Aloo really lacked flavour and depth to the sauce. Dhansak seemed to have curry leaves added and was rather flat.'* RW. Hours: 12-2 / 6-12.

Please send us your reports. See pages 339 & 340 or go online at www. patchapman.co.uk

ISLE OF MAN

2 on the map on previous page

Area: Off the English N W. coast.
Population: 76,000

Douglas

SAAGAR TANDOORI

1 South View, Queens Prom 01624 674939

Mr and Mrs Chowdhury and Mr Jaigirdar might give you a disc if you show them this Guide at their 60-seater: *'the best I've been to.'* RR. *'One time we tried the special Kachee Biriani – 12 hours' notice required to prepare it. It's partially cooked Basmati rice layered over meat marinated in spices, yoghurt and herbs then cooked in the oven – perfumed with saffron. £25 for two. Delicious. Next time we brought friends and tried Kurzi lamb – 24 hours' notice is required for this extravaganza (c£50 for four). We've yet to try £75 whole leg of lamb marinated in fresh ground spices with lamb mince meat cooked in the oven. Starters, sides, rice & breads for four included.'* AN. Hours: 12-2 / 6-12.

MILLENIUM SAAGAR   NEW ENTRANT

1 Sherwood Tce, Broadway, IM2 4EN   01624 679 871

Established in 2002 by the youthful Hamid Chowdhury, it's on two floors of a Victorian terraced building with the lounge/bar area and dining room on the first floor. Manager is Navin Aynikkal, from Mumbai in India. Chef Fakhruddin Bellary was born in Bangalore and grew up in Mumbai, where he worked in various hotels as an Indian master chef. Starters include: Punjabi Spiced Cod £7.25; Fresh Mussels £7.95; Minced Veal Kebabs £7.25 - with cream cheese, accompanied by a Mango and Pineapple Chaat Masala Salad; Cheese and Chilli Melt £3.75 - served on a Naan Bread with Olive Oil. Mains include: Spice Crusted Monkfish £16.95; Chicken Paneer Kofta £11.95; South Indian Lamb Curry £12.95. They offer all the 'usual' curries, veg side dishes of which Black Lentils with tomatoes and cream £4.75 is notable. Reports please. Hours: 6-11, Friday to 12. www.millenniumsaagar.co.uk

Ramsey

SPICE OF LIFE

8 Peel Street, Ramsey   01624 816534

'We enjoyed the food, and would have done had it been in Manchester' GB. *'Bizarre note on the door, We do not serve drunks.'* DMCC.

SCOTTISH ISLANDS
THE WESTERN ISLES
2 on the map on page 309

Area: The Outer Hebrides or Western Isles comprise an island chain off the Scottish Population: 26,000.

Isle of Bute (Rothsay)
INDIAN PAVILION

7 Argyle St, PA20 0AT   01700 504988

Est. 1993 by Bobby Mahey, 30-seater. Dave Mahey cooks north and south Indian and Goan food. Del Ch 95p. Hours: 5-12.30.

Isle of Lewis (Stornaway)
STORNOWAY BALTI HOUSE

24 South Beech, HS1 2UG   01851 706116

46-seater previously Ali's T/a, now owned by Mohammed Ahmed - Moe to his friends. T/a: 10% disc. Hours: 12-2 / 5-11.

Isle of Skye (Portree)
SPICE HUT INDIAN

Bayfield Road, IV51 9EL   01478 612681

Formerly the Ghandi. 'Difficult to find – at the rear of the big car and coach park near the Tourist Information Centre. A bizarre experience. We turned up at 1 to find "Closed" on the door. However, we tried the door anyway and it opened. Two bored looking Asian teenagers were folding napkins, and one lethargically showed us to a table in the otherwise totally deserted restaurant. He took our order with his now customary lack of charm, and we prepared for the worst. However, the food arrived very promptly and was actually delicious. Vegetable Rowghon was fragrant and packed with fresh tomatoes. Garlic Chicken Tikka was equally good. It is an enormous shame that a clearly excellent chef is having his hard work marred by a front of house crew displaying such shameless amateurism.' CC. 'Good.' G&MP.

ORKNEYS
4 on the map on page 309

Area: 70 small islands 16 km north of mainland Scotland.
Population: 19,500

Kirkwall
DIL SE

7 Bridge Street, KW15 1HR   01856 875242

70-seater, opened by Anwar Hussain in June 2005. His pink restaurant is simply and nicely decorated with traditional embroidered wall hangings and seats a considerably seventy diners. 'I find that it's the side dishes I enjoy the most, I could live off dhal and I love Sag Aloo. My mouth still waters when I think of it.' df. Menu Snapshot: Bombay Roll £3.50 - sheek kebab rolled in a deep-fried Indian pancake with fresh onions, served with our mint dip and salad; Tandoori Mixed Grill £12.95 - tandoori chicken, chicken and lamb tikka, sheek kebab, tandoori king prawn and nan - hooray for the nan and king prawn!; lamb Tikka Achari £7.95 - with a tangy mango twist; Colli Bhaji £2.75 - spiced cauliflower florets; Coconut Rice £2.30. Hours: 4 - 11. dilserestaurant.co.uk

SHETLANDS
5 on the map on page 309
Population: 22,000

North of Orkney and the northernmost part of the UK are 100 Shetland islands, of which the main one is known as Mainland.

Lerwick
RABA INDIAN

26 Commercial Rd, ZE1 0LX   01595 695554

'Well-cooked Indian cuisine at reasonable prices.' AIE. 'As a regular visitor to Shetland, and a far more regular visitor to Indian restaurants (assisted, of course, by your reliable guide), I have always enjoyed my visits to the Raba over the last 15 or so years. Over the last couple of years I have noted a great improvement culminating in as wonderful a curry as I have enjoyed anywhere in Britain. It was nearly full when I arrived (mid-evening), reflecting the popularity of the Sunday buffet, but I desired spicier things. I ordered Chicken Jal Frezi as my

main dish, here being so hot as to justify a warning by the considerate waiter as to its spice strength. Only after I had convinced him that I had ordered and enjoyed the selfsame dish before did he accept my order! His cautious comments were justified by the dish upon arrival, as it was indeed very, very hot. but absolutely delicious, with copious amounts of chicken breast pieces in a sauce thick with peppers, onions and tomatoes. The accompanying Vegetable Pilau was another enormous portion, rich with fresh green and root vegetables, not to mention mushrooms - a lovely dish in it's own right. Two light and fresh Chupattis completed my meal, washed down with a perfectly-chilled bottle of Kingfisher. My total bill for these delights came to little more than £12, a veritable bargain, especially in a captive-audience land such as Shetland. The service was excellent, by the way, and very prompt and professional. I can't wait to go back, despite the obvious expense of getting there. Please give this wonderful establishment the attention and credit I feel is due.' DW. Hours: 12-2 / 4.30-12. Sun buffet: 1 -11. Adults £9.50/Kids £6.

ISLE OF WIGHT

6 on the map on page 309

Area: Off S.E. English coast, county status.
Population: 133,000

TIFFIN ROOMS   NEW ENTRANT
Bonchurch Manor, Bonchurch Shute,
PO38 1NU   01983 852868

This grand old country house is a small smart hotel on the southern tip of the island a mile west of Ventnor. Its rooms have en-suite bath or shower, most with a garden or sea view (av price c£45 per room). Its USP is the dining room, a tiny 20-seater called the Tiffin Room, which, incredibly, only serves south Indian food, with

cooking by the idiosyncratic Ms Shuba Rao from Bangalore. *"I metamorphosed from a psychologist to chef and restaurateur by chance."* It opened in 2004, and though your editor is mentioned on their website, the owners had did not informed us about. Fortunately AG reported on it (see later). Menu snapshot: Three starters, Masala Dosa, Vegetable Pakora and Mysore Bonda , deep-fried spicy potato balls dipped in gramflour batter, all £3.50 and all served with coconut chutney. Mains: Six items inc Pepper Beef Tamil Style, slow-cooked in red onion and pepper sauce and served coconut rice; Chicken Chettinaad, simmered in tamarind, spices and coconut served with fresh lemon rice; Andhra Fish in a coconut, tamarind and coriander sauce served with coconut rice, all £14.50 and Vangi Bath with Onion, Tomato and Yoghurt Salad,£6.50. Desserts: 4 inc Sweet Pongal, slow-cooked rice and lentil *cooked in milk. "Polite and attentive service was from two eastern Europeans. The food is of extremely high quality, though not 'chilli-hot'. My Dosa maybe didn't match that of Ravi Shankar (NW1) but it was light and well-spiced. Jackie's Bonda was similar, though maybe short of Jaffna's (SW17) standard. You certainly get your money's worth. Portions are huge. The mains were equally impressive. I had the fish, delicate and flaky and J had the Vangi – not oily. We also had rice and Pooris, light, fluffy and hot. But boy, we were stuffed at the end of it! This is by some distance the best Indian restaurant that has ever graced the island."* AG. Should you stay the night, ignore the English breakfast. Go instead for the south Indian breakfast (pre-booking essential) of Uppahittu with vegetables (semolina cooked with vegetables), or Masala Dosa with Sambar and Chutney, or Idly with Sambar and Chutney. Finally we just have to give you this quote from Clive Aslet, in The Times: *"If the Michelin Guide cared more about proper food, rather than the degree of starch on the napkins, it would give Bonchurch [Tiffin Room] a star".* Readers of this Guide know how much your editors' despair of the tyre-men's star system (non-system) in the Indian sector. How refreshing to find the opinion echoed by a respected journalist. Hours: Ring to book your meal. www.thetiffinroom.com

YOU SAY OK – IOW.
You might get a discount if you show them this Guide.
COWES: COWES TANDOORI   40 High St. ~ 01983 296710 At Ashid Ali's 64-seater DB *'loves the Podina Gusht and Garlic Chicken'* and L&CH found 'Tasty Sheek Kebabs'. Hours: 12-2/6-12.

NEWPORT: NABAB PALACE   84 Upper St, James St. ~ 01983 523276. Jila Miah's 54-seater serves *'good, competent curries and accompaniments at reasonable island prices* [10% disc Guide readers].' L&CH. *'Decor clean and comfortable, service efficient. Starters: King Prawn – fresh and well cooked. Chana Puri – well spiced. Veg Dhansak good. Tarka Dal very good. Garlic Nan – plenty of fresh garlic.'* aG. Hours: 12-2 / 6-12.

NORTHERN IRELAND

Shares a land border with the Republic of Ireland (Eire).
Population: 1.6 million

Curry still hasn't grabbed this part of the world in the way it has on the 'mainland'. We have just 35 establishments on our database all over the province. Compare this with Bradford W Yorks and you'll get the picture. There are fewer curry establishments per head of the population than in any other place in Britain. However, the number of curry restaurants has increased by 30% in the province in 3 years. That's a good statistic for the media. We'd dearly love more reports, please.

Belfast

ARCHANA

53 Dublin Road, Belfast   02890 323713

'I'm sure you'll not remember me; I gave you initial training in Macs.' [course I remember you Ann]. 'I don't like hot spicy food but I do like tasty food and when I asked the waiter for help, he took a lot of time and trouble to recommend a dish which turned out to be delightful and suited my taste perfectly. My partner had their mixed grill and said it was the best he's ever tasted – so with compliments flying I thought you ought to know, just in case they're not in your guide! We love good food and always go back to restaurants that please us - this will definitely be one of them. Great web site by the way.' AO. 'Visited last weekend around 7. Quite the most expensive (over £9 for a Dhansak without rice, for example) and poorly cooked food I have eaten in many years of eating curry. All our meals had barely cooked onion in them and my Sag Aloo had the consistency of a child's meal. Other diners sending back their rice as cold. Service surly, almost aggressive. Your sign on the door, needs taking down.' GT. Who's right? Reports please.

CAFÉ INDIA   NEW ENTRANT

42-46 Malone Road Belfast   02890 666955

'newly opened. on two levels. some unusual dishes here. quality excellent. quantity smaller than usual. décor unusual: wooden floors with wooden beams in the roof and pale painted walls. service polite and attentive. comfort well spaced out comfortable chairs. the pops didn't arrive but house starter was particularly good. small portions but tasty and well marinated. G&MP.

JHAMA

133 Lisburn Road, Belfast   02890 381299

110-seater. *'We found the Tandoori Crayfish superb and different £11.95.'* CD. Hours: 12-2/5.30-11.30. Branch: Tamarind, Carrickfergus; Bithika T/a, Belfast.

MOCHUL

62 Botanic Avenue, Belfast   02890 326677

Established 1984 and taken over in 1998 by H.Sirpal. Formerly Maharaja. Seats 80 diners. Specials: Tikka Special £7.95 – marinated chicken, mild sauce with mangoes and banana. Pakora Curry £5.95 – fairly hot, with yoghurt, gramflour and Punjabi spices. Paneer Makhani £6.95 – chef's own paneer, mild buttery sauce. Kebabs (Delonly): Donner, Sheesh, Chicken Tikka etc available from £3 and Chicken Burger with salad . Del: £1 Ch. Hours: 12-2/5-12

SONALI

701c Lisburn Road, Belfast   02890 666833

Formerly Ghandi. *'The food took a fairly long time to arrive, but this proved to be more of a case of care being taken with every dish than sloppy service. One immediately noticeable feature of the entire meal was the restrained use of ghee for which the chef is be commended. Each dish was fresh and light with its own distinctive taste well brought out. The top of my list of Belfast curry houses.'* DMCD.

EIRE

Republic of Ireland
Shares a land border with Northern Ireland.
Population: 3.5million

Dublin

JAIPUR
TOP   100

41 South Gt Georges St, Dublin 01 677 0999

'Chic and modern, fifty seater in the south of the city. Friendly and helpful staff, a mixture of Indians, Irish and Chinese. Nicely decorated and inviting. complimentary Popadums a 'traffic light' array of Chutneys. Modern interpretation of dishes. Jaipur Jugalambandi €12 - enjoyable selection of Aloo Tikka, Tandoori King Prawn, Tandoori Salmon, lamb Tikka and Tandoori Chicken Wing, all served with five concentrated and intensely flavoured, different sauces. Excellent Nalli Ghost €20 really well cooked, tender lamb leg of the very best quality, lovely rich taste served with a thin sauce

that did compliment the flavour of the meat. Very nice Nan €3 – coriander blending well with the lamb. Fair Tarka Dal €4.50 - bit thin. Good restaurant.' RW. Real Indian chefs, real Indian food. Welcome to our Top 100. Branches: Jaipur, 21, Castle Street, Dalkey: 01 285 0552; Jaipur, 5, St James's Terrace, Malahide: 01 845 5455; Jaipur Ongar, 35 Main St, Ongar Village, Dublin 15. 01 640 2611 www.jaipur.ie

RAJDOOT   RE-ENTRANT

28 Clarendon St, Westbury Centre Dublin 2
00 3531 679 4280

The first in Dublin and still one of the best.

SHALIMAR   TOP 100

17 South Gt Georges St, Dublin 2 01 671 0738

'A rarity – an Indian restaurant run by Indians! Upmarket decor, de rigeur for this art of super-cosmopolitan Dublin, with light and airy main room, subdued colours and Bauhaus simplicity in the furniture. Some sixty-four guests are attended to by knowledgeable and discreet staff. Limited menu choice, but authentic dishes and modern interpretations, all very nouvelle cuisine. Complimentary Popadums. Tandoori Masala €8.99- exquisite, thin medallions of best tender, perfectly cooked beef, interspersed with layers of tomato and red pepper, with three loops of different sauces - outstanding. Raan E Sikandari €18.95 - had a lot to live up to and succeeded brilliantly, a stunning bottom thigh joint of lamb, the meat partially cut away, but left enough to pick up and gnaw at, well marinated and cooked to absolute perfection, with a really hot and spicy marinade. Splendid Nan, light and fluffy, lovely perfume from the coriander leaves. Tarka Dal €6.95 - without doubt the best I have ever had – perfect blend of garlic, onion and lentils.' RW. Welcome to our top 100. Hours: 12-2.30 / 5-11.30; 12 Fri & Sat.

Galway

EASTERN TANDOOR

2 Spanish Parade, Galway   0191 564819

'Eight Popadums with pickles - sweet mango, chilli and Lime all Pataks. Prawn Puri €6.30 - mild but tasty. Eastern Delight €10.90 - plenty for two and good mix. Beef Balti €13.50 euro - very mild as was the Madras! Chicken Jalfrezi €13.40 - bland. Bhindi €6.50 euro - fresh and good, Pullao Rice enough for six! Nan good, Chapatti €1.50 too thick for me. Excellent decor and service.' NC. T/a: 20% disc.

Kenmare

THE VELVET   NEW ENTRANT

Henry Lane, Kenmare, Co Kerry, 064 79837

Opened in 2007. 'We usually have a curry on the menu, as

authentic as possible and made from absolute scratch.' Owner. ' Your books have been enormously helpful!' 'DK. Hours: 6.30-10. closed Mon.

YOU SAY OK.

You might get a discount if you show them this Guide.

CO.WICKLOW, GREYSTONES: CHAKRA BY JAIPUR
Meridian Point Centre. 01 201 7222 See Dublin entry for details.

SCOTLAND
Population: 5 million

In 1965, much to the Scots' disgust, the age-old mainland Scottish shires and counties were amalgamated into nine large counties (or regions). In 1996 new changes resulted in only three staying totally unchanged (**D&G, Fife and Highland**). Two others have the same boundaries but new names: **Borders** became **Scottish Borders**, while Central once again became **Stirling**. **Tayside** is no more, being split into two (**Angus and Perth & Kinross**). Part of **Grampian** has been retained, with its western part returning to **Moray**. Northern **Strathclyde** has become **Argyll & Bute**, while the rest of **Strathclyde**, and the whole of **Lothian** have been split into sixteen Unitary Authorities, administering the larger cities and surrounds. For the time being, and until Scotland itself takes all these changes for granted, we retain in this Guide, the nine former counties (listing their ancient shires and/or new names within them, as relevant). Scotland's population of just over 5 million (less than that of central London) occupies a land mass nearly half that of England, though most of her curry houses are in and around the large cities. We'd adore a huge postbag of Scottish reports for our next Guide please.

DUMFRIES & GALLOWAY

Contains Kirkcudbrightshire (centre) and Dumfriesshire (east),referred to as Galloway. and Wigtownshire (west).

Area: Southwest Scotland
Population: 148,000
Adjacent Counties:
Cumbria, Scottish Borders,
Strathclyde

Dumfries

JEWEL IN THE CROWN

48 St Michael St, Dumfries   01387 264183

Good curryhouse where you might get a disc if you show them this Guide. Hours: 12-2.30 / 6-11.

FIFE

Area: East Scotland
Population: 355,000
Adjacent Counties:
Lothian, Tayside

YOU SAY OK - FIFE.

You might get a discount if you show them this Guide.

CUPAR: ARMAAN OF CUPAR, 102-104 Bonny Gate – 01334 650600. Habib Chowdhury opened in 2005 with 80 seats which on Fri & Sat nights are busy. On other days you might get a disc if you show Mr Chowdhury this Guide. Specials: Chicken and lamb Parsi £7.95. Del: 4m, £2.50. Hours: 12-2 / 5-11.

CUPAR: PASSAGE TO INDIA, 76a Crossgate   01334 650677. Zahid Raja's 50-seater serves North Indian curries and accompaniments. Del: 8m, £1 Ch. Hours: 4.30-10.30; 11 Fri & Sat.

GLENROTHES: NURJAHAN Coslane, Woodside Road – 01592 630649. Manirul Isl's 110-seater *'is decorated to a very highstandard. Roomy carver-chairs at all tables. Truly magnificent meal. Spotless. More than generous quantities. Waiters very polite and helpful. The best quality we have ever tasted. A superior restaurant in every aspect.'* MAJF. Hours: 12-2 / 5-11; 12 Fri. & Sat; 4-11 Sun.

St Andrews

BALAKA BANGLADESHI
AWARD WINNER

3 Alexander Pl, Market St   01334 474825

Even before you enter Abdur Rouf's upmarket and sophisticated 52-seater, note the frontage floral display. He has won awards for it. The unique feature is the huge kitchen garden at the rear, in which Mr Rouf grows all his own herbs and many vegetables. More foliage inside with palms dividing tables and hand stitched Bangladeshi tapestries on the walls. Balaka's unusual ne means a 'swan'. Unusual dishes on the menu include Mas Bangla – salmon marinated in lime, turmeric and chilli, fried in mustard oil, garlic, onion, tomato and aubergine. I had the privilege of being trained to cook this dish by chef Abdul Monem which I reproduced at a lecture at St Andrews University for the Chemical Soc and all of Mr Rouf's friends. I hope they enjoyed it as much as I did. We then moved on to the restaurant for a fabulous meal. amazingly the restaurant has no tandoor, which is detectable in the flavours of the breads and tikkas. But that aside, Mr Rouf's team continues to provide outstanding food in superb surroundings. We have lots of contented customer reports. All show a friendly, caring patron, and here's proof: 'Is still excellent.' m. 'We dined here with a large party of friends from the Netherlands and around the world. The evening was a tremendous success – wonderful food and service.' tgm. 'Nice decor, good service. Good portion of wonderful Afghani Gosht. anon. 'Not bad curries.' t&km. It seems to me it's always busy, and if you are really lucky you might just see Sean Connery on the nearby golf course. please book your table. Credit cards accepted. Cobra, £4.90 a pint, house wine £11.95 a bottle. Del: 20m, £2 Ch. Comfortably in our a-list. Hours: 12 - 3 and 5-12.30. Sunday lunch closed. www.balaka.co.uk

GRAMPIAN

Contains Aberdeenshire, Banff, Kincardine and Morayshire, all formerly known as Grampian.

Area: North East Scotland
Population: 537,000
of which Aberdeen 212,000
Adjacent Counties:
Highland, Tayside

Aberdeen

CINNAMON

476 Union Street, Aberdeen 01224 633 328

Opened in 2005 by Khalia Miah. His restaurant is stylishly decorated inside and out. A fairly small frontage, but never the less, impressive. Two gun metal grey planters, planted with cacti are situated either side of the entrance door. Inside, beige brick walls, round mirrors with the restaurants logo engraved, wooden black slatted screens provide privacy for diners and a striking paprika red, metal stair case, takes customers upstairs to the gallery dining area. Menu Snapshot: Malai Tikka £4.95 - rich creamy yoghurt sauce with a hint of cardamom and white pepper; Pani Poori £4.45 - puffed crispy wheat biscuits, filled with spiced chicken, peas and potatoes; Ginger and Cinnamon Tiger Prawns £6.95; Saffron Stuffed Red Pepper in Cottage Cheese £11.50 - coloured pepper sauce diced cottage cheese and coloured pepper cooked with tomatoes and onion, tempered with mustard, curry leaves, cinnamon and clove; Okra Pachandi £7.10 - fried okra, mixed yoghurt, ground coconut, cumin seeds in coconut milk sauce; Tamarind and Dried Red Chilli Rice £3.05; Date and Almond Naan £3.45; Pomegranate and Coconut Chutney £1.40. Licensed: stocks Cobra. Hours: 12-12. Branch: Cumin, 25, Victoria Terrace, Kemnay, Aberdeenshire.

Elgin (Morayshire)

AL BAHAR NEW ENTRANT

156 High Street, Elgin   01343 545000

'An upstairs restaurant in a vast, cavernous and almost windowless room, sporting decor in pink, featuring unusual lamps. Elevator Muzak as background music. Everything is clean, toilets are spotless, service is swift and friendly (although a little bit stern in the beginning). The parathas, nans and popadums sometimes taste like the oil/ghee/butter that was used is a bit stale, but the curries make up for that. Chicken Jalfrezi, Lamb Tikka, Methi Gosht and Napali Balti have always been a revelation. The vegetables seem to be fresh, the meat well marinated, the chillies have a decent kick. Rice is being served on the plate. Cobra from tab available. I normally pay for a main course with saag aloo, 2 cobras and popadums ca 19 pounds. Always a pleasure to return, even if the presentation lacks a bit'. DP

YOU SAY OK - GRAMPIAN
You might get a discount if you show them this Guide.

ELGIN: QISMAT   202 High St. 01343 541461. Est1987 by Liaquat Ali. 100 seats. Modern, brightly decorated with wooden polished floor, palms, coloured seat pads and a/c. Del: £10 min, Elgin only. Hours: 12-2 / 5-11.30. Branch: Qismat, Millamburn Rd, Inverness.

ELLON: NOSHEEN 5 Bridge St. 01358 724309. Est1989. 92-seater owned by Khalid Ahmed. Decorated rather lavishly in crimson ceiling and chairs, cream walls, green tablecloths and brass light fittings. S Banquet A: £14.50 – Pops & onion, Pakora, Bhoona or Korma, Patia, Pullao Rice and Nan – for 2. T/a: 10% disc. Del: £12 min Ellon, £18 min outside. Hours: 5-11.30; 12 Sat. New branch Peterhead, see below.

INVERURIE: BANANA TANDOORI 56 Market Pl. ~ 01467 624860. Est 1987 by Syed Mujibul Hoque. 'Waiters efficient and friendly. Buffet night worth a visit.' cw. Hours: 12-2.30 / 5.30-11.30.

PETERHEAD, ABERDEENSHIRE: KACO 5 IN I TAKEAWAY NEW ENTRANT 15 Queen Street AB42 1TN. ~ 01779 474674. Khalid Ahmed's new Kaco (pron Kayco) seats just 20 in this small fishing village, pop 20.000. Av meal for 2 c£12.00. Best sellers are CTM, Chicken Qundari and Chilli Naan. Hours: 12 to late Mon - Sat /5-11 Sun. Branch: Nosheen, Ellon. www.kacodelites.com

TURRIFF, ABERDEENSHIRE: MOONLIGHT TANDOORI NEW ENTRANT34 Balmellie St AB53 4DU ~ 01888 562636 Hours:12-2 / 5-11. T/a 10% Disc. Del: 3m on £10. NK.

HIGHLAND

Contains Caithness, Inverness, Nairn, Ross.& Cromarty and Sutherland and small parts of Argyll and Moray.

Area: North Scotland
Population: 212,000
Adjacent Counties:
Grampian,Strathclyde,
Tayside

Inverness

QISMET TANDOORI

1b, Millamburn Rd, Inverness 01463 716020

Established in 1998 by Liaquat Ali; your host is pictured on the T/a menu and he might give you a disc if you show him this Guide. Seats 100 and is brightly decorated with polished wooden floor and chairs, white tablecloths, palm trees and spot lighting. Specials: Chicken Tikka Sonali, with finely chopped ginger, green chillies and onion, medium hot. Mazedar, lamb tikka with Worcester sauce, lemon juice, cream and cheese. T/a: 10% disc. Hours: 12-2 / 5-11.30.

Nairn

AL RAJ

25 Harbour Street, Nairn 01667 455370

Mobarok Ali's 70-seater has helpful waiters who might give you a disc if you show them this Guide. Hours: 12-2 / 5-11.30.

LOTHIAN

The region of Lothian has been disbanded, the larger cities and surrounds split into a number of Unitary Authorities. For the time being, we are sticking to the old Lothian in this Guide.

Area: Mid Eastern
Scotland
Population: 774,000
of which Edinburgh
is 454,000
Adjacent Counties:
Central, Fife, Scottish
Stirling, Strathclyde

YOU SAY OK
You might get a discount if you show them this Guide.

COATBRIDGE: PUNJAB EXPRESS   22 West Canal St, ML5 1PR ~ 01236 440880. Est 1993 by the Dhanda brothers, Kally and Tari. It is situated in what used to be the station master's accommodation in part of the former Coatbridge Station House, closed by Lord Beeching in 1963. Built in 1899, the building still has many the period features. Downstairs, in the former ticket office, is the Pullman Lounge.

Edinburgh
Includes Blackhall, Dalry, Greenhill, Roseburn, Stockbridge and Viewforth

(Leith is entered separately)

FAR PAVILION   TOP 100

1 Craigleith Rd, Stockbridge, Edinburgh W
0131 332 3362

Est. 1987, this 125 seat restaurant has menus from Chef Abdul Aziz and an award-winning wine list. The Scotsman's Gillian Glover says *'the walls bore dimpled panels of buttoned velvet. Even the staff were upholstered.'* Remains in our TOP 100. The Guide-readers disc eases the bill as does the e-a-m-a-y-l Tuesday 6.30-10, £11.95 and lunchtime buffet. T/a: 10% off. Hours: 12-2 (weekdays)/5.30-12; closed Sun. except Dec.

KHUKURI

W Maitland Street   0131 228 2085

Nepalese specials, eg: Bhenda Momo, steed spicy minced lamb, Bara, thick lentil pancake, garlic, ginger, spices, both served with Nepali dip. Trisuli Poleko Macha, marinated baby fish, cooked in tandoor, served with green salad. Kukhura Hariyali, spicy yoghurt sauce, mint, coriander, green chillies. Solukhumbu Bhenda, from East Nepal, long slices of lamb stuffed with mint, in spicy sauce of onions, garlic, ginger, tomato. Aloo Ta Bodi, potato, Bamboo shoots, black-eye beans. Hours: 12-2, except Sun / 5.30-1.30; 12 Fri & Sat; 11 Sun.

KHUSHI'S

9 Victoria Street EH1 2HE   0131 220 0057

Established 1947 therefore the first in the city. *'Good and as busy as ever. Nice short menu, good helpings, very good meat, perfectly marinated. Fair service, nice Italian waiter. Clean, light-painted decor, very clean toilets. Good comfort on padded benches and formica tables. Excellent big starters. No alcohol, but most people brought big jugs (2-3 pints) of beer from the pub next door. Madras was now a Vindaloo; Bhuna and Korma could have been Madras.'* NKC. BYO Hours: 12-11; 10 Sun. Branch: Khushi's of West Lothian, Mid Calder.

LANCERS BRASSERIE   TOP 100

5 Hilton Place   0131 332 3444

70-seater opened in 1985 by Wali Udin JP, managed by Alok Saha. Head chef is Badrul Hussain. Beautifully decorated, stylish restaurant for business and special occasions. Pink suede on the walls, tiled floor, highly polished tables. Dinner for One c£20 - Assorted Kebabs - lamb, chicken, fish and vegetable kebabs; Chicken Tikka Masala - mild sauce; lamb Pasanda - with almond sauce; Sag Panir - spinach and cheese; Sabzi Pullao - vegetable rice; Naan and coffee. Menu Snapshot: Murghi Chaat £4.95 - small pieces of chicken cooked with tomatoes, and cucumber in hot and spicy sauce; Panir Cutlet £3.55 - shallow fried cheese cutlet; Ghee Bhat £2.45 - buttered basmati rice with fried onion; all stuffed Naan £2.75. Hours: 12-2.30 / 5-11.30.

MEZRAAN SOUTH INDIAN
NEW ENTRANT

14, Broughton Street, Toll Cross, EH3 9JH
0131 229 5578

'Very nice guy, about 6'1" remembered us from before. He suggested the Thali, chicken or lamb, I ordered the lamb, amazing, never tried it before! Big dish with compartments. Very good Puri, all came hot.' NKC. Menu Snapshot: Diwani Handi £7.95 - tender lamb, thick sauce, tomatoes, peppers and dry apricot; Bagara Baingan £4.95 - aubergine, Hyderbadi-style; Bikaneri Chaan Masala £3.95 - chickpeas with onions and yoghurt; Masala Dosa £6.95 - rice pancake with vegetable stuffing, Sambar (lentil) and Coconut Chutney; Paneer Makhani £5.35 - cheese simmered in smooth tomato sauce with a hint of fenugreek - all sounds delicious!

MOTHER INDIA   NEW ENTRANT

5, Infirmary Street   0131 524 9801

Here's one for the books (or the Guide at any rate!) We all know of the rivalry between Glasgow and Edinburgh. . Who could for see that well known restaurateur from the former would open a branch in the latter! Monir Mohammed is the man in mid 2008, at the former Baraka. Full height plate windows, stone wall tiles, some Indianised dressings and to quote witty journalist Jonathan Trew in Metro.co.uk *'black flock wallpaper covering one wall. There is some irony in the idea that what was once a cliché of old-school curry houses has now become hugely fashionable. I moan like a broken record about every restaurant turning to tapas-style serving.'* [me too - Ed], *'but it works here. There are some 40-odd dishes on the menu and just under half of them veggie. Almost all of them are under a fiver. Snapshot: Baked King Prawn with fennel and mustard seeds £5.50 - boldly flavoured and the seeds popped in the mouth; Chicken Achari £4.75 - cooked in pickle that was mouth-wateringly sour; Baby Aubergines and Potatoes £3.90 - in a rich tomato sauce melted to the touch. A lot of Indian restaurants cook meat in the tandoor before boiling it in a sauce. The shrivelled end-results look like Keith Richard's. Here, all the meat was tender. The lamb in the Saag £4.75, fell into moist chunks. Curry and battered fish? It's practically Scotland's national dish. The service was quick and cheery.'* JT. Hours: 12-10.30. www.motherindia.co.uk

SHAMIANA   TOP 100

14 Brough St, Edinburgh   0131 228 2265

First opened in 1977, taken over in 1992 by co-owner brothers Nadim (manager) and Mohammed (head chef) Butt. Seats 37. Specialises in Pakistani Kashmiri cuisine. *'I have been a regular customer of this excellent restaurant for around seven years and have been consistently impressed by the quality of your food. I also appreciate the professional manner in which the restaurant is run, and that last orders are taken*

at 10, thus restricting clientele to genuine curry enthusiasts.' TN. *'The food at Shamiana is excellent and the standard during the last ten years has been first class'* A&AM. *'Another excellent meal. My business colleagues look forward to further frequent visits now that our office headquarters are located around the corner'.* TAS. *'Very good menu, set meal £12.95 a head. Strangely small quantities but excellent, top notch, melt in the mouth lamb. Very good Keema and Peshwari Naans. All food hot to the table.'* NKC. *'We hadn't booked, it was midweek, it was packed, we got the penultimate table. Popadums crispy, good chutney tray, but naughty, naughty – don't put tomato ketchup in the cachumber ever again! Samosa, was shaped like a spring roll, but tasted very good. Main course portions good. Pat ordered his beloved Methi Chana Gosht, with spinach, fenugreek, fresh oriental herbs and hot spices, and pronounced it authentic and delicious. I had the Pakistani equivalent of CTM – Kashmiri Chasni Tikka, spicy, and equally good. Rice and breads enormous.'* DBAC. Great to see Kulfi Pista, Gulab Jan and Garjar Halwa on the dessert menu. Hours: 6-10.

SINGAPORA

69 N Castle St, Edinburgh   0131 538 7878

Malaysian-Singaporean 65-seater owned and managed by chef C Pang. Decor is *'dominant decorative wood and high ceiling reminiscent of colonial-style romance, the waitresses in national dress.'* AG. Satay: Chicken, Beef, King Prawn or Tofu, marinated, skewered and char grilled, served with a delicious peanut sauce (five sticks). The Malay Kari – chicken, beef, or vegetables in a coconut base, and Redang Beef, the national dish curry. You might get a disc if you show them this Guide. T/a: 10% off. Del. Hours: 12-2.30 / 6-10.30. Sun. closed winter.

VERANDAH   A-LIST

17 Dalry Rd, Edinburgh   0131 337 5828

At our Awards ceremony, the Award for best in Scotland was ungraciously received by another Scottish restaurant in another city. We graciously therefore transfer the Award to this highly deserving and highly appreciative restaurant. It's a tiny 40-seater, and the first opened (in 1981) by Wali Tasar Uddin, MBE, JP. It is now run by his nephew, Foysol Choudhury, who describes it as 'reassuringly low-key' serving northern Indian and Bangladeshi cuisine. It's a pretty, relaxing restaurant with cane chairs and Bamboo-slatted wall blinds, a clever and effective illusion. DBAC says: *'I first ate there, well, let me see, a very long time ago, the decorations were unfussy, in fact simple but never-the-less effective and the food served in generous portions.'* We continue to get many appreciative reports: *'First class restaurant by any standards. The welcome and the ambience of this establishment is all that once could wish for, when sitting down to dine. The welcome is friendly, the staff attentive and the food is flavoursome and well prepared. We have been before and do recommend it. We are*

fortunate in having restaurant so this calibre in Edinburgh.' anon. *'The staff were very polite and welcoming with an excellent neat table. The candle was a beautiful touch. Been before but only for a T/a, even better sitting in. Would definitely return. Thank you staff, you were all fabby!'* LH. *'coming here for two years, and always recommend it.'* FC. *'We have been coming here for twenty five years, you may think us biased. However, although visiting once a year, we have never had a poor meal. The extremely high standard of food, delicate flavours of creamy lamb Pasanda £6.25 and Chicken Tikka Masala £6.25, are a bench mark, which other restaurants can only hope to approach. Even after a years absence, the warm family welcome sets the mood for an excellent experience. Portions generous, menu extensive and meals very reasonably priced.'* CKL. *'I visit quite often, always friendly, excellent food, prices reasonable. Everything is clean, including the toilets. There is no background music, which is very good, as I hard of hearing. Friends and colleagues always impressed.'* ADK. *'Second to none.'* PS. You have to visit their website to see the array of stars who have visited here, to name just two: Clint Eastwood and Cliff Richard. Weekday Lunch Menu: £5.95 per person Menu Snapshot: Mach Kebab £2.95 - fish cooked with garlic, ginger and coriander leaf; Murgh £5.95 - chicken cooked with mango pulp, cream and mild spices; Palok Gagor Cashew Nut £3.95 - fresh spinach, carrots, nuts, medium hot. Del: £15. Hours: 12-2.15 / 5-12.

YOU SAY OK - EDINBURGH
You might get a discount if you show them this Guide.

EDINBURGH: CELLARS NEW ENTRANT 3 York St. EH1 3EB
~ 0131 557 9899 *'My initial impression was not good; the waitress
was not particularly welcoming and didn't offer drinks, luckily the
food more than made up for this. I started with the Chicken Chilla
(£3.95); described as chicken on a lentil pancake it was in fact a
light wrap generously filled with moist chicken cooked in with peppers
- delicious. For main I had Lal Mass (£8.90) a lamb dish from
Rajasthan. There was a good portion of tender lamb cooked in a
medium hot sauce with a pleasant tomato flavour. They don't make
Naan but the Chapati was fine. It has a number of steps down to it
which may cause problems for those with impaired mobility.'* MC.
www.9cellars.co.uk

IGNITE 272 Morrison St.   0131 228 5666. Owner: Mr Khan
Good reports received.

KEBAB MAHAL 7 Nicholson Square   0131 667 5214. *'Very
good place, probably the 2nd oldest in Edinburgh. Have eaten in and
had T/a.'* NKC. *'Recommended. Not upmarket or designer, but the
food is extremely good and consistent and also quite cheap.'* Dr DD.
Hours: 12-12; 2 Fri & Sat.

OLOROSO 33 Castle St. nkc. ate here with his family and had
a, *'super duper meal.'* More reports needed, please. Menu
Snapshot: Tandoori Quail with Potato Chat £6.50; Today's Curry
£8 - with Rice and Popadums; Aloo Muttar £5.50 - Pentland
potatoes with peas in a light tomato curry sauce served with Puri
(flat bread); Punjabi Salmon £6.50 - served with the warm
Turmeric Rice; Bread Pakora £4.50 - homemade bread stuffed
with, cheese, onions and spices, served with mint dip.

TIPPOO SAHIB 129a Rose St. 0131 226 2862. A Pakistani 60-
seater restaurant opened in 1982 as the Shanaz by the Parvez
family and renamed in 1996 *'Chicken Mancharry, tandoor-cooked,
with freshly grated chilli, garlic and ginger, Chicken Nentara,
cooked with onions and methi, and Massalidar Gosht, meat cooked
with pickles, and Karela Gosht meat with bitter gourd. First class
quality food, staff and atmosphere. Reasonable prices.'* RC. Hours:
12-2 / 5-12; Sat. 12-11.30; Sun. 5-11.30.

ZEST 15 North St Andrew St. 0131 5556 5028. Pretty cafe–
style licensed restaurant, polished wooden floors, glass shelves,
tubular steel chairs and pastel colours. Seats 55 diners. Del: 2m,
£15 min. Hours: 5.30 - 11.30. Specials: Kashi Gar Masala.
Branch: Eastern Spices and Bombay Feast.

Leith

BRITANNIA SPICE   AWARD WINNER

150 Commercial Street, Britannia Way, Leigh
                                      0131 555 2255

Once it was known that the ex Royal Yacht Britannia
was to be retired in derelict Leith docks, Wali Tasar
Uddin decided to open a restaurant to assist the
regeneration of the area, now called Ocean Terminal.
He chose the former Glenmorangie Whisky warehouse
at the dock entrance. He hired Arshad Al to design the
venue to reflect the *'gracious lady of the seas'*, which had
taken up residence within sight of the new premises. It
opened in 1999. This gorgeous nautically-themed
restaurant, seating 130 diners, (served by frequent buses
from the city centre) has blue chairs, polished wooden
tables and floors, brass railings and blinds that look like
sails and is is perfect stop-off after you have visited the
the Yacht or the other people-magnet, the Scottish
Executive building. The menu is divided by countries -
Bangladeshi, Thai, Nepalese, North Indian and Europe
– mix and match, if you like! Menu Snapshot: Tom Kha

Gai £3.95 - (Thai) chicken in a rich coconut soup,
flavoured with fresh galangal, lemon grass, kaffir lime
leaves and mushrooms; Maccher Bhorta £3.95 -
(Bangladesh) baked fish, minced with onions, green
chillies, mushrooms and fresh coriander leaves,
tempered with mushroom seeds; Shatkora Gosht £9.95 -
(Bangladesh) tender pieces of lamb cooked in a medium
hot sauce with rinds of a the Shatkora citric fruit, lemon
leaves and Bengali chillies; Special Chicken £11.95 -
(Bangladesh) diced king prawns, wrapped in thin filleted
chicken and cooked in a rich and mild sauce; Pad Ho Ra
Pa Kub Nua £10.95 - (Thai) thinly sliced pieces of beef,
stir-fried with a selection of traditional Thai spices and
basil - hot; Chicken Panaeng £8.95 - (Thai) medium to
hot, with lime leaves, red pepper, coconut milk and red
chilli paste; Himalayan Momo £9.95 - (Nepal) minced
meat mixed with spices, enclosed in pastry and
traditionally steed; Mixed Tandoori £15.95 - (Northern
India) lamb and chicken tikka, sheek kebab, tandoori
chicken, king prawn served with salad, Naan and mild
sauce; Palok Gajor Cashew Nut £6.95 - spinach, carrot,
cashew nuts, medium hot. *'What a great restaurant, lovely
surroundings, great courteous service and the food is just up
with the very best. We had Chicken Tikka Chasni Masala bit
more spicy than your average CTM and Methi Murgh. The
Aloo Jeera was simply divine, the Okra tasty, if a bit oily. TOP
100 stuff no doubt, elegant.'* T&KM. *'Very, very tiny helpings
- beautifully plated. Very, very expensive.'* NKC. *'Whilst on
business, my colleague and I found ourselves staying at the
Holiday Inn Express (adjacent to the restaurant). We walked
past the restaurant at 7 - it was empty, deciding on a beer first.
Returned at 8.30 - it was packed, despite this we got a table!
Excellent starters of Assorted Kebabs. Main courses: Northern
Indian Garlic Chicken with hot sauce, Harrey Masaley Ka
Gosht, cubes lamb in green masala or coriander, mint, green
chilli, curry leaves and spices, a superb, best ever tarka Dal.
Very impressive, worthy of its guide entry. Will visit again!'*
DL. For the totally unadventurous there is a small
choice of English dishes – steak, roast chicken etc. Del:
£10 min, 5-mile radius. Hours: 12-2; Sunday closed / 5-
11.45 daily. britanniaspice.co.uk

GULNAR'S PASSAGE TO INDIA TOP 100

46 Queen Charlotte St, Leith   0131 554 7520

Mohammad Ridha Saleh's 82-seater Passage, serves
north Indian and Kashmiri food. *'Many are the nights I've
spent there feeling like a desert king, being fed the most
amazing food under the drapes that give the establishment the
air of a Bedouin tent. One Arabic dish at Gulnar's especially
emphasises this feeling: Helahil, chicken cooked with sweetcorn,
onion, fresh coriander and chilli, served on a bed of rice with
salad, a superb dish with a wonderful mix of flavours. Try
Halabcha, spiced and roasted aubergine cooked in the tandoor
with chicken, yoghurt, tomatoes, onions, garlic, chilli and
coriander, a hot dish that tantalises the tastebuds; Aloobora –
spicy potato balls filled with minced lamb. Potahari Sang –
minced lamb fried with fresh herbs and spices, garnished with*

coconut, wrapped in a puri. Rooflifter, lamb and chicken marinated, tandoor-cooked and prepared with mint, nuts and spices. An incredible edible experience.' gr. 'Recommended by several people, but to be honest we thought it sounded a bit too good to be true. We soon realised that all that accolade was not exaggerated. We went for the atmosphere mainly, but were very thrilled with the variety and quality of the exotic food. A great cheer to a marvellous place which had given us one of the best nights out in the UK for a long, long time.' FA. Hours: 12-2 / 5.30-12; 1 Sat.

Mussleburgh (Fisherrow Harbour)

CHUBARA   NEW ENTRANT

The Quay Complex, 131, New St. EH21 6DH
0131 665 1066

Charan Gill MBE opened his new venture, costing a reported £1.35 million, followed by £650,000 on refurbishment. Situated just five miles from the centre of Edinburgh on the A1 at the picturesque harbour of Fisherrow in Musselburgh, overlooking the Firth of Forth, it's not hard to see what attracted Charan to The Quay. Chubara, means 'penthouse,' and is situated in on the third floor, with full glass windows, looking out over the fishing boats, yachts, beaches and out over to the Firth of Forth. Menu Snapshot: All Indian brigade here, so expect authentic curries and accompaniments, like - Aloo Tikki - mashed potatoes, coriander, ginger, garlic and spinach, deep-fried and served with chickpea curry - a particular favourite; Lal Mass - lamb cooked with Jaipuri spices, served with boiled rice and Jeera Aloo; Chicken Sagwala - fresh spinach cooked with chicken on the bone, served with Jeera Pullao Rice and Aloo Gobi. Reports please. www.thequaycomplex.com

STRATHCLYDE

Area: Central west Scotland
Population: 2,255,000
of which Glasgow 578.000
Adjacent Counties:
Borders,
D & G, Central,
Highland, Lothian

Strathclyde (meaning "valley of the River Clyde") is an historic subdivision of Scotland, and was one of the regional council areas of Scotland from 1975 to 1996. It contains the former counties of: Argyle, Ayrshire, Dunbartonshire, Lanarkshire and Renfrewshire. For this edition we are continuing to use the old region of Strathclyde here, but we point out that Northern Strathclyde has become Argyll & Bute, while the rest of Strathclyde is divided into a number of Unitary Authorities, administering the larger cities and surrounds.

Glasgow

Includes Battlefield, Finnieston, Hillhead, Muirend, Nitshill, Pollockshields, Scotstoun, Townhead

Glaswegians are at pains to tell us that Glasgow curries are 'the real thing, the best anywhere' .. 'everywhere else is a pale imitation, especially the pakoras', writes one person frequently. The reason is a largely Pakistani population, and this means gutsy, spicy Kashmiri/Punjabi-style curries, as are found in Southall and Bradford, which are quite removed from the Bangladeshi curry house formula. Put another way, Glasgow's curries are the authentic thing, once tasted, never forgotten. The argument about whether Glasgow or Edinburgh is best for curry or the curry capital is fatuous. Glasgow has come a very long way since its tenement-block, 6 pub-closing, Mars-bar-loutishness reputation. Modern Glasgow is breathtaking. Its Indian restaurant scene is as good as it gets and ever-improving. Here are your favourites:

THE ASHOKA

108 Elderslie St, Glasgow   0141 221 1761

Balbur Singh Sumal opened Glasgow's first Ashoka in 1968. He went on to found a big group (see next entry) but this one is no longer part of the group. It was taken over in 1995 by the Purewal brothers and in 2002 by Cyrus.(Syrus or Siroosh) Bavarsagh, who holds court with a crew of waiters in kilts. Starters Snapshot: Stuffed Poories £5.45, choice of sweet and sour prawn, spicy chicken, chana or mushroom folded into a puri; Chicken Numbo Lassan £5.95 - spicy golden fried chicken, with a garlic lemon mayonnaise dressing; Bharvan Shimla Mirch £5.95 - green pepper stuffed with chicken, rice, spices, herbs and a hint of chilli - very popular in Uttar Pradesh north India's largest state. Mains: Nashili Garlic - lamb, chicken or seafood, ginger, garlic fried with

Punjabi home-style sauce and cognac; Gujarati Chilli Peas - chilli, peas and a touch of sweet. Chef Abpaz has some Parsee specials: Chicken Abpaz - black bean sauce, green peppers, mushrooms and onions; Patra Ni Macchi - fish cooked with coriander, coconut and spinach, both £12. Chicken or Lamb Dampokhet £14 - slow baked until tender and sealed with a puri top. Lunch and dinner. www.ashokaglasgow.co.uk   Reports please.

THE ASHOKA GROUP

There have been Ashoka restaurants in Glasgow since 1968. Balbur Singh Sumal grew the number to six during the 1980s (including the original at Elderslie Street, noted above). The remainder, became part of Charan Gill's Harlequin Group which he sold to Sanjay Majhu in 2005. It claims to be Europe's largest chain of Indian restaurants, (turnover £15m). It is in rapid expansion-mode especially focusing on cheap food and fast food. Yet despite that you tell us that the service and food is at a very high standard, high enough for us to have given one of their restaurants the BEST IN SCOTLAND award in 2007. The group's portfolio at the time of writing is 17 restaurants. They operate a central reservations, T/a and freephone Del 'hotline': 0800 195 3195. There's also a cookbook (one recipe of which requires you to use lychees to make their lamb Rogan Josh!!!). while spices can be bought at www.ashokaspiceshop.com. Head office, 23 Crow Rd, G11, 0141 342 5200 www.harlequinrestaurants.com

ASHOKA AT THE MILL   A-LIST

500 Corselet Rd, G53   0800 195 3195

Ashoka at the Mill is described as the group's 'jewel-in-the crown'. It is indeed located in a 'medieval' farmhouse /old mill. The location is off the M77 at j3 – go west half a mile along the A726, turn left and follow the signs, and suddenly you've left industrial Glasgy behind and combines an historic setting with a classy contemporary twist in its vast interior. The Grand Buffet is the centrepiece. family Room with a 'cyber-jungle mural and more gadgets and gizmos than the S.S. Enterprise' will keep the kids quiet. The food, according to IMCT: *'is not all Indian, but it's all at the Ashoka standard worth travelling for.'* Specials include Goanese fish and prawns, Kala Mirch Masala, sliced chicken breast in a peppery, tangy herbal sauce. Buffets Mon - Thurs from 5: £11.95; Friday 12-6.30:£10.95; from 6.30, £14.95; Sat 5-6.30: £10.95; from 6.30, £14.95 Sunday 5 -6.30: £10.95; from 6.30:, £12.95. Weekend Lunch Special (Sat / Sun) 50% off all a la carte curries. Hours: Mon-Thurs: 5-11; Fri:12-12; Sat: 4 -12; Sun: 4-11. Seema and Rajesh Saraf manage the place and were presented with the best in Scotland category of the renowned Cobra Good Curry Awards. [albeit after a rather ungracious start]. Said Rajesh: *'I particularly proud to receive this award against stiff competition as it is chosen by Pat Chapman's Curry Club, Britain's first and foremost authority on Asian food, based on his own mystery shopper reports and customer feed back. So thank you to all our regular diners at the Mill!'*. Hours: Mon-Thurs: 5- 11; 12-12 Fri; 4-12 Sat; to 11 Sun.

THE OTHER ASHOKA (HARLEQUIN GROUP) GLASGOW RESTAURANTS : All 0800 195 3195 unless stated.

ASHOKA BEARSDEN 9 Kirk Road, Bearsden, G61. Opened in 1997. Franchise owner Imtiaz Aslam. Decor rich creams and deep browns colonial artefacts and Indian antiques and bric-a-brac–sitars, tablas, swords and even bullets adorn the walls, with subtle traditional Indian lightingKids free Sun when accompanied by an adult. Pre-Theatre Menu £8.95 served 5-6:30. Hours: Sun-Thurs: 5-11; 12 Fri & Sat.

ASHOKA HILLSHEAD 19 Ashton La, Hillhead, G12. (behind Hillhead Underground Station). Absorbing Indian market scene mural. Thali Lunch £4.95 or 2-course Lunch Menu £6.95, Mon-Sat 12- 5. Pre-Theatre Menu £11.95 served 56:30. Hours: Mon-Thurs: 12 -12; 1 Fri & Sat; 1 -12 Sun.

ASHOKA REGENT BRASSERIE 99 Cowgate, Kirkintilloch, G66 1JD 0141 776 7617. Take the M80 to J3 then the B757. The 2007 new-look refurbishment is popular. Reports please.

ASHOKA SHAK Phoenix Leisure Park, Linwood. In 2001 this first branch opened at the former 'Harry Ramsden's', close to Glasgow Airport. Thali lunch at £4.95, Mon-Sat. Hours: Daily 12-11.

ASHOKA SHAK Showcase Leisure Park, Baillieston, G69 7TS. (Opened 2001 as a fast food outlet. Since then it has been given a 'sassy' new design. Thali lunch £7.95, Mon-Sat.

ASHOKA SOUTHSIDE 268 Clarkston Rd, Glasgow. Raj and colonial décor with period pictures, photographs, artefacts and memorabilia adorning the walls. Pre-Theatre Menu £8.95, daily from 5-6:30. Hours Sun-Thurs: 5-11.30; Fri/Sat: 5-12.

ASHOKA WEST END 1284 Argyle Street, G3. Opened 1982 near Kelvingrove Art Gallery and Museum on the corner of the longest street and shortest road in the city. Pre Theatre Menu £8.95: 5-7. 25 seats upstairs, 35 downstairs Kids eat free on Sundays when accompanied by an adult. Hours Sun-Thurs: 4-12.30; Fri & Sat: 5-1.

SPICE OF LIFE 1293 Argyle Street. Behind Hillhead Underground Station, it attracts the suits in the daytime, and the young crowd at night. Modern murals and lights which subtly change as darkness falls. Take a pre-dinner aperitif in the cocktail bar before ascending to the balcony where the booths and tables for two await. Kids free Sun when with an adult. 2 course lunch £5.95, Thurs/Fri. Pre-Theatre Menu £8.95 served daily from 5-7. Hours: 12-2 Thurs & Fri / 5-12.

CAFÉ INDIA

171 North St, Charing Cross   0141 248 4074

North street can be found at Charing Cross and runs parallel to the M8 motorway and is accessed from St Vincent Street or Kent Road. It sits across the road from the Mitchell Library. Described (by its owner Abdul Sattar) as 'Britain's first-ever designer buffet restaurant'. It certainly has changed since it opened in 1979, its seating by 1999 having reached a monumental 560 seats. The ground floor is open-plan and bright. The seats are expensive high-backed pale wood with pink or blue upholstery, depending which zone you are in, and there are some alcove tables. The area called the galleries in the lower floor is moody, with darker reds and wrought iron. There is provision for self-service via a smart counter. Both floors have eye-catching artwork and light fittings. Young clientèle love it and their set

meals, which are a speciality, and the Friday/Saturday e-a-m-a-y-ls (at £12.50). Sattar it seems is proud of the fact that he served 1160 diners in a single day. T/a: 10%. Hours: 12-12; Sun. 3-12. Cafe India branches: 253 Gallowgate, Glasgow 0141 552 1448; 29 Albion St, Glasgow - +44 141 552 5115. www.cafeindiaglasgow.com

CHAPATI 1

2017 Dumbarton Road   0141 576 0118

Chain of eleven takeaways, est. 1983 by Iqbal S Gill each of which has its own personnel, but are overseen by Deepa Gill (service) and Harnak Singh (chef). Curries, Kebabs and Pizza. Prices are not cheap for T/a: Onion Bhajia £2.25, Mango Chutney 70p, Potato and Cauliflower Curry £3.50. Most ordered dishes: Karahi Chicken and Chicken Jullander. Hours: Sun.-Thurs. 4-12.30; Fri. / Sat. 4-1.30. Branches: (All Glasgow area) Chapati 2, 1576 Dumbarton Rd, 0141 954 3154; Chapati 3, 339 Dumbarton Rd, Partick, 0141 337 1059; Chapati 4, 20 Byres Rd, 0141 334 4089; Chapati 5, 354 Paisley Rd W, 0141 427 6925; Chapati 6, 468 Dumbarton Rd, Dalmuir, 0141 952 9210; Chapati 7, 182 Paisley Rd W, Renfrew, 0141 885 2313; Chapati 8, 5 Lennox Dr, Faifley, 01389 879914; Chapati 9, 3 Greenock Rd, Bishopton, 01505 862 222; Chapati 10 39 Main St, Busby, 0141 644 1971; Sajjan, 2372 Dumbarton Rd, Yoker, 0141 951 1839. Neelim, 1590 Dumbarton Rd, Glasgow, 0141 959 6265.

KAMA SUTRA

331 Sauchiehall Street   0800 195 3195

In 1996, it opened (opposite the Dental Hospital) to widespread curiosity, with the locals speculating as to what might be about to happen behind the stylish frontage. The venue's PR machine added to the mystery: *'the legend comes alive over a candlelit cornucopia of exotic eastern cuisine. Be it a romantic dinner-a-deux, or a fun night out with friends, you can indulge in the food of love, every which way you want. Private affair? The salubrious 80-seat suite downstairs provides the perfect backdrop for special celebrations by night.'* Phew! Don't need any aphrodisiacs here then! The sultry and sassy design innovation caused a sensation, and the sniggering soon stopped. The minimalist elements of wood, iron, slate and stone are appealing. During daytime the venue is frequented by the suits: Lunchtime 'Quickie' Buffet £5.95 Mon-Sat: 12-3.30). Buf: Mon/Tue eves £11, 6.30-9.30. Pre-Theatre Menu (£7.95) 3.30-6.30 daily and Sun 5-6.30. Hours: 12-12; -12.30 Fri-Sat; 5-12 Sun.

KOH I NOOR   TOP 100

235 North St, Charing Cross   0141 204 1444

Glasgow's earliest Indo-Pak opened in 1961, and boasts to be the originator of the famous e-a-m-a-y-l buffet nights (Mon.-Fri. 7-9). Authentic Indian and Pakistani design with authentic Asian decor, with hanging rugs, arches etc. *'Fabulous decor.'* DBAC. Northern Indian formula curries. Its 150 seating is now small in comparison with other Glasgow venues, but is still big

considering the national average of 50, and it's still very busy. *'Not only was the service friendly and helpful but the food arrived very promptly, considering the number of people there. The Chicken Dansak was excellent and the naan breads terrific'.* RA. *'Excellent. Samosas so filling, had to leave most of my main course!'* SF. *'Starters very impressive, quantities large. Garlic Nan not for the faint-hearted: beautiful. Chicken Tikka Chasini and Chicken Nentara memorable.'* HB. *'Absolutely superb. In a class of its own.'* BS. We have a difference of opinion here. *'Average, not Top 100, food not good enough.'* T&KM. *'Visited on three consecutive nights, although had to pay a hefty £26 for Popadums, starter, main course rice and Nan. Still think it currently the best Indian I've tried. lamb Lyallipour - eyewatering hot, so succulent and tasty. Garlic Chilli lamb - superb. Quick service, highly efficient, polite. My girlfriend Brigit - not a spice freak like me requested a mild curry. The waiter sensed that something was wrong, whisked here Okra Korma away and brought back a different one, declaring this would be palatable and indeed it was.'* DP. Hours: 12-12; -1 Fri & Sat.

INDIA QUAY   NEW ENTRANT

181, Finnieston St. G3 8HE   0141 221 1616

'Caters for 200 diners, who can enjoy fantastic food with

fantastic views towards the Finnieston Bridge. Head Chef: Kashmir Sing, experiments, making interesting starters such as

Pheasant Pakora and Venison Bhajia.' TM. Reports Please.

MASALA JAK'S

The Quay, Springfield Quay   0800 195 3195

'Back in the Great American Gold Rush of 1849,' says owner Harlequin Liesure's spin, *'thousands of prospectors headed to the USA to panhandle for gold. Many found fortunes, thousands died, a few found fame, but perhaps the most famous of all was Jagir Singh, known as 'Masala Jak', who left the Punjab for the USA. Jak found no gold, but did find fortune when he introduced the cowboys of the Wild West to the delights of Indian Cuisine. His fame travelled across America, a legend was born. Old tales tell that the words*

'Masala Jak' derived from Mister Jagir Singh, maybe true – maybe not'. Decidedly not! It's all PR spin! But the food at the 120-seat, 3,500 sq ft Quay is good. The group plan to roll out branches nationwide. Hours: 12-11. See Ashoka group above).

MISTER SINGH'S INDIA   TOP 100

149 Elderslie Street   0141 204 0186

Satty Singh owns this 90-seater restaurant, as its eponymous title suggests, and like other Glasgow restaurants, as part of the Harlequin Group (see Ashoka above), it benefits from group marketing and purchasing muscle. Decor combines ethnic and traditional Scottish with stark white walls and dramatic bursts of cobalt blue creating a magical Mediterranean milieu, and hand-carved wooden balustrades and mirrors. Manager Jil Ahmed, and the waiters wear kilts and the girls wear salwars; Younis Ahraf (who wears chef's whites, by the way) does curried Haggis! And we hear that there's a French influence at work in the kitchens too. *'Without question the best I have visited! Vast menu. Fantastic food, good portions. Booking essential, even midweek. Brandy-drinkers beware. They have a 200-year-bottle of Napoleon's brandy at £35 a shot!'* GD. *'For me, it is a 'must' when I travelling to Glasgow! The food is so good and tasty, particularly the Chilli Garlic Chicken.'* RA. *'We must have been the second couple to enter the restaurant but within 30 minutes the whole place was packed and we took this to be a very good sign indeed. We were impressed by the amount of food on the plate. When the main course arrived I can only say it was the best curry I have ever tasted and that includes my own, spicy hot but very tasty. One of the finest curries in the country'.* GC. Lunch, Mon-Fri: 12-5, £6.95. Pre-Theatre from 5-6.30, £8.25 Weekend Brunch, Sat: 12-5, Sun 2.30-5, £6.95 (one child under 12 eats free for every adult dining a la carte) Football Package: £14.95: 5-course lunch plus free taxi to the big match available for all home games (booking essential). Hours; 12- 11.30; -12 Fri & Sat; 2.30-11.30 Sun.

MOTHER INDIA   TOP 100

28 Westminster Terrace   0141 221 1663

A well-known Glasgow landmark, Mother India opened its doors for business in 1992, and is run by Monir Mohammed. *'The jewel of Glasgow. Small unpretentious restaurant, Top 100 no doubt about it!'* t&km. *'I've been an avid user of your Curry Guide since 1995 an have travelled the length and breath of the UK always with a copy under my arm! I have eaten curry in most cities and cook my own when at home. I was amazed that Mother India was not in the TOP 100. I've eaten in every TOP 100 in Edinburgh and Glasgow and in Edinburgh, the best in my opinion is Shamiana and in Glasgow, Mother India. The service, atmosphere and quality of food are second to none in the city. Really fresh ingredients with excellent use of spices cooked to perfection. Cumin Chicken and Courgette - excellent. lamb Saag - melt in your*

mouth staff. Some times, I am tempted away to Ashoka or one of the other TOP 100 Restaurants but always return to Mother India for a better fix! They even do a, Sunday to Thursday, 'eat as much as you can,' menu for £12.50 - fantastic value. Make it a top 100!' JT. Ok,Ok. Mother India has a very relaxed atmosphere and although the restaurant is licensed you can BYO (wine & beer, no spirits). Snapshot:: Spiced haddock; chicken with spinach leaf; kheer (rice pudding). Lunch £6.95; Pre-theatre £7.95 (Fri & Sat £8.95); Dinner £12.95 - £16.95. Seats: 120. Hours: 12-2 / 5.30-11.

MOTHER INDIA'S DELICATESSEN, BEARSDEN. 0141 942 3643. Opened in 2007, by Monir Mohammed, it's not an eatery. Like it says on the tin, it's where you buy spices and ingredients and chilled Mother India ready meals. It won't be a surprise if Indian delis start popping up all over the central belt.

MURPHY'S PAKORA BAR   TOP 100

1287 Argyle S, Glasgow   0141 334 1550

Like Mr Singh's above, it's now part of the Harlequin Group, but still retains its owner Teresa Doherty, she with a good eye for sound bites: *'It was love at first bite! As we sank our baby teeth into our first chunk of pakora, there were loud karahis of more mum!'* [groan] *'The word Pakora, to a Scot, slips off the tongue as easily as haggis, neeps and tatties. It's one of those snacks that can be eaten at any time of day or night – one bite is never enough. At Murphy's the chef's a Scot (R. McGregor) which is why there's Haggis Pakora. Beam me up, Scotty.'* CW. And there are 30 others incl Chilli. Or there are Pizzas – traditional or with an Indian twist. Of course, it is a licensed bar, selling, well Murphy's of course! Takeaway: 10% off. Hours: 12-12; 1 Fri & Sat.

RAWALPINDI

321 Sauchehall St. G2 3HW   0141 832 4180

'This restaurant is one my friends and I go to regularly. Good prices and quality, unlike others nearby that are overpriced. Pakora, from £2.50 - excellent, Mixed Vegetable Curry £5.45 ,from buffet was good value. lamb Curry £5.75 was quite gristly. Service was if anything a bit over eager - the fact that I was still eating, should have been a clue that I was not finished yet! However, as the restaurant was quiet, they were possibly just overstaffed. Reservations about the lamb curry were probably due to the festive season and normally no problems. A slightly disappointing visit to a dependable restaurant, but I'm sure I'll be back. Would recommend it a a good basic Indian.' JK. Menu Snapshot: Chicken Chat £2.95 - drumsticks marinated in spicy yoghurt and lemon juice just barbecued in the clay oven and cooked in a tangy sauce served with salad; Onion Bhajia £2.75 - original or rings (rings sound good! I wonder if they are like the fried onions rings, the ones you get in a Pub - hope so!) served with sauce and salad; Egyptian Kebab £9.45 - chicken, tomato and mushrooms, on skewer with full garnish; King Prawn Lalpari £10.50 - with red wine and green chillies. T/a: 10% disc. Hours: 5-11; 1am Fri & Sat; 1pm- 12.30 Sun.

WEE CURRY SHOP

7 Buccleuch St, Glasgow   0141 353 0777

Everything about this eatery is small, including the menu – smaller than a paperback book. *'Really good. Very wee indeed. Seats approximately 20 with one chef and one waiter. Vegetable side dishes seem to have low priority. My pal has been eating here for years.'* GG. The menu has also probably the smallest selection we have ever seen. However, as the saying goes, better to cook one dish well than ten badly. There are only four starters to choose from: Vegetable or Chicken Pakoras, Aubergine Fritters and Mutter Paneer Puri. There are a few more mains to choose: six Chicken dishes, prices from c£6 to £8; one lamb, a Karahi dish; four Vegetables eg: Aloo Sag, Black Eye Beans and Broccoli and one Dal. To accompany your curries, there is Basmati Rice , Garlic Potatoes, Chupatti 60p, Paratha and Raitha £1.20. We agree: you don't need anything more! Wee branches: Byres Rd, 0141 339 1339 and Ashton Lane, 0141 357 5280, near Cowcadden tube. Part of Mother India group.

YOU SAY OK – GLASGOW
You might get a discount if you show them this Guide.

BATTLEFIELD, G42: ALISHAN   250 Battlefield Rd ~ 0141 632 5294. 48-seater est 1987 by M Ayub Quereshi. Menu Snapshot: Chef's Platter £9.50, chicken, lamb, vegetable, mushroom, fish pakora; chicken chat; chicken and lamb tikka; shiekh kebab; spiced onions and pops - what a feast! to share with friends! T/a: 10% disc. Del: 5m, £10 min. Hours: 5-12.

POLLOCKSHIELDS, G4I: AMBALA SWEET CENTRE 178 Maxwell Rd.~ 0141 429 5620 Franchise operated by Mrs S Ahmad. (See Ambala, Drummond St, London, NW1.) As well as the counter T/a sweets and snacks, chef Akmal cooks a small range of curries for the 26-seat restaurant. 'lamb Bhoona is amazing!' df. Alcohol not allowed. No credit cards. Hours: 10-10.

TRADESTON, G5: VILLAGE CURRY   129 Nelson St ~ 0141 429 4610. 'Superb. Religious place, no alcohol, no BYO, must be Halal as 90% of customers of Asian appearance. Very good middle range menu, not short or too long. Good quantities, very good prompt service. Good comfort, amazing decor. We were taken upstairs to an excellent restaurant, all fitted out in dark, polished tables and chairs, nice stone coloured walls, huge red/yellow/gold paisley ceiling drapes to give a huge tent effect. Being a Friday night, we booked. Hive of industry - eating!' nkc. Branches: 132 Nelson St, Tradeston, Glasgow. 0141 429 8555; 1005 Paisley Rd W, Bellahouston, Glasgow. 0141 427 0060. www. villagecurryhouse.co.uk

ZEERA   181 Kirchintilloch Rd, G64.~ 0141 772 9393. Toni Ghani and his father, also Toni have been designing and building Indian restaurants for well over a decade and have recently taken up ownership of Zeera. Distinctive, with its expansive windows that look into a tasteful furniture – South African black marble floor tiles, black walls, and comfy leather chairs in the dining area.

Helensburgh

CAFE LAHORE

33 West Clyde Street   01436 674971

'Light, clean and simple decor. Helpful, cheerful and friendly

service. Very varied menu, one of the biggest I've seen. I opted for the buffet, with enormous starter of Mixed Pakora, eight main dishes, two rices and bread. Nan disappointing, hard as leather. However, if you order fresh, you are in for a treat – small is the size of a moderate coffee table! Quite fantastic Lassi and Chai. Excellent Lal Toofan. Recommended.' RT. Menu Extracts: Fish or Paneer Pakora, Garlic Okra, Chicken lyallpuri, green chilli and coriander; Hasina, tender lamb, marinated, onions, capsicums, tomato, baked in tandoor, sauce, served on sizzler; Mix Hot Rice, fried rice, chicken, lamb, prawns, fresh green chillies, served on hot sizzler. Buffet Nights: 6-11, £9.95, children under 12 half price. T/a: 10% disc. Del: £15 min. Hours: 12-2.30 / 5-12; 12 Fri & Sat.

SCOTTISH BORDERS

Formerly called Borders. Contains four burghs Peeblesshire, Roxburghshire, Selkirkshire and Berwickshire.

Area: Southeast Scotland
Population: 110,000
Adjacent Counties:
D & G, Lothian,
Northumberland,
Strathclyde

YOU SAY OK
You might get a discount if you show them this Guide.

EYEMOUTH: JAMUNA 9 Market St. TD14 5HE. ~ 01890 1007

GALASHIELS: SWAGAT   36 Market St. TD1 3AA. ~ 01896 750100. *'Well lit, comfortable little place. Service is good. Very tasty Jalfry.'* GMCG. Hours: 12-2/5-11.

HAWICK: SHUCONDA BALTI HOUSE 4 Station Bldg, Dove Mnt Pl. TD9 7AA. ~ 01450 373313. BM Talukder's 50-seater Bangladeshi curry house. Hours: 12-2 /6-11.30.

STIRLING

Formerly called Central. Includes most of the former county of Stirlingshire (except Falkirk) and the south-western portion of the former county of Perthshire.

Area:
Mid Scotland
Population: 88,000
Adjacent Counties:
Lothian, Strathclyde,
Tayside

Drymen

DRYMEN TANDOORI

5-7 Stirling Road, Drymen   01360 660099

65-seater, est 1994 by Sohail Wahid who might give you

a disc if you show him this Guide. *'Does quite a tasty little number of average curries, a tad on the expensive side and carry out staff at least are a little unfriendly and disinterested.'* T&KM. T/a: 10% disc. Del: £10 min, 5-mile radius. Hours: 12-12.

Stirling

RANA'S NEW ENTRANT

37, Friar Street, FK8 1HA   01786 463 075

'Stylish, modern 60 seater in centre of town, decorated somewhere between a Berni Inn and a Pizzeria.Pakistani and Sikh staff, all knowledgeable and courteous. Lasan Prawn £4.95, superb, well presented, delicious, seriously aromatic, yet delicate, served with delicate sauce and crisp salad. Lamb Jaipuri Jeera £7.95 perfect balance of spices, mouth watering sauce, encasing the best lamb tikka I have ever had, moist and tender. More restaurants need to sell Garlic and Paneer Naans, fabulous, moist, crisp base, particularly light, despite topping. Only cloud, was a loudmouth cockney/Essex boy, who thought that shouting at the staff would endear him to his parents, who were visible seething. A stunningly good meal.' RW. Cabaret, as well as a good meal, sorry I missed that one! Hours: 12-11.

TAYSIDE

(Inc Angus, Kinross and Perthshire)

Area: East Scotland
Population: 395,000 of which Dundee 141,000
Adjacent Counties: Central, Fife, Grampian, Highland, Strathclyde

Dundee

ASHOKA EXPRESS

3, Wellgate Centre, Dundee   0800 195 3 195

Harlequin Leisure Group, (see Glasgow) has entered the fast food market with the combined name of Ashoka Express/Italy Express which the Group hope to roll out all over the UK. The dual entrance into the food court - from both the rear and the front of the Wellgate - means that it is always very busy. It offers a range of curries and 'meal deals'. Hours: 12-11. Branch: Ashoka Shak, Camperdown Leisure Park, Dundee, DD2 3SQ. Fast food but with sit-in area.

DIL SE   AWARD WINNER

99 Perth Road, Dundee   01382 221501

Abdour Rouf's 150-seat Dil Se restaurant (pron dill see and means, 'from the heart.') was presented with the Dundee Civic Trust Award for its outstanding contribution to the improvement of the city when it opened in 2003. Billed as the largest Bangladeshi restaurant in Scotland it specialises in Bangladeshi, Indian and Thai cuisine Clients dress up to eat here, as the modern and stylish air of this restaurant requires it. The fresh, organic ingredients, herbs and vegetables, are grown in the garden behind its sister establishment, The Balaka, St Andrews. Locally produced salmon is also a speciality, served marinated in chilli, coriander and cumin - delicious and healthy! *Its sister restaurant, the Balaka in St Andrews, Fife has been thrilling curryholics, myself included, and winning prestigious Curry Club awards for 21 years. Decor is modern and minimalist and the toilets are like a fake leopard skin coat - absolutely spotless. The Dil Se menu is a carbon copy of The Balaka's and every last morsel of food is cooked to order. 'Please be patient,' says the blurb on the front page. 'Good food is like art and like at it takes time.' We kicked off with chilli pickle - careful, friends, this red hot stuff will seriously blow your tights off - and a pile of popadums that were so fresh I'm surprised they didn't try to slip the haun. Then ce the real starters - Chicken Tikka and a Shi Kebab. Simple Chicken Tikka is always a smart option if you want to judge any Indian - or, in this case, Bangladeshi restaurant. The Tikka at Dil Se was perfect. Every mouthful burst with flavour - particularly when smeared thickly with the awesome chilli pickle - and I loved the tasty little burnt bits. From the list of fifteen or so chef specials, I tried the Mas Bangla, salmon fillet, marinated in lime juice, turmeric, green chilli and several other spices then fried in mustard oil with garlic, onion, tomato and aubergine. Believe it or not, it tasted even better than it sounds, and special doesn't even begin to describe it. I said it before and I'll say it again, why can't more curry houses start using salmon. It always works well'.* T Cowan, Dundee Record. This is an outstanding, caring restaurant, and following the tradition of its sister, the Balaka in St Andrews, Fife, we took great pleasure in giving it our Best in scotland award 2004/5 award. Del: 20m, £2 min Hours: Sun-Thurs 5-1; 12-1 Fri & Sat. Open Christmas Day. Branch: Balaka, St Andrews. .

YOU SAY OK
You might get a discount if you show them this Guide.

PERTH: MANZIL 13 York Pl. ~ 01738 446222. Rana Ali 's 85-seater. Hours: 12-2 / 5-11.30. Branch: Tandoori Knights, Princess Street, Perth (t/a only).

TANDOORI NIGHTS 12, Princes St. ~ 01738 441277. 38-seater est 1998. Specialities: Chicken Nashedar c£7 – barbecued chicken or lamb in a spiced cream based sauce with cashew nuts and flavoured with brandy. Menu also has Turkish kebabs, Italian Pizzas and European Dishes. T/a: 10% disc. Del: free in Perth. Hours: 5-12; 1 Sat.

WALES

Population: 2.9 million

For Wales as with England, the Guide runs alphabetically in county and town order. In 1996 a large number of Unitary Authorities replaced the six Welsh counties (regions) which had themselves replaced the age-old shires and smaller counties in 1965. To provide a convenient geographical division of Wales in this Guide, we retain the six former counties (listing their shires within them). With a population of under 3 million, (nearly matched by Greater Manchester alone) and under 300 curry restaurants in the whole of Wales, (there are more in London SW) we cannot say Cymru is big on the nation's favourite food. As ever, we would very much welcome a plethora of Welsh reports for next time.

CLWYD

Contains Denbighshire, Flintshire and Wrexham and (recently) Conway.

Area: North Wales
Population: 421,000
Adjacent Counties:
Cheshire, Gwynedd,
Powys, Shrops

Deeside (Shotton)

BENGAL DYNASTY   A-LIST

106 Chester Road East   01244 830455

Monchab Ali bought a former guest house in 1991 and converted it into a stylish, spacious restaurant. In 2001, the restaurant reopened after having had a complete face-lift at a cost of over £200,000. A stunning new entrance, bigger windows, change of interior colour, new floor. It is air-conditioned, purpose-built, airy and elegant, luxury and a fabulous Demonstration Kitchen allows diners to see the technical wizardry of the Corporate Chef Partha Mitra and his brigade preparing and cooking their north Indian and Bangladeshi dishes. The smartly-furnished restaurant managed by Rico is fully-licensed, and seats 92 in modern comfort and the roomy lounge bar, takes 40. It has disabled access. The menu includes Kashmir Rezala, Chicken Bondhu, Satkora (citrus) Gosth and Bengal Fish Curry. *'Truly exceptional place. Immense size – huge. Politely greeted and guided to bar.The food was just the business. This restaurant is well worthy of its Best in North Wales rating.'* MW. *'Outstanding.'* waj. The Dynasty's Bangladeshi food festival was raved over by locals, as were the cookery demos, sometimes from Monchab himself. T/a: 15% disc. Del: £12 min, 5-miles. Hours: 12-2.30 / 5.30-11.30; 12.30-11. Branch: Bengal Dynasty Northwich, Cheshire and Llandudno Gwynedd. www.bengaldynasty.com

PLAZA AMANTOLA

Welsh Rd, Sealand   01244 811383

Opened in 1997. A pretty restaurant decorated in reds and greens with soft, comfortable sofas to relax on while taking coffee and liqueurs after a satisfying spicy meal. Seats 300 diners in two rooms. *'Incredibly impressive looking restaurant. A large and imposing free-standing building by the main North Wales Coast Road (A55) and right opposite RAF Sealand. Large car park complete with fountain and elephant statues leads to an elegantly decorated interior. Friendly knowledgeable staff, some of whom are noticeably local! Extensive menu, though the special dishes have made up names, which I found detracted from the cuisine. Very nice Chicken Chat £3.20, very light and remarkably grease free Puri with pleasant and delicate taste of its own. Topped with lovely combination of small pieces of tender chicken in a mouth watering sauce topped with a generous sprinkle of Chat Masala. lamb Rogan Josh £6.50 - just as good, excellent pieces of lamb, free of fat and gristle, served in a tasty, tangy sauce rich in herbs and spices. This was served with a light and fluffy, mould of al-dente Pullao Rice £1.85 - well perfumed and lump free. A smashing meal.'* RW. *'Overall an excellent lunch.'* DB. T/a: 10% disc. Del: 5m, min Ch £15. Hours: 12-2 / 5.30-12; 12-12 Sat & Sun.

YOU SAY OK
You might get a discount if you show them this Guide.

FLINT: VERANDA 15 Chester St. ~ 01352 732504. Chef owner, Adbul's *'food is very tasty, the staff friendly and welcoming. If you get a table at the back, you can catch a glimpse of the cooking in the kitchen. Chicken Tikka flambée: they pour Sambuca onto the sizzling platter and flames shoot two feet in the air.'* DV-W. Snapshot: Ostrich Tikka £4, with salad; Mussels £9.50, in a lively broth of chillies and curry leaves; King Prawn Gratin £11.50, barbecued with butter sauce, topped with cheese Del: £10 min. Hours: 12-2.30/5-11; 12-7 Sun Buf.

FLINT: RAJ BALTI 70 Chester St. ~ 01352 733633. *'Chicken Phal consistently good, as hot as a phal should be. Good portions, excellent. BYO.'* SA&AP.

LLANGOLLEN: SPICE LOUNGE 36 Regent St. ~ 01978 861877. *'Service polite, smart and efficient. Pops & picks excellent. Started with Chicken Chat, excellent, succulent. Sheek Kebab and Aloo Puri , good. Main courses: Chilli Masala (inc PR), very red, very hot, superb flavour. lamb Dhansak, good. Very tender lamb Pasanda, but sauce was colour of CTM. House Special Balti, very filling, well worth the extra pence. Fresh, hot Pullao Rice and excellent, stinking of garlic, Garlic Nan £1.40. Hot towels and complimentary brandies served. Overall a great meal.'* MPW. Hours: 12-2, Sat & Sun only /6-12 daily.

Wrexham

CHIRK TANDOORI

1 Station Av, Chirk, Wrexham   01691 772499

'Smart, well-ordered, staff exceptionally polite, helpful and efficient. Meal for four was truly outstanding in every aspect. I ordered Prawn Phall (not on the menu) which was one of the best I have ever tasted – hugely prawned and no evidence of the dreaded Campbells Tomato Soup syndrome! My three friends were equally impressed.' DC. Hours: 6-11.30.

JAMUNA

18 Yorke Street, Wrexham	01978 261142

'Service excellent, hot food, tasty good portions, although my husband would like more sauce with Jalfrezi. plenty of chicken in Dhansak and Balti, well presented. Reasonably priced house wine.' DV-W. T/a: 10% disc, min £13. 20% disc, min £17. Menu Extracts: Murghi Masala £11.20, half spring-chicken, creamy sauce of minced meat; Chana Special £6.95, tomatoes, green peppers, onion, chick peas, bhuna sauce; Service: 10%.

DYFED

Contains Cardigan, Carmarthenshire & Pembrokeshire.

Area: West Wales
Population: 356,000
Adjacent Counties:
Glam, Powys,Gwynedd

Carmarthen

TAJ BALTI

119 Priory St, Carmarthen	01267 221995

Opened in 1995 by Lias Miah who might give you a disc if you show him this Guide. *'My husband and I always enjoy their fare. Elegant decor, service excellent and friendly, with superb food. Muted traditional music, intimacy of individual booths, a special atmosphere. Tandoori Mixed Grill declared the best ever.'* JF. Hours: 6-12.

Llanelli

ALI RAJ   NEW ENTRANT

Bryn Yard, Trinity Rd, New Dock,	SA15 2AB
	01554 777727

'Really is great, food and hospitality. Ali feels that as they are so far from Cardiff and there are so many restaurants in the area, they don't get a chance to be entered for awards. Always busy and food always to the same standard. Impressed with cleanliness, tables and chairs wiped down at end of night.' DV-W. Menu Snapshot: Chicken Roll £2.35, crispy rolled pastries filled with chicken; Spinach and Chicken/Lamb Balti £5.70, served with Naan.

YOU SAY OK
You might get a discount if you show them this Guide.

LLANELLI: BENGAL LANCER 43 Murray St. ~ 01554 749199. 78-seater opened by Ahmed Ali in 1986. Muzaffar heads the cooking. Hours: 12-2.30/6-12. Branch: Anarkali , Swansea.

LLANELLI: VERANDAH 20 Market St. ~ 01554 759561. 64-seater est 1985 by Mr A.Khalique. Bright turmeric walls, indigo carpet and shelving with chilli-red and orange chairs and sofas.

Special: Charga Mossalla (half spring-chicken, with tomatoes, green peppers & red wine). Hours: 6-12; 12.30 Sat.

TENBY: BAY OF BENGAL 1 Crackenwell St. ~ 01834 843331 *'A lovely venue with some excellent restaurants. Very good meal at The Bay of Bengal. Beautifully furnished, restaurant looks out to the sea, food matched the view. Chicken and Chickpea for Linda and King Prawn Bhuna for me - so many prawns!'* MG.

GLAMORGAN

Contains West, Mid & South
Glamorgan.

Area: South Wales
Population: 1,346,000
Adjacent Counties:
Dyfed, Gwent, Powys

In 1996, the counties of West, Mid and South Glamorganshire were disbanded in favour of 11 Unitary Authorities to administrate the 11 large towns (incl Newport) in the area. For Guide convenience we have retained the former Glamorgan geography. For Newport see Gwent.

YOU SAY OK
You might get a discount if you show them this Guide.

BARRY: MODERN BALTI 290 Holton Rd. ~ 01446 746787. Est1982 by A Akbar. Menu Snapshot: Chicken Nugget Tikka £2.40 - the kids will love that one! Balti Tandoori Grill £3.55' chicken and lamb tikka, sheek and balti kebab, with salad and mint sauce. Pakora Masala £3.90, spicy potato, vegetables in a thick spicy sauce; lamb Kalia £5.60, with chillies, garlic potatoes, coriander leaves: hot spicy sauce. Hours: 5.30-12.30; 1.30 Fri & Sat.

BARRY: SHAHI NOOR 87 High St. ~ 01446 735706. Owner Maybur Rahman. Hours: 12-2.30 / 6-12.

BRIDGEND: CAFÉ BANGLA 53 Nolton St ~ 01656 750070. M Uddin's 55-seater. Snapshot: Jhinga Caldeen £8.50, king prawns cooked with garlic, ginger, lime juice, cream, coconut and mixed spicy chillies; Goa lamb Vindaloo £8, marinated lamb cooked with fresh green chillies, paprika, tomato purée, fenugreek and coriander; Komola Chicken £8, spiced chicken in a rich orange sauc.. Sun Buffet: £8 adult, £5 children. T/a: 10% disc. Hours: 5.30-11; 11.30 Fri & Sat; 1-10 Sun. www.cafe-bangla.com

CAERPHILLY: CASTLE GATE 5 Castle View Shopping Centre, Nantgarw Hill, Nantgarw, Caerphilly 029 2088 1106. Koysar Hussain's venue is part of the Empire Group, see next entry. Hours: 12-2 except Friday / 5-12. www.empiregroup.inf

CARDIF, TREFOREST: CINNAMON TREE NEW ENTRANT Tonteg Road, CF37 5UA ~ 01443 843222. 108-seater, oened 1998, just off the A470, between Cardiff and Pontypridd. Hours: 6-10.30; 12-10 Sun

CARDIFF, PONTCANNA: CINNAMON TREE, 173, Kings Rd, CF11 9DE. 029 2037 4433. Branch of above.

CARDIFF WENTLOOG: CINNAMON TREE Peterstone Lake Golf Club, CF3 2TN. 01633 689 082. Branch of above.

Cardiff

BALTI EMPIRE

157-159 Albany Rd, Roath	029 2048 5757

Owner Mujib Mohammed created the Empire Group, a group of six South Wales-based Asian restaurants formed with an aim to "raise the standard of Asian

cuisine" in South Wales. They now Official Restaurants of Cardiff County Council Festival, and are currently holders of a number of regional awards, including the South Wales Echo Indian Restaurant of the Year. They We have also set up an annual Asian Food & Culture Festival. All six off the curryhouse menu with all your favourites. Members: Castle Gate Caerphilly (above), Bay Leaf, Jinuk and Mujib's Cardiff and Indian Empire, Caldicot, Gwent. Hours: 12-2 except Friday / 5-12. www.empiregroup.info

BAY LEAF

29 High St,Llandaff, Cardiff   029 2056 7400

Mohammed Sai established it in 2000 in the historic settings near the Cathedral. Quality Indian food at a competitive price, in a pleasant atmosphere. Hours: 12-2 except Friday / 5-12. www.empiregroup.info

CAFÉ NAZ   A-LIST

8 Mermaid Quay, Cardiff   029 2049 6555

Cafe Naz maintains a classic Indian identity with ultra modern fittings. Customers are welcomed in the bar and seating area complete with a crescent of fashionable, soft minimalist seats facing a chic wooden bar. The service is polite without being stuffy, a standard which is maintained throughout the evening. Cafe Naz's family ownership and management have created a warm, caring environment, a rarity in restaurants of this high calibre. The food is simply divine, and at its currently deflated prices, is a treat not to be missed. Views of Cardiff bay and St. David's hotel are enhanced in the summer when meals are served on the balcony. Entertainment includes a vast (yet amazingly unobtrusive) screen silently playing the best of Bollywood and occasionally traditional Indian dancers. The on-view kitchen is behind glass and you can watch the cooks at work. The menu contains 30 starters 32 main courses and a extensive wine and beer list. The non veg platter is a feast for two, with two types of chicken (tikka and tandoori), lamb seek kabab, pakodi each given in ample portions. Set Lunches: c£8 or c£6. Del£12, 2m. Hours: Mon to Thurs 2 - 3/ 5-12 Sat & Sun: 12 -12. Branches, London E1. Cambridge.

JINUK

185 Cowbridge Rd Et, Canton   029 2038 7778

Shahin Ahmed's venue is part of the Empire Group Restaurant, see Balti Empire, earlier. Quality Indian food at a competitive price, in a pleasant atmosphere. Hours: 12-2, not Friday /5-12. www.empiregroup.info

JUBORAJ   A-LIST

10 Mill La, Hayes, Cardiff   029 2037 7668

Cardiff's Juboraj Group, consisting of five quality

restaurants, three in Cardiff, one in Newport and the other in Swansea were awarded Best Business to the Community Award at the Welsh Awards 2003 held at St David's Hall, Menu snapshot: Starters include Bhajees, Samosas, Pakoras, kebabs and Tandoori items. Main courses: Karahi Duck - tender pieces of duck barbecued and tossed in medium spices with onions, tomatoes and green peppers; Chicken Shashlick, cooked in the clay oven with green peppers, onions and tomatoes, served with a mild sauce; Machli Biran, salmon steak delicately spiced & gently fried Sag Paneer, spicy spinach and cottage cheese; Paneer Chilli Masala, with fresh green chillies and Special Fried Rice, with eggs, peas, onions, almond and spices. Desserts include Sticky Toffee Pud, Apple and Blackberry Crumble. This branch is *'fairly large, comfortable restaurant, good reputation, very popular. Visited by Tom Jones'* [wow!] *'In my opinion, one of Cardiff's best. Another visit, and the food once again was excellent.'* JB. *'Food excellent, service not.'* G&MP. *'Celebrating a Liverpool FC's nail-biting penalty shoot out victory, we took the Guide's advice and headed for this restaurant. Service initially prompt, but as the fans from both sides descended, things got a little hectic at times! Popadums and Kebabs (Shami and Sheek) both excellent. Main courses, Chicken Madras, Chicken Sagwalla accompanied by Pullao Rice, Nan and Tarka Dal, excellent! Food a little more expensive, guess that was a result of its town centre location! Will visit again – hopefully when no footy!* DL. Hours: 12-2 / 6-12. Branches 11 Heol Y Deri, Cardiff 029 2062 8894, also 84 Commercial St, Newport 01633 262646 and 20 Wind St, Swansea. 01792 649944.   juborajgroup.com

JUBORAJ LAKESIDE

Lake Road West Lakeside 029 2045 5123

Love the chairs in this restaurant, made from cane with wicker and upholstered in a richly coloured paisley styled material and a scrolled back, really nice. See above. Hours: 6-11.

MUJIB'S   NEW ENTRANT

Caerphilly Rd, CF14 4AD   029 2069 1515

Owner, Mujib Mohammed opened here at the Former Cross Inn) It provides Indian and oriental cuisine at the same table at a competitive price, in a pleasant atmosphere. A feature is the bar with illuminated aquatic pumps and black corian bar surface. The restaurant has its own smaller white corian bar. It is part of the Empire Group Restaurant, see Balti Empire, earlier. Hours:12-2, not Friday /5-12.   www.empiregroup.info

SPICE MERCHANT

The Big Windsor, Stuart Street, Cardiff Bay
                                              029 2049 8984

Mike Ahmed spent £450,000 to give the Windsor

Hotel, an historic docklands pub, a new identity. Spice Merchant, is a modern ground and first floor 180 seater. The first floor lounge and restaurant seats up to 130. Ahmed is also actively involved in promoting the Indian Food festival – a yearly event, held in Aberystwyth. Snapshot: Fish Tikka, cod marinated in yoghurt with mild spices and herbs; Pepper Chicken or Lamb, large whole green pepper stuffed with extra spicy and garlic chicken tikka or lamb tikka, both £3. Mains: Jalander Gusht, lamb cooked with spices in curry sauce, £7; Chengi Kapso, Prawns cooked in delicately flavoured oriental sauce with potato and tomato, £7.50; Maslee Bengal Trout, cooked with tomatoes, chillies, coriander and bombay duck sauce, £7.50; Khatlama, chicken or lamb, Bhuna style curry including green chilli and coriander, then deep fried in paratha and served with pilau rice and salad for a complete meal, £10.50. Branch: 8 Park Pl, Cardiff. www.spicemerchantcardiff.co.uk

Kenfig Hill

MUKTA MAHAL

104 Pisgah Street   01656 746000

'Once a Bingo Hall. Spacious layout with large water fountain. It is possible to have a Thai / Indian mixed meal - the only problem - what to choose! Quality of food very good indeed with excellent service, even on busy nights. Worth a detour off the M4 at junction 36. Highly recommended.' KN. Thai Specials: Tord Mun Pla, deep-fried spicy fish cakes with cucumber, salad, delicate sweet and sour peanut; Yum Woonsen, spicy glass noodle salad with prawns and chicken; Gaeng Mad Sa Man Gai, spicy Muslim chicken curry, sweet potatoes, coconut milk, peanuts; Pla Rad Prik, crispy fish fillet topped with a hot chilli and garlic sauce. Indian Specials: Chicken Pakora; Chicken Makhani, tossed in butter, yoghurt, fresh cream, tomatoes and spices, lamb Tikka Mahal, green chillies, garlic, coriander; Keema Rice. T/a: 10% disc. Hours: 12-2.30/5.30-12; 12.30 Fri & Sat; 12-12 Sun.

Swansea

ANARKALI

80 St Helen's Road, Swansea 01792 650549

Fully licensed and air-conditioned 60-seater established by A Rahman way back in 1978. Such long-standing gives it an assurance, experience and confidence with a long list of regulars. Menu Extracts: Crab Malabar, made from flaked fresh crab, sautéed with spices. Mahasha, cabbage leaves stuffed with lamb mince, rice and selected green herbs, sweet and sour flavour. Goan lamb Vindaloo, marinated lamb with hot chilli, fresh green chilli, paprika, tomato puree, fenugreek and coriander. Sun Buffet: c£9 eat as much as you like. Hours: 5.30-12, 2am Sat; 12-12 Sun.

BONOPHOL BANGLADESHI

93 Sterry Road, Gowerton 01792 875253

Bonophol means 'forest flower'. The exterior is elegantly picked out in attractive tones of green and gilt, and this theme continues inside, with with chandelier, modern Bangladeshi art and forty cane chairs. Menu Extracts: Murg Nawabi, barbecued chicken, blended with fresh herbs and spices, garnished with chopped spiced egg. Mr Imran has moved on (See Phool Koli later) and we need reports please about Bonophol. Sun Buffet: 12-5, c£7 adult, c£5 children. T/a: 10% disc. Del: £10min, 4m. Hours: 5.30-12; 12.25 Fri & Sat; 12-12 Sun.

LAL QUILA

480 Mumbles Rd, Mumbles   01792 363520

'Everything is spotless with quick and friendly service. I particularly like the Chicken Methi with lots of fresh fenugreek. Food generally good.' JD. *'Very stylish, airy atmosphere with wonderful views over Swansea Bay. Over-formal, but efficient service and excellent, unusual menu – ostrich and monkfish. Fair portion of Mangalorian Fish Curry and excellent Aloo Paratha. Quality and nice for a change.'* IB. *'Restaurant was quiet, only about a dozen other diners. Flat screen TV's on each wall, showing Bolywood films, different. Food very good, staff very friendly. Recommended.'* DV-W.

MIAH'S

St Paul's Church, St Helens Rd 01792 466244

Abdu Miah opened it in 2001 in a former church. It's not the first curryhouse in a church, but done well it does lead interesting venue, and yes, the décor is done well here. The bar is now the high altar, picked out with gothic arches in its front panels. Over it is a funky modern chandelier. Tables line the blonde wood floor. Your eye is drawn to the sweeping staircase, which shows off the huge stained-glass gothic window, and up to the fabulous vaulted roof. The stairs sweep left and right and take you to the balcony. But you can't eat the décor. We have desisted entering Miah's before because you tell us of uncaring service, excess red colouring and cold food. But of late we have had more cheering reports, and we'd like more please. The menu offers all the Bangladeshi curryhouse favourites, and there is a section called the 'connoisseur's menu' with a selection of chef's specials. Prices a bit higher than average. Lunch and dinner daily.

PHOOL KOLI BANGLADESHI
TAKEAWAY   NEW ENTRANT & NEW TOP 100

64 Lone Rd, Clydach, SA6 5HU   01792 846147

After 17 years at the helm of one of Swansea's top restaurants, Mohammed al Imran and his partner Samad

PHOOL KOLI BANGLADESHI TAKEAWAY

64 Lone Road, Clydach,
Swansea, SA6 5HU
01792 846147 / 846028
Hours: 5.30 - 11.15 daily

Go north out
of Swansea on
the A4067,
under the M4
and Clydach
is right there.

Uzaman have opened a new venue near Swansea city. Phool Koli, meaning 'Flower Bud' is a Takeaway venue. The food is Bangladeshi / Indian, cooked by chefs led by Shamin Ahmed, who has worked in top restaurants London and Swansea. Menu Snapshot: Komola Chicken or Lamb £5.20, rich orange sauce; Sali Gosht £5.20, lamb cooked with dry apricot, dressed with thin slices of potatoes; Kulcha and Lasson Naan £1.80, fresh garlic, onions, coriander. And Imran guarantees an exceptional quality of the food matched with an above average level of service and customer care. This gives the new venture a distinct advantage over the competition, and it is this pedigree which has brought Phool Koli to the early notice of this Guide. Knowing Imran, we are making it a Top 100. And he will no doubt give you a discount if you show him this Guide. Hours: 5.30-11.15.

Pictured: Mr Imran is on the right. His partner Mr Uzaman is alongside , with Chef Ahmed in the whites. Note the 2007 Good Curry Guide.

KARMA 3 3 Victoria Rd. ~ 01792 477848. Opposite Swansea Leisure Centre, Karma's frontage is very striking, decorated with blue mosaic, so you can't miss it. Furniture, wood and wrought iron, was specially imported. The restaurant is deceiving in size, in fact it is quite big, with dining rooms upstairs and down. Licensed. Sun Banquet, served between 12-10: adult £7, child £4.50. Mon-Sat 2 course lunch, just £4.95. Hours: 12-2/6-11

NAWAB 12 Christina Street ~ 01792 470770. Opened in 1976. Mr Miah (manager) Del: 2m, £10.

GWENT
Monmouthshire

Area: South west
Wales
Population: 454,000
Adjacent Counties:
Glamorgan, Gloucs,
Herefordshire and Powys

In the 1996 reorganisation, Monmouthshire was restored for some purposes and Gwent for others, including for this Guide. Newport became an independent Unitary Authority, and we retain it here.

Abergavenny

SHAHI BALTI

5 Mill Street Abergavenny   01873 792011

'Having gone to visit friends, they chose the venue and booked a table – good job too – very popular with locals and those from out of town. Had a drink in the tiny bar, whilst table was readied. Chose a rather unimaginative Chicken and Potato Balti, pleasantly surprised, tasty indeed, good value at £6.50. Suggested a vegetable Thali for friend, who is unused to eating spicy food. Very impressed, a very appetising selection with ample portions. One other thing to note - Nan's, tasty, substantial.' MD. Hours: 6-11.30.

Caldicot

INDIAN EMPIRE

Park Wall Crick, Caldicot   01291 431144

Kazad Uddin's venue is a member of the Empire Group, (see Cardiff). *'Situated 3m from the Welsh border town of Chepstow and 12m from the city of Newport on the A48, this giant 180-seater is well positioned with ample parking. Inside is pristine with background music creating a very relaxed atmosphere. The friendly waiters and excellent service makes sure that your visit is memorable and you return again. I made two visits to meet the Manager Tufayer Ahmed and the Chef Abdul Boshor to see the food preparation. The Kitchen was clean and tidy and there was always someone with a mop ready to clean up any spillages. All the cooking instruments*

were cleaned once finished with. Chef showed me how they prepare their bases and rice for the day, which were Masala, Korma, Curry and Pillau Rice. From experience on my two visits the bases were cooked with fresh ingredients and the meals were also cooked to a high standard with fresh spices and nice presentation for the customer. Chef said, "if customers spend good money the customer deserves good food." The kitchen staff were very synchronised with everyone knowing their part to play from prep work to the customers final dish on the table. As for the the food, my wife and I ordered Chicken Tikka Masala twice (one was madras hot), a Keema Naan, a plain Naan, Keema fried rice, pillau rice and chips.' [CHIPS???] 'The food was all I expected it to be hot, fresh and spicy. I highly recommend this restaurant. Once a month it has a buffet night.' MJ. Hours: 12-2 except Fri / 6-11.30. www.indianempire.co.uk

Crumlin

RAJDOOT

17 Main Street Crumlin   01495 243032

'Feeling hungry on the way home from Newport one night. Have tried it a few times since, even though it is quite away from my home, about 10m. I particularly like the Roghan Gosht, which was rich and creamy with a good portion. The Rajpoot Thali was excellent with a very good fruit salad. £21 for two.' PH. Hours: 5.30-12, 12.30 Fri & Sat.

Monmouth

MISBAH TANDOORI   A-LIST

9 Priory Street, NP25 3BR   01600 714940

D Miah opened his 80-seater restaurant in 1990. It is situated in the historic Market town of Monmouth. The restaurant itself is situated by the Monnow, it is also in the immediate vicinity of Monmouth castle and the ancient Market square. The restaurant is in an ideal position for visitors, being located conveniently close to the main A40 dual carriageway. Brum is less then 1 hour, Newport, 20 mins, Bristol 40, Cardiff, 35. This comfortable venue exudes customer care. Mr Miah's Misbah attracts celebs, and he's delighted to tell you about them (ask him – each one has a tale). Chef A Rahman heads the chef brigade. Menu Snapshot: Bengal Fish Mossala (freshwater fish from Bangladesh cooked in tomato and onion, Zahan Special, medium, aubergines, spinach, potato, chickpea, mixed vegetables; Jamdani all mild, chicken cooked with cheese, cream c£7.95; Spicy Wing Masala £4.95; Baigan Aloo Masala £5.95, aubergine and potato; Shahi Rice £3.95, almond, sultanas, peas, onion and spices; Special Nan £2.25, stuffed with vegetables, egg, cheese and spices. *'As good as all the reports I have read: clean, friendly, basic menu, good service. Strangely quiet for a Friday night though. Excellent*

Chicken Jalfrezi and Pullao Rice. Excellent.' IB. 'Warm, personal welcome. Intimate friendly service. Appealingly presented tables. All senses catered for. Wonderful food, succulent meat, stupendous prawns - all flavours beautifully blended, a richly textured Tarka Dal. Fluffy and exotically flavoured Rice and above all FRESH Mango! Gastronomic excellent.' GL & DT. 'Have visited for over five years. Exceptionally high standard. Feels like home.' JT. 'Popadums and chutneys arrived immediately. Exciting menu with authentic dishes. Clean toilets.' S&DT. 'Food superb and promptly served.' HE. 'The quality of the food is a good mix between the comfort blanket of the traditional and the innovative and new.' AR. 'Delicious, wonderful food, lots of lovely vegetarian dishes.' J&HA. Super stuff. Misbah has been in our Guide since it opened. In our last Guide (2007/8, we awarded it the ultimate: Best in Wales. Such an Award can lead to criticism and it did.We got one *'disappointed'* report (but just the one) from JC. Min Ch: £10.00. Set dinner: £11.95 per person. T/a: 10% off. Hours: 12-2.30, 2 Fri & Sat / 6 - 11; 5.30-11.30 Fri & Sat. www.misbahtandoori.co.uk

Newport

DELHI   NEW ENTRANT

131, Caerleon Rd, NP19 7BZ   01633 222281

'Warm welcome, friendly staff. When the Popadoms arrived, the waiters warned us that one chutney as particularly hot; he was right, but it was delicious. Chicken Tikka and Onion Bhajia were quickly polished off. Undoubtedly the best Chicken Biryani, wonderful mixture of vegetables in sauce.' JH. Menu Snapshot: Jinga Puri, king prawns, thick sauce, served with puffy bread; Badami Passanda, chicken with mild fruit sauce, cashew nuts and cream; Persian Birany, mixture of chicken, pineapple, sultanas, cashew nuts, omelette, served with curry sauce; Half and Half, Pullao Rice and chips! well, that will please the kids, won't it! Hours: 5.30 to late.   www.delhi-restaurant.co.uk

JUBORAJ

84 Commercial Street, Risca   01633 262646

'Good decor, classy, almost temple-like, very clean and inviting. Welcoming, friendly staff, attentive. Good and pricey menu. Very tasty, fresh Mixed Starter – onion bhajia, meat samosas and chicken pakora, small portion. lamb and Prawn Madras with Pullao Rice and Aloo Gobi, very good portions with generous sauce, not at all oily, flavoursome. Delicious Chicken Tikka Masala. Special Fried Rice a bit disappointing, seemed very similar to Pullao Rice. All in all very good.' PAH. Menu Extracts: Juboraj King Prawn, cooked in shell; Coriander Chicken, fillets, ground coriander; Kohlapuri, hot and spicy chicken, turmeric, cumin, coriander, green chillies. Hours: 12-2 / 6-12. juborajgroup.com

YOU SAY OK - NEWPORT, GWENT
You might get a discount if you show them this Guide.

BALTI NITE 8 Gladstone St, Crosskeys ~ 01495 271234 40-seater est 1995 by Chef Abdul KahimSpecials include: Chicken Kohlpuri £6, hot and spicy with turmeric, cumin, coriander and green chillies; Nilgiri Mirch £6, sautéed lamb with coconut, ginger, mint and coriander leaves and Ayre Mossala £7, Bangladeshi freshwater (boal) oven baked in sauce with coriander leaves, green peppers, green chillies, spinach, ginger and mustard, Del: 3m, £20 min. Hours: 5.30-12.

CWMBRAN, LLANFRECHA: NR CWMBRAN, THE RAJ GATE NEW ENTRANT Cweleon Rd, Llanfrecha, Nr Cwmbran, NP44 8DQ   01633 875155   Hours: 12-2 (not Fri(/5.30-11. therajgate.co.uk

GWYNEDD

Contains: Caernarfonshire and Merionethshire and for the purposes of this Guide, Anglesey.

Area: North Wales
Population: 240,000
Adjacent Counties:
Clwyd, Dyfed, Powys

Abersoch

EAST MEETS WEST

The High Street Abersoch   01758 713541

Opened 2006. *'Modern establishment in heart of quaint village. Open, light and airy interior, subtly decorated. Run by young and friendly staff, service efficient and cheerful. Excellent Reshmi Kebab single, large, succulent well spiced kebab, topped with a large, well cooked omelette. Nice, crisp salad, but yoghurt sauce would not have gone amiss. Superb lamb Balti Rogan Josh, tangy, beautifully balanced sauce, plenty of tomatoes, well cooked onions and peppers. Stuffed with good cuts of tender lamb, though gristle and tough lumps were present. They take the translation of Balti literally, my curry was served in a copper plated stainless steel bucket! Very well cooked Chapati for two, soft, moist but not doughy or salty. Very enjoyable, highly recommended. Up to Top 100 standard.'* RW. Menu Extracts: Bengal King Prawns, hot with green chillies, bay leaves, cinnamon; Agni, Chicken or lamb Tikka cooked with onions, peppers, flambéed in brandy; Egg Nan; Keema Paratha. Hours: 6 to late.

Llanberis

SPICE OF LLANBERIS

32 High Street, Llanberis   01286 871983

In Abdul Jalil 2005 took over the Balti Raj and renamed it. There are sixty seats and chef Suruk Miah cooks up Bangladeshi styled curries, including Shere e Bangla

£6.50 - medium dry spiced chicken and lamb tikka with spring onions, green peppers, herbs, garlic and mushrooms served with vegetable curry sauce; Sylheti Chicken £6.50 - marinated, sliced chicken, lightly spiced, medium hot sauce, boiled eggs, green peppers - recommended with Pullao Rice; Jomuna Issa £6.50 - prawns, medium sauce, garlic, ginger, coriander leaves. Cobra, £2.90 a bottle, house wine £8.50 a bottle. You might get a disc if you show Mr Jalil this Guide. Hours: 5-11. Branch: Polash Balti, 28, Penlawst, Pwllheli.

Llandrindod Wells

CHELEE SPICE

Emporium Bldg, 2 Temple St   01597 823844

Opened in 1995 by Abdul Khalique. Korma and Tikka Masala are his most popular dishes. Menu Snapshot: Nargis Kebab £2.85, boiled egg covered with a thin layer of minced lamb cooked in a clay oven and garnished with a delicate sauce; Spiced Potato and Garlic Mushrooms £2.75, soft, fluffy spiced potato balls served with salted mushrooms in garlic butter; Tandoori Mixed Grill £9.10, lamb and chicken tikka, tandoori chicken, sheek kebab, king prawn and nan; Salmon Spice £6.95, salmon steak, lightly spiced, garnished with coriander and spring onion, Peshwari, Onion, Coriander, Vegetable or Garlic Nan all £1.60 each. Hours: 5.30- 1.30; 1 Fri & Sat.

Llandudno

BENGAL   DYNASTY   A-LIST

1 North Parade, Llandudno   01492 878445

Manikur Ahmed opened his 86-seat Bengal Dynasty the day before Bangladesh Independence Day, in 1988. Llandudno is a really fabulous seaside town with gorgeous Georgian buildings running in an arch along the waterfront. Lewis Carroll wrote Alice in Wonderland in this seaside resort. The Bengal Dynasty is situated upstairs in three dining rooms in one of these fine buildings. Popular dishes include: Jalfrezi, Masala, and Korai Specials:: Chicken Bondhuk; lamb Satkora Bangladeshi citrus fruit; and Macher Tarkari, a Bangladeshi fish dish. All Tandoori dishes are served with green salad and mint yoghurt. *'I was about to settle for fish & chips when I saw it, upstairs above a shoe shop. I had lamb Tikka to start and then Chicken Bhuna, which was excellent.'* AG *'King Prawn Butterfly followed by my usual main courses. A very accomplished meal. Keema Nan was the highlight together with a homemade Kulfi. Gets my vote.'* JL. *'Service was welcoming, prompt and polite. Pops and chuts fresh and crisp. Main meals were large, everything was hot and well presented. An enjoyable experience, but not outstanding.'* SR. *'Menu was wide and varied. Popadums and chutneys excellent. Raita exceptional. All meals were*

served piping hot with hot plates and the portions were satisfying. Waiters were very accommodating in making changes to dishes for our individual tastes. Smart, clean and tasteful surroundings. Highly recommended.' NC. T/a: 15% disc. Cobra, £2.90 a bottle, house wine £8.95 a bottle. You might get a disc if you show Mr Ahmed this Guide. Hours: 12-2.30; 4.30 on Sun/ 6-11.30. Branches: Bengal Dynasty, Deeside Clwyd & Northwich, Cheshire.. www.bengaldynasty.com

Porthmadog

PASSAGE TO INDIA

26 Lombard Street   01766 512 144

'We have been visiting for nearly twenty years and have seldom had a bad meal. The restaurant is relatively small and gets very busy at weekends and throughout the summer. It is advisable to book, unless the visit is scheduled for a winter weekday evening. Your patience and preplanning will invariably be rewarded by good food and unhurried service. The portions are very generous and the Vegetable Roghan Josh £4.50, is always particularly good. There is something on the menu to satisfy even the most confirmed and critical curry lover.' n&jg. Menu Snapshot: Chicken or lamb Naga £6.95, cooked with garlic, onion, and the extremely hot Naga Morich chilli. Hours: 6-11.

POWYS

Contains Montgomeryshire, Radnorshire and Brecknockshire

Area: Central East Wales
Population: 130,000
Adjacent Counties:
Clwyd, Dyfed, Glamorgan,
Gwent, Gwynedd, Herefordshire,
Shropshire

Buith Wells

BILASH   NEW ENTRANT

Bilash, 17 High Street, LD2   01982 551786

Light, bright and airy restaurant. White walls, linen tablecloths, minimalist clean decor.' *Very friendly, popular local curry house. Will cheerfully cook what / however you want a dish. The mild version of their Nawabi Masala £7.95 is superb.* SS-L. They tell us: '*Unlike some restaurants the take-away section is separate from the restaurant so you can eat your meal without being disturbed by people coming in and out. The take-away waiting area looks directly into the kitchen, so you can watch your food being freshly prepared in an environment that is busy but hygienic.*' Menu Snapshot:

Misti Masala £7.95, chicken tikka, prawns, onion, capsicum, fresh cream, almond, coconut powder, honey, herbs and spices; Duck jalfrezi £8.50, sauce of onion, green chillies, coriander, tomato, fairly hot; Chicken Poonir Kufta £7.95, chicken with meat balls and cheese. Hours: 5-11.30, Fri & Sat till late. www.bilash.net

Llansantffraid

TANDOORI PLAICE TAKEAWAY

Waterloo Hse, Llansantffraid   01691 828152

Est 1994 by Shoakoth Ali. Menu Extracts: Keema Chana Masala, minced lamb, chick peas, masala sauce; Pista Nan, pistachio nuts; Green lamb Masala, lamb pieces with peas, green herbs, touch of cream, butter. Credit cards not accepted. Hours: 5-11.30; 12 Fri & Sat.

Newtown

SHILAM

49 Broad Street Newtown   01686 625333

'*I had been recommended to visit and it certainly did not disappoint. Clean, fairly modern surroundings. Service very friendly and prompt. Good all round menu. Superbly presented, very good food, garnished platters rather than the traditional oval stainless dish. Tandoori Trout starter exceptional and Vindaloo had lots of bite. Loads of green chillies in very hot Jalfrezi. Most impressed.*' kn. Menu Extracts: Bangol Maslee £6.75, spicy trout. Chicken Green Masala £5.75, tandoori chicken, freshly ground chilli, coriander, onion, green pepper, garlic, ginger, spinach, lime, pickle flavoured sauce, served with salad. Hours: 5.30 -12; 2am Fri & Sat.

PREEM

Pool Road, Newtown   01686 625534

Mehoraz owns this 80-seater. Head chef: Shim Uddin. cooks Bangladeshi style curries. Menu Snapshot: Stuffed Pepper £2.95, chicken or lamb or vegetable; Tandoori Duck £7.95; Tandoori Cocktail £9.95, chicken and lamb tikka, king prawn, sheek kebab, tandoori chicken served with plain naan; Chicken or lamb Delight £12.95, with cointreau, cream and almonds. Min Ch: £10. Del: 3m, £15 min. Hours: 5-12.

LITTLE INDIA

Laguna, Talang, Phuket, Thailand   076 270 673

Thailand is truly amazing, like its PR says. It's clean and orderly. Thai women and men are beautiful and gentle, albeit 20% are transsexual. Thai scenery is stunning. Thai food is phenomenal. And it draws in the tourists, no more so than the island of Phuket, and its town, Patong. Parts of it are frankly awful. It heaves with tourists, Thai lady-girls (transsexuals), tarts, ineffective sales persons, fast-food joints, stinking smells, no-parking, and little, if any culinary excellence. It was smashed by the 2004 Tsunami, but it's back. Patong, though charismatic for the odd moment; is fortunately avoidable. By contrast, Laguna, Phuket is one of Thailand's most sought-after resorts. It's a huge, select, glamourous, gated seaside complex made up of five very upmarket, hotels, apartments and million pound villas. Robbie Williams stays there.

Laguna was built on an old tin mine, and the holes and scars caused by decades of surface-digging, have been filled with sea water from the nearby beach, which has created wonderful lagoons, hence the name Laguna. Each hotel is linked by these lagoons; just wait on the jetty and within ten minutes a boat (with driver), will pick you up. The hotels all have expensive restaurants: Thai, seafood, Italian and continental. Do you have any Indian restaurants we ask? No they all reply, but we do themed buffet nights, – Thursday is Indian night! We decided that this wasn't for us, and a bit over-fed on Thai food, we decided to see what was going on outside the complex. There is a sprawling, fast-growing town. One part is pure Thai (for the hotel workers) complete with markets and a Tesco, (yes the very same – are big in Thailand) whilst near the complex are fashionable shops, which wouldn't look out of place on Bond Street, selling beautiful coloured Thai silks made into everything from cushion covers to ball gowns; handbags made from sting rays and reptile skin including snake (belts were complete with heads! - yuk!); highly trendy and polished steel cutlery. There is also a very smart 24-hour surgery; we passed one evening and saw three uniformed staff relaxing on a sofa, waiting for tourist business. There are plenty of restaurants of all ilks. We had been several times to this resort and each time we had noticed, but ignored a very small restaurant, with an equally small frontage, which always looked closed. In

desperation for a fix, we finally tried Little India. Expecting a mere takeaway, we were greeted by a cheerful young man and two pretty Thai waitresses, one of whom handed us a menu. Fully licensed too – things are looking up! We ordered a large G&T each and a bottle of red wine. The menu isn't huge but perfectly adequate, with a selection of favourites. We ordered and waited for our food. If we thought it was going to be a mediocre curry house, offerings as are to be found elsewhere in Phuket, how wrong we were. This was true Indian food. What did we eat? Well, quite a lot, including freshly-roasted popadoms, served with a china tray of four home-made relishes, very good podina (coriander and mint), mango chutney, mixed pickle and pink pickled onions (70 Bahts)! Vegetable samosas, two large triangles, served with salad (140B); Onion Bhajias, huge plate, one portion was enough to feed four! (50B) All main courses were served in individual bowls, with some of those fabulously trendy spoons. We enjoyed Butter Chicken, 300B, but the cooked proper way. It was wonderful, barbecued chicken pieces, smothered in a rich red sauce, decorated with cream. The Lamb Biryani, 200B, was lovely, though the rice was a little over-cooked for me, but was cooked in delicious meat stock. The Potato and Cauliflower, 210B was the best we have ever tasted, so fresh and a Stuffed Paratha, made especially for Pat, 80B was divine. Who was this creator of this wondrous food? It turned out to be the young man, Raj,

the chef-owner who told us he had cheffed at Delhi's Maurya Sheraton. In eight days we ate at Little India two more times. That's how good Raj's food is and it cost less than £30 with drinks. While we were there quite a lot of Indian tourists (from both UK and India) came in, took one look at the menu and left, doubting the menu would deliver anything resembling Indian food, saying 'we'll get a pizza'. We suggested to Raj that he wrote the menu in Hindi/Urdu as well as English to convince them he knew his cooking. Those that did stay were won over, as we were. In the words of many a reporter, we will return.

Contributors

This Guide is possible thanks to the many Curry Club members, and others, who have sent in reports on restaurants. Especial thanks to the following regular, prolific and reliable reporters (apologies for any errors, duplications, omissions (tell us if we did), and for the tiny print necessitated by space considerations).

A: Martin Abbott, Gloucs; Colin Adam, Kilwinning; Ray Adams, Kimberley; Meena Ahamed, London; F. Ahmed, Salisbury; Stephen Albrow, Norfolk; Diane Aldsworth, email; Alex, email; Paul Allen, Chatham; Maria Allen, Milton Keynes; Tony and Lesley Allen, Rugby; Harri Ahola, Espom, Finland; MF Alsan, Rugby; G Amos, Wirral; Capt R Anclive, BFPO 12; Apryl Anderson, Ponteland; Bill Anderson, Berwick Upon Tweed; Karen Andras, Nottingham; Andy from Aus; Lisa Appadurai, Benfleet; Richard Arch, e-mail; Pete Archer, Tamworth; Robin Arnott, Strafford; Mrs M Asher, Woodford Green; Dave Ashton, Warrington; Jo Ashton, Elland; Allan Ashworth, York; Berry Ashworth, Compton Bassett; Michelle Aspinal, Chester; Darius Astell, Southampton; Rachael Atkinson, Cheshire; Simon Atkinson, N5; Y Atkinson, IOM; Claire Austin, Stoke; Arman Aziz, N4.

B: Tom Bailey, Alresford; John Baker, Loughton; Kim Baker, BBC; Raji Balasubramaniam, Bangalore; Mridula Baljekar, Camberley; Jan & Randolph Baller, Nantwich; David Bker, Cranleigh; Kim Baker, Hatfield; Mr & Mrs ML Banks, Enfield; Keith Bardwell, Hertford; Ian Barlex, Ilford; Trevor Barnard, Gravesend; Christopher Barnes, Ashton; Derek Barnett, Colchester; Tony Barrel, Hounslow; R.Barry-Champion, Market Harborough; Joanne Bastock, Saltash; Mike Bates, Radcliffe; Shirley Bayley, Worthing; Karin and Angela, Rugby; Mr MJ Beard, Stafford; Joyce Bearpark, Murcia Spain; Dave Beazer, Cornwall; DJ Beer, Ross-on-Wye; Derick Behrens, Bucks; Ian Bell, Cheshire, Matt Bell, Derbys; P Bell, Carlisle; Sam Bell, Coventry; TW Bennett, Sherborne; Becky Benson, Worcs; John Bentley, Northampton; Ron Bergin, Gerrards Cross; Ian Berry, Goole; Ian and Jan Berry, Sheffield; Martyn Berry, SE3; Michael Berry, email; Shirley and Nick Bertram, Surrey; Kenneth Beswick, Lincoln; DJ Betts, Bexhill; Jonathan Bick, Cardiff; Brian and Anne Biffin, Fleet; Colin Bird, Welwyn Garden City; BH Birch, Hyde; Jim Birkumshaw, Derbys; James Birtles, Manchester; Chris Blackmore, Bristol; David Bolton, Lichfield; Mrs C Bone, Norfolk; A Boughton, SE27; L le Bouochon, Jersey; J Bowden, email; Mrs I Bowman, Rochester; Julie Bowman, email; Robert Box, Knottingley; Alan Boxall, Burwash; Sean Boxall, Andover; F Boyd, Stranraer; Iain Boyd, Wealdstone; Pippa Bradley, Walsall; Roderick Braggins, Peebles; Amanda Bramwell, Sheffield; Susan Brann, Worthing; Dave Bridge, Wallasey; Michael E Bridgstock, Northants; Sandra Brighton, Nelson; Steve Broadfoot, Anfield; John and Susan Brockington, Sutton Coldfield; Paul Bromley, SE13; Robert Brook, London; Rose Brooke, Oakham; Nigel John Brooks, Stoke-on-Trent; David Brown, Leeds; IA Brown, Fernhurst; Janet Brown, email; Mark Brown, Scunthorpe; Steve Brown, Twickenham; DA Bryan, York; Rachel Bryden, email; RC Bryant, Witney; Robert Bruce, Thornaby; Heather Buchanan, Inverness; Dr TM Buckenham, SW11; Mrs J Buffey, Sutton Coldfield; LG Burgess, Berkhamsted; DA Burke, London, A Burton, Weston-super-Mare; Bob Butler & family, email; Sanah Butt, Middlesex.

C: A C, email; D Cadby, Swindon; Barry Caldwell, Chesterfield; David Caldwell, Brownhills; Stan Calland, Kingsley; Hugh Callaway, Cleethorpes; Duncan Cameron, Fordoun; Frank Cameron, Dundee; HS Cameron, Wirral; Alex Campbell, Ramsey Campbell, Wallasey; Hartley Wintney; Mrs E Campbell, Harrogate; N Campbell, Edinburgh; Josephine Capps, Romford; L Carroll, Huddersfield; James Casey, Wilts; Peter Cash, Liverpool; Mark Caunter, Guildford; TM Chandler, Farnborough;

Desmond Carr, N8; J Carr, Birkenhead; TO Carr, Warrington; BR Carrick, Wakefield; DL Carter, Huntingdon; Mrs M Carter, Colchester; Madeline Castro, Bury St Edmunds; Dr WF Cavenagh, Norfolk; Judith Chambers, Heref; Neil Chantrell, Warrington; Hilary J Chapchal, Leatherhead; Mr & Mrs DR Chapchal, Leatherhead; DBA Chapman (Ed), Haslemere; John Chapman, Leics; OD Chapman, e-mail; Paul Chapman, Leighton Buzzard; Charlie and Linda, Zakynthos, Greece; Mr & Mrs Chatfield, Wimborne; Rajender Chatwal, Bicester; Dr GT Cheney, Salhouse; Paul Chester, Cuffley; Kathryn Chitty, Merseyside Quest PR Ltd; Chris Isitt, Cholsey; Dave Christian, IOM; Sqn Ldr PF Christopher, Ferndown; Martin Churchill, Ross-on-Wye; Alexis Ciusczak, Capistrano Beach, CA; Imogen Clist, Les Routiers in Britain, email; Peter Clyne, SW11; VA Coak, Penzance; Alan Coates, Sheffield; Louise Coben-Sutherland, Enfield; Neil Coburn, SW11; CH Coleman, Sussex; Robin Collier, Mid Calder; Chris Coles, Biggin Hill, Billy Collins, Wirral; Glen Collins, Durham; Mrs J Collins, Portsmouth; CJ Comer, Basingstoke; Rhys Compton, Cheltenham; John Conyebeare, Cardiff; A Conroy, Durham; Joseph Coohil, Oxford; Neil Cook, Royston; Peter Cookson, Notts; Mr LW Coombes, Devon; Alan & Margaret Cooper, Llansteffan; Kim Cooper, Basildon; DW Cope, Whitchurch; Dr JC Coppola, Woodstock; Will Coppola, Oxford; Nigel Cornwell, Orpington; John Costa, Tunbridge Wells; MJ Cotterill, Bristol; Ron A Couch, email; T.Cowan; Dundee Record; Stephen Cowie, SW16; Steve Cowling, Shrops; Julie Cozens, Oxon; Dr AM Croft, Cornwall; Roderick Cromar, Buckie; Simon Crosby, Kent; C Cross, Poole; Yasmin Cross, Huddersfield; Major & Mrs FJB Crosse, Salisbury; Robert Crossley, Huddersfield; F Croxford, Edinburgh; Frank and Elizabeth Crozier, Redruth; Gordon Cruickshank, Banffshire; R Cuthbertson, Southampton.

D: S Daglish, Scarborough; P Dalton, Wirral; Jan Daniel, Felpham; Mr & Mrs PE Dannat, Eastleigh; Martin Daubney, Hitchin; Gary Davey, W4; Alasdair Davidson, Heswall; Adrian Davies, NW3; Gwyn Davies, Wirral; Mrs JC Davies, Leeds; Josephine Davies, Swansea; Lucy Davies, Essex; Paul Davies, Chiddingfold; Mrs G Davies-GoV, Marlow; Shelley Davies, Bristol; Colin Davis, Tatsfield; Martin Dawe, London; Ian Dawson, Mirfield; DM Day, Preston; Michael Day, West Bromwich; Angela Dean, Solihull; Peter Deane, Bath; Gary & Katy Debono, High Wycombe; David Dee, Ruislip; Elizabeth Defty, Co. Durham; Neil Denham, The Netherlands; R Dent, Bishop Auckland; Les Denton, Barnsley; Richard Develyn, St Leonards; Nigel Deville, Uttoxeter; Ken Dewsbury, Somerset; Richard Diamond, Romsey; Phil Dicey, Cyprus; RC Dilnot, Broadstairs; Graham Divers, Glasgow; Geof Dixon, Durham; James Dobson, Burscough; S Dolden, Rochester; R Dolley, W11; Donna, Worthing; Clive Doody, Surrey; Keith Dorey, Barnet; Neil Downey, Worthing; Sarah Dowsett, Swindon; Jane Driscoll, Cape Province; Mrs J Driscoll, BFPO; Hazel Drury, Bromborough; Diane Duame, Wicklow; Eric Duhig, Hornchurch; Sheila Dunbar, Pinner; James Duncan, West Kilbride; Jon Dunham, Northants; Mark Dunn, E18; Rachael Dunn, Hemel, Robin Durant, Brighton; Martin Durrant, Chester; Avishek Dutt, London, Mr & Mrs JA Dywer, Birmingham.

E: A Edden-Jones, Bristol; Bruce Edwards, Norwich; Dave Edwards, Rugeley; Fred and Hilary Edwards, Worthing; CM Eeley, Witney; Rod Eglin, Whitehaven; Wendy Elkington; Ray Elliott, Worcester; Chris Ellis, email; H Ellis, Worthing;

Peter Ellis, London, PT Ellis, W'rtn; Stuart and Christine Ellis, email; Mrs G Elston, Woodley; Tony Emmerton, Chorley; Mark Evans, SW5; Mr & Mrs A Evans, Manchester; Brian Exford, Derbys.

F: Colin Fairall, Hants; Gary Fairbrother, Crosby; J.M.Fairhurst, Baldock; Hazel Fairley, Guildford; Chris Farrington, Cherry Hinton; Graham Faulkner, Dorking; Joy Fawcett, Sheffield; John Fearson, Bucks; Denis Feeney, Glasgow; Kevin Fenner, Rothley; Bill and Laraine Field, Newcastle-upon-Lyme; RC Field, Hants; Stephen Field, Norton; Mick Fielden, Glossop; AJ Finch, Enfield Wash; Duncan Finley, Glasgow; Maureen Fisher, Woodford Green; Bernard Fison, Holmrook; John Fitzgerald, Great Missenden; David Flanagan, Orkney; Gerry Flanagan Pepsi Co Germany; Merly Flashman, TN12; Colin & Toni Fleet, Dorset; Dr Cornel Fleming, N6; KD Flint, Kempsey; Fiona Floyd, Truro; Sarah Flynn, Beds; Stephen & Elizabeth Foden, Lynton; Chris Fogarty, Enfield; Gareth Foley, Porthcawl; Neil Foley, Essex; IE Folkard-Evans, Manchester; Jonathan Follows, Wilmslow; SR Tracy Forster, Beds; Rod Fouracres, Glos.; Rosemary Fowle, Midhurst; John R Fox, King's Lynn; John W Fox, Doncaster; Linda Foye, Barry; Theresa Frey, Fareham; Chris Frid, North Shields; Steve Frost, Kingston; Ben Fryer, Worthing; Derek Fulford, York; Alan Furniss, Wraysbury; June Fyall, Bronwydd; Mrs MAJ Fyall, Dyfed.

G: Gail & Brendan, Orme; Stephen Gaines, Middlesex; MJ Gainsford, Burbage; Leo Gajsler, Geneva; Harry E Garner, London; Steve Garrod, Hull; Mrs FE Gaunt, Stonehouse; Phillip Gentry, Bexleyheath; Brian George, Wolverton; Nick & Julie Gerrard, Gwynedd; CM Gerry, Cyprus; G Gibb, SE21; Robert (Bob) Giddings, Poole; Michael Gill, Leeds; Emma Gillingham, Huddersfield; Andrew Gillies, Edinburgh; AV Glanville, Windsor; Ms D Glass, Liverpool; A Glenford, Lincoln; Gillian Glover, The Scotsman; Johanne & Mark Glover, Nottiingham; Nick Goddard, Stevenage; Andrew Godfrey, Seer Green; Matthew Goldsmith, Burgess Hill; Mr & Mrs A. Goldthorp, Halstead; John Goleczka, Pensford; Michael Goodband, Perhore; Mrs A Gooding, Aylesbury, email; Bryn Gooding, Corfu; Nigel Goodrich, Thornhill, Scotland; Dr G Gordon, Kidlington; Mrs J Gorman, Strood; Ian Gosden, Woking; Bill Gosland, Camberley; Mr and Mrs J Gough, Brough; Chris Goulden, Andover; David Gramagan, Formby; DC Grant, Enfield; Kathryn Grass, Wigan; Alan Gray, Erskine; DR Gray, sw11; A Greaves, Chester; Andrew Greaves, Derbys; Rachel Greaves, Tavistock; Denise Gregory, Notts; Jonathan Green, Cathays, Michael Green, Leicester; Nigel Green, Orpington; Richard Green, Gerrards Cross; Sheila Green, Barrow; A Gregor, Boston; Frank Gregori, NW10; Andrew Grendale, Ingatestone; A Griffiths, Milton Keynes; JK Greye, Bath; M Griffiths, Northampton; Dave Groves, Walsall; Lynda Gudgeon, Roopa Gulati, London; Willenhall, Louis Gunn, Chelmsford.

H: Jackie Hale, e-mail; Karen Haley, Telford; John Hall, Cullercoats; Andrew Halling, Leigh; Stephen Hames, Bewdley; Alan Hamilton, Wakefield; Tina Hammond, Ipswich; Geoff & Janet Hampshire-Thomas, Kirkland; Neil Hancock, Derby; Ray Hancock, Chester; David T. Hanlin, email; Dorothy Hankin, Fordingbridge; David T. Hanlin, Solihull; Sharon Hanson, Derby; Glynn Harby, Knaresborough; Martyn Harding, Powys; Roger Hargreaves, Stoke; J Harman, Brentwood; Gerald Harnden, Westcliff-on-Sea; Justin Harper, Hemel; Dawn Harris, Dubley; Paul Harris, BFPO; David

Harrison, Dursley; Mr and Mrs I Harrison, Warwick; Mark Harrison, Oxon; Patrick Harrison, Cambridge; Louise Hartley, Edinburgh; David Harvey, SE24; S Harwood, Lewes; John K Hattam, York; Sally Haseman, Surbiton; Christopher & Linda Haw, Dewsbury; Andy Hayler.com; Ann & David Haynes, Bournemouth; John Haynes, Saffron Walden; DI Hazelgrove, West Byfleet; M Hearle, Tunbridge Wells; Kevin Hearn, Newcastle; Bernice Heath, Nottingham; Jane Helmich, South Wales Argus; Andy Hemingway, Leeds; Terry Herbat, Barnsley; Georgina Herridge, W9; Andy Herrin, yellow fingers.co.uk; T & M Hetherington, Preston; Victoria Heywood, Burton; Roger Hickman, N1; Stuart Hicks email; Pat & Paul Hickson, Chorley; Janet Higgins, Blackburn; Mrs S Higgins, Blackburn; Mrs B Higgs, Cotty; Dave Hignett, Newcastle-upon-Tyne; Alec Hill, Wigan; Carolyn Hill, Nottingham; Stephen Hill, Chesterfield; Barry Hills, Surrey; David Hindle, W5; Bharti Hindocha, Richmond; Daniel Hinge, Bishop Auckland; Mrs MJ Hirst, Kent; SC Hodgon; Daniel Hodson, Abingdon; Peter Hoes, Bingley; Bernard Hofmiester, Berlin; P Hogkinson, Sheffield; Duncan Holloway, Windsor; Kevin Hooper, St Austell; Linda Horan, Wirral; Will H Horley, Barnsley; Peter Hornfleck, Farnborough; Jerry Horwood, Guildford; Dr MP Houghton, Rugby; Neil Houldsworth, Keighley; Nigel & Rev Erika Howard, JK Howard, Enfield Wash; P Howard, Hornchurch; David & Val Howarth, Derbs; Mrs J Howarth, Oldham; Mat Howarth, Burton Upon Trent; Kathy Howe, Carlisle; Simon Howell, Gillingham; Bruce Howerd, Tongham; Lynn Howie, Sanderstead; Deh-Ta Hsiung, London; Jan Hudson, Hemel Hempstead; Tom Hudson, Jarrow; Chris Hughes, Wraysbury; Paul Hughes, Detroit; Paul Hulley, Stockport; SP Hulley, Reddish; HL & S Humphreys, Stoke-on-Trent; AG Hunt, Southend-on-Sea; John & Frances Hunt, Langport; Paul Hunt, Essex; Roger Hunt, Sidmouth; Vince Hunt, Manchester; Penny Hunter, Brighton; Sheila Hunter, Dundee; Humayan Hussain, Journalist; Dr M Hutchinson, Gwynedd; Mike Hutchinson, Stafford; Mrs V Hyland, Manchester; Jeffrey Hyman, email.

I: DM Ibbotson, Sheffield; Nick & Mandy Idle, Ossett; Ken Ingram, Leeds; G Innocent, Dawlish; Mrs G Irving, Redditch; Chris Issit, Chosely; Robert Izzo, Horsham.

J: Dr AG James, Wigan; O Jarrett, Norwich; Sue Jayasekara, Essex; Sally JeVries, Heathfield; L Jiggins, Dagenham; Bal Johal, email; G John, Wirral; Maxine & Andrew Johnson, Leiden; Colin Johnson, Southall; Peter Johnson, Droitwich; Paul Jolliffe, Exeter; CML Jones, St Albans; Clive Jones, nw; Gareth Jones, Tonypandy; Kate Jones, Leiden; Mark Jones Newport, Gwent; RW Jones, N9; Shirley Jones, SE13; WA Jones, Flints; Wendy Jones, Clwyd; Michael Lloyd Jones, Cardiff; Esther Juby, Norwich; Sylvia & Adrian Judd, Pontefract; Surjit Singh Jutla, Reading.

K: Tessa Kamara, W13; Sarah Kaikini, Surrey; AD Kantes, Northants; Chris Keardey, Southampton; Anthony Kearns, Stafford; David R Keedy, T & W; Russ Kelly, Seaforth; Prof. and Mrs Kemp, Royston; D Kennedy, Edinburgh; Mr & Mrs MJB Kendall, Hook; David Kenny, Kenmare; David Kerray, Akrotiri; John Kettle, Dover; John Kettle, Crewe; JS Kettle, Banbury; Saul Keyworth, Essex; M. Arif Khan, London; Stephen Kiely, N16; John Kilbride, Glasgow; Cleo Kinder and Toby Kinder, SE17; David King, Biggleswade; Mike King, Sussex; John & Jane Kingdom, Plymouth; Alyson Kingham, Oldham; Mark Kirby, Ashtead; Frances Kitchen, Langport; Peter Kitney, Banbury; J & P Klusiatis, Reading; Drs Heather & Mark Knight, Oxford; Ana Knowles, Walton on Thames; Drs MJ & A Krimholtz, SW14.

L: Caz Lack, Kent; Martin Lally, Chester; Colin Lambert, Bucks; John Lambourne, Majorca; Mrs Langley, email; Alan Lathan, Chorley; Clive

Lawrence, email; Cass Lawson, Swindon; Ronnie Laxton, London; Jonathan Lazenby, Mamhilad, Gwent; Gary Leatt, St. Brelade, Jersey; Andrew Lecomber, Durham; DH Lee, Waltham Abbey; Mark Lee, e-mail; Jackie Leek, Dartford; Simon Leng, Wakefield; David Leslie, Aberdeen; Russell D Lewin, NW2; A Lewis, Sherborne; CK Lewis, Maidenhead; Margaret Ann Lewis, Ashford; R Lewis, Rayleigh; Pat Lindsay, Hants; David Lloyd, Walgrave, N'ton; David Lloyd, Oswestry; Eleanor & Owen Lock, Geneva; Peter Long, Cheltenham; J Longman, Bodmin; John Loosemore, Orpington; DA Lord, Hove; Julia & Philip Lovell, Brighton; AP Lowe, Tolworth; Paul Lowe, Stourbridge; Peter Lowe, Lewes; Mr & Mrs DN Luckman, Horley; Jeremy Ludlow, Dorset; Mrs H Lundy, Wallasey; Graeme Lutman, Herts; Tim Lynch, Romford; Jamie Lyon, Burscough.

Mac/Mc: M Mcbryde, Watford; Loraine McClean, Poole; Alan McIntyre, Northumberland; David Mackay, Twickenham; Darren McKenzie, T&W; David Mackenzie, Darlington; Ir Macmillan, Lincoln; Deb McCarthy, E6; Patrick McCloy, N8; Vanessa McCrow, Teddington; David McCulloch, NW11; Michael McDonald, Ellesmere Port; David McDowell, Telford; BJ McKeown, Seaford; Ian McLean, Brighton; Dr and Mrs J McLelland, Mid Calder; Alan & Jean McLucas, Solihull; Dr FB McManus, Lincoln; Alan McWilliam, Inverurie.

M: Chris Mabey, Swindon; Fiona Maddock, Guildford; Rakesh Makhecha, Harrow; Paul Lowe, Stourbridge; Chloe Malik, email; Richard Manley, Wirral; Cherry Manners, Hatfield; Emma and Peta Manningham, email; E Mansfield, Camberley; Clive Mantle; Mark of Melbourne; JF Marshall, Bedford; Geraldine Marson, Winsford; Colin Martin, Nuneaton; Derek Martin, Marlow; Jane Martin, SW19; PR Martin, Southend; J Mason, Southport; DJ Mason, Cleveland; LJ Mason, Leeds; John Maundrell, Tunbridge Wells; Gilian May, Hayes; Peter F May, St Albans; Simon Mayo, Farnborough; Simon Meaton, Andover; John Medd, Nottingham; Tim Mee, Harrow; Sue & Alf Melor, Hanworth; Nigel Meredith, Huddersfield; Sujata Mia, Middlesex; Andy Middleton, Rotherham; H Middleton, Coventry; Simon Mighall, St Neots; PJL Mighell, Canterbury; Robert Miles, Herts; Catherine Millar, BFPO; DR Millichap, Horsham; BW Milligan; AJ Millington, Woodford; Sally Millington, N10; Mr & Mrs P Mills, Mold; Mary Mirfin, Leeds; Al Mitchell, Belfast; Jonathon Mitchell, Alton; F Moan, Cuddington; Sarah Moles, Buxton; Jon Molyneaux, Peterborough; Mrs SE Monk, Gisburn; Steven Montgomery, Monash, Australia; AV Moody, Portsmouth; Christy Moore, Dublin; Christy Moore, London; DM Moreland, Willington; S Morgan, Feltham; Tim & Katherine Morgan, Scotland; Ian Morris, Gwynedd; Miranda Mortlock, Suffolk; Peter Morwood, Wicklow; A Moss, Colchester; Caroline Moss, Solihull; K Mosley, email; Paul Motley , email; Mrs L Muirhead, Glasgow; David Muncaster, Stoke; Andy Munro, Birmingham; Joan Munro, Leyburn; Annette Murray, Thornton Cleveleys; JL Murray, Enfield; RG Murray, Carlisle; Drs Heather & Harry Mycook.

N: Simon Nash, Cheshire; Mrs PG Naylor, Salisbury; Hugh Neal, Kent; Jeff Neal, Bolton; Marcus Neal, Liss; Rob Neil, Ashford; A Nelson-Smith, Swansea; Liam Nevens, Stockton; Tony Newbold, email; Rebecca Newman, Hayes; Tony Newman, Margate; J Newsom, Lancing; Jan Newson Southgate, N14; Clive Newton, Northwich; John Nicholson, Bromborough; Nick, e-mail; P & D Nixon, Basildon; Mrs DA Nowakowa, Tiverton; Robert Nugent, SE31; Canon Peter Nunn, Glocs; Jody Lynn Nye, Illinois.

O: Beverley Oakes, Essex; AM O'Brien, Worthing; Eamon O'Brien, Holland; Pauline O'Brien, London; DC O'Donnell, Wetherby; Elise O'Donnell, Wolverhampton; Mary O'Hanlon, Dr

M. Ogden, Barnsley; Ann Oliver nee Cridland, email; N Oliver, London; Helensburgh; Sheila Openshaw, Hants; David O'Regan, Leeds; Joanne Osborne, Bromborough; Steve Osborne, Bucks; Chris Osler, email; Jan Ostron, Felpham; Judith Owen, SW6; William & Sue Oxley, Southampton.

P: Trevor Pack, Rushden; RH Paczec, Newcastle; M Padina, Mattingley; Mr & Mrs GG Paine, Coventry; Keith Paine, Tilbury; GJ Palmer, Gainsborough; RS Palmer, Norfolk; Mrs A Parker, Birmingham; Mr GM Parker, Birmingham; John MF Parker, North Yorks; Philip Parker, Matlock; Roger Parkes, Petersfield Curry Club; Bill Parkes-Davies, Tunbridge Wells; Angela Parkinson, Clitheroe; Nick Parrish; Brian Parsons, email; M Parsons, Fareham; Roy Parsons, Richmond; Donald Paterson, East Grinstead; GM Patrick, London; Paul, email; Mrs PA Pearson, Bristol; Mrs G Pedlow, Hitchin; David and Dandra Peet, Surrey; Mrs Barrie Penfold, Bourne End; J Penn, Southampton; Elaine & Martin Perrett, Dorchester; AJW Perry, Bristol; Graham Perry, Truro; Ian Perry, Essex; MJ Perry, E17; Ian Pettigrew, Edinburgh; J Pfeffer, Manchester; Christopher Phelps, Gloucester; Adrian & Angela Phillips, Ammanford; Diane Phillips, Hyde; John Phillips, Wrexham; Jonathan Phillips, Saffron Walden; Steve Phillips, Wokingham; Colin Phipps, Scarborough; Sara Pickering, Northolt; Jack Pievsky, Pinner; Dr Dirk Pilat, e-mail; Mike Plant, Essex; Susan Platt, Bury; Rod Plinston, Reading; D Pool, SE2; K Pool, Leyland; SR Poole, Runcorn; Tony Pope, Derbys; Steve Porter, Walsall; Julia Pounds, Brighton; RL Power, Sutton Coldfield; Dave Prentice, Dartmouth; Steve Prentice, Devon; Tim Preston, Barrow; Alison Preuss, Glencarse; Jeff Price, Bristol; Mr J Priest, Sawbridgeworth; Dr John Priestman, Huddersfield; D Pulsford, Marford; Janet Purchon, Bradford; John Purkiss, York; Steve Puttock, Chatham; Julie Pyne, County Down.

Q: Sheila Quince, E11.

R: Jon R, W5; Diane Radigan, Welling; Harish B Raichura, Reading; Rohit Rajput, email; Kevin Ramage, Berwick; Clive Ramsey, Edinburgh; Pradeep Rao, Derby; Alison Ratcliff, Halstead; KJ Rayment, Hertford; RC Raynham, Chelmsford; CR Read, Epsom; Mark Read, Romford; Guy Reavely, Surrey; Kim Reeder, South Shields; Debbie Reddy, W12; Francis Redgate, Nottingham; Steven Redknap, Ashford; I Reid, Fife; Lorraine Reid, Edinburgh; Duncan Renn, Dursley; Jon Restall, Ealing W5; Kevin Rhodes, Largo Florida; Richard, email; Derek Richards, Bewdley; Sean Richards, Dover; Michael & June Richardson, Hull; Simon Richardson, Gainsborough; Steve Ridley, email; Mike Ridgway, Buxton; Mathew Riley, se3; Laurence Ritchie, Ilkeston; Lindsay Roberts, Lancaster; Margaret Roberts, Rubery; Peter Roberts, Shipston; Stewart & Anne Robertson, Leamington; Simon Roccason, Willenhall; Pat Roche, Chislehurst; J P Rockery, Leicester; KG Rodwell, Harston; R Ronan, IOW; John Roscoe, Stalybridge; Brian Roston, Pontefract; John Rose, Hull; WJ Rowe; Steve Rowland, Matlock; Gareth Rowlands, email; the Royston family, East Sussex; Mrs EM Ruck, Darlington; DC Ruggins, Chalfont; JA Rumble, Rochford; Sue & Mike Rumfitt, Bedford; Paul Rushton, Nottingham; K Ruth, w1; Bob Rutter, Blackpool; EJ Ryan, Effingham; N Ryer, Mansfield.

S: George and Mrs J Sadler, Thetford; MB Samson, Herts; Pauline Sapsford, Milton Keynes; MR Sargeant, Cornwall; Mark Sarjant, Guildford; GM Saville, Egremont; Mike Scotlock, Rayleigh; Mike Scott, Holmer Green; MJ Scott, SE26; Nicky & Don Scowen, Romford; Tim Sebensfield, Beeston; L Segalove, SN2; M Seefeld, W5; Patrick Sellar, Maidstone; Richard Sellers, East Yorks; Philip Senior, Liverpool; N Sennett, Hull; David Sewell, Aldershot; Mrs DA Seymour, Burnham-on-Sea; Richard Shackleton, Wakefield; Brian Shallon, Camberley; Sarah Shannon, B'hm; Jeane Sharp, St Albans; Mark Shaw, Swindon; Michelle Shaw, Ilford;

What we need to know

We need to know everything there is to know about all curry restaurants in the UK. And there is no one better able to tell us than those who use them, i.e. YOU. We do not mind how many times we receive a report about a particular place, so please don't feel inhibited or that someone else would be better qualified. They aren't. Your opinion is every bit as important as the next person's. Ideally, we'd like a report from you every time you dine out – even on a humble takeaway. We realise this is hard work so we don't mind if your report is very short, and you are welcome to send in more than one report on the same place telling of different occasions. Please cut out the forms alongside. Or you can even use the back of an envelope or a postcard, or we can supply you with more forms if you write in (with an S.A.E., please). Alternatively, you can use the website <patchapman.co.uk> Go to Restaurant Reports and follow instructions.

If you can get hold of a menu (they usually have takeaway menus to give away) or visiting cards, they are useful to us too, as are newspaper cuttings, good and bad, and advertisements, scanned or mailed. So, please send anything along with your report. They are also used when preparing the next edition of this Guide. We do not pay for reports but our ever-increasing corps of regular correspondents receive the occasional perk from us. Please join them. Please send us your report after your next restaurant curry.

Thank you.

Pat Chapman
Founder, The Curry Club
PO Box 7, Haslemere
Surrey, GU27 1EP

E-mail it to
pat@patchapman.co.uk

Restaurant Report Form

Photocopy or scan this form. Mail it or e-mail it to the address below.
Whenever you have an 'Indian' meal or takeaway, The Curry Club
would like to have your opinion.

Your Name and address: ....

....

Your phone number .... Your e-mail address ....

Restaurant name: ....

Street no and Street name: ....

....

Town: .... County: ....

Postcode: .... Telephone: .... e.mail: ....

Website: .... Date Visited: ....

REPORT

Please tell us everything – your first impressions, the welcome, cleanliness, your table – was it appealing? Nice things waiting for you on it? The menu, quantities, quality, service, background music, comfort, decor. Irritating or pleasing? The food? How were the toilets? First visit? Been before? Would you go back? recommend to friends? Overall was the restaurant TOP 100, good, bad, indifferent, appaling?

Restaurant Update Information

Photocopy or scan this form. Mail it or e-mail it to the address below.

Your Name and address ....

....

Your phone number .... Your e-mail address ....

Even if you do not fill in a report overleaf, you may be able to give us vital information, such as that below.

DO YOU KNOW OF ANY: NEW CURRY RESTAURANT OPENINGS:

Restaurant name: ....

Street no and name: ....

Town: ....   County: ....

Postcode: .... Telephone: ....

DO YOU KNOW OF ANY: CURRY RESTAURANT CLOSURES OVER THE LAST FEW MONTHS

Including any listed in this Guide

Restaurant   name:

....

Street no and name: ....

Town: ....County: ....

Postcode: .... Telephone: ....

DO YOU KNOW OF ANY: HYGIENE OR OTHER OFFENSES

Please back up with a local press cutting if possible

Restaurant name: ....

Street no and name: ....

Town: ....County: ....

Postcode: .... Telephone: ....

YOUR FAVOURITE RESTAURANT(S)

If possible, in descending order, best first

Restaurant name: ....

Street no and name: ....

Town: ....County: ....

Postcode: .... Telephone: ....

ANY OTHER CURRY RESTAURANT INFORMATION

Please continue on separate sheets of paper if required

Please return your info to: The Curry Club, PO Box 7, Haslemere, Surrey. GU27 1EP

Town Index

THE DISTANCE BETWEEN GOOD & GREAT

KEEP WALKING
JOHNNIE WALKER

Entertain in Style

As any creator of gourmet items will tell you, a drink or dish stands or falls on the quality of its ingredients. Recognised by experts as the definitive premium whisky, **Johnnie Walker** is a brand synonymous with quality, premium Scotch whisky, which makes it the World's favourite.

Many people don't put in enough thought when it comes to pairing food and alcohol – but its important. Whilst wine or beer are the most common accompaniments to food today, whisky is fast becoming popular with food aficionados heralding a time for change.

Johnnie Walker Black Label blended Scotch whisky is particularly popular with the Asian community because it beautifully complements the rich flavours of subcontinent cuisine. Its depth of character set it apart from any other Scotch whisky.

To best understand the pairing of whisky and food, one has to understand the various flavours and aromas found in the blend. **Johnnie Walker Black Label** is a blend of over 40 select malt and grain whiskies each of which has been matured for a minimum of 12 years, some considerably longer.

However there are four predominant flavours and aromas that cut through:

Earthy Smoke – you may be able to detect the smell of a bonfire

Fresh Fruits – Look for the aromas of apple skins, pears, oranges or green grass

Rich Fruits – You may be able to detect the smell of rich figs or sultanas.

Creamy Vanilla – the smell of sweet vanilla, not unlike ice-cream or toffee.

The Perfect Match

No matter what your taste is, **Johnnie Walker Black Label** will complement a variety of menus, bringing to life the best flavours. The below dishes go very well with the various flavours and aromas of **Black Label**:

Starters	Main Course	Rice	Deserts
Adraki Lamb Chops	Murgh Makhani	Chicken Biryani	Zarda
Chilli Prawns	Rogaan Josh	Mutton Pulao	Gajjar Halva
Murgh Achari Kebab	Mutton Korma	Vegetable Biryani	Gulab Jamun
Papri Chaat	Navratna Korma	Vegetable Pulao	Bread Pudding
Paneer Stuffed Samosas	Paneer Makhani		Kulfi
	Dum Aloo		

KEEP WALKING.

JOHNNIE WALKER.

Dining in is the new dining out

THE NEW CURRY BIBLE
THE ULTIMATE MODERN
CURRY HOUSE RECIPE BOOK

PAT CHAPMAN

Curry Club Cookbooks

patchapman.co.uk

Something for the weekend
(and the other five days)

From the original Cobra Premium Beer to the Cobra Bite range of flavoured lagers, with Cobra Light, Cobra Zero% and King Cobra in between, the Cobra range has a beer for every occasion.

cobrabeer.com

BEST UK INDIAN RESTAURANT AND BEST IN THE MIDLANDS 2007/20

(2008)

WARDS 2006

5

COMING TO A SUPERMARKET NEAR YOU SOON